1. 9
16/

S

Volume 2

**The unaccepted design for the 1936 Accession issue
submitted by Edmund Dulac which later formed the
basis of the issued King George VI values 7d. to 1s.**

Photo: National Postal Museum, London

Stanley Gibbons

Great Britain

Specialised Stamp Catalogue

Volume 2
King Edward VII
to King George VI

Eighth Edition

Stanley Gibbons Publications Ltd
London and Ringwood

By Appointment to Her Majesty The Queen
Stanley Gibbons Ltd, London
Philatelists

Published by **Stanley Gibbons Publications Ltd.**
Editorial, Sales Offices and Distribution Centre:
5 Parkside, Christchurch Road, Ringwood,
Hants BH24 3SH

© **Stanley Gibbons Publications Ltd 1989**

1st edition—February 1967
   Reprinted—April 1967
2nd edition—July 1970
   Reprinted—September 1970
3rd edition—March 1974
4th edition—May 1978
   Reprinted—June 1979

5th edition—May 1980
6th edition—March 1984
7th edition—November 1986
8th edition—October 1989

Item No. 0286 (89)

ISBN 0 85259 227 2 (limp)

ISBN 0 85259 232 9 (cased)

Printed and bound in Great Britain by
Butler & Tanner Ltd, Frome and London

Contents

Contents

Checklists

King Edward VII

King George V

King Edward VIII

King George VI

Acknowledgements

In preparing this new edition we are very grateful to members of the Great Britain Philatelic Society and others who have contacted us. In particular our thanks go to Dr R. W. Powell, FRPSL and Mr W. A. Wiseman, FRPSL for their help. We are again grateful to members of the staff at the Post Office and especially Mrs Jean Farrugia, the Archivist.

The illustrations of the essays of King Edward VII for 2½d., £1 and £5, originally from the De La Rue archives, are shown with kind permission of Christie's-Robson Lowe. We also thank the Great Britain Philatelic Society and Royal Philatelic Society for permission to use certain illustrations from their publications.

STANLEY GIBBONS PUBLICATIONS LTD.

Preface

After the switch to surface printing in 1855 there were no further major changes in Great Britain stamp production for the remainder of Queen Victoria's reign. Design concepts, process, printer, even the Queen's portrait, remained unchanged. The new reign, when it came, altered nothing, except the monarch's portrait, and it was not until the accession of King George V that the mould was finally broken. Thereafter change was rapid. The King's considerable interest in philately and stamp design led from the unsuccessful Downey Heads to the 1912 profile designs, the magnificent high value Seahorses and ultimately, to the 1934 photogravure series. It was a period of innovation. De La Rue lost their hold on the stamp printing contracts to be replaced by Harrison & Sons, commemorative stamps appeared for the first time and the venerable typography process gave way to the flexibility of modern photogravure.

The next two reigns pushed forward the science of stamp design. Contrast the simplicity of the King Edward VIII definitives or Dulac's striking 1937 Coronation stamp with the staid efforts of the Victorians. By 1952 modern concepts of stamp design and production were in place. It is not surprising that such a period of radical change has always attracted the collector so this second volume of the Great Britain Specialised Catalogue has always been popular.

Much research continues to be done on the stamps from this period and this edition contains much revised information and a number of new discoveries. One of the most important of the latter, the 1902–11 De La Rue £1 green showing watermark inverted, has taken over 80 years to come to light. The major revision in the King Edward VII section is amongst the Departmental Officials where new introductory notes, contributed by Mr W. A. Wiseman, FRPSL, provide the background to the conception and use of the Inland Revenue, Government Parcels, Office of Works and Army issues. Additional overprint varieties appear in the Government Parcels and Army listings.

For King George V much work has been concentrated on the interesting story of the Downey Heads. It has been possible to study material originally held by a Deputy Master of the Royal Mint and by the J. A. C. Harrison archive. Much of this new information has been used to expand the coverage of the fascinating essay and proof material. In the photogravure section the unissued 6d. purple with lighter background has been added.

Additional "SPECIMEN" overprints appear amongst the King Edward VIII issues and the introduction to the King George VI low value definitives has been rewritten.

The Stamp Booklet appendix has been revised following the publication of the first three parts of the major work by Dr Jean Alexander and Mr L. F. Newbery. The condensed notes previously provided for underprints on the issues of King Edward VII and King George V have been expanded to an actual listing, although it has not been possible, at this stage, to quote prices. An additional appendix now provides listings for the Guernsey and Jersey issues under German Occupation between 1940 and 1945.

The continual demand for scarcer or more unusual material is reflected in the prices quoted in this edition. The levels of most basic stamps remain fairly static, but those for proof material and varieties continue to forge ahead in many instances.

We are grateful for the assistance of the many collectors, who have further provided information for this new edition. We are always happy to receive details of discoveries for possible listing in the G.B. Specialised Catalogue, or of fresh information which can be incorporated into subsequent editions.

David J. Aggersberg
Robert H. Oliver

Stanley Gibbons International Ltd.

HEAD OFFICE, 399 STRAND, LONDON WC2R 0LX

Auction Room and Specialist Stamp Departments. Open Monday-Friday, 9.30 a.m. to 5 p.m.

Shop. Open Monday–Friday 9.30 a.m. to 6 p.m. and Saturday 10 a.m. to 4 p.m. **Telephone 01-836 8444 and Telex 28883 for all departments.**

RINGWOOD OFFICE

Stanley Gibbons Publications, 5 Parkside, Christchurch Road, Ringwood, Hants BH24 3SH. Telephone 0425 472363. Telex 41271.

OVERSEAS BRANCHES

Stanley Gibbons (Australia) Pty. Ltd., P.O. Box 863J, Melbourne 3001, Australia. Telephone (01 0613) 670 3332 and Telex AA 37223.

Stanley Gibbons (Singapore) Pte Ltd., Marina Square, P.O. Box 0001, Singapore 9103, Republic of Singapore. Telephone 336 1998 and Telex RS 38398 SINGSG.

Stanley Gibbons Publications Ltd. has overseas agents and distributors for Australia, Austria, Belgium, Canada, Denmark, Finland, France, West Germany (inc. West Berlin), Hong Kong, Israel, Italy, Japan, Luxembourg, Netherlands, New Zealand, Scandinavia, South Africa, Switzerland, United States, West Indies and Caribbean. Please contact the Ringwood address for details

Introductory Notes

The aim of this catalogue is to classify in specialised form the stamps of Great Britain, to give distinguishing numbers to them and to quote prices which are current with Stanley Gibbons Ltd. at the time of going to press and at which they will supply if in stock.

Catalogue Numbers

All *Specialised Catalogue* numbers include a prefix letter or letters; shades normally have a number in brackets and subsequent varieties have letter identifications.

Essays, Die Proofs, Plate Proofs, Colour Trials, etc. do not have catalogue numbers which should therefore be described in full.

For each basic stamp a cross-reference is included to the S.G. catalogue number in the 1990 edition of the Gibbons *Part 1* British Commonwealth Catalogue.

Prices

Prices quoted in this catalogue are the selling prices of Stanley Gibbons Ltd. at the time the book went to press. They are for stamps in fine condition; in issues where condition varies prices may be higher for the superb and lower for the sub-standard. The unused prices for stamps of King Edward VII and King George V are for lightly hinged examples. Unused prices for stamps of King Edward VIII and King George VI are for unmounted mint (though when not available unmounted, stamps are often supplied at a lower price). Prices for used stamps refer to postally used examples. All prices are subject to change without prior notice and no guarantee is given to supply all stamps priced, since it is not possible to keep every catalogued item in stock.

If a variety exists in more than one shade it is priced for the commonest shade and will be worth correspondingly more in a scarcer shade. Except where otherwise stated varieties are priced for single examples and extra examples required to make up positional blocks or booklet panes would be valued as normals.

Cylinder blocks containing varieties are indicated by an asterisk against the price (which includes the cost of the variety).

King Edward VII Controls are priced for unused corner pairs according to perforator type. Controls of the King George V Downey Head issues in Section NA are priced likewise, but all other typographed Controls, including the postage dues, are priced as unused singles, extra stamps being valued as normals. Controls and/or cylinder numbers of photogravure issues are priced for appropriate blocks according to circumstances, their size being stated in the lists.

Prices quoted for stamps "on cover" are for a single example of the stamp concerned on cover. Covers bearing either multiples of the stamp or other values used in conjunction with it will generally command a higher price.

The prices quoted for booklet panes are for panes with good perforations and complete with the binding margin. Prices for complete booklets are for those containing panes with average perforations as it is unusual for all panes to be well perforated.

Guarantee

All stamps supplied by Stanley Gibbons Ltd. are guaranteed originals in the following terms:

If not as described, and returned by the purchaser, we undertake to refund the price paid to us in the original transaction. If any stamp is certified as genuine by the Expert

Committee of the Royal Philatelic Society, London, or by B.P.A. Expertising Ltd., the purchaser shall not be entitled to make any claim against us for any error, omission or mistake in such certificate.

Consumers' statutory rights are not affected by the above guarantee.

Expertisation

We do not give opinions as to the genuineness of stamps. Expert Committees exist for this purpose and enquiry can be made of the Royal Philatelic Society, 41 Devonshire Place, London W1N 1PE, or B.P.A. Expertising Ltd., P.O. Box 163, Carshalton Beeches, Surrey SM5 4QR. They do not undertake valuations under any circumstances and fees are payable for their services.

Correspondence

Letters should be addressed to the Catalogue Editor, Stanley Gibbons Publications Ltd., 5 Parkside, Christchurch Road, Ringwood, Hants BH24 3SH, and return postage is appreciated when a reply is sought. New information and unlisted items for consideration are welcomed.

Please note we do not give opinions as to the genuineness of stamps, nor do we identify stamps or number them by our Catalogue.

To order from this Catalogue

Always quote the *Specialised Catalogue* number, mentioning *Volume 2, 8th Edition,* and where necessary specify additionally the precise item wanted.

Detailed Introductory Notes

Before using the catalogue it is important to study the "General Notes" as these explain the technical background of the issues in question. They are to be found at the beginning of the relevant sections.

Items Excluded

In dealing with varieties we record only those for which we can vouch, namely items we have seen and verified for ourselves.

Watermark Illustrations

The illustrations show watermarks as seen from the *front* of the stamp, except for the Multiple Cypher watermark described under the King George V Typographed and Postage Due "General Notes" sections. Here the watermark is illustrated as seen from the *back* of the stamp; the side usually chosen for inspection.

Quantities Sold

This information is based on figures published by the Post Office.

National Postal Museum Archive Material

During 1984 and 1985 surplus GB material from the National Postal Museum archives was included in three auction sales. The lots offered were mostly imprimaturs, which were handstamped on the reverse to indicate origin, and specimen overprints. This material is included in special entries, under headings clearly indicating their origin. Where items included in these sales had been previously listed a dagger is shown alongside the catalogue price.

It should be emphasised that only items from lots which were sold at the sales of 26 April 1984, 19 February 1985 and 5 September 1985 are covered by the catalogue entries.

Symbols and Abbreviations

†	(in price column)	does not exist
—	(in price column)	exists or may exist, but no market price is known (a blank conveys the same meaning)
I.	(above price column)	control imperforate selvedge (partially perf. margins are regarded as imperf.)
P.	(above price column)	control selvedge perforated through
*	(against price of a cylinder block)	price includes a listed variety
*	(against cylinder number)	an "abnormal" cylinder (see General Notes to Section ND)
from	(preceding price column)	several items listed, such as a number of different types, for which only the commonest is priced
Cyl	cylinder	
mm.	millimetres	
M/S	manuscript	
No.	number	
NPM	The National Postal Museum, London	
Pl.	plate	
R.	row (thus "R. 6/4" indicates the fourth stamp from the left in the sixth horizontal row from the top of a sheet of stamps)	

Unused Prices. The unused prices for stamps of King Edward VII and King George V are for lightly hinged examples and those quoted for stamps of King Edward VIII and King George VI are for unmounted mint.

The King Edward VII Issues

General Notes

PRINTING CONTRACTS. When King Edward VII came to the throne on 22 January 1901 the contract of 1899 between De La Rue and the Inland Revenue for printing stamps had nearly ten years still to run. Discussions about designs started almost immediately and De La Rue produced a series of paste-ups, incorporating the new King's head into the existing Queen Victoria designs. In the event only the ½d., 1d., 2½d. and 6d. values emerged with completely new designs, the remainder closely resembling their 1887 predecessors. From about 1908 it was decided to replace certain bicoloured values with monocoloured stamps and this process was still going on when the King died on 6th May 1910.

At about that time De La Rue were given formal notice of termination of the 1899 contract and were informed that they had failed to win the tender for further supplies. The new contractors, Harrison & Sons, took over from De La Rue on 1st January 1911. The new King George V stamps were not then ready and in April 1911 it became apparent that the stock of King Edward stamps would be insufficient to tide them over. Arrangements were made for printings to be taken from the King Edward plates but Harrisons did not have the necessary machines for printing bicoloured stamps and could only print the monocoloured ones so the remainder were printed at Somerset House. These are known as the King Edward VII Provisional Printings. They did not entirely cease until June 1913.

PAPER CONTRACTS. At the time of the King's accession the contract for the supply of all paper for British postage stamps, dated 1897, was with R. D. Turner & Co. of Roughway Mill, Tonbridge and still had four years to run. In 1904 it was renewed for a further period of seven years to October 1911. Although Turners did not get the subsequent paper contract for King George V stamps they continued to supply the Inland Revenue with Imperial Crown watermarked paper up to the end of the provisional printings.

ARRANGEMENT. Each value has been dealt with in turn, together with booklet panes, through changes of colour, perforation and printer, followed by the list of plate markings, printings, plating index and control and pricing schedules as appropriate. The preliminary Essays, Proofs and Colour Trials appear before the beginning of the list and Essays, Die Proofs and Colour Trials of the completed values are given under their respective values.

NEW HISTORICAL SOURCES. During the 1970s an immense amount of new and important historical material has been opened to inspection. This includes the De La Rue archives (including the De La Rue/Inland Revenue correspondence), the British Library material from the Inland Revenue and the Inland Revenue files themselves. All these have provided a new understanding of the basic processes behind the issue of Edwardian stamps over the post office counter and have enabled a new look to be taken at old ideas and material.

On the ½d. and 1d. there is still much work to be done and the task of identifying the official plate numbers has yet to be achieved. Owing to the number of plates and the mass of information in existence this will take some time to complete. Nevertheless, in this edition, the tables describing the plate markings have been revised to give the present position on these two values. The work on identifying the remaining values to the £1 with the official plate numbers, using archive and other material, has been completed so that the 3d., 4d., 6d., 7d., and 1s. are now provided with listings to include their official plate numbers. The high values are dealt with in the same way. It was felt that to continue with cross references to the previously published " philatelic " plate numbers would be confusing and, accordingly, these are now not given. Prices are quoted in separate tables for identifiable plate pieces.

INVALIDATION. Stamps issued in the reign of King Edward VII were invalidated on 1 April 1930. The stamps of Queen Victoria had, according to the Post Office guide, been invalidated in 1924. Stamps issued in the reigns of King George V, King Edward VIII and King George VI were invalidated on 1 March 1972.

PAPER

Mill Sheets. All the paper emanating from Roughway Mill for the printing of postage stamps was in one size, i.e. in sheets of 22¾″ × 22⅞″, each sheet being known as a " mill sheet ".

Imperial Crown

Anchor

Two watermarks were used: Imperial Crown and Anchor.

The Anchor watermark was used only for the 2s. 6d., 5s. and 10s. values and the mill sheet consisted of 224 Anchors comprising four panes each of 7 horizontal rows of 8 stamps.

The Crown watermark was arranged in two ways in the mill sheets. For all the remaining values, except the 9d., there were 480 crowns arranged as follows:

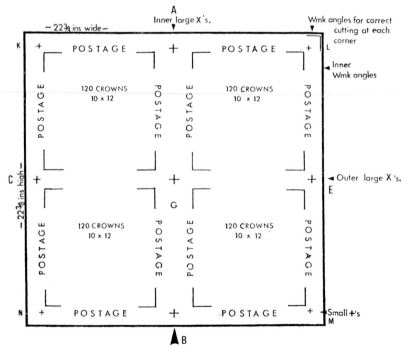

Diagram of 480 Crown Mill Sheet

(Everything within the outer rectangle is part of the watermark except the references to the number of crowns)

480 Crown Mill Sheet. In addition to the Crown watermarks each mill sheet incorporated a number of other features in the watermark. In the margins of each pane of 120 crowns was the word " POSTAGE " in double-lined capitals, repeated twelve times. In addition there was a watermark angle piece at each corner of each pane (16 in all) and another one in each corner of the mill sheet, so that each mill sheet had 20 watermark angle pieces. The four corner angles marked where the mill sheet had to be cut out of the continuous reel of paper in which it was made, such a reel being technically known as a " web ". Occasionally, due to folds in the paper, these normally unseen watermark angle pieces can be found. There are also four small crosses and five large crosses in the watermark in the positions shown and indicated by capital letters outside the rectangle. Finally on every mill sheet of this paper there is a single-lined capital letter in the position shown in the middle between the 11th and 12th rows from the top. The letters D, E, F and G are known but their purpose is unknown.

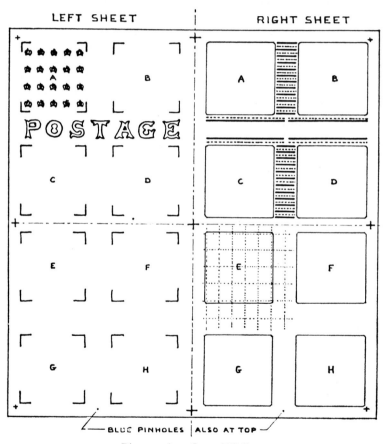

Diagram of 320 Crown Mill Sheet

320 Crown Mill Sheet. This was employed only for the 9d. value and has similar features to those of the 480 crown paper except that the word " POSTAGE " is different and there is no letter in the watermark. The letters indicating the panes are referred to in the listing of the 9d. value.

Post Office Sheets. The mill sheets were invariably guillotined by the printer into " Post Office sheets ". These varied in size according to value. When printed the mill sheet was cut down the central vertical line of three crosses giving two post office sheets of 240 crowns each for the $\frac{1}{2}$d to 7d. values.   For the other values printed on 480 crown paper, i.e. the 10d., 1s. and £1, each 240 crown sheet was further sub-divided along the horizontal row of large crosses into post office sheets of 120.   The 9d. value was only issued in post office sheets of one quarter of the mill sheet, i.e. with 80 crowns.

Recognising the Halves of the Mill Sheet.   The plating of Edwardian stamps is greatly simplified by the ability of the collector to recognize from which half of the mill sheet, left or right, any piece has come.   This can be done for any piece showing an undamaged corner selvedge, and any piece showing part of a letter in the watermark.

Examination of the 480 crown paper diagram shows that a cut along the line of crosses A, D and B (also called the "inner watermark crosses") leaves two halves, whose crosses are a mirror image of each other—that is if the sheet were folded exactly in half along the line A, D and B the watermark crosses on each half would fall exactly over each other. From this fact it is possible to assign each corner piece unequivocally to its correct half of the original mill sheet.

The essential details of the situation are shown in diagrams X and Y.   The collector should place the crown of the corner stamp on his piece over the crown in each diagram in turn.   He will find that in one or other case the watermark cross seen in the selvedge will fall close to or over *one* of the crosses on the diagrams (i.e. large or small cross).   The one that shows the closer fit will indicate from which side of the mill sheet his piece has come. To be more precise the diagrams show the positions of the crown relative to the inner corner angle pieces, but these are not always easily seen, hence the crown itself should be used.

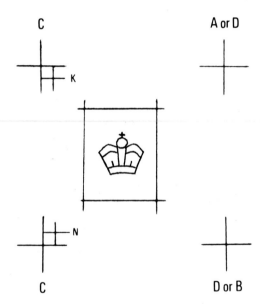

Diagram X.   Left Sheet Corner Crosses
(*Actual size*)

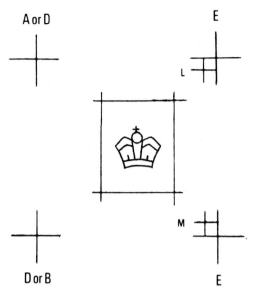

Diagram Y.   Right Sheet Corner Crosses
(*Actual size*)

The letters given to the corner crosses in the above diagrams relate to those in the diagram of the 480 crown mill sheet and a reference to this will show to which side of the mill sheet the corner piece belongs.

If the lines of the centre rectangle are taken to be the lines of the watermark angle pieces then the diagrams apply equally to both Imperial Crown watermark papers and also to the Anchor paper. Deciding the halves of the Anchor mill sheet is of no plating importance, hence the emphasis in the diagrams on the Imperial Crown paper.

The centre crosses A, D and B are hardly ever found complete. Being normally cut vertically only a small part of the horizontal arm may show. Similarly as crosses C, D and E are often cut in a horizontal direction only a small short piece of one vertical arm may show. The centre cross D may not show at all. The large crosses C, D and E are shown both above and below the rectangle in the diagrams because they occur in the centre of the mill sheet and can therefore relate either to an upper or a lower pane. Crosses A, K and L can only relate to upper panes and B, M and N to lower panes.

With a little practice the collector will be able to assign practically all his corner pieces to left or right sheets but deciding whether they come from upper or lower panes is more difficult and sometimes impossible.

More detailed information about this will be found in Part 19 of the series of articles on these issues by W. A. Wiseman in *The GB Journal* for October 1978.

Other Aids to Plating from the Watermark. The watermark words " POSTAGE " in the 480 crown mill sheet can also be useful in plating and positioning studies. If the stamps are perfectly printed relative to the watermark the " T " of " POSTAGE " falls exactly over the perforation gutter between the 6th and 7th stamps in the top and bottom rows, and opposite the perforation gutter between the 5th and 6th rows on each side of each pane where it occurs. The first three stamps in any horizontal direction from any corner of any pane show no sign of " POSTAGE " unless the watermark is displaced, whereas in the vertical direction no sign of the word can be seen beside the first two stamps. Hence no corner block of four ever shows part of " POSTAGE ".

Paper Quality. All the paper supplied was specified to be " animal tub-sized cream wove " of a certain weight per ream. The contracts had provision for checking the quality but in practice there was some variation. For example some stamps are found on paper with distinct ribbing, giving the appearance of laid paper. The cause of this is not clear but it is not a different paper, being manufactured in the web like the rest.

Types of Paper. Three types of paper were supplied to the printers. *Ordinary paper* was supplied initially to De La Rue for printing all values. This was surfaced before printing to varying degrees, sometimes sufficiently for surface rubbing to occur after printing, this showing as smudging of the details of the impression. It was generally white in appearance but there is some variation and a few pieces show significant toning but not sufficient to affect the perceived shades to any appreciable degree.

In April 1905 the Inland Revenue gave approval for *chalk-surfaced paper* to be used and thereafter this was supplied to De La Rue. It was used for the 1½d., 2d., 3d., 4d. green and brown, 5d., 6d., 9d., 10d., 1s. and 2s. 6d. values. The silver test is the only conclusive means of identifying the chalky paper. There are significant variations in the degree of surfacing and in later printings the paper is more heavily loaded, resulting in a more opaque, stiffer and weaker paper. The colour varies from brilliant white to distinctly yellowish, the majority being white or off white and these variations do have a significant effect on the perceived shades. The more highly toned papers cause the green head plate ink to appear yellower and the purple one to appear darker than normal.

The actual surface of this paper also varies considerably. Sometimes it seems to be unstable to such an extent that it is impossible to find even large mint blocks of some printings which do not show very severe rubbing. The pale purple head plate shade of the 1½d. value is caused by such paper. It is difficult to find blocks of four on chalky paper which do not show some signs of rubbing under a glass. The more highly toned paper usually shows much less rubbing than normal and pieces on brilliant white paper showing no signs of rubbing are very rare.

The chalky paper silver test. A piece of pure silver (better than 90%) is drawn over the surface of the paper and leaves a black line if chalky. This may, in fact, be rubbed out but even so some collectors are reluctant to use it and have tried other methods, such as an ultra violet lamp, but these other tests cannot be relied upon. The silver only needs to be drawn lightly over the surface to work but both the paper surface and the silver must be clean. The ideal tool is a piece of wire about 1 mm. diameter carefully rounded at the end and then polished with silver polish before use which can then be used to draw the finest of lines. Used stamps are liable to be dirty and it is advisable to try in several places and even then the test will occasionally fail.

Post January 1911 *paper.* Identical paper manufactured by R. D. Turner was furnished to Harrisons and Somerset House for the provisional printings, and the same paper had been supplied previously to De La Rue. The reason for the difference in the quality of the printing is that ever since 1879 De La Rue had been plate-glazing the paper, whereas Harrison and Somerset House did not. At first, therefore, their printings displayed a coarser surface and uneven thickness. In the late summer of 1912 Harrison arranged for Samuel Jones to plate-glaze the paper at an additional cost and later Harrison supplied Somerset House with paper plate-glazed and ready for printing. Hence the later provisional printings are distinguishable by the better finish of the paper and clearer impressions.

PRINTING PROCESS. All King Edward VII stamps were surface-printed. This process is also known as *letterpress* and philatelists usually refer to it as *typography.*

In typography the engraver cuts away from the soft steel die those parts of the design which are *not* to be printed. The ink roller is applied to the surface only of the electrotyped plate and the resulting impression has no depth of ink to it and feels flat under the fingertips compared with line-engraved stamps.

PLATES

Layout of Plates. The layout of the crowns and other watermark features on the mill sheet decided essentially the layout of the plates themselves and to a large extent dictated printing techniques.

The illustration of the 480 crown paper shows that the crowns are set out in two pairs of two panes, each pane having 120 crowns in 10 horizontal rows of 12. Between each vertical pair of panes a gap was left whose vertical dimension was exactly equal to that of a stamp. This gap is called the "interpane gutter". Obviously each crown watermark located the position of one stamp image on the plate, and hence each plate comprised two panes with 120 stamps, the upper and the lower. Round each pane was a coloured line, known as the "marginal rule", but the interpane gutter was treated differently in different values.

The monocoloured values (½d., 1d., 2½d., 3d., 4d. orange, 6d. and 7d.) had this space filled with 12 sets of 4 lined blocks or "pillars" and the marginal rule crossed the gutter at each end, while in the bicoloured values the gutter was blank and the marginal rule did not cross it at any point.

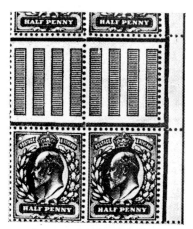

<table>
<tr><td>Interpane Gutter with Pillars
and Continuous Rules</td><td>Blank Interpane Gutter
Coextensive and Short Bar Rules</td></tr>
</table>

These pillars and rules all formed part of the plate (see under " Plate Markings "). Thus every plate printed on the 480 crown paper comprised 240 stamp images, that is, it was 240 " set ", except as indicated below for the 10d. and £1 values and for the 4d. value, where the brown duty plates were in fact 120 set.

In the £1 value each stamp covered three watermark crowns, so there were only 40 stamps in each pane and 80 on the plate. The marginal rule was arranged as for the other monocoloured values, except that there were 11 vertical pillars in each section of the interpane gutter instead of 4, there being four sections.

The 2s. 6d., 5s. and 10s. values were arranged as the other monocoloured values except that there were 8 sets of 4 pillars in the interpane gutter. Hence these plates were 112 set.

⊥

```
┌─────────────────────────────────────┐
│                                     │
│                                     │
│                  W                  │
│                                     │
│                                     │
└─────────────────────────────────────┘
```

4 horizontal and 48 vertical Lined Blocks
(alternately red and purple)

```
┌─────────────────────────────────────┐
│                                     │
│                                     │
│                  X                  │
│                                     │
│                                     │
└─────────────────────────────────────┘
```

. . . . . (Guillotined) . . . . .

```
┌─────────────────────────────────────┐
│                                     │
│                                     │
│                  Y                  │
│                                     │
│                                     │
└─────────────────────────────────────┘
```

4 horizontal and 48 vertical Lined Blocks
(alternately red and purple)

```
┌─────────────────────────────────────┐
│                                     │
│                                     │
│                  Z                  │
│                                     │
│                                     │
└─────────────────────────────────────┘
```

⊤

Layout of 10d. Printers' Sheets

In the bicoloured values the 10d., which was printed on the 480 crown paper, was arranged in four panes each of 4 horizontal rows of 12. The head plates were made up as one unit of four such panes and were therefore 192 set. The duty plates were 48 set each, so that each pane comprised one plate. These were numbered from 1 upwards (see under " Plate Numbering ") and it is likely that No. 1 was placed at the top, No. 2 second and so on but this is not absolutely certain and it is conventional to give the four panes the letters W X, Y and Z as shown in the diagram.

The sheets were guillotined between X and Y panes to form post office sheets of 96 and the blank interpane gutter between these two was exactly the same as between the panes of any other bicoloured value. Between the W and X and Y and Z panes there are two rows of crowns over which no stamp images appear. To prevent fraudulent use of this watermarked paper the interpane margin was filled with long horizontal pillars (or " lined blocks " as they are called to distinguish them from those on the monocoloured values) separated by short vertical lined blocks. There are two lines of blocks in the purple head plate ink and two in the red duty plate ink in each gutter, so that the crowns which do not have stamps on them are each covered by one head/duty pair. The lined blocks formed no part of either the head or duty plates.

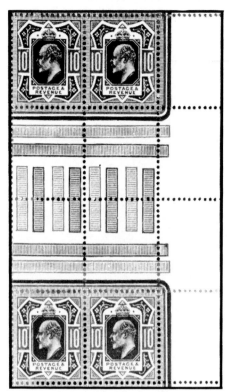

Horizontal and vertical lined
Blocks or Pillars separating
the 10d. Panes

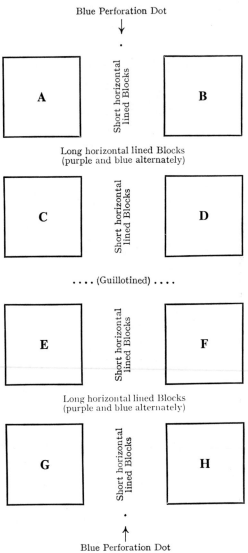

Layout of 9d. Printers' Sheets

The 9d. value, being printed on the 9d. paper, had head plates comprising eight panes of 20 stamps each (4 horizontal rows of 5 stamps), being 160 set. The duty plates were separate units, each plate being one pane in size, i.e. 20 set. Again, each duty plate had a number but the layout of these is obscure and it is conventional to give them letters as shown in the diagram.

The printers' sheets were guillotined between CD and EF panes to form post office sheets of 80 and the interpane gutter between these was blank. The positions of the interpane blocks are indicated in the above diagram. They did not form part of the plate.

Plate Making. All plates used for printing King Edward VII stamps were made by De La Rue. They were mostly copper electrotype plates, backed with solder and given an electrolytic coating of "steel" before use. They were made essentially in the same way as the master plates made by the Royal Mint and a full description of this is given in Gibbons *Stamp Monthly* for March 1973, p. 176. However there was one major difference: the Royal Mint pressed the working plates from master plates while De La Rue generally made them from recently-struck leads.

A few De La Rue plates, especially the duty plates of the 4d., 9d. and 10d. values, were made from master plates. This meant one striking only of the necessary leads, but that for the 9d. duty plates took place in Victorian times. The only other strikings of duty plate leads for King Edward stamps were for the 1½d. value, for which one plate was made and used, and the 1s. value for which two plates were made but not used.

De La Rue Striking Books. Records of the striking of all leads were kept in special books, known as "Striking Books". The contents of numbers 5 and 6 referred to King Edward VII stamps and these survived the war but were broken up and put on the market in December 1975. Earlier books were badly damaged during the Second World War.

Each piece cut from these books is unique, usually giving the plate number and date of striking. Each entry refers to one "warrant", i.e. official instruction to make a plate or plates, hence the original books formed a record of every plate made, either individually or collectively, together with the striking of surplus leads for repair of plates but such a striking is not evidence of specific use. Each entry had a cut down die proof attached recording the die from which the leads were taken.

The pieces cut from the Edwardian Striking Books are listed in abbreviated form and an illustration of one of these is shown under the ½d. value.

In addition to striking leads from the die for stamps, plate making from leads also involved the striking of leads for ancillary purposes, such as the marginal rules, pillars, etc.

Plate Numbering. 324 Great Britain plates were made by De La Rue bearing the head of King Edward VII. Of these 56 were fiscal plates. They were, however, all numbered in sequence from 1 to 324. This is called the "current number". In addition to this the successive plates for each value were numbered consecutively from 1 onwards and these are the true plate numbers. The combined numbers comprise the full plate number and are expressed thus: 4/264, the 4 being the plate number for that value and the 264 its current number.

For the collector the interesting number is the plate number but the current number is also useful as it was allotted in the order in which the plates were actually made, with insignificant exceptions, and so helps to date them. Moreover both numbers are essential for anyone referring to official records.

Duty plates were given a single plate number, each value having its own series starting from 1. Thus every 20 set duty plate of the 9d. value had its own sequential number in the series of all the 20 set duty plates made from 1886 onwards. The 1½d., 2d., 5d. and 1s. were similar in that respect but the 4d. and 10d. had plate number series starting from 1901, independent of the Victorian series.

All these plate numbers, both head and duty, were incorporated into the non-printing margin of the plates, so that they could be read by the printers and others using them. Thus no plate numbers of King Edward stamps were ever printed on sheets of stamps but when registration and proof sheets were taken for record purposes, the Inspector certifying the sheets almost invariably recorded the plate number or numbers on the sheet. From this, and from many other clues, it has been possible to correlate various features on the plates, minor flaws, etc., with a given plate number and thus assign official plate numbers to plates which have hitherto been known under their philatelic numbers.

SHEET MARKINGS. Various markings are found on the sheets as described below.

Registration Piece. Above and below the marginal rules of Nos. 6 and 7 at the top and bottom of the sheet there is a thin bar with a projection in the middle, upwards at top and downwards at bottom, sometimes referred to as a "T" mark. At the bottom and below this and at the top above it there is a coloured dot where the paper is invariably pierced by a needle. The dots were to ensure correct registration of the sheet in the perforating machine.

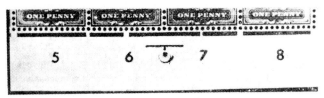

Die I Registration Piece

The "T" together with a short length of marginal rule, were all incorporated into a die used to strike leads, called a "registration (piece) die". A consequence of this was that the marginal rules in the area concerned required special treatment. Details of this are given in the *GB Journal* for January 1975, p. 18. In the 9d. value this registration die was replaced by a single tiny blue dot at top and bottom exactly between the A and B and G and H panes. For convenience this is called the "perforation dot".

Marginal Rules. The three types of marginal rule are to be seen in the two illustrations above under "Layout of the Plates". They are:—

Continuous. The rule is virtually without any breaks.

Coextensive. The rule is divided into regular lengths, each about the width or height of the adjacent stamp.

Short bar. The rule is divided into short lengths, sometimes of a regular size, but bearing no relationship in size to the neighbouring stamp. They were almost invariably much shorter than coextensive rules.

Their purpose was to help protect the adjacent stamps from the impact of the printing rollers. They came from leads struck from an appropriate die, e.g. a separate one for the vertical and horizontal rules.

In the *continuous rule* plates the gaps between adjacent pieces of the rule were filled in by hand work which is often visible at the perforation gutters. This included joining in the short piece of rule formed by the registration piece die. In late 1902 this policy was abandoned because it was so time consuming and thereafter the plates were made with coextensive rules. The short bar rules, and in a few cases the coextensive rules, were made by chopping up what had originally been continuous rule.

At first the *coextensive rule* was made from the existing dies (being left unjoined), including the registration piece die. For some reason this was not satisfactory and in 1904 a new registration piece die was introduced, known as Die II. This can be distinguished from Die I in having a tiny white dot in the rule below No. 6 in the bottom row and over No. 7 in the top row.

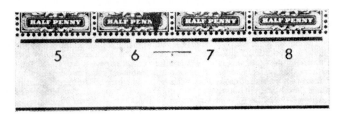

Die II Registration Piece

The 6/7 rule variety. In the Die I period there was some doubt about the best method of dealing with the rules over and under the 6th and 7th vertical columns. It was a consequence of using the registration piece die that when the leads were assembled in the chase prior to electroplating there were gaps in the rule under the middle of the 6th and 7th stamps in the bottom row and over the same stamps in the top row. In the bottom row the right-hand gap was about half the size of a normal gap between adjacent coextensive rules whilst in the top row it was the left-hand gap which was narrow (see illustration of the Die I registration piece). This is more fully explained in *The GB Journal* for January 1975, p. 18 already referred to above.

These gaps could either be left as they were, filled in or a new gap opened out under the perforation gutter between the 6th and 7th columns and all these options were taken in the Die I period. Pieces with the gaps filled (with or without narrow gap under 6/7 gutter) are known as being the "6/7 rule" variety and are found on the ½d., 1d. and 6d. values, pieces with unfilled gaps being confined to the ½d. and 1d. There are no variations in the Die II registration piece.

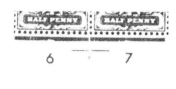

Without gap under R. 6/7   With new narrow gap under R. 6/7

Die I Registration Pieces with Gaps Filled
(the 6/7 rule variety)

Exceptions. In the Edwardian stamps there were exceptions to the arrangements mentioned above. The 4d. green and brown head plate 4/250 with coextensive rules had a quite unique arrangement in this area of the plate, top and bottom. The plates of the 4d. orange and the 7d. values had no registration piece, and the rules were from new dies specially made for the purpose. Perforation dots are found under and over the 6/7 perforation gutters but how they were located on the plate is not known.

The marginal rules of the head and duty plates of the bicoloured stamps do not coincide at any point except in the 5d. value where they coincide horizontally over each pane (this was because the duty plates were used for the Victoria issues where the tablet positions are a little higher than on the Edward stamps and in consequence there is a correspondingly large gap at the bottom of each pane).

For the bicoloured stamps the rules were made from different dies, those close to the stamps being from "inner line" dies and those further away from "outer line" dies. The inner line dies included the registration piece die and represented something that was fixed to ensure correct perforation registration. The outer line dies included neither a registration piece nor a perforation dot. To ensure the correct registration of the head and duty plate printings it was necessary to have provision on the printing plates for some adjustment and this was done by making the outer line plates adjustable. As it was inconvenient to manoeuvre the whole plate the outer line plates became divided up into sections. For diagram see next page.

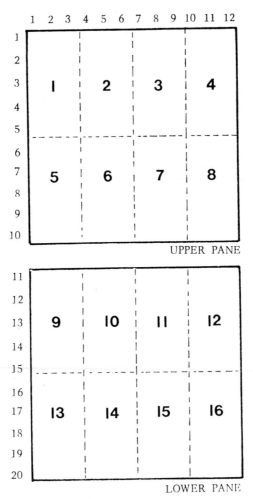

Diagram of Sections of Outer Line Plates

Mostly these sections comprised five horizontal rows of three stamps and there were thus 16 sections in each 240 set plate which are numbered as in the above illustration. Normally these sections would only be of academic interest, but Somerset House transferred some sections of one duty plate of the 2d. value onto another, thus providing an interesting field of study.   Such partial substitutions were also made on the 9d. and 1s. where bits of both head and duty plates were moved about and added to as occasion demanded.

King George V plates began with the rules over and under the 6th and 7th stamps in the same state as they had been for the later King Edward VII plates.   Later King George V plates were invariably made so that the rules in this area of the plates looked exactly the same as those in any other area.   This was done by opening out a gap under the 6/7 column perforation gutter and closing those under and over the stamps themselves.   The traces of this work can be found on the master plates in the National Postal Museum. For further information on these matters see *The GB Journal* for February 1975, p. 26, and for January 1977, p. 14.

CONTROLS. The letters date back only to 1882 (being first used for the 1881 1d. Lilac, Die II) and were used by De La Rue to assist in the financial control of the stocks of paper. Prior to the Edwardian period they were changed at irregular intervals but in the new reign they were at first changed annually in October.   Towards the end of 1903 the Inland Revenue requested that a figure be added to the control letter to represent the year and that this figure be changed on 1 January in each year.   Hence on 1 January 1904 the figure " 4 " was added to the current letter, which was " C ".   Thereafter the letters were changed annually at about the end of the first quarter so that each year date appears in combination with two different letters.   In the listing of the controls in this catalogue the dates given refer to the first reported dates of issue, not those when the changes were made by the printers.

In the King Edward VII issues only the ½d. and 1d. values had Controls .and these are listed and priced.

D4

A 11

With Continuous Rule   With Coextensive Rule

Above are illustrated two typical ½d. Controls.   (The marginal rules have been fully described earlier in these notes.)

½d. value. The Controls were made up from type as required and were attached to the presses used by De La Rue. In the ½d. value Controls "A" and "B" are located under the 11th stamp in the bottom row but all the others are below the 2nd stamp. Control letters "A" (including the "A" in "A 11") and "B" are set in sans-serif capitals and the rest in serifed capitals.

1d. value. Controls appear under the 11th stamp in the bottom row and all letters are in sans-serif capitals.

The perforation types are fully illustrated and described in Appendix 1. The few whole sheets of early Controls of both the ½d. and 1d. seen to date are Perf Types V4 or V4A. More information about Controls can be found in *The GB Journal* for November 1974, p. 127, October 1975, p. 106 and November 1975, p. 128.

Prices. The King Edward VII Control lists are set out according to the various perforation types.   Prices are therefore for unused *corner pairs* with side and bottom selvedge intact. Controls in Section NA are also priced thus. Note that all other King George V typographed Controls are priced for single unused examples with Control attached.

PLATE MARKINGS. These are markings which are found on the marginal rules. They have been used by collectors for the purposes of identifying the different plates but they were never placed there by the printers for that purpose.   As already explained the plates had their numbers engraved on them but outside the printing area.

The following diagrams show typical markings found on the marginal rules and are shown here for reference purposes in connection with both King George V stamps and King Edward VII issues, and some of them are only seen on the former.

Two small dots   Cut with   Cut   Oval dot
(top/base)   central dot

Examples of Plate Markings

Descriptions in the Lists. Markings in the bottom marginal rule are given a position relative to the letters of the wording in the value tablet. Hence " Cut under (N)N of 7th " indicates a cut under the second N of PENNY of the 7th stamp in the row.

Markings in the vertical rules at the side are given a position in millimetres from the bottom of the rule. Thus " Cut 19th right side, 7 mm " indicates a cut on the right side of row 19 at a point 7 mm from the bottom of the rule. For greater accuracy the measurement is taken to the centre of the marking.

The marks found on the Edwardian issues can be divided between those employed by De La Rue and Harrisons and those placed there by Somerset House.

De La Rue and Harrison Markings. These generally take the form of straightforward cuts through the rule or half cuts. They are essentially linked to the side of the mill sheet upon which the plate was used. Thus plates found on left-hand halves have a cut or pair of cuts under odd numbered stamps in the bottom row, while those found on right-hand halves have them under even numbered stamps. In some instances this system was extended round the right-hand corner of the bottom row. Thus cuts right of the 20th row are found on right-hand sheets, right of the 19th row on left-hand sheets and right of the 18th row on right-hand sheets and so on.

The cuts appear to have indicated the position on the press from which the sheets were printed. Some plates started life without cuts. This happened when the plate was paired with another having a single cut, which gave the information required, thus obviating the need to make an additional mark or cut.

It is rare to find cuts filled up on De La Rue sheets, i.e. almost invisible ones, as generally when a plate was moved from one side of the press to the other, or to another machine requiring a different marking, the earlier cuts were left unchanged. Hence on some plates, especially in the ½d. and 1d. values, bottom rows can be found with a number of cuts under different stamps, some odd and some even, each one presumably representing a different position for the plate. Sorting these out in chronological order is quite a problem and the matter is confounded by the very occasional practice of moving a plate and not making a new mark. Thus it is possible to find sheets with left-hand sheet marks but which are in fact right-hand sheets, and vice versa.

Additional marks under the 6th and 7th stamps must not be confused with the normal gaps found on coextensive plates (see under " The 6/7 rule variety ").

Somerset House Markings. These can be divided into four types which can be summarised as " date cuts ", " ink dots ", " guillotine dots " and " plate dots ".

Date cuts. In 1911 it became the practice to mark the bottom marginal rule with two cuts under the 11th stamp to denote " 1911 " with a single cut under another stamp to indicate the month, e.g. a cut under the 7th for a printing made in July. In the 1½d. value a " V " mark was made instead of a cut. The first printing in 1912 of the 2d. value had two dots under the 12th stamp. On all other values two cuts were placed under the 12th stamp, all others (including De La Rue cuts) being filled up, sometimes so perfectly that it is often very difficult to locate the positions of the original ones. Printings in 1913 retained the old 1912 cuts.

Ink dots. From April 1912 a white dot was inserted right of the 20th, 19th or 18th rows of the 6d. value. An existing dot was completely removed before a new one was inserted and the change took place every time a different ink was used and they are therefore helpful in dating different printings. The 5d. value has a similar mark right of the 20th row which was placed there in 1913 but it is not known whether this has any connection with the ink.

Guillotine dots. Coloured dots in monocoloured stamps, and in the colour of the head plate ink in bicoloured stamps, were sometimes placed down the line of the centre mill sheet watermark crosses (A, D and B) to guide the guillotine cut between left and right halves. They are sometimes useful in recognising the left or right half of the mill sheet.

Plate dots. In the King George V issues Somerset House marked the plates with a white dot smaller than the ink dots to indicate the plate number for the particular value. This was placed in the marginal rule over the top row of each pane, the stamp number being determined by the plate. Thus a dot over the 2nd stamp would indicate plate 2 of that value. This occurred in some values from the 1½d. upwards. In the case of later plates of the 6d. where these dots occur it is likely that they were put there for this purpose but not certain.

Scoops. So-called " scoops " occur on some King Edward VII and King George V plates but they happened through accident rather than intention. They are found on the outside of marginal rules in constant positions throughout the life of the plate and in varying degrees. They occur close to screws that fix the plates to the underplates. They are valuable for plate recognition.

Other Markings. Other markings are found mainly on King George V issues and some are illustrated. In most instances their purposes are not understood and some may have come about accidentally but they are helpful for plating purposes.

PLATE VARIETIES. A plate variety is a flaw on a stamp caused by an imperfection on the plate which has been transmitted to the stamp in the course of printing. Such a variety will be constant and will appear on every stamp printed from that position of the plate, sometimes in different states, unless it is discovered and subsequently corrected. There are other flaws which may be found on more than one copy which are not necessarily constant; they may be due to foreign matter adhering to the plate and therefore of a transient nature. They cannot be classed as plate flaws.

There are thousands of flaws on Edwardian and Georgian stamps and it is our policy to list only the more prominent ones whose positions have been established and we also quote the particular plate where this is known.

Displaced Cliché

SUBSTITUTED AND DISPLACED CLICHES. It is known that in early Victorian times De La Rue made repairs by cutting out old clichés and substituting new ones. However, records do not show whether this practice continued in the Edwardian period. Such a substitution may sometimes be revealed by the new cliché being slightly out of alignment but this was not always so.

It is now clear that the majority of the known examples of displaced clichés are due to other causes, such as deformation of the plate under stress, and they are in fact quite common. In view of this the varieties previously listed as " Substituted cliché " are now described as " Displaced cliché " and a few have been added.

PLUG REPAIRS. When a small area of a plate was unsatisfactory one method of repairing it was by drilling out the offending area, putting a copper pin in the hole, knocking it flat and re-engraving that part of the design which was originally faulty. This is known as a "plug repair". Often this was done so well as to be unnoticeable but some obvious examples are known on the 1d. value where a typical one is illustrated. Other very similar varieties exhibiting small circles on the stamps exist but they are not necessarily plug repairs.

CLICHÉ LOCATION. When listing varieties where the plate number is known we quote this first " Pl. " or, in the case of bicoloured stamps, " Pl. H " or " Pl. D " for head or duty plate. This is followed by the row number and the position in the row from the left, thus " R. 6/4 " means the fourth stamp from the left in the sixth horizontal row from the top.

PRINTING

LAYOUT, ETC. The size and layout of the mill sheet governed the techniques of printing. Monocoloured low values were printed from two plates laid down side by side on to the undivided mill sheets. The 2s. 6d. to £1 values were printed from a single plate on both sides of the mill sheet.

De La Rue printed the bicoloured values from two pairs of plates, one of each pair being a head plate and the other a duty plate, and the duty plates, which received the non-fugitive ink, were printed first. However, Somerset House used only one pair of plates, i.e. 240 set instead of 480.

Before printing the paper was gummed and after printing the sheets were interleaved, stacked and left to dry for some days under Inland Revenue control.

CONTROL OF PRINTING. Printing was controlled by the Inland Revenue at every stage, even when done at Somerset House. The first step was for the Accounts Branch to issue the printers with a "Warrant" in money terms in units of mill sheets. Thus a warrant for £200,000 in sheets of 480 at £4 per sheet of the 2d. value meant 100,000 sheets of 240. The printers were supplied with the precise quantity of paper needed and when invoicing for stamps supplied had to account for all paper wasted

Printing of the ½d. and 1d. was continuous and warrants were issued for them, but for the other values it was usual for warrants to represent about one year's supply. They were numbered consecutively and dated. The number of printings of each value and their approximate dates are known. It is not, however, possible to identify every printing by shade or ink. In the tables of printings the numbers assigned to the printings bear no relationship to the warrant numbers.

Where we have been able to introduce Printing Schedules in this edition the dates given relate to the period during which the stamps were being printed. In the lists the dates for the introduction of the chalk-surfaced paper refer to the earliest recorded date of appearance to the nearest month and these are usually a month or two after printing. Thus in the 5d., for instance, the 5th printing was the first on chalk-surfaced paper and took place during February/March 1906 and the first recorded use was in May 1906. Several dates hitherto accepted for the introduction of this paper have been shown not to accord with the printing dates and have had to be amended in this edition.

The above refers to De La Rue printings. Similar information about Harrison printings is not available but dates of many of the Somerset House printings are known

PRINTING VARIETIES. A number of different types of varieties are due to printing problems rather than plate making.

Watermark Varieties. It is extremely rare for a sheet to be printed on paper without watermark. Most stamps without watermark come from rows adjoining the selvedge and result from misplacement of the watermark. This accounts for stamps showing parts of the word "POSTAGE" in the watermark.

Most inverted watermarks come quite normally from booklet panes, being printed from special plates which have half the clichés inverted. Inverted and often misplaced watermarks from sheets, due to the more or less square sheets having been fed from the wrong way up, are quite rare.

Reversed watermarks occur more often in the King George V issues and result from the paper having been gummed on the wrong side. Similarly, watermarks may be found both inverted and reversed.

Recession Flaws. The pressure required for surface-printing causes the paper to be slightly embossed, i.e. it is slightly raised at the back. In bicoloured printing, where the impressions of the head and duty plates come together there is a tendency for the head plate not to print properly in the area of the "embossing" caused by the duty plate. This produces what is known as a "recession flaw", which may vary from printing to printing but will remain constant within a printing. The best known examples of this type of flaw are the "no cross on crown" varieties of the 10d. value, where the cross can be found in all stages of recession (but not all cross on crown varieties are due to this cause). Other examples are known, including the loss of frame lines.

Offsets and Double Prints. An "offset" (more accurately termed "setoff" but this is not used in philately) is simply a reverse impression on the back of a stamp taken from the sheet below in the stack due to the ink being still wet and the absence of an interleaving sheet. Such items are outside the scope of S.G. catalogues.

However, if the two sheets without interleaf are slightly shifted whilst the ink is still wet, the offset impression will make a faint non-coincident second impression on the face of the original sheet. This appears like a "double print". It is important to distinguish between offset impressions, where the second impression is faint by comparison, and true double prints where the paper has passed through the press twice. These varieties are rarely found on Edwardian stamps but more often occur on Georgian stamps, especially the Downey Head issues.

INKS AND SHADES

A. De La Rue Printings. Research by M. R. Fox (see *The GB Journal* for March 1975, p. 44) has shown that in the King Edward VII period De La Rue always used the same composition of ink for the same value. Stamps were held by both De La Rue and the Inland Revenue as standards for colour matching of subsequent printings (see notes under "Specimens" in Appendix 4).

The inks for the monocoloured values and the duty plates of the bicoloured were " singly fugitive", that is they were affected only by mineral solvents. The 6d. value and the head plates of the bicoloured values were printed in doubly fugitive inks, that is inks which were affected by both mineral and aqueous solvents. The latter were compounded mainly of vegetable dyes and were relatively unstable in that they could be affected by even the moisture in the air.

The green head plate ink was especially sensitive, and it is possible to detect what appears to be a slightly blue look in even well-preserved mint stamps. The vast majority of unused stamps today can be assumed to show much the same perceived shades as they did when they were printed. Naturally the same cannot be said for used copies as many have been carelessly soaked off paper, resulting in the ink going first blue and then pale yellow, depending upon the degree of exposure to water.

However, easily perceived shade variations are found in all De La Rue stamps of this period, sometimes even on the same sheet of stamps. In general variation in depth of colour is of less importance than difference in tone. As already mentioned under "Types of Paper—Chalk-surfaced Paper" the toning of the paper does affect the perceived shades.

B. Somerset House Printings. It is known that Somerset House made numerous experiments with printing inks on the Provisional Issues but they have not yet been fully studied. We have therefore not attempted to make any alterations to our listing of these shades, although more perceived shades exist than are listed. Some footnotes relating to Somerset House shades will be found in the text and so do not need to be repeated here.

C. Harrison Printings. Harrison inks are virtually unknown but it is clear that different ones were tried in some values. It is not known if there was close liaison with Somerset House in these matters.

Fluorescent Inks. Under the influence of invisible ultra violet rays some colouring matters give off visible light of various colours. In Edwardian times the compounds doing this were essentially artificial dyes derived from a chemical compound called "aniline". Hence inks that show fluorescence, especially when they give off orange or golden orange light, are called "aniline" shades. Though occasionally found in De La Rue printings, fluorescence is common in certain values printed by Harrison and Somerset House. Where they occur they are indicated by " (F) " after the shade description.

Collectors are warned that ultra violet lamps can be dangerous if incorrectly used and care should be taken to ensure that glasses are worn when the light is on and the skin exposed as little as possible.

GUM. The gum was invariably applied to the paper before printing. It varies in texture and colour, especially in De La Rue printings. There are no consistent differences between the gum used by De La Rue and that in the provisional printings except that the latter always have white gum and the former are sometimes darker; hence pieces with darker gum can be safely assigned to De La Rue issues.

PERFORATION. All De La Rue and Somerset House issues gauge 14 all round. Harrison issues gauged 14 to start with and were then changed to 15×14 to equalise the breaking force required to separate stamps along the horizontal and vertical gutters. For details about the various perforators see Appendix 1. They were designed to perforate half mill sheets.

BOOKLETS. Booklets first appeared in 1904, although discussions on them had taken place in the previous reign. Special plates were made comprising 20 horizontal rows of 12 stamps with an interpane gutter between rows 10 and 11 to ensure that the crowns on the mill sheet would fit.

Each horizontal row had the first three stamps upright, the next three inverted, followed by a narrow vertical gutter (to allow for the binding margins) and then again three upright and three inverted stamps. This meant that half the stamps from booklets have the watermark inverted. The introduction of the central vertical gutter caused the crowns to be displaced left or right on all stamps and the outside stamps sometimes have part of the word " POSTAGE " in the watermark.

The first booklet issued contained 24 1d. stamps and sold at 2s. 0½d. The next four booklets were sold at 2s. The first of these contained 12 1d. stamps and 23 ½d. stamps. In the next three issues the make-up changed to 18 1d. stamps and 11 ½d. stamps. This meant that one pane in the booklet comprised five stamps and the sixth position was taken up by a St. Andrew's cross.

De La Rue made three 1d. plates and four ½d. plates and to provide for the panes of five ½d. stamps one pair of plates had the St. Andrew's cross in the 3rd and 4th and the 9th and 10th positions in alternate rows.

The booklet panes are listed after the sheet stamps and the complete booklets are listed and priced in Appendix 2.

COIL STAMPS. Not many Edwardian coil stamps have been authenticated and no attempt has been made to list them. All were made up from ordinary sheets with joins on the back by the various promoters of the coin-operated dispensing machines. They were not made by the printers of the stamps in Edwardian times. Further information on this subject will be found in a series of articles by G. H. R. Homer-Wooff and Peter J. Jones which started in *The GB Journal* for February 1977.

Apart from authenticated coil join pairs, single copies of coil stamps can sometimes be identified by a close examination of the perforations to check the method by which they were separated.

First in the field was Mrs. Kermode who conducted an official trial for the Post Office, installing machines at the House of Commons and at Threadneedle Street B.O. in July 1906. The stamps were delivered sideways, separated by a knife and dispensed. The 1d. stamp No. M5 was employed and this would have *cuts through the perforations at both sides*. In 1907 the machine was modified to give vertical delivery and the stamps were pulled from the machine by the purchaser, thus showing *no cut marks*. These machines were supplied to the Post Office and commercial undertakings and were in use for many years. The 1d. stamps Nos. M5/7 were most commonly used with these machines but all values up to 1s. are known to have been issued from coil machines.

In 1907 experiments were made with the German Abel machine, later patented by the British Electric Automatic Machine Co. and known as the BEAM machine. This gave vertical delivery dispensing the stamps into a delivery box so that they show knife *cuts at top and bottom*. Nos. M5/7 were used. The machines were less successful and were withdrawn in 1914 with the advent of war with Germany.

Between November 1910 and January 1911 there was a short-lived experiment with the Rex machine which was adapted to affix the stamp on to the envelope. At first it employed whole sheets joined together and later half sheets which had been divided vertically. This produced a horizontal strip of stamps which were then issued singly after a three bladed knife had cut through the perforations on three sides. Thus stamps would show *cuts on all four sides* and only No. M5 was employed.

Finally, in 1910 there was an unsatisfactory experiment with the Kingsway machine which was designed to attract a revenue by displaying advertisements every time it was operated. This also used complete sheets joined together in a continuous roll. First it severed a horizontal strip of twelve stamps which was fed forward for cutting and dispensing stamps singly. The first marginal stamp might show pulled perforations on one side but the rest would have *cuts on all four sides,* and again No. M5 was used.

DISTINGUISHING THE PROVISIONAL PRINTINGS. This is a difficult subject as there are no simple infallible tests that can be used. However, there are a few tests by which some stamps can easily be assigned but in other cases it is usually necessary to look at a combination of factors. We start by describing some general tests and then go on to deal with each value in turn.

Perforation
Stamps perforated 15 × 14 were printed only by Harrison. It is worth while having the 2½d., 3d. and 4d. values in this perforation as their shades and appearance in most cases match the Harrison perf. 14 printings and they are therefore valuable reference material.

Except for the 6d. value all stamps on chalk-surfaced paper were printed by De La Rue.

Stamps perforated by the horizontal Type H1 comb machine can only be printed by De La Rue, whilst the ½d., 1d., 3d. and 4d. perf. 14 from the horizontal Type H2 machine must be Harrison printings and the £1 from the same machine must be printed by Somerset House. These can be identified by the selvedge by reference to the descriptions in Appendix 1.

In this connection it is possible to distinguish the use of vertical and horizontal comb perforators from single stamps without selvedge. Many perforators have imperfections such as uneven spacing of pins, pins out of alignment or of uneven size, etc. Place a ruler along one edge of the stamp and note any irregularities. Then transfer it to the opposite side and see if the same irregularities are repeated exactly. If this is so on the vertical sides then the stamp as been perforated by a vertical comb perforator. Similarly, repeated irregularities on the horizontal sides will reveal a horizontal comb perforator.

Paper
Differences in the quality of the paper affect the standard of printing and thus the general appearance of the stamps. The provisional printings are generally coarser because of the imperfections of the paper. In consequence under the glass the edges of the design are seen to be blurred with sudden changes of direction, whereas in the De La Rue products the edges are sharp and free flowing without changes of direction. This is a general characteristic which lasted until the introduction of the plate glazed paper towards the end of the Somerset House printings. However it does not apply to the 6d. value on chalky and other surfaced papers.

Shades

Study of the inks used can provide a valuable method of recognition of the two products. Somerset House tried many different inks and it is sometimes possible to follow their progressive use through different values as the same characteristics appear in different values at about the same time. The most important colours are the purples and greens used for the head plates and the reds and blues used for the duty plates, generally but not exclusively in the bicoloured values.

Purple inks. The early provisional purple inks show very red compared with the slate-purple of De La Rue. Later they became much closer to the De La Rue colour. During this period various purples appear which show a strong golden fluorescence under ultra violet light. These fluorescent inks vary from reddish purple to the full deep slate-purple found in the early to middle 1912 printings of the 1½d. value. After this there was a reversion to redder purples, generally called plum, easily distinguishable from the De La Rue slate-purple and non fluorescent. The last Somerset House printings, especially of the 5d. and 9d. values, were in deep purple, darker even than the De La Rue slate-purple on chalky paper. The Harrison purple was redder than De La Rue. For the 6d. value see below.

To summarise, reddish looking purples are Harrison or Somerset House printings, the dark purples are Somerset House but the slate-purples may be De La Rue or Somerset House.

Green inks. The early Somerset House greens are generally darker than those of De La Rue. Later they began to get a closer match and it is sometimes difficult to distinguish them, especially in used condition. In the 2d. value some issues were made in an ink with a distinct olive appearance, far yellower than any De La Rue product.

To summarise, duller, darker greens and those with a clear olive look are Somerset House printings.

Red inks. The red provisional inks are much duller than the corresponding De La Rue ink, even when fairly close in shade. The early red printings were more scarlet than De La Rue but later they were more carmine. For example those 1s. values showing the dark green head plate and scarlet frame plate can never be muddled with De La Rue products but later printings are more difficult. The carmine ink used in later printings of the 2d. value suffused through the paper or failed to dry properly, hence it shows through the back, making it easily recognised. Such effects are never seen on De La Rue printings.

To summarise, the provisional reds are duller than the De La Rue ink and are often more scarlet in shade.

Blue inks. The De La Rue blue is unmistakable. It is a brilliant light ultramarine with a pale look about it compared with any provisional printing. The early provisional printings of the 9d. are in a bright blue but deeper and more violet than the De La Rue ultramarine. Later this gave way to a pale ink but it is still dull. After these the provisional blues became very dull, with a touch of grey in them. Later still they were displaced by brighter blues but duller than the early bright blue and the De La Rue ink.

To summarise, the De La Rue blue is a brilliant shade against which all the others appear dull except for the first bright blue.

Individual Values

½d. The green is generally darker, duller and bluer than De La Rue products but a wide range of provisional inks was used and some confusion may arise. See notes after No. M3.

1d. The provisional shades are generally duller. The rose-red shade has a distinct orange look to it, while the carmines generally look deeper and bluer but there are some confusing shades. Shades showing fluorescence can only be from provisional printings. See notes after No. M6.

1½d. The purple diagonal line in the S.E. corner is always thick on Somerset House printings due to a fresh make ready but this is not an infallible guide as a few De La Rue stamps also show it thus. Normally De La Rue printings have this line thin. See notes after No. M10.

2d. Because a new duty plate was introduced in 1912 the duty tablets of later Somerset House printings have thick, even frame lines and well formed corners which are not rounded. Most of these can also be recognised by their ink (see under " Red inks " above).

2½d. The Harrison perf. 14 stamps always show a dull blue shade quite unlike any De La Rue product and they are nearly always poorly centred.

3d. The Harrison perf. 14 issues are on lemon paper whereas the De La Rue printings on ordinary paper are on orange-yellow. This is best seen from the back. Again, the Harrison printings are generally badly centred.

4d. The Harrison orange is bright, the only case where the provisional printing is consistently distinctly brighter than the De La Rue printings. De La Rue stamps are deeper, duller and with a touch of grey or red in them.

5d.   See notes about shades after No. M30. The majority of the unused stamps on the market are from Somerset House printings.

6d.   This value is very complicated as there are De La Rue ordinary and chalk-surfaced papers and Somerset House ordinary, "Dickinson" coated and chalk-surfaced papers. The early provisional printings on ordinary paper were of a dull reddish purple which later became even darker.   The "Dickinson" coated and chalk-surfaced papers produced very fine printings and the latter rarely shows rubbing, unlike the De La Rue chalky paper printings.   The chalky provisional printings are easily confused but the provisional ink is darker (without being slate) than the De La Rue.   The paper is always white.   See further notes under Nos. M34 and M36.

7d.   This is a very difficult value to assign with confidence and we cannot add anything to the notes which appear under No. M38.

9d.   Owing to the mixture of blue and purple none of the provisional printings can be confused with the ultramarine of De La Rue and the Somerset House purples are generally redder.

10d.   The provisional purple ink begins reddish, usually with a scarlet duty plate.   These scarlet inks are generally fluorescent and cannot be confused with De La Rue stamps which are basically carmine.   The later slate-purple head and carmine duty plate inks cause more difficulty, especially when printed on plate glazed paper, but the inks are duller, especially the carmine.

1s.   The early head and frame plate inks are quite different from the De La Rue inks while the later inks, being darker and duller than the De La Rue issues, should also present little problem.

2s. 6d.   The comments about the purple shades above generally apply to this value.

5s.   This is the most difficult value of all in which to assign single copies of the different printers.   As stated in the notes after No. M52 the De La Rue ink tends to show through the back of the stamp but this is not a completely reliable guide.

10s.   This is the only value in which a blue ink was used where the difference in shade between the two printers is not very great.   However, the comments above about blue inks remain valid.   The De La Rue ink is an ultramarine, a bright light colour, light in the sense of having a white look about it as it is not a pale colour.   The Somerset House blues are duller, with a deeper violet or purple tone.

£1.   This value is not easy to distinguish, even for experts.   The De La Rue green is bluish whilst the Somerset House is a deeper, richer green.

Used Stamps

Used examples in good, clean, unrubbed condition and with dated postmarks can form the basis of a useful reference collection, the dates often assisting in the assignment to the printers.

STAMPS OVERPRINTED "SPECIMEN" OR "CANCELLED". As with those of the Victorian issues they are listed in the basic lists after the varieties. Some overprint types are listed under National Postal Museum Archives as they are only known from this source. The various types of overprint are illustrated in Appendix 4 where further information is given.

Essays, Proofs and Colour Trials

ESSAYS.   The earliest King Edward VII essays were paste-ups on the then current Queen Victoria stamps and they were followed by black and white photographic essays and some coloured ones for the new designs.   Then came the abortive "Transvaal" essays and the "Canada" head essays.   Essays in private hands from these groups are listed at the conclusion of these notes.   Essays for the 2d. Tyrian plum and for the 1910 7d. value show a further advance in essay production as they were on highly glazed photographic paper in various colours.   They are listed under their respective values.

DIE PROOFS.   De La Rue took proofs from their dies at various stages of making the die and they are known as "progressive die proofs".   Die proofs of the head only are listed after the essays.   Completed die proofs for the monocoloured values and the separate head and duty die proofs for the bicoloured values are listed under the values concerned.

They are normally on thin white glazed card cut to about 90 × 60 mm. As with the Victorian die proofs they frequently bear signatures, initials or instructions in manuscript and are generally handstamped " BEFORE HARDENING ", " AFTER HARDENING " or " AFTER STRIKING " and dated.

These are followed by the pieces cut from the De La Rue Striking Books, information about which is given above under " PLATES ". The dates written on these rarely include the year date and in a few cases where they do it may be incorrect due to reasons for which the books were kept originally. These dates relate to those on the " AFTER STRIKING " die proofs.

PLATE PROOFS. These will be found listed after the Die Proofs.

COLOUR TRIALS. The only colour trials made by De La Rue for the first issues were those for the 1d. value in 1901, for which a 20 set plate was made, and those ordered in December 1901 for the 2½d. owing to the decision not to print it in purple and blue.

The 1909 colour trials for the 1½d., 2d. and 4d. values were for two purposes: to decide whether the designs were satisfactory for printing in monocolour and to choose colours for the planned monocoloured series. It was decided that the 2d. design would not be suitable, hence the change of design for the abortive Tyrian plum and the need to make colour trials for this.

The 1910 colour trials for the 4d. were made following complaints that the selected orange colour was not satisfactory, but nothing came of these. Colour trials were also made for the 1910 7d. value.

Colour trials were also made for the 6d. value but the date of these and their purpose are not known.

All the colour trials are listed under the appropriate values after the die and plate proofs. The 1911 colour trials of Edward VII stamps made by Harrisons were for the King George V stamps and are listed there.

Series A   Series B

1901 "Paste up" of the Victorian "Jubilee" Issue

The ½d. to 1s. values (except 4½d.) and the 1d. lilac. The portrait of the Queen was cut from the design and a lithographed head (in appropriate colour) of King Edward VII substituted.

Series A	½d. to 1s. Mounted on card with a three-quarter face likeness of K.E. VII facing left. 12 values exist	*Each* £2500
Series B	As above, but with a quarter-face likeness facing left	*Each* £2500

In addition, the frame and likeness of the 1d. lilac stamp exists in three other states.

Aa	As in series **A**, but portrait reversed	£3000
Bb	As in series **B**, but portrait reversed	£3000
C	Similar to A but portrait engraved instead of lithographed	£3750

Transitional Essays. These show hand painted alterations to the Victorian stamps. The values known are the 1½d., 2d., 3d., 4d., 5d., 9d., 10d. and 1s. They all had a crown superimposed above the Queen's head.

The portrait for the issued stamps was executed by Emil Füchs, an Austrian artist who also prepared a new design for the ½d., 1d., 2½d. and 6d. stamps. The remaining values of the issues were similar in design to their Victorian predecessors, but with the incorporation of the Crown above the head.

1901 Essays of the Suggested Design for the ½d., 1d., 2½d. and 6d. Stamps

Frames produced from temporary copper plates and pasted on card.

(1) Proof in black of the frame, inscribed " POSTAGE: REVENUE ". A photograph of the
   King's head inserted £1250
(2) As above, but inscribed " POSTAGE & REVENUE ". An engraved head inserted   ..   £1250
(3) As above, but the King's head differently placed in the oval £1250
(4) As above, but printed in various colours. Red, green, or purple on pink ..   ..   *From* £1100

Eight different essays were prepared for the 2½d. stamp, differing in the design
of the value tablets. Photographic frames with heads inserted. Mounted on
card dated "July 10th 1901 " ..   ..   *Each* £850

Essays for 2s. 6d., 5s., 10s., £1 and £5

Artist's sunken sketches. Head and Crown from a proof, and backgrounds
similar to the issued design hand painted in black and white   ..   *Each from* £1350

It was originally intended to have a £5 stamp, but no plate was made, and
the value passed from currency. Die proofs for this will be found listed after
the £1 value.

Die Proofs

Large Head

Small Head
Solid Background

Small Head
Cleared Background

Approved Head

Die proof of the large size head in black on white glazed card, used for ½d., 1d.,
2½d., 6d., 7d., 2s. 6d., 5s. values

Stamped " 27 JUN 01 " and " BEFORE HARDENING " £500
Stamped "AFTER HARDENING " and endorsed "27/6/01" and initials in M/S £500
As last but without date £500
Stamped "2 NOV 01" and "BEFORE HARDENING" with head cleared..   ..   £500

Die proof of the small head on solid background on white glazed card, used for
the 1½d., 3d., 4d., 9d., 10d. and 1s. values

Without marking £500
Stamped "1 AUG 01" and "BEFORE HARDENING" and endorsed "Die" in M/S   £500
Stamped "4 SEP 01" and "BEFORE HARDENING" and endorsed "Unified" in
M/S £500
Endorsed " After Hardening " in M/S £500
Stamped " 5 SEP 01 " and " AFTER HARDENING " £500

As last but head partly cleared by thin white contour line, used for 2d. and 5d.
values

Without marking £500
Stamped "5 SEP 01" and "AFTER HARDENING" £500

The die proof of the " extra large size head ", previously listed here, has been deleted as
this was struck in connection with colonial stamps and is therefore outside the scope of
this Catalogue.

Approved Frame with Value Tablet Blank

Die proof on white glazed card

Without marking £500
Stamped "AFTER HARDENING" and " 1 AUG 01 " £500

The dies for the ½d., 1d. and 6d. were made from this master die, also the 2½d. value
with modifications.

Head and Frame

Approved Head and Frame Without Value

Die proof of complete design except the value, for ½d., 1d. and 6d. values. In black on white glazed card

Endorsed in reverse " ORIGINAL DIE " above and with " P.6." below in M/S	£950
Stamped " 1 AUG 01 " and " BEFORE HARDENING "	£750
Stamped " 1 AUG 01 " and " AFTER HARDENING "	£750
Without markings (cleared borders)	£650

Die Proofs from the De La Rue Archives

On card 92 × 60 mm unmounted with traces of gum or paper on the back

Large sized head

With circular uncleared surround, stamped " 5 JUN 01 " and " BEFORE HARDENING " and endorsed " Die & Punch " in M/S ..	£500
With boxed uncleared surround, stamped " 27 JUN 01 " and " BEFORE HARDENING " and endorsed " Original P.1 " in M/S ..	£450
As last but stamped " 2 JUL 01 " and " BEFORE HARDENING " and endorsed " Original die. No. D.1." in M/S	£250

Small head on solid background

Stamped " 31 JUL 01 " and " BEFORE HARDENING " and endorsed " Die " in M/S ..	£400
Stamped " 1 AUG 01 " and " BEFORE HARDENING " and endorsed " Die " in M/S ..	£200
Stamped " 5 SEP 01 " and " AFTER HARDENING " and endorsed " Original P.20. Solid ground "	£450

Small head partly cleared with thin white contour line

Stamped " 5 SEP 01 " and " AFTER HARDENING " and endorsed " Original P.21. White ground "	£400

Approved head and frame without value

Stamped " 1 AUG 01 " and " BEFORE HARDENING " and endorsed " Original Die P.6." in M/S ..	£600
As above but without markings ..	£450

"Transvaal" Essays

Some months after the first Edwardian stamps were issued, further essays were prepared at the request of the King, who it is believed favoured the design of the Transvaal stamps to that of the ½d., 1d., 2½d. and 6d. of Great Britain.

Type 1   Type 2

Essays were prepared in October 1902 in the above Types.

Type 1. As illustrated
Type 2. As Type 1 but with thin line painted in between the oval of the King's head and the frame in approximately the same colour as that of the frame.

25

Essays from the De La Rue Archives

Type 2, each mounted on card with manuscript " Cancelled "

In red numbered " 2 "		£1000
In green numbered " 5 "		£1000
In black and purple numbered " 8 "		£1000

The remaining six essays were acquired by the National Postal Museum and comprise essays in black and red numbered " 1 ", in carmine numbered " 3 ", in black and green numbered " 4 ", in black and blue numbered " 6 ", in blue numbered " 7 ' and in purple numbered " 9 ".

It is believed that this set of nine essays represents all the colours that were used. Any others which have been recorded at various times result from inaccurate descriptions or colours that have faded.

Type 1

Die Proof on white glazed card

In black £1000

Printed from a plate and mounted on card. Perf. 14

In black and red, red, carmine, black and green, green, black and blue, blue, black and purple,
purple .. .. *From* £800
Examples are known to exist off card.

Type 2

Printed from a plate and mounted on card. Value tablets and crown touched
in by hand with white paint. Perf. 14

In black and red, red, carmine, black and green, green, black and blue, blue, black and purple,
purple .. .. *From* £800
Examples are known to exist off card.

As above but pasted on card and numbered

No. 1 for 1d.	Black and red	..	..	..	..	..	..	..
No. 2 for 1d.	Red ..	..	..	..	..	..	..	..
No. 3 for 1d.	Carmine	..	..	..	..	..	..	..

} *Each* £800

1903 "Canada Head" Essays

Prepared by De La Rue using the head employed for the 1903 issue of Canada.

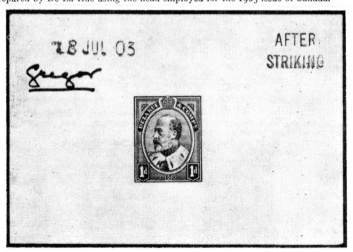

Die 1.   Small Head

Die Proof.   Die 1 in black on glazed card

Stamped "8 JUN 03" and endorsed "Turner" in M/S	£850
Stamped "10 JUN 03" and "AFTER STRIKING" and endorsed "Gregor" in M/S	£850
Stamped "28 JUN 03" and "AFTER STRIKING" and endorsed "Gregor" in ink..	£850
Stamped "28 JUL 03"	£850
Undated but endorsed "Mr. T" in M/S	£850

Die 2.   Large Head.   Heavily shaded

Die Proof. Die 2 in black on thick glazed card

Stamped "8 JUN 03" and endorsed "Turner" in M/S	£1000
Stamped "27 JUL 03"..	£1000
Stamped "28 JUL 03" and "AFTER STRIKING" with "Zinc" in M/S	£1000
Undated but endorsed "Mr. T" in M/S	£1000
Without markings	£1000

Colour Trials

Die 2.   Imperforate

On thick wove paper, plate glazed both sides
In ochre-brown, carmine-red, dull green .. .. *From £650*

On thick proof card
In pale orange, ochre-brown, carmine-red, pale dull green, pale blue .. .. .. *From £650*

On thin wove paper. Wmk. Rosette.   No gum
In dull orange, ochre-brown, carmine-red, ultramarine .. .. *From £650*

On thin wove paper.   No watermark.   With gum
In dull orange, ochre-brown, carmine-red, ultramarine, dull green .. .. .. *From £650*

On very thin high quality wove paper.   No watermark or gum
In carmine-red *£650*

Photographic Essays

The frames of the 2d., 4d., 9d. and 1s. values mounted on card, with the head of the King inserted.   This head was a smaller edition of that used for the 1903 issue of Canada.   Touched in by hand in white paint .. ..   *Each £1500*

1911 Colour Trials

The Edward VII colour trials of 1911, formerly listed here, will now be found at the end of the General Notes to Section NA since they relate to the first Georgian stamps.

CHECKLIST OF KING EDWARD VII DEFINITIVES

Description	Spec. Cat. No.	S.G. Nos.	Page
De La Rue Printings on Ordinary Paper			
½d. blue-green	M1	215–16	30
½d. yellow-green	M2	217–18	32
1d.	M5	219–20	40
1½d.	M8	221–22	49
2d. green & red	M11	225–26	55
2d. Tyrian plum	M14	266a	60
2½d. purple on blue	M15	—	61
2½d. blue	M16	230–31	61
3d.	M19	232–32a	66
4d. green & brown	M23	235–36	69
4d. orange	M25	239–41	72
5d.	M28	242	74
6d.	M31	245–46	78
7d.	M37	249–49a	83
9d.	M39	250–51	85
10d.	M42	254	89
1s.	M45	257	92
2s. 6d.	M48	260	96
5s.	M51	263–64	98
10s.	M53	265	100
£1	M55	266	101

De La Rue Printings on Chalk-Surfaced Paper

Description	Spec. Cat. No.	S.G. Nos.	Page
1½d.	M9	223–24	50
2d.	M12	227–29	56
3d.	M20	232b–34	66
4d.	M24	237–38	69
5d.	M29	243–44	74
6d.	M32	247–48	78
9d.	M40	252–53	85
10d.	M43	255–56	89
1s.	M46	258–59	92
2s. 6d.	M49	261–62	96

Harrison Printings Perf 14

Description	Spec. Cat. No.	S.G. Nos.	Page
½d.	M3	267–71	34
1d.	M6	272–75a	43
2½d.	M17	276	63
3d.	M21	277–77a	66
4d.	M26	278	72

Harrison Printings Perf 15 × 14

Description	Spec. Cat. No.	S.G. Nos.	Page
½d.	M4	279–79a	35
1d.	M7	280–82	44
2½d.	M18	283–84	63
3d.	M22	285–85a	66
4d.	M27	286	73

Somerset House Printings

Description	Spec. Cat. No.	S.G. Nos.	Page
1½d.	M10	287–89	51
2d.	M13	290–92	58
5d.	M30	293–94	75
6d. (ordinary paper)	M33	295, 297–300	78
6d. (" Dickinson " coated paper)	M34	301	79
6d. (chalk-surfaced paper)	M35, M36	296, 303	79
7d.	M38	305	84
9d.	M41	306–08	86
10d.	M44	309–11	90
1s.	M47	312–14	93
2s. 6d.	M50	315–17	97
5s.	M52	318	98
10s.	M54	319	100
£1	M56	320	101

CHECKLIST OF KING EDWARD VII BOOKLET PANES

Spec. Cat. Nos.	Description	From Booklets Nos.	Listed Below Cat. No.	Page
MB1, MB1a	6 × ½d. De La Rue	BA2–5	M2	33
MB2, MB2a	5 × ½d. De La Rue and one green cross	BA2–5	M2	33
MB3, MB3a	6 × ½d. Harrison	BA6	M3	35
MB4, MB4a	5 × ½d. Harrison and one green cross	BA6	M3	35
MB5, MB5a	6 × 1d. De La Rue	BA1–5	M5	41
MB6, MB6a	6 × 1d. Harrison	BA6	M6	43

Postage Issues (1902-13)

WATERMARKS. The ½d. to 1s. have watermark **W12** (Crown). The 2s. 6d., 5s. and 10s. have watermark **W9** (Anchor). The £1 has three Crown watermarks on each stamp.

FUGITIVE INKS. As these stamps are printed in fugitive inks (*see* under " Inks and Shades " in the General Notes) the colours are particularly liable to suffer through immersion in water. Badly affected stamps are virtually worthless.

PRICES FOR STAMPS IN USED CONDITION

For well-centred, lightly used examples of stamps in Section MA, add the following percentages to the prices quoted.

De La Rue printings—3d. (M19/20) +**35%**, 4d. orange (M25) +**100%**, 6d. (M31/32) +**75%**. 7d. (M37) and 1s. (M45/46) +**25%**, all other values +**50%**.

Harrison printings—all values and perforations +**75%**.

Somerset House printings—1s. (M47) +**25%**, all other values +**50%**.

1902-11. ½d. Green, Type M1

Cat. No.	S.G. No.	Perf.	Paper	Shades	Unused	Used
1902 (JANUARY 1).		**BLUE-GREEN.**	**PERF. 14.**	**DE LA RUE**		
M1	215/6	14	Ordinary	(1) Dull blue-green	60 ✔	30 ✔
				(2) Blue-green	60 ✔	30 ✔
				(3) Deep blue-green	8·00	1·50

	Block of four	3·00	2·50
	Used on cover	†	60
a.	Watermark inverted ..	£900	
e.	Displaced cliché (Pl. 20, R. 19/12) horiz. pair	£150	
f.	Do. (Pl. 20, R. 20/12) corner pair	£125	
g.	Diagonal scratch (Pl. 11, R. 19/6)	35·00	
h.	Bottom frame broken (Pl. 33, R. 20/5)	25·00	

i.	Split frame (Pl. 20, R. 11/8)	38·00
j.	Split left frame (several exist) .. .. .. *From*	28·00 ✔
k.	Left frame broken (Pl. 24c, R. 11/6)	25·00
l.	Minor frame breaks *From*	12·00
s.	" Specimen ", Type 15 ..	£100
t.	" Cancelled ", Type 18 ..	

Nos. M1*e/f* are displaced upwards and often darker in shade.

M1*g*
Extends up
to R. 18/6)   M1*h*, M2*i*   M1*i*   M1*j*   M1*k*, M2*ha*

Perforation 14 (Nos. M1 and M2).

Types: see Control List.

Die Proofs

In black on white glazed card :

Without marking	£500	
Without marking, endorsed		
" A. S. Roberts "	£475	
Without marking but initialled		
" EF " (E.Fuchs)	£475	
Cut down, endorsed " As		
approved by Mr. Fuchs " ..	£180	
Endorsed (M/S) " 25/VI/1901		
Emil Fuchs "	£475	
Endorsed (M/S) " 21 Aug EF "	£475	

Endorsed " 21 AUG 01	
BEFORE HARDENING " ..	£475
Endorsed " 22 AUG 01 AFTER	
HARDENING "	£475
Endorsed (M/S) " Working Die	
No. 17 26-9-01 "	£475
Endorsed (M/S) " Jan 1907	
After Striking "	£475

Endorsed " AFTER STRIKING " with signatures dated:
"7 JULY 03", "4 AUG. 04", "12 APR. 05", "15 APR. 05", "10 AUG. 05",
"21 FEB. 06", "5 APR. 06", "20 JUN. 07", "3 APRIL 08", "23 JUN. 08",
"23 DEC. 08", "3 MAR. 09", "2 APR. 10", "1 DEC. 10" .. .. *Each £475*

In green on white glazed card :

Partly engraved proof of value tablet and left half of frame £1250

Die Proof from the De La Rue Archives

On card unmounted with traces of gum or paper on the back

Cut down (85 × 43 mm), endorsed " As approved by Mr. Fuchs " £600

Pieces Cut from the Striking Books

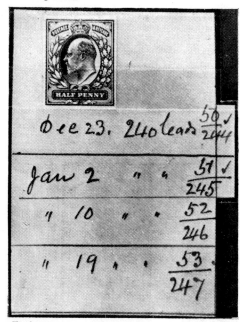

Typical Example showing Dates, Plates and Leads

Each piece is unique and the value of any one piece depends to some extent upon its condition. A full listing is beyond the scope of this Catalogue but we include one for each value and a few special items. For further information see General Notes under " De La Rue Striking Books ".

Struck on plain paper cut to size with various endorsements comprising dates, plates and/or number of leads

½d. value	*From £300*
½d. and 1d. values on same piece	*From £600*

Plate Proofs. No watermark, imperf.

Blue-green on yellowish paper	28·00
Ditto, diagonally overprinted " CANCELLED "	28·00
Blue-green on thick surfaced card	28·00

Cat. No.	S.G. No.	Perf.	Paper	Shades	Unused	Used
1904 (NOVEMBER 26). YELLOW-GREEN. PERF. 14. DE LA RUE						
M2	217/18	14	Ordinary	(1) Pale yellowish green	50✓	20✓
				(2) Yellowish green	50✓	20✓

oth colours

	Block of four	2·50	1·50
	Used on cover	†	30
a.	Watermark inverted†	1·75	1·25 ✓(1)
b.	Raised crown in watermark (corner block of 4) (Pl. 41b, 49b, 52c, 53a, and 55, R. 19/2)		45·00
c.	With St. Andrew's Cross attached	£110	£110
ca.	Ditto watermark inverted	£110	£110
d.	Doubly printed	£9750	
	The bottom rows of one sheet with control H9 showed 13 stamps with partial or full doubling		
e.	Displaced cliché (Pl. 20, R. 20/12) corner pair	£110	

f.	Right frame broken (Pl. 18c, R. 10/12)	38·00	
g.	Split left frame (Pl. ?, R. 1/5)	38·00	
h.	Left frame broken (Pl. ?, R. 4/3)	38·00	
ha.	Left frame broken (Pl. 24c, R. 11/6)	38·00	
i.	Bottom frame broken (Pl. 33, R. 20/5)	38·00	
j.	Minor frame breaks *From*	10·00	
s.	"Specimen", Type 17	£150	
t.	"Specimen", Type 22		
u.	"Cancelled", Type 20		

†No M2a. The prices are for booklet stamps. Inverted watermarks from sheets are worth much more but can only be differentiated by marginal copies or multiples differing from the booklet format of 3×2.

Many cracks and breaks in the frame lines are known. We illustrate and catalogue five major examples.

M2*f*	M2*g*	M2*h*

Booklet Panes of Six
From Booklets BA2/5

MB1	Watermark upright	10·00	MB1a	Watermark inverted	15·00
s.	"Specimen", Type 17 ..	£900	as.	"Specimen", Type 17 ..	£900
t.	"Specimen", Type 22 ..		au.	Cancelled St. Andrew's	
u.	Cancelled St. Andrew's			Cross, Type A ..	50·00
	Cross, Type A ..	50·00	av.	Cancelled " E.C.'A' ",	
v.	Cancelled " E.C.'A' ",			Type B	50·00
	Type B	50·00	aw.	Cancelled " E.C.'U' ",	
w.	Cancelled " E.C.'U' ",			Type C	50·00
	Type C	50·00	ax.	Cancelled " E.C.K ",	
x.	Cancelled " E.C.K ",			Type D	50·00
	Type D	50·00			

Booklet Panes of Five with One Green St. Andrew's Cross

MB2/a, MB4/a

From Booklets BA2/5

MB2	Watermark upright	£180	MB2a	Watermark inverted	£180
s.	"Specimen", Type 17 ..	£900	as.	"Specimen", Type 17 ..	£900
t.	"Specimen", Type 22 ..		au.	Cancelled St. Andrew's	
u.	Cancelled St. Andrew's			Cross, Type A ..	70·00
	Cross, Type A ..	70·00	av.	Cancelled " E.C.'A' ",	
v.	Cancelled " E.C.'A' ",			Type B ..	70·00
	Type B	70·00	aw.	Cancelled " E.C.'U' ",	
w.	Cancelled " E.C.'U' ",			Type C ..	70·00
	Type C	70·00	ax.	Cancelled " E.C.K ",	
x.	Cancelled " E.C.K ",			Type D	70·00
	Type D	70·00			
y.	Cancelled "London Chief				
	Office, E.C.", Type E ..				

Type E has not been recorded in panes with watermark inverted.

Die Proof. In black on white glazed card
St. Andrew's Cross dated "24 JAN. 06 " £950

Plate Proof. Imperf. without watermark
In issued colour on poor quality buff paper .. .. 12·00

Specimen overprints from the National Postal Museum Archives

Booklet pane of five with St. Andrew's Cross label at top left.
Perf. 14, watermark Type W12 (inverted)
"Specimen", Type 15

Booklet pane of six. Perf. 14, watermark Type W12 (inverted)
"Specimen", Type 15

Cat. No.	S.G. No.	Perf.	Paper	Shades	Unused	Used

1911 (MAY 3). YELLOW-GREEN. PERF. 14. HARRISON

M3	267/71	14	Ordinary	

		Unused	Used
	Block of four	6·50	3·00
	Used on cover	†	3·00
a.	Watermark inverted†† ..	3·75 ✓ʃ	2·75
b.	Watermark sideways ..	—	£9000
c.	No watermark		
d.	Imperf. (pair)	£5500	
e.	With St. Andrew's Cross attached	£150	£150
f.	Do. watermark inverted ..	£150	£150
g.	Gash in crown (Pl. ?, R. 12/11)	85·00	
h.	Major frame breaks (Pl. 64b, R. 18/10)	85·00	
ha.	Major frame break (Pl. 57b, R. 17/7)	85·00	
i.	Minor frame breaks *From*	12·00	
j.	Vertical scratch below beard to stamp below (Pl. ?, R. 1/8)	50·00	
k.	Major bottom frame break and damage (Pl. 59b, R. 20/3)	85·00	

	Shades	Unused	Used
(1)	Dull yellow-green	1·10 ✓	40 ✓
(2)	Dull green	1·75 ✓	40 ✓
(3)	Deep dull green	8·00 ✓	2·00 ✓
(4)	Deep dull yellow-green (very blotchy print)	35·00	20·00
(5)	Pale bluish green	22·00	22·00 ✓
(6)	Bright green (fine impression) (June 1911)	£150	£110
(7)	Deep bright green	£150	80·00

		Unused	Used
l.	Cross on Crown almost missing (Pl. 63b, R. 19/20 Nos. 1/3) .. .. *Each*	60·00	
m.	Left of Crown broken (Pl. 63b, R. 20/5)	50·00	
s.	"Specimen", Type 22 ..		

††No. M3*a*. The prices are for booklet stamps. Inverted watermarks from sheets are worth much more but can only be differentiated by marginal examples or multiples differing from the booklet format of 3 × 2.

The Harrison printings, with the exception of the two bright green shades, have a very flat appearance when compared with the De la Rue issues. There is less white in the design, and the shading extends well up to the sides of the Crown. The pale green shade (No. M3(5)) is the nearest approach to the De la Rue colour, but is bluer. The bright green shades are distinct ; on No. (7) the design is rather spotted (Plate 64b).

In the Harrison printing the lines in the veining of the leaves and on the King's neck are noticeably strengthened.

M3/4*g*   M3/4*h*

M3*ha*   M3*j*
(Extends to R. 2/8)   M3*k*

M3*l*

M3/4*m*

Perforation 14
Types: see Control List.

Booklet Panes of Six
From Booklet BA6

MB3 Watermark upright   20·00
   t.   Cancelled "London Chief
      Office, E.C.", Type E

MB3a Watermark inverted   30·00
   as.   "Specimen", Type 22   ..
   at.   Cancelled "London Chief
      Office, E.C.", Type E

Type E has not yet been recorded on panes with watermark upright.

Booklet Panes of Five with One Green St. Andrew's Cross
From Booklet BA6

MB4 Watermark upright   £250
   t.   Cancelled "London Chief
      Office, E.C.", Type E

MB4a Watermark inverted   £250
   as.   "Specimen", Type 22   ..
   at.   Cancelled "London Chief
      Office, E.C.", Type E

Specimen overprints from the National Postal Museum Archives

Booklet pane of six. Perf. 14, watermark Type W12

"Specimen", Type 15, watermark upright
"Specimen", Type 15, watermark inverted

Booklet pane of five with St. Andrew's Cross label at top left.
Perf. 14, watermark Type W12

"Specimen", Type 15, watermark upright
"Specimen", Type 15, watermark inverted

Cat. No.	S.G. No.	Perf.	Paper	Shades		Unused	Used
1911 (OCTOBER 30).		**GREEN.**	**PERF. 15 × 14.**	**HARRISON**			
M4	279/9a	15 × 14	Ordinary	(1)	Dull green	20·00	25·00 ✓
				(2)	Deep dull green	24·00 ✓	20·00 ✓
	Block of four		95·00 £120	(3)	Deep dull green (very		
	Used on cover		† 65·00		blotchy print)	£400	£180
g.	Gash in Crown (Pl. ?, R.			(4)	Pale bluish green	20·00 ✓	18·00
	12/11)		£100				
h.	Major frame breaks (Pl.						
	64b, R. 18/10)		90·00				
m.	Left of Crown broken (Pl.						
	63b, R. 20/5)		40·00				

4 v very pale b—g   ✓

Perforation 15 × 14
Types V3 and V3A

Controls. Prices are for unused corner pairs
Printed by De La Rue

Control	Date				H1	H1A	V1 or V4	V2	V2A or V4A
(a) *With continuous rule*									
Blue-green									
A	Jan. 1902 ..	..	..	..	2·00 ✓	3·00	55·00	†	38·00
B	Dec. 1902 ..	..	..	..	2·00 ✓	15·00	38·00	†	38·00
C	Oct. 1903 ..	..	..	..	3·00	70·00	3·00	†	22·00
C 4	Feb. 1904 ..	..	..	..	2·00 ✓	55·00	3·00	†	12·00 ✓
D 4	Apr. 1904 ..	..	..	..	2·50	—	20·00	†	55·00
Yellow-green									
D 4	Nov. 1904..	..	..	..	38·00	†	28·00	†	55·00
(b) *With coextensive rule*									
Blue-green									
B	Mid 1903 ..	..	..	..	22·00	†	15·00	†	70·00
C	Oct. 1903 ..	..	..	..	5·00	60·00	55·00	†	12·00
C 4	Jan. 1904 ..	..	..	..	3·00	70·00	3·00	†	3·00 ✓
D 4	Apr. 1904 ..	..	..	..	2·00	70·00	2·00	†	10·00
Yellow-green									
D 4	Nov. 1904 ..	..	..	..	2·00	55·00	2·00	†	—
D 5	Mar. 1905 ..	..	..	..	2·00 ✓	28·00	6·00	†	—
E 5	Sep. 1905 ..	..	..	..	2·00	70·00	5·00	10·00	2·50
E 6	June 1906 ..	..	..	..	2·00	†	†	70·00	2·25
F 6	Aug. 1906 ..	..	..	..	2·00 ✓	28·00	†	14·00	2·00
F 7	July 1907 ..	..	..	..	12·00	†	†	10·00	2·50 ✓
G 7	Sep. 1907 ..	..	..	..	3·00	†	†	2·00	2·00
G 8	July 1908 ..	..	..	..	3·00	60·00	†	3·00	3·00 ✓
H 8	Oct. 1908 ..	..	..	..	2·00	15·00	†	2·00	2·00 ✓
H 9	Aug. 1909 ..	..	..	..	28·00 ✓	†	†	3·00	3·00 ✓
I 9	Nov. 1909 ..	..	..	..	3·00	†	†	2·00	2·00 ✓
I 10	July 1910 ..	..	..	..	2·00 ✓	70·00	†	3·00	2·50 ✓
J 10	Oct. 1910 ..	..	..	..	2·00 ✓	†	†	2·00	2·00

One example is known of Control F6 and several of Control E5 with Perf. Type V2(a).
A single example of Control I 10 with bottom margin perforated through has been seen with " o " omitted.

Printed by Harrison

Perf. 14

Control	Date				Perforation Type			
					H2	H2A	V1	V1A
A 11	May 1911..	..	..	..	4·00 ✓	4·00 ✓	12·00	60·00

Control A 11 (Perf. Type H2A) is known with the watermark inverted.

Perf. 15 × 14

					V3	V3A
A 11	Oct. 1911..	..	..	..	40·00	70·00

The H2 perforator is known in variations a, c, d and e and the H2A perforator in variations c, d and e. An exceptionally wide margin is needed to show the 14 holes of variation e.

At least two examples are known with perforator as Type V3 but having no extension hole in the bottom margin.

A vertical post 5 mm. high midway between two sheets and appearing 7½ mm. below their bottom stamps is occasionally seen on corner pieces of the Harrison printing perf. 14. This may have served a similar purpose to the guillotine dot of the De La Rue printings but seems only to have had a limited use. It is known for a few control corner pieces from Plates 54 and 60b and on S.E. corner pieces from Plate 59b. The latter can be identified by a white spot which appears in the top left inner frame of R. 20/12. Reports of any sightings for other plates or values would be welcomed.

The so-called " A 17 " Control results from ink build up between the tops of " 11 " and is found on some pieces perf. 14 from Plates 54 and 58c.

Plate Markings

A great deal of research on the Plates of the ½d. and 1d. values has been undertaken by the King Edward VII Study Circle of the Great Britain Philatelic Society, but more remains to be done. The findings to date are embodied in the information that follows. It is probable that a few more 1d. plates were used.

In the plates with coextensive rule all are Die II except where Die I is stated. Further information about this and the "6/7" Rule will be found under "Marginal Rules" in the General Notes. See also under "Registration Piece".

To distinguish between left-hand sheets and right-hand sheets see under "Recognising the Two Halves of the Mill Sheet" in the General Notes.

Before this study can be completed much more material needs to be seen, preferably in the form of complete bottom strips. In the lists of Plate Markings a plate marking *preceded by a dagger* indicates that there remains some uncertainty about this item. The nature of the uncertainty is shown in the Control Schedules where a plate number *followed by an asterisk* means that the item has been reported previously but has not been confirmed during the present study but when *followed by a dagger* its existence has been deduced but not actually confirmed from the sighting in a bottom or side strip.

Anybody possessing such items is requested to submit them to the Editor for examination and this applies also to any marginal rule portions bearing cuts, etc. that do not agree with those listed—for instance a plate with a continuous rule of the 1d. with control A having a first cut under the 3rd stamp is one that the Study would very much like to see, and the same for the ½d. with cuts under 3rd or 6th.

All the Plate Numbers are arbitrarily allocated philatelic numbers but it is hoped eventually to be able to correlate these with the official plate numbers.

The ½d. plate has now been added as Plate 71 with Continuous Rule, but no cuts have been seen, so more information is required. Corner pieces of this plate had been confused with those of Plate 9, as both have a prominent flaw in the marginal rule below 11th at the upper left. Both plates started with Control A, but whereas right-hand sheets were given for Plate 9, those of Plate 71 are left-hand. 71 is thought to have served as a master plate, with 9 a successful copy.

With Continuous Rule

Plate	Features
†1a	2 cuts under LFP of 3rd, damage starts in 12th rule
1b/d	Added cuts under PE of 2nd, FP of 6th and EN of 7th, damage to 12th rule extends
†2a	2 large cuts under LFPE of 4th
2b, c	Added cut under NN of 2nd and ¾ cut (base) under FP of 3rd
2c	Added cut under LF of 1st
3	Cut under PE of 8th
†4a	Cut under E of 5th
4b	Added cut under FP of 1st
4c	Added cut under PE of 2nd
4d	Side change with added cut likely for D4
5a	Cut under P of 4th, bottom rule temporarily damaged at right corner
5b	Added cut under P of 1st
6	Deleted. Now part of Plate 4
7	Deleted as being redundant
†8a	Cut under PE of 1st
8b, c	Added wide and fine cuts under PE of 8th and fine ½ cut (base) under FP of 4th
†9a	Large cut under ENN of 8th. Distinctive rule flaw below 11th, as for Plate 71
9b	Added cut under P of 3rd
9c	Added cut under P of 1st
9d	Added cut under LF of 2nd
9e	Added 2 cuts under NY of 7th
9f	Added cut under FP of 4th
†10a	Cut under PE of 1st
10b	Added cut under FP of 2nd but only control triple seen for either state

Plate	Features
†11	Fine cut under P of 2nd
12	Deleted. Now part of Plate 24
13	Cut under P of 5th. Left B control, wide break under 11/12
14	Deleted. Now part of Plate 11
16	Deleted. Now part of Plate 65
†18a	Cut under F of 4th
18b	Added cut under P of 7th
18c	Added cuts or breaks to right of R. 20 (12 mm.), and R. 18 (4 mm.). Rule below 12th becomes dropped
†19	Cut under N(N) of 8th
21	Deleted. Now part of Plate 4
22	Deleted. Now part of Plate 2
†23	Slanting cut under FP of 4th, 2 cuts under FPE of 5th
†24a	1½ cuts under P of 7th
24b	Added 2¾ cuts (base) under LF of 6th
24c	Added 2 sloping cuts under ALF of 4th
24d	Added cut under FP of 3rd, rule below 12th dropped. Thinned rule opposite 19th row
†65a	3 cuts under 7th below F, N(N) and Y
65b	Added cut under EN of 2nd
65c	Added cut under 5th reported
†66	Cut under PE of 3rd
67	Cut under PE of 6th
69	3 cuts under 7th, below F, PE and N(N)
70	2 cuts under 6th, below L and P
71	Distinctive flaw below 11th as for 9a (only control strip of 3 seen and no cuts known)

With Coextensive Rule

Plate	Features
†15	Die I, 6/7 Rule. Cut under PE of 1st
†20	Die I, Cut under (P)E of 3rd
†25a	Die I, 6/7 Rule. Large cut under AL of 1st
25b	Added cut under P of 8th
†26a	Die I, 6/7 Rule. Cut under FP of 2nd
26b	Added cut under PE of 1st (finer than Pl. 15)
26c	Added cut under LF of 11th
†27	Die I, 6/7 Rule. 2 sloping cuts under ALF of 6th
†28	Fine cut under P of 1st. Right of centre pillars, 2 plug-like breaks (16½, 18½ mm.)
29	Cut under PE of 2nd. From control E 6 the right of rule under 1st damaged

Plate	Features
†30a	Thin sloping cut under P of 3rd
30b	Added cut under FP of 4th
32	Cut under FP of 4th
33	1½ cuts under PE of 5th
†34a	Cut under N(N) of 7th
34b	Side change for control G8 strip of 3, no cut seen
35a	Cut under AL of 6th
35b	Added ½ cut under L of 4th
35c	Added ½ cut (base) under PE of 8th, ½ cut (base) under H and irregular cut or break under FP of 9th (with right control F 6)

With Coextensive Rule—*continued*

Plate	Features
36a	Cut under PE of 8th. Poor alignment of rules and clichés, particularly under 4th and 9th
36b	Cut to right of 20th (3 mm.)
36c	Added cuts under FP of 2nd, PE of 4th and ¼ cuts or nicks under and right of Y of 1st and NN of 12th (with right control F 6)
36d	Added ¾ cut (base) under AL of 1st
†37a	Cut under PE of 10th
37b	Added ½ cut under P of 3rd, hollow rule under 2nd with control I 9
†38a	Cut under NN of 9th
38b	Moved by E5, but no cut made under 6th
38c	Added cut under FP of 4th
38d	Added ¾ cut (base) under PE of 3rd
39	Slanting cut (left to right) under PE of 8th
40	Deleted. Now part of Plate 36
41a	No cuts; right-hand sheets, minute dot under H of 2nd
41b	Added ½ to full cut (base) under HA of 2nd
42a	No cuts; right-hand sheets, 1 mm. registration piece gap under P and small dot under PE of 7th
42b	Added cut under P of 3rd
43a	No cuts; left-hand sheets, ¾ mm. registration piece gap under P of 7th, distinct scoop under AL of 9th; "flag" at top of S.E. corner "bit" Rule left of 19th dented (outer) (10½ mm.)
43b	Added cut under N(Y) of 7th
43c	Added cut under FP of 3rd
44	Deleted. Now part of Plate 47
†45a	Cut under FP of 11th
45b	Added cut under PE of 5th
45c	Added 1½ cuts under PE of 1st
†46a	Cut under P of 12th
46b	Added cut under P of 8th
46c	Added 1½ cuts under F of 3rd
46d	Added cut under FP of 1st
†47a	¾ cut (base) under HA of 1st
47b	Added large cut under P of 5th
48	Deleted. Now part of Plate 42
49a	Cut under P of 4th
49b	Added cut under P of 3rd
49c	Moved back but no new cut made under 4th
50	Deleted. Now part of Plate 37
51	Deleted. Now part of Plate 43
†52a	No cuts; right-hand sheets, tapered rule below 2nd narrowing to right
52b	Added large semi-circular cut under PEN of 3rd
52c	Added cut, sometimes closed at base, under PE of 8th
52d	Added cut under E of 7th
53a	Irregular cut under HAL of 6th
53b	Added irregular cut under PE of 5th
53c	Moved back, but no new cut made under 6th
†54a	Cut, sometimes double, under PE of 1st
†54b	Harrison usage, but side cuts not yet seen
55	Cut under EN of 4th
56	Deleted. Now part of Plate 43
57a	Slanting cut, running down from left, under FP of 8th
57b	Added cut right side of 19th row (6 mm.)
58a	1½ cuts under HA of 1st. Faint flaw under FP of 11th
58b	Added cut under HA of 4th
58c	Added cut 18th right side (8 mm.)
†59a	Cut under H of 2nd
59b	Added cut 17th right side (7¾ mm.)
60a	2 cuts under EN of 3rd
60b	Added cut 18th right side (11 mm.)
61	Cut under P of 5th. 2 cuts 19th right side (11¼, 14¼ mm.)
62	Deleted. Now part of Plate 54
63a	Cut under A of 6th
63b	Added cut 19th right side (10½ mm.)
64a	Cut under (N)N of 7th
64b	Added cut 20th right side (10½ mm.). Later a coloured line developed right of left corner "bit"
†68	No cuts; right-hand sheets, ¾ mm. registration piece gap under P of 7th (the S.W. corner "bit" is more to left and lower than that of Plate 42a)

The corner "bits" can be of help in differentiating Plates 42, 43, and 68.

Index to Marginal Markings

Bottom Margin, stamp numbers

Stamp No.	Plates
1	2c, 4b, 4c, 5b, 8a, 8b, 9c, 9d, 9e, 9f, 10a, 10b, 15, 25a, 25b, 26b, 28, 36d, 45c, 46d, 47a, 47b, 54, 58a, 58b, 58c
2	1b/d, 2b, 2c, 4c, 9d, 9e, 9f, 10b, 11, 26a, 26b, 29, 36c, 36d, 41b, 59a, 59b, 65b, 65c
3	1a, 1b, 2b, 2c, 9b, 9c, 9d, 9e, 9f, 20, 24d, 30a, 30b, 37b, 38c, 42b, 43c, 46c, 46d, 49b, 52b, 52c, 52d, 60a, 60b, 66
4	2a, 2b, 2c, 5a, 5b, 8b, 9f, 18a, 18b, 18c, 23, 24c, 30b, 32, 35b, 35c, 36c, 36d, 38b, 38c, 49a, 49b, 55, 58b, 58c
5	4a, 4b, 4c, 13, 23, 33, 45b, 45c, 47b, 53b, 61, 65c
6	1b/d, 24b, 24d, 27, 35a, 35b, 35c, 53a, 53b, 63a, 63b, 67, 70
7	1b/d, 9e, 9f, 18b, 18c, 24a, 24c, 24d, 34, 42a, 42b, 43b, 43c, 52d, 64a, 64b, 65a, 65b, 65c, 69
8	3, 8b, 9a, 9b, 9c, 9d, 9e, 9f, 19, 25b, 35c, 36a, 36b, 36c, 36d, 39, 46b, 46c, 46d, 52c, 52d, 57a, 57b
9	35c, 38a, 38b, 38c
10	37a, 37b
11	9a, 26c, 45a, 45b, 45c, 58a, 58b, 58c, 71
12	36c, 36d, 46a, 46b, 46c, 46d

No cuts: 41a, 42a, 43a, 52a, 68
Basal scoop under NY of 4th: 8, 9, 24, (28), (47), 60, (63)
Basal scoop under HAL of 9th: 9, 13, 28, (29), 30, 32, (34), (37), 38, 41, 43, 46, 47, (63), (68)

The scoops are sometimes very slight on the plates shown in brackets.

Right Margin, row numbers

Row No.	Plates
17 ..	59b
18 ..	18c, 58b, 60b
19 ..	24d, 57b, 61, 63b
20 ..	18c, 36b, 36c, 36d, 64b

Centre pillars: 28

Control Schedule

As corner copies with full selvedge can be used to identify from which side of the mill sheet they come, Controls are recorded from both left and right sheets in the table which follows. See General Notes under "Recognising the Two Halves of the Mill Sheet".

As already stated an asterisk means that the plate with the particular control has been reported but not confirmed by the present study and a dagger indicates that its existence has been deduced but not actually confirmed from the sighting in a bottom or side strip. Plate numbers shown in brackets are those which have changed sides with a particular control. Such plates acquire an additional sub-state, but they do not appear in the previous Table, since they lack the corresponding cut. They do, however, feature in the table below and some likely positions, for which cuts were not needed, deduced from the controls have been given.

Control			Plates with which it was used
			Left Sheets
A	..	..	1a, 4a, 5b, 8a, 10a†, 13, 65a, 66, 69, 71
B	..	..	1a*, 4b, 5b, 9c†, 10a*, 13†, 15, 20†, 23†, 24a, 65a†, 66†, 71
C	..	..	9e†, 10a†, 15†, 20, 23†, 24a†
C 4	..	..	2c†, 9e†, 18b†, 20, 23, 24a†, 25a†, 26b, 65c†
D 4 blue-grn.			2c†, (4d†), 9e†, 18b, 20, 23†, 24d, 25a†, 26b†, 28, 33, 34a
D 4 yell.-grn.			24c, 28, 30a, 33, 34
D 5	..	..	28, 30a, 33, 34a, 37b
E 5	..	..	28, 30a*, 33, 34a, 37b
E 6	..	..	28, 33, 34a, 37b
F 6	..	..	28, 33, 34a, 37b, 42a*
F 7	..	..	28, 33, 34a, 37b†, 42a*
G 7	..	..	28, 33, 34a, 37b, 39, 43a, 47a
G 8	..	..	28†, 36d†, 37b, 43a, 45a†, 47
H 8	..	..	37b, 38d, 42b†, 43a, 45a, 45b, 47a
H 9	..	..	37b†, 38d, 42b, 43a, 45b, 47a, 52b
I 9	..	..	37b†, 42b, 43a, 43b, 43c, 45c, 46c, 46d, 47a, 49b, 52b, 52d, 53a, 53b, 54*
I 10	..	..	43c, 45c, 46d, 47a†, 53b, 58a
J 10	..	..	43c, 46d†, 47b, 54a, 58a, 60a, 61, 64a
A 11 (14)	..	..	57b, 59b, 63b
A 11 (15 × 14)			57b†, 59b†, 63b†

Control			Plates with which it was used
			Right Sheets
A	..	..	2a, 3, 5, 8b, 9a†, 11, 67
B	..	..	1b†, 2a†, 11, 18a, 19†, 26a†, 67, 70
C	..	..	1b†, 2b†, 9d†, 11†, 18a, 19, 26a†, 65b†
C 4	..	..	1b†, 4c, 10b†, 18a, 19†, 24b, 24c, 26a†, 27†
D 4 blue-grn.			1b†, (2d†), 4c†, 9f, 18a*, 18c, 19†, 24c, 25b, 27, 29, 32
D 4 yell.-grn.			18c, 27, 29, 32, 35a, 36a
D 5	..	..	29, 32, 35a, 36a, 37a, 38b
E 5	..	..	29, 30b, 32, 36a, 36b, 38b
E 6	..	..	29, 30b*, 32, 38b, 39
F 6	..	..	27*, 29, 32, 35b*, 35c†, 36c†, 38a, 39, 41a
F 7	..	..	35b*, 36c†, 38b†, 39, 41a, 68†
G 7	..	..	35b*, 36c†, 38b, 41a, 42a, 43a, 68†
G 8	..	..	(34b†), 38b, 41a, 42a, 46a†, 68†
H 8	..	..	38, 38c, 41a, 41b, 42a, 46a, 46b, 49a, 52a, 68
H 9	..	..	41b, 42b†, 46b, 49a, 52a†, 53a
I 9	..	..	41b, 46b, 49c, 52c, 53a, 55, 57a, 68†
I 10	..	..	41b, 49c, 55, 57a, 59a*
J 10	..	..	41b, 49c, 53c, 55, 57a, 58b, 59a, 63a
A 11 (14)	..	..	54b, 58c, 60b, 64b
A 11 (15 × 14)			58c, 64b

1902-11.   1d. Red, Type M2

Cat. No.	S.G. No.	Perf.	Paper	Shades	Unused	Used
1902 (JANUARY 1).	**RED.**		**PERF. 14.**	**DE LA RUE**		
M5	219/20	14	Ordinary	(1) Scarlet	50✓	15✔
				(2) Bright scarlet	50✓	15✔
				(3) Deep bright scarlet	3·50✓	1·25✓
				(4) Rose-carmine	20·00✓	15·00✓

all 3 shades

	Block of four	3·00✓ 1·00✓
	Used on cover	† 1·50
a.	Watermark inverted* ..	2·00✓✓✓ 1·25
b.	Raised crown in watermark (R. 19/2) (corner block of 4)	60·00
c.	Imperf. (pair)	£7500
d.	Imperf. margin at bottom of top pane	£1500
e.	Displaced cliché (Pl. 30c, R. 20/12) corner pair	60·00
f.	Displaced cliché (Pl. 51, R. 20/12) corner pair	70·00
g.	Plug repair, N.E. of value tablet and top frame break N.E. corner (Pl. 9, R. 12/12)	£100
h.	Plug repair below ON of ONE	£110
ha.	Plug repair below P of POSTAGE (Pl. 9, R. 20/12) ..	90·00
i.	Frame broken at right (Pl. 70a, R. 19/12)	35·00
j.	Flaw in E of ONE and P of PENNY (Pl. 58a, R. 20/8)	30·00
k.	Spot under E of PENNY (Pl. 58a, R. 20/10)	25·00
l.	Left frame thinned and vertical scratch (Pl. 9, R. 19/11, control E 5)	25·00

m.	Major plate crack (Pl. ?, R. 3 or 13/12)	50·00
ma.	Ditto. Continued (Pl. ?, R. 4 or 14/12)	50·00
n.	Spot under V of REVENUE (Pl. 50b, R. 20/11) ..	25·00
o.	Tail to E of REVENUE (Pl. 53a/c, R. 20/10) ..	25·00
oa.	Major plate crack (Pl. 53a, R. 20/12)	60·00
p.	No top to Crown (Pl. 85, R. 20/11)	30·00
q.	Minor frame breaks *From*	12·00 ✓
r.	Cracked plate (various) *From*	12·00
ra.	Inner frame broken at right (R. 1/3 of booklet pane with watermark upright) ..	
s.	"Specimen", Type 15 ..	90·00†
t.	"Specimen", Type 16 ..	£150
u.	"Specimen", Type 17 ..	£170
w.	"Specimen", Type 22 ..	
x.	"Cancelled", Type 20 ..	

*No. M5a. The prices are for booklet stamps. Inverted watermarks from sheets are worth much more but can only be differentiated by marginal examples or multiples differing from the booklet format of 3 × 2.

Numerous plug repairs are recorded in articles in *The GB Journal*, Vol. 7 pp. 42, 59 and 73.

Many cracks and breaks in the frame lines are known on the 1d. value. We only list some of them. For further information see *Cracked Units on K.E. VII 1d.* by H. S. Doupé; published by the G.B. Philatelic Society.

†No. M5s exists from NPM archive sales.

M5j, M6ab, M7a

M5g

M5i

M5k, M6ac, M7b

M5*n*

M5*l*
Repaired with Control
E 6 (possibly substituted cliché)

M5*m/ma*

M5*oa*
Later retouched

M5*o*

M5*p*

M5*ra*, M6*d*

Perforation 14
Types: See Control List.

Booklet Panes of Six
From Booklets BA1/5

MB5 Watermark upright		15·00
s. "Specimen", Type 17	..	£1000
t. "Specimen", Type 22	..	
u. Cancelled St Andrew's		
Cross, Type A		50·00
v. Cancelled "E.C.'A'",		
Type B	.. ..	50·00
w. Cancelled "E.C.'U'",		
Type C	.. ..	50·00
x. Cancelled "E.C.K",		
Type D	.. ..	50·00

MB5a Watermark inverted		22·00
as. "Specimen", Type 17		£1000
au. Cancelled St. Andrew's		
Cross, Type A	..	50·00
av. Cancelled "E.C.'A'",		
Type B	.. ..	50·00
aw. Cancelled "E.C.'U'",		
Type C	.. ..	50·00
ax. Cancelled "E.C.K",		
Type D	.. ..	50·00

Essays from the De La Rue Archives

Stamp size design with photographic centre and bromide frame on card:

Lettered " B " and stamped " 19 APR 1901 " £1500
With larger " & ", lettered " A "and stamped " 23 APR 1901 " £1500

Stamp size photographic essay on card showing larger space between laurels and portrait:

1d. value without markings £1500

This was approved on 8 May 1901 by Emil Fuchs on behalf of the King subject to the laurel and oak being narrower to allow more space between the portrait and the frame.

Die Proofs in black on white glazed card :

Without marking	£550	Endorsed " AFTER HARDEN-ING 20 AUG 01 "	£475
Without marking but initialled (M/S) " EF "	£500	Endorsed " AFTER STRIK-ING " (various dates) ..	£475
Endorsed (M/S) " As approved by Mr. Fuchs 19 Aug " ..	£500	Endorsed " Working Die No. 16 "	£500
Endorsed " BEFORE HARD-ENING 20 AUG 01 " ..	£475		

Die Proofs in scarlet on gummed paper. Watermark Crown

Four impressions struck as two vertical pairs £5000

Die Proofs from the De La Rue Archives

On card unmounted with traces of gum or paper on the back:

Essay in die proof form by F. W. Pearce with approved frame but with beard and hair of head plate not approved £1200
Complete die proof with uncleared surround, without markings £650
Cut down proof of frame plate (27 × 32 mm) £800

Pieces Cut from the Striking Books

See notes under the ½d. value.

Struck on plain paper cut to size with various endorsements comprising dates, plates and/or number of leads

1d. value.. .. .. *From* £300

See under ½d. value for pieces with ½d. and 1d. together.

Plate Proofs. All imperf. and without watermark

Pale or deep green on thin white card .. .. *Each* 22·00
Carmine on thin white paper .. .. 28·00

The above proofs are known with double, and with triple impressions *Each* 28·00

Bright scarlet on poor quality buff paper .. ' .. .. 12·00
Bright scarlet on white wove paper .. .. 40·00

Colour Trials. Made from a special plate of 20 electros

1901. Watermark Crown, Imperf. or perf. 14

Dull purple, black on red, purple on red .. .. *From* £750

1906. Watermark Crown. Imperf. or perf. 14. Trials for a suggested change of colour

Blue-geranium, cerise, deep carmine, carmine-red, carmine-lake, carmine-rose and dull rose .. .. *From* £750

For the 1911 Colour Trials see under Section NA.

Specimen overprints from the National Postal Museum Archives

Booklet pane of six. Perf. 14, watermark Type W12

"Specimen", Type 15, watermark inverted
"Specimen", Type 16, watermark upright
"Specimen", Type 16, watermark inverted

Cat. No.	S.G. No.	Perf.	Paper	Shades	Unused	Used

1911 (MAY 3). RED. PERF. 14. HARRISON

M6	272/75a	14	Ordinary	(1) Rose-red	1·75 ✓	4·00 ✓
				(2) Deep rose-red	2·75 ✓	4·00 ✓
Block of four		10·00	40·00	(3) Intense rose-red	£250	55·00 ✓
Used on cover		†	6·00	(4) Pale rose-carmine	32·00	7·50 ✓
a. No watermark (Pl. 58b) ..		75·00	35·00	(5) Rose-carmine	35·00 ✓	9·00 ✓
ab. As *a.* Flaw in E of ONE and				(6) Deep rose-carmine	£250	£110
P of PENNY (Pl. 58b, R.				(7) Aniline rose (F)	£110	75·00 ✓
20/8)		£110		(8) Aniline pink (F)	£250	£110
ac. As *a.* Spot under E of				Some of the rose-red shades		
PENNY (Pl. 58b, R. 20/10)		£100		show slight fluorescence.		
b. Watermark inverted ..		5·50	4·50			
c. Bottom frame broken (Pl.						
61b, R. 20/9)		25·00				
d. Inner frame broken at right						
(R. 1/3 of booklet pane with						
watermark upright)						
s. "Specimen", Type 22 ..		£100†				
t. "Cancelled", Type 21						
imperf.		35·00 ✓				

Some shades of this value are difficult to classify. The best method of checking M6 Nos. (4) (5) and (6) is to use the identical perf. 15 × 14 shades for comparison purposes. The rose-red shades of Harrison are quite different from the scarlet of De la Rue. and little difficulty should be encountered here. M5 (4) is brighter than M6 (5). The latter has less white in the design, and the shading extends well up to the sides of the crown.

M6*a* occurs in shades of brick-red and was probably a trial printing.

The plates which were used for the provisional printings, like those of the Halfpenny value, were probably resurfaced before use.

†No M6*s* exists from NPM archive sales.

M6/7*c*

Perforation 14
Types: See Control list

Booklet Panes of Six
From Booklet BA6

MB6	Watermark upright	15·00	MB6a	Watermark inverted	35·00
b.	No. 3 and 6 on pane		*as.*	"Specimen", Type 22 ..	
	showing displaced		*at.*	Cancelled "London Chief	
	clichés .. *From*	£140		Office, E.C.", Type E	
t.	Cancelled "London Chief			(*shades*) ..	
	Office, E.C.", Type E ..				

Specimen overprints from the National Postal Museum Archives
Booklet pane of six. Perf. 14, watermark Type W12

"Specimen", Type 15, watermark upright
"Specimen", Type 15, watermark inverted

Cat. No.	S.G. No.	Perf.	Paper	Shades	Unused	Used

1911 (OCTOBER 5). RED. PERF. 15 × 14.   HARRISON

M7	280/82	15 × 14	Ordinary	(1) Rose-red	18·00	10·00
				(2) Deep rose-red	50·00	15·00
	Block of four	25·00	22·00	(3) Rose-carmine	5·00	3·00
	Used on cover	†	15·00	(4) Deep rose-carmine	12·00	6·00
	a. Flaw in E of ONE and P of			(5) Pale rose-carmine	8·00	3·00
	PENNY (Pl. 58b, R. 20/8). .	40·00		(6) V. pale " "	240 (retail 20)
	b. Spot under E of PENNY					
	(Pl. 58b, R. 20/10)	35·00				
	c. Bottom frame broken (Pl.					
	61b, R. 20/9)	35·00				

Perforation 15 × 14

Types V3 and V3A

Controls. Prices are for unused corner pairs

Printed by De La Rue

Control	Date				H1	H1A	V1 or V4	V2	V2A or V4A
(a) With continuous rule									
A	Jan. 1902..	..	..	..	2·00	14·00	3·00		2·50
B	Dec. 1902..	..	..	..	2·00	12·00	2·00		3·00
C	Oct. 1903..	..	..	..	2·00	10·00	3·00	†	9·00
C 4	Feb. 1904..	..	..	..	2·00	12·00	2·00	†	18·00
D 4	Apr. 1904..	..	..	..	10·00	60·00	5·00	†	—
D 5	July 1905..	..	..	..	22·00	†	22·00	†	—
(b) With coextensive rule									
C	Oct. 1903..	..	..	..	10·00	55·00	18·00	†	15·00
C 4	Feb. 1904..	..	..	..	3·00	70·00	55·00	†	—
D 4	Apr. 1904..	..	..	..	2·00	55·00	2·00	†	18·00
D 5	June 1905..	..	..	..	2·00	70·00	2·00	†	—
E 5	Aug. 1905..	..	..	..	2·00	†	2·00	2·00	2·00
E 6	July 1906..	..	..	..	3·00	60·00	†	60·00	2·00
F 6	Sept. 1906..	..	..	..	2·00	60·00	†	3·25	2·00
F 7	July 1907..	..	..	..	2·00	55·00	†	3·00	2·50
G 7	Oct. 1907..	..	..	..	2·00	70·00	†	2·00	2·00
G 8	July 1908..	..	..	..	12·00	†	†	2·00	2·00
H 8	Oct. 1908..	..	..	..	2·00	22·00	† V1A	2·00	2·00
H 9	July 1909..	..	..	..	2·00	28·00	†	3·00	10·00
I 9	Oct. 1909..	..	..	..	2·00	55·00	†	2·00	2·00
I 10	July 1910..	..	..	..	15·00	70·00	†	2·00	2·50
J 10	Sept. 1910..	..	..	..	2·00	28·00	†	2·00	2·00

At least six pieces are known of Control E 5 with Type V2(a).

Single examples of the following control varieties are known:—

A single of Control D 4 with imperf. bottom margin, Type H1, with the " 4 " almost omitted.

A corner strip of three of Control F 7 perf. Type V2 with the " F 7 " almost omitted.

A pair of Control G 7 from Plate 23 with the watermark inverted.

Examples occur where the control (e.g. I 9) is repeated under the 10th, 9th, 8th, 7th, etc., stamps, each impression fainter than its predecessor. Such examples are always perforated by the Type V2A perforator with right feed. The variety is caused by the comb head picking up the ink from the control, which had not properly dried, and at each descent of the comb a progressively fainter control became printed in the bottom margin. This variety has been seen with controls E 5, E 6 and G 7.

Printed by Harrison

Perf. 14

Control	Date						H1	Perforation Type		
								H2A	V1	V1A
A 11 (c)	Sept. 1911	..	..	..	••	..	38·00	†	†	†
A 11 (w)	May 1911	..	..	..	••	..	15·00	5·00 ✓	15·00	17·00

Perf. 15 × 14

A 11(c)	Oct. 1911	••	••	••	••	••	V3 10·00 ✓	V3A 17·00

The H2 perforator is known in variations a, c, d and e and the H2A perforator in variations c, d and e.

(c) "close" and (w) "wide" refer to the space between the figures (1½ mm. and 2 mm. respectively).

want M6 (1) rose 1d   A 11(c)

Plate Markings

See notes under "Plate Markings" of ½d. value.

With Continuous Rule

Plate	Features
†1a	Cut under PE of 10th
1b	Added cut under (P)E of 4th
1c	Added cut under PE of 8th
†2a	Cut under PE of 7th
2b	Probably added cut under an even numbered column
2c	Added slanting cut under NE of 11th
†3a	Crossed cuts under EP of 4th
3b	Added cut under P of 5th
3c	Added slanting cut under PE of 10th
4	¾ cut (base) under PE of 10th
5	Cut under NE of 11th
6	Cut under EP of 12th
7	Cut under P of 12th
8	Deleted. Now part of Plate 14
†10	Cuts under E(N) and NN of 1st, N(N) of 5th and O and NE of 6th
†11a	Cut under (P)E of 5th
11b	Added cut under P of 2nd
11c	Added cut under EP of 11th
12	Deleted as being redundant
†13	Cut sloping down, left to right, under (P)E of 4th
†14a	½ cut (base) under (P)E of 9th, ½ cut (top) or damage under PE of 7th
14b	Added cuts under E(N) and N(Y) of 8th. Many rule breaks, including break or cut under (N)N of 10th. Rule below 12th drops during right control C 4
†16a	Cut under PE of 8th
16b	Added cut slanting down from left to right under (E)N of 7th
†17a	Cut under E(P) of 5th
17b	Added cut under E(P) of 4th
†18a	Cut under NE of 6th
18b	Added cut under P of 9th
†19b	Cut under (P)E of 2nd, under PE of 8th and break or cut under N(Y) of 10th
†20a	Cut under (P)E of 2nd
20b	Added cut under PE of 3rd
29	Deleted. Now part of Plate 2
32	Deleted. Now part of Plate 17
†68a	Cut under P of 6th
68b	Added cuts under PE and N(N) of 5th
†69	Cut under E(N) of 7th
†70a	Cut sloping up left to right under (P)E of 6th, 2 pips (top) under N(E) of 8th
70b	Added cut under EP of 12th
72	Cut under PE of 9th
73	Cut under P(E) of 8th
†74a	Stamp 20/11, with control A, has disturbed shading over & RE
74b	Added ¾ cut (base) under P of 12th
75	Cut under (P)E of 8th differing from that on Plate 16
76	Cut under (P)E of 1st (Official Plate 1/1)
77	Cut under (N)E of 1st
†78a	Double cut under P of 10th
78b	Cut or cuts added, including under P of 11th leaning slightly forward
†79	Thick and thin cuts under P and E of 1st. Basal nicks in rule below gutter 10/11 and ON of 11th
80a	Cut under (P)E of 7th
80b	Added cut under PE of 4th and ¾ cut (top) below gutter 9/10
81	Cut under PE of 2nd
†82	Cut under P of 4th, seen only on a strip of four of MO37, but although this overprint is believed to have constant variety, upward projection from lowest inner oakleaf of control stamp, R. 20/11, confirmation of bottom strip required
†86	Cuts under PE of 2nd, (P)E of 4th and NN of 7th with right control C 4
87	Cut below (P)E of 4th but differing from Plate 13
88a	Cut sloping down, left to right, under PE of 4th
88b	Added wide cut under (P)E of 3rd
88c	Probably added cut under an even numbered column

From control pieces with features not seen in the above plates it is thought that about another six plates may eventually be included. Each should have a cut or cuts that differ, perhaps only slightly, from the foregoing and any likely pieces should be submitted to the Editor.

With Coextensive Rule

Plate	Features
†9	Die I. ¾ flat-topped cut (base) under PE of 1st (Plate 49 cut has a pointed top)
15	Deleted. Now part of Plate 30
21a	Cut under (P)E of 3rd (less curved right side and narrower base than Plate 37a)
21b	Added ¾ cut (top) under PE of 10th. This was formerly Plate 37 and items from control E 6 and later and previously listed as Plates 21a/b now belong to Plate 37
†22a	¾ cut (base) under PE of 4th
22b	Added diamond-shaped cut under PE of 2nd
†23a	Sloping cut under E(N) of 4th
23b	Added cut under P of 3rd
24a	Cut under PE of 5th
24b	Added wide ½ cut under NN of 2nd
25a	Cut under (N)E of 6th, widening to two cuts
25b	Added ¾ cut (base) under PE of 12th
†26a	Cut under (O)N of 6th, thin and regular
26b	Added cut under P of 11th; changes from left to right during control G 8
26c	Added ½ cut (base) under NE of 2nd; with control H 8 comes from left and right
27	Cut under N(N) of 7th
†28a	Full and ½ cut (base) under P of 8th
28b	Added diamond-shaped cut under PE of 1st and ½ cut (top) under NE of 6th
†30a	Die I. Cut under P of 2nd; slanting crack under NE of 12th
30b	Added ½ cut (base) under EP of 10th
30c	Added cuts under O and (N)E of 6th
†31	1½ cuts under NE of 2nd; with none added for first change of side (information wanted about second change)
†33a	2 thick cuts under NE of 6th
33b	Added ½ cut (base) under P of 10th; short rule left of 11th
†34a	½ cut (top) under NE of 11th
34b	Added fine cut and dot under PEN of 9th (probably due to wear)
34c	Added cut 20th right side (5 mm.)
34d	Added cut 19th right side (8½ mm.)
†35	½ cut (base) under EP of 2nd; change of side with control F 6
36	Cut under (P)E of 8th. Rule below 12th dropped from control E 5; change of side with control G 7
37a	Cut under (P)E of 3rd (more curved right side and wider base than Plate 21a)
37b	Added cut under PE of 2nd. Plate 37 now contains controls E 6 to H 8 items of Plate 21a/b, whilst the original E 5 item becomes Plate 21b

With Coextensive Rule—*continued*

Plate	Features
†38a	Cut under PE of 2nd
38b	Added 2 double cuts under NN of 7th
39a	Dot under EP of 1st
39b	Added 2 irregular cuts under PEN of 4th
40a	Curved semi-double cut under PE of 2nd
40b	Added 2 cuts under EPE of 5th. None added to bottom rule for side change with control G 7
41a	Thin "v" cut under (P)E of 5th. Side changed with no added cuts during control G 7
41b	Added ¾ cut under (P)E of 4th
42	Wide cut under (O)N of 6th
†43a	½ cut (base) under Y of 7th
43b	Added cut or dot under P of 1st
†44a	Cut under P of 5th
44b	Added fine sloping cut under (P)E of 11th
†45	2 fine cuts under ON of 6th; right end of 10th cut away during right control G 8
†46a	2 ragged cuts under NE of 6th
46b	Added ½ cut (base), 1 cut and ½ cut (base) all under NEP of 5th
47a	Cut under NY of 7th
47b	Added cut under P of 5th
47c	Added 3 fractional sloping cuts (base) under EP of 2nd; 10th rule broken under Y and left section dropped
†48a	1½ cuts under P of 8th
48b	Added 1½ cuts under (E)N of 7th
†49	½ cut with pointed top (base) under PE of 1st (Plate 9 had a flat-topped cut). A temporary change to right side with control I 10, so additional cuts likely
50a	Cut and minute ½ cut under EP of 1st
50b	Added cut under EP of 4th
†51a	½ cut (base) under PE of 2nd and cut or break on 19th right side (11 mm.)
51b	Added ½ cut (base) under EP of 1st
52a	Ragged cut under PE of 3rd
52b	Added ½ cut under (N)E of 1st
†53a	Irregular cut under (P)E of 4th
53b	Added sloping cut under EN of 3rd and ¾ cut (base) under (O)N of 6th
53c	Added cuts under PE, (N)N and Y of 7th
†54a	Irregular cut under (P)E of 5th

Plate	Features
54b	Added cut under PE of 4th and 2 ½ cuts (top) under (P)E of 8th
55	Deleted. Now part of Plate 53
†56	Irregular cut under N(N) of 5th. Changes to right side with control I 10 so further cuts likely
†57a	2 very close cuts under N(E) of 6th and dot at top left end of 12th rule; 5 cuts in centre rule to right of pillars (2.0, 6.7, 13.5, 17.5, 21.5 mm. up)
57b	Added 2 cuts under PEN of 5th and cut under EP of 8th
†58a	½ cut (top) under NY of 7th
58b	Added ½ cut under N(N) of 1st and 2 cuts or breaks under EPE of 8th. Several flaw varieties
59	2 thick sloping cuts under ON of 6th. A proof on buff paper has fine cut or break under P of 11th, no examples seen on issued stamps
60	Small ½ cut (base) under PE of 2nd
61a	½ cut (base) under P of 4th
61b	Added large cut under NN of 9th and cut 17th right side (8½ mm.). Some previous I 10 and J 10 control items now constitute Plate 84
62a	Very fine cut (top) under EP of 5th
62b	Added big cut under PE of 11th, cut 19.b right side (12 mm.)
62c	Added cut under 18th right side (11 mm.)
63a	½ cut (base) under NE of 3rd
63b	Added cut 17th right (12½ mm.)
63c	Added cut 20th right (9½ mm.)
64	Deleted. Now part of Plate 48
65	¾ cut (base) under EN of 7th
66a	½ cut (base) under P of 8th (ragged)
66b	Added cut under EP of 10th (coarse and cut 18th right side (10½ mm.)
67	Deleted. Now part of Plate 44
†71	Die I, 6/7 Rule. Cut under P of 7th
†84	½ cut (base) under EP of 4th (the similar ½ cut of Plate 61 is under P). Some I 10 and J 10 control items originally with Plate 61 belong to Plate 84
†85a	Die I, 6/7 Rule. Cut under (P)E of 6th
85b	Added cuts under EP and P of 8th

There are indications that one or two more plates could exist.

Index to Marginal Markings

Bottom Margin, stamp numbers

Stamp
No.   Plates

1 9, 10, 28b, 39a, 39b, 43b, 49, 50a, 50b, 51b, 52b, 58b, 76, 77, 79
2 11b, 11c, 19b, 20a, 20b, 22b, 24b, 26c, 30a, 30b, 30c, 31, 35, 37b, 38a, 38b, 40a, 40b, 47c, 51a, 51b, 60, 81, 86
3 20b, 21a, 21b, 23b, 37a, 37b, 52a, 52b, 53b, 53c, 63a, 63b, 63c, 88b, 88c
4 1b, 1c, 3a, 3b, 3c, 13, 17b, 22a, 22b, 23a, 23b, 39b, 41b, 50b, 53a, 53b, 53c, 54b, 61a, 61b, 80b, 82, 84, 86, 87, 88a, 88b, 88c
5 3b, 3c, 10, 11a, 11b, 11c, 17a, 17b, 24a, 24b, 40b, 41a, 41b, 44a, 44b, 46b, 47b, 47c, 54a, 54b, 56, 57b, 62a, 62b, 62c, 68b
6 10, 18a, 18b, 25a, 25b, 26a, 26b, 26c, 28b, 30c, 33a, 33b, 42, 45, 46a, 46b, 53b, 53c, 57a, 57b, 59, 68a, 68b, 70a, 70b, 85a, 85b
7 2a, 2b, 2c, 14a, 14b, 16b, 27, 38b, 43a, 43b, 47a, 47b, 47c, 48b, 53c, 58a, 58b, 65, 69, 71, 80a, 80b, 86
8 1c, 14b, 16a, 16b, 19b, 28a, 28b, 36, 48a, 48b, 54b, 57b, 58b, 66a, 66b, 70a, 70b, 73, 75, 85b
9 14a, 14b, 18b, 34b, 34c, 34d, 61b, 72, 80b
10 1a, 1b, 1c, 3c, 4, 14b, 19, 21b, 30b, 30c, 33b, 45, 47c, 66b, 78a, 78b, 79, 80b
11 2c, 5, 11c, 26b, 26c, 33b, 34a, 34b, 34c, 34d, 44b, 62b, 62c, 78b, 79
12 6, 7, 25b, 30a, 30b, 30c, 57a, 57b, 70b, 74b
Basal scoop under NY of 4th: 17, 20, (24), (44), 47, 82
Basal scoop under ONE of 9th: 2, (9), 10, 13, 20, (22), 24, 25, 28, 30, 31, (33), 35, 38, 39, 41, 42, 43, 44, 46, (48), 50, 54

The scoops are sometimes very slight on the plates shown in brackets.

Right Margin, row number

Row No.	Plates	Row No.	Plates
Centre Pillars: 57a, 57b			
17	61b, 63b, 63c	19	34d, 51a, 51b, 62b, 62c
18	62c, 66b	20	34c, 34d, 63c

Control Schedule

For the significance of the asterisks, daggers and brackets and other information see the notes under the Control Schedule for the ½d. value.

Control	Left Sheets	Plates with which it was used — Right Sheets
A	2a†, 5, 11a, 11c†, 14a, 69†, 72, 76, 77, 78b†, 79, 80a, 88b	1a†, 3a†, 4, 6, 7, 11b†, 16a, 68a, 69†, 70a, 70b†, 73, 74a†, 74b†, 75, 78a†, 80b, 81, 87, 88a
B	2a, 3b†, 11c†, 14a†, 17a, 18b†, 63b†, 79†	1a†, 1b, 1c, 3c†, 7, 10†, 13†, 16a, 18a†, 19†, 20a†, 68a†, 69†, 82†, 86†, 88c
C	2a†, 9, 16b†, 17a†, 18b*, 20b†	1c†, 3c*, 10†, 13, 14b, 16a*, 19*, 30a
C 4	9, 11c, 16b†, 17a, 18b†, 20b†, 71	2b†, 3c†, 7, 10†, 13†, 14b†, 19b, 30a, (79b†) 82†, 85a†, 85b†, 86†
D 4	2c†, 9, 11c†, 17a†, 18b, 20b, 21a, 24a, 27, 71†	2b†, 3c, 7, 17b, 22a, 22b, 23a†, 25a, 26a, 28a, 30a, 31*, 85b
D 5	9, 18b, 21a, 24a, 27, 34a	7, 22b†, 23a, 25a, 28a, 30b, 33a. 35
E 5	9, 21a, 24a, 26b, 27, 34a	21b, 23a, 25a, 25b, 28a, 30c†, 33a, 35, 36
E 6	9, 24a, 26b†, 27, 28b*, 34a†, 37a	23a†, 25b, 28b†, (28c†), 30c†, 33a†, 35†, 36†, 38a, 42
F 6	9, 24a, 27, 35†, 37a†, 38b*, 39a, 41a, 43a	23a, 24b, 36, 38a, 40a, 42
F 7	9†, 37a, 38b*, 39a, 41a, 43a	23a, 31*, 36†, 38a†, 38b*, 40a, 42
G 7	35†, 36†, 37a, 39a, 40b, 41a, 42*, 43a, 44a	23a, 31, 36, 38b, 40a, 40b, 41a, 45, 46a†
G 8	23b, 26b†, 26c†, 31†, 34a, 35†, 36†, 39a, 43a†, 44a	25b, 26b†, 31† 33a†, 37b†, 41b, 42*, 45, 46a, 48a†
H 8	23b, 26b†, 26c†, 31†, 34a, 35† 39b, 43b, 44a†, 47a, 49, 50a, 52a, 53b, 53c, 54a	25b†, 26c, 31†, 33a†, 37b, 41b†, 44a, 45†, 46a, 48a, 50b, 51a, 53a
H 9	47b, 49, 52a, 53c†, 54a, 58a†	46a, 48a†, 50b, 51a, 53c, 57a*
I 9	34a, 44a†, 46b, 47b†, 49, 52a, 56, 58a	25b†, 33a†, 47c, 48a, 50b, 51a, 57a, 59, 84†
I 10	34a*, 49, 51b*, 52a, 58a, 62a	48a†, 49†, 50b, 56†, 57b, 59, 60, 84
J 10 ..	34b, 44b†, 48b, 49†, 51b, 52a, 52b, 58a, 62a, 63a, 65	25b, 33b, 48a, 54b, 56*, 58b†, 59, 60 61a, 66a, 84
A 11 (c) (14)	61b	58b? (see note below), 62b
A 11 (w) (14)	34b†, 62b, 63b	34c, 66b
A 11 (c) (15×14)	34c, 34d, 61b, 62b*	62c, 63c

Since some examples of No. M6 are known to have varieties peculiar to Plate 58b it is included in the above table, although neither the control nor the sheet side are yet known.

1902-11. 1½d. Purple and Green, Type M3

Cat. No.	S.G. No.	Perf.	Paper	Shades	Unused	Used

1902-05. PURPLE AND GREEN. PERF. 14. DE LA RUE

A. 1902 (MARCH 21). Ordinary paper

M8   221/22   14   Ordinary

		(1) Dull purple and green 15·00 6·00 ✔
		(2) Slate-purple and green 12·00 4·75 ✔

Block of four .. .. ..   60·00   40·00

Used on cover .. .. ..   †   12·00

a. Watermark inverted ..   —   £400

b. Damage in tablet (Pl. D4, R. 1/7) .. ..   50·00

ba. State 2 Redrawn leaves and tablet retouched (Pl. D4, R. 1/7)   75·00

c. Tablet repair (Pl. D4, R. 2/7) .. ..   75·00

d. Retouch left of tablet and around large figure I (Pl. D4, R. 10/2) .. ..   75·00

e. Deformed leaf (Pl. D4, R. 19/1) £300   £100

f. Frame broken at bottom (Pl. H1, R. 20/2) .. ..   50·00

g. Frame broken at right (Pl. H1, R. 20/3) .. ..   50·00

s. "Specimen", Type 15 ..   £100

Nos. M8*d*/*e* are the same varieties as K29*e*/*f* listed in Volume 1 and ascribed to Duty Plate 4 and Duty Plate 2.

M8*b*
Damage in tablet (State 1)

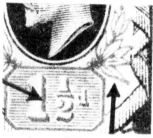

M8*ba*
Redrawn leaves and tablet retouched (State 2)

M8*c*

Retouch repair between frame and figure "I"

M8*d*

M8*e*

M8*f*

M8*g*

B. 1905 (AUGUST). Chalk-surfaced paper

M9	223/4	14	Chalky		

	Block of four	£100	45·00	(1) Pale dull purple and green	25·00 5·50 ✓
	Used on cover	†	20·00	(2) Slate-purple and bluish green	20·00 4·25 ✓
c.	Frame broken at left (Pl. H5, R. 6/4)	£100		(3) Deep slate-purple and bluish green	40·00 15·00 ✓
e.	Frame broken at top left ..	40·00			
s.	"Specimen", Type 17 ..	£200			
t.	"Cancelled", Type 18 ..	—†			
u.	"Cancelled", Type 20 ..	£400			

In the De la Rue printings, the uppermost line at the top of the fringe in the S.E. corner is usually faint.

†No. M9t exists from NPM archive sales.

M9c   M9e

No. M9c is a first state of No. M10c.

Perforation 14
Type H1 only

Die Proofs in black on white glazed card:

Head plate only

Without marking	£550	
Endorsed "BEFORE HARD-ENING 20 NOV 01" ..	£500	
Endorsed "AFTER HARDEN-ING 27 NOV 01"	£500	
Endorsed "AFTER STRIKING 29 NOV 01"	£500	
Cut down and endorsed on back "Duplicate proof of Head die for 1½d. stamp registered 1 Feby 1902" in M/S ..	£400	

Duty plate only

Endorsed "After Striking 19 APR 06"	£500

The date on this proof is not the striking date for Plate 7, nor any other plate.

Unfinished Die Proof of proposed monocoloured issue

With manuscript "Cancelled" and initials	£800

Die Proofs from the De La Rue Archives

On card unmounted with traces of gum or paper on the back:

Head plate only, without markings £650

Die for proposed monocoloured issue:

With uncleared surround, endorsed " Cancelled " in M/S £1100

Pieces Cut from the Striking Books

See notes under the ½d. value.

Struck on plain paper cut to size with various endorsements comprising dates, plates and/or number of leads

1½d. head plates .. .. *From* £300
1½d. duty plate 7 dated "Jan 11" (1904) £350
1½d. duty plate with 2d. head plate and 6d. plate all together £950

Partly finished die for proposed monocoloured issue

Endorsed "This die partly finished/Chgd. 25 Aug 10 " £1100

Colour Trials

Following the decision to print the 1½d., 2d. and 4d. values in one colour, Warrants were issued for the colour trials for two purposes. First to decide whether the existing designs were suitable for printing in monocolour and second to select which colours should be used. Nine Warrants were issued, three for each value each on three different papers. These were for the normal white 480 crown paper, the yellow 480 crown paper used for the 3d. value and finally on three different papers tinted in colours not then in production and therefore without watermark. It is not known for certain how many colours were printed, but those actually submitted are known. De La Rue printed the purple inks in different depths and submitted what were the basic combinations several times over. 28 samples for each value were submitted to the Inland Revenue on 19th March 1909.

The colour names given are descriptive of the actual colours submitted but have been simplified in some cases. The colour " Tyrian plum " is included as it was selected for the abortive 2d. monocoloured although existing examples of the colour trials bear little resemblance to the colour actually used for it. No names or descriptive notes were given to the trials.

The tinted papers have white backs. As only three tinted colours were used other colours given in earlier editions are omitted. The colours may not have been consistent over the whole supply.

All are perforated 14

On white paper. Watermark Crown

In carmine-lake, carmine, orange, orange-yellow, sage-green, dull blue-green. deep blue, violet, purple, Tyrian plum, brown, deep brown, olive-brown, slate   *From* £800

On yellow paper. Watermark Crown

In scarlet, green, four shades of purple .. ..   *From* £800

On tinted paper. No watermark

In three shades of purple on pink; two shades of purple on orange, black on orange; red on blue, purple on blue .. ..   *From* £800

On 16th March 1910 the deep brown shade was selected for the proposed new monocoloured stamp and work began on a new combined head and duty plate which was left unfinished owing to the death of the King.

Cat. No.	S.G. No.	Perf.	Paper	Shades		Unused	Used
1911 (JULY 13).		**PURPLE AND GREEN.**		**PERF. 14. SOMERSET HOUSE**			
M10	287/89	14	Ordinary	(1) Reddish purple and bright green		25·00	9·50
			Block of four	65·00	35·00	(2) Reddish purple and yellow-green (Oct. 1912)		25·00 ~~90~~ 10	9·50✓
	c.	Used on cover	†	30·00				
		Frame broken at left (Pl. H5, R. 6/4)	85·00		(3) Dull reddish purple and bright green (Sept. 1911)		20·00	6·00✓
	f.	Do. (Pl. ?, R. 8/4)	85·00					
	g.	Do. (Pl. ?, R. 9/4)	85·00		(4) Dull reddish purple and green (1912)		13·00	6·00✓
	h.	Do. (Pl. ?, R. 10/4)	85·00		(5) Dull purple and green (some F)		13·00	6·00✓
	j.	Cracked plate	40·00		(6) Deep plum and deep green		£110	50·00
				(7) Slate-purple and green (some F)		18·00	10·00✓

(8) Pale slate y green   30

51

In the Somerset House printings, the uppermost line at the top of the fringe in the S.E. corner is thick, and sometimes broken. Many stamps show damage to the circle round the medallion, and the frame lines are sometimes pitted, as though the plate had suffered corrosion.

With the exception of No. (7) all shades of purple appear redder when placed side by side with stamps from the De la Rue printings. Some of the above shades of purple are met with again on the 5d., 6d., 9d. and 1od. values.

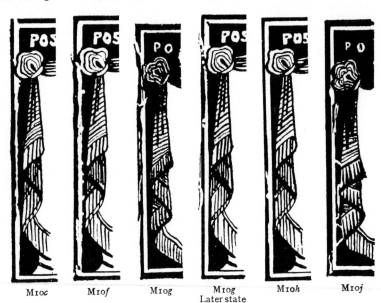

| M1oc | M1of | M1og | M1og Later state | M1oh | M1oj |

No. M1oc is a second state of No. M9c.

Perforation 14

    Types V1   V1A

Specimen overprint from the National Postal Museum Archives

    Perforated 14, watermark Type W12

    "Specimen", Type 22

Plate Descriptions

Official Pl. No.	S.G. Pl. No.	Features

Head Plates (Inner Line)

1/60	H1	Continuous rules. Square corners at the interpane margin (all other bicoloured head plates with continuous rules have rounded corners). Cut under 2nd. Used only by De La Rue
2/64	H2	Continuous rules. Cut under 1st. Used only by De La Rue
3/66	H3	Continuous rules. No markings. Used only by De La Rue
4/249	H4	Coextensive rules. No markings in first state (see Printings). Used by De La Rue and Somerset House
5/263	H5	Coextensive rules. Tiny diagonal white line below middle of 2nd on most De La Rue printings. Used also by Somerset House
6/271	H6	Coextensive rules. Square dots at the interpane margin (all other bicoloured head plates with coextensive rules, except one, have curved corners). Cut preceded by nick under 2nd in De La Rue printings. Used also by Somerset House

Duty Plates (Outer Line)

4	D4	Continuous rules at sides only. Used only by De La Rue
5	D5	Continuous rules at sides only. Used only by De La Rue
6	D6	Continuous rules all round but with breaks in horizontal rules every third stamp. Upward bulge under 2nd about the 9th De La Rue printing. Also used by Somerset House
7	D7	Coextensive rules. Used only by Somerset House

These features identify the plates in their original states. Later states are indicated under the list of printings.

Printings
De La Rue

No. of Printing	Date	Plates Left sheet	Right sheet	Notes

Ordinary Paper (No. M8)

No. of Printing	Date	Plates Left sheet	Right sheet	Notes
1	Feb./Aug. 1902	H2/D4	H1/D5	
2	Jan./Feb. 1903	H2/D4	H1/D5	
3	Nov./Dec. 1903	H2/D6	H1/D5	
4	July/Aug. 1904	H2/D5	H1/D5	
		H2/D6	H3/D5	

Chalk-surfaced Paper (No. M9)

No. of Printing	Date	Plates Left sheet	Right sheet	Notes
5	May/June 1905	H2/D6	H3/D5	
6	Dec. 1906/Feb. 1907	H4/D6	H3/D5	
7	Oct./Dec. 1907	H4a/D6	H5/D5	Cut preceded by nick under 1st in H4a
8	Dec. 1908/Feb. 1909	H4a/D6	H5/D5	
9	Dec. 1909/Jan. 1910	H4a/D6a	H6/D5	Upward dent under 2nd in D6a
10/12	1910	H4a/D6a	H6/D5	

The chalky paper used at about the time of the 7th and 8th printings had a very unstable top surface and stamps from these printings are heavily rubbed and found in the so-called " pale purple " shade.

The exact dates of the introduction of Plates H5 and H6 are uncertain.

Somerset House

No. of Printing	Date	Plates	Notes

Ordinary Paper (No. M10)

No. of Printing	Date	Plates	Notes
1st	May 1911	H6a/D6a	H6a has added V cuts under 5th (denoting May) and two wide spaced cuts under 11th for 1911
2nd	Aug. 1911	H6b/D6a	H6b has marks under 2nd, V cuts under 5th and wide 1911 cuts all filled up. Cut under 8th (denoting August) and narrow date cuts under 11th added and purple dots over and under 12th stamp in top and bottom rows of each pane
3rd	Jan. 1912	H6c/D7	H6c cuts under 8th and 11th filled up. Cuts added under 12th to left of " 1 "
4th	Feb. 1912	H5a/D7	Diagonal line under 2nd removed; date cuts added under 12th under " 1 " and purple dots added as in H6b
5th	About Aug. 1912	H4b/D7	Cut and nick under 1st filled up; narrow thin date cuts under 12th to right of "1"; purple dots added as in H6b

The dates and numbers of printings after the 4th are at present obscure. The printings were on a substantial scale but probably not continuous.

At the time of the fourth printing a fluorescent head plate ink in slate-purple was used and H6c, which had been exposed to it, began to be badly corroded, with faults in the printing design appearing all over it. This plate was not used again and H5a was used with new inks, apparently until King George V stamps became available in sufficient numbers.

Price Schedule

Plate Combination Head/Duty	Left or Right sheet	Printing Usage	Recognisable Piece	Price per Pair
De La Rue				
(a) Ordinary Paper				
H1/D5	Right	1 to 4	S.W. corner	60·00
H2/D4	Left	1, 2	Corner	70·00
H2/D6	Left	3, 4	Pair with horiz. green cont. rule. only	80·00
H3/D5	Right	4	S.W. corner	90·00
(b) Chalk-surfaced Paper				
H2/D6	Left	5	Pair with horiz. green & purple cont. rules	80·00
H3/D5	Right	5, 6	Pair with horiz. purple cont. rule only	£100
H4/D6	Left	6 only	S.W. corner	£150
H4/D6	Left	6 to 12	Pair with horiz. green cont. rule and coext. purple rule	65·00
H4a/D6	Left	7, 8	S.W. corner	£110
H5/D5	Right	7, 8	S.W. corner or interpane pair with curved corner pieces	85·00
H4a/D6a	Left	9 to 12	S.W. corner	95·00
H6/D5	Right	9 to 12	S.W. corner or interpane pair with square corner dots	95·00
Somerset House				
H6a/D6	—	1st	S.E. corner	45·00
H6b/D6	—	2nd	S.E. corner	40·00
H6c/D7	—	3rd	S.E. corner or interpane pair with square corner dots and green coext. rule	32·00
H5a/D7	—	4th	S.E. corner	45·00
H4b/D7	—	5th	S.E. corner	65·00

Prices are quoted for pairs, although single examples are sometimes adequate for identification.

Before attempting to identify recognisable pieces from De La Rue printings it is necessary first to establish whether an item comes from a left or right sheet, thus for H1/D5 "corner" means any corner of a right sheet, and so on. For this purpose reference should be made to the General Notes under "PAPER. Recognising the Halves of the Mill Sheet".

See also in the General Notes under "PLATES", "SHEET MARKINGS" and "PLATE MARKINGS".

1902-11. 2d. Green and Red, Type M4

Cat. No.	S.G. No.	Perf.	Paper	Shades	Unused	Used

1902-10. GREEN AND RED. PERF. 14. DE LA RUE

A. 1902 (MARCH 25). Ordinary paper

M11   225/26   14   Ordinary

Block of four	80·00	35·00
Used on cover	†	12·00

a. Distorted tablet ("Rhombus", state 1) (Pl. D3, R. 1/1) £150

b. Double frame break (Pl. D3, R. 6/4) .. .. .. 60·00

c. Bottom right tablet corner raised (Pl. D4, R. 3/12) .. 60·00

d. Shading line below d thinned (Pl. D3, R. 10/2) .. 45·00

e. Displaced 2nd dot at upper right (Pl. H1, R. 6/6) .. 60·00

f. Scratch through O (P. H1, R. 18/12) .. .. .. 85·00

g. Irregular shading on right side of tablet (Pl. D3, R. 9/3) .. .. 45·00

(1) Yellowish green and carmine-red   18·00   4·00 ✓

(2) Pale greyish green and carmine-red (1903)   18·00   4·00

(3) Pale greyish green and scarlet-vermilion (1903)   £110   40·00

(4) Grey-green and carmine-red (1904)   18·00   4·00 ✓

s.   "Specimen", Type 16   ..   £100

M11a, 12b

M11b
Later retouched

M11c, 12e

M11d, 12g
Later retouched on M12

M11g, M12n
The irregular shading
extends behind the value

M11e, 12h

M11f, 12i

B. 1906 (APRIL)   Chalk-surfaced paper

M12   227/29   14   Chalky

Block of four	£150	40·00
Used on cover	†	20·00

a. Watermark inverted .. ..
b. Distorted tablet ("Rhombus", state 1) (Pl. D3, R. 1/1) £180
c. As last, state 2 .. .. £110
d. Deformed tablet (Pl. D4, R. 5/9) £300
e. Bottom right tablet corner raised (Pl. D4, R. 3/12) .. 75·00
f. As last, retouched (bottom tablet corner still raised but no longer joined to lowest frame line) .. .. .. 50·00
g. Shading line below d thinned (Pl. D3, R. 10/2) .. 50·00
h. Displaced 2nd dot at upper right (Pl. H1, R. 6/6) .. 75·00
i. Scratch beside O stronger (Pl. H1, R. 18/12) .. £100
j. Lower left frame lines both broken ("Magnus" flaw) (Pl. H3, R. 8/3) .. .. — £110

(1) Pale grey-green and carmine-red   22·00   6·00 ✓
(2) Dull blue-green and carmine (1907)   40·00*/80* 20·00 ✓
deep 275
(3) Pale grey-green and scarlet (1909)   25·00 *7S* 6·00 ✓
(4) Grey-green and scarlet (1910)   22·00   6·00 ✓

k. Flaws in oak leaves and frame break (Pl. H1, R. 15/11) .. .. — 85·00
l. Big R (Pl. H2, R. 6/8) .. 75·00
m. 3rd E of REVENUE shortened and flaw under it (Pl. H2, R. 5/8) .. .. .. 85·00
n. Irregular shading on right side of tablet (Pl. D3, R. 9/3) 45·00
o. Top shade line of tablet broken and joined to "2" (Pl. D4, R. 10/1) .. 45·00
s. "Specimen", Type 17 .. £200†
t. "Cancelled", Type 18 .. —†
u. "Cancelled", Type 20 ..

†Nos. M12s and M12t exist from NPM sales.

M12c   M12d, 13b   M12f, 13d

M12o, M13h

M12j   M12k   M12l   M12m

Perforation 14
   Type H1 only

Die Proofs.   In black on white glazed card (head plate only):

Without marking £550
Endorsed "BEFORE HARDENING
  19 DEC 01 " £500

Cut down and endorsed on back
  " Duplicate proof of Head die
  for 2d stamp registered 15
  March 1902 " (M/S) £450
Endorsed " AFTER HARDEN-
  ING 27 DEC 01 " £500

The Victorian die was used for the duty plate 5.

Pieces Cut from the Striking Books

See notes under the ½d. value

Struck on plain paper cut to size with various endorsements comprising
  dates, plates and/or number of leads

2d. head plates .. .. *From £400*

See under 1½d. value for piece which includes 2d. value.

Colour Trials

See the notes under " Colour Trials " for the 1½d. value.

The following were submitted to the Inland Revenue on 19th March 1909:—
All perforated 14

On white paper. Watermark Crown

In carmine-lake, carmine, orange, orange-yellow, sage-green, dull blue-green,
  deep blue, violet, purple, Tyrian plum, brown, deep brown, olive-brown, slate .. *From £850*

On yellow paper. Watermark Crown

In scarlet, green, four shades of purple .. .. *From £850*

On tinted paper. No watermark

In two shades of purple on pink, black on pink; two shades of purple on orange;
  red on blue, two shades of purple on blue .. .. *From £850*

No colour was selected.

Cat. No.	S.G. No.	Perf.	Paper	Shades		Unused	Used

1911 (AUGUST 8). GREEN AND RED. PERF. 14 SOMERSET HOUSE

M13	290/2	14	Ordinary	(1) Deep dull green and red		12·00	4·50 ✓
	Block of four		45·00 35·00	(2) Deep dull green and carmine		10·00	4·50 ✓
	Used on cover		† 30·00	(3) Deep dull green and bright carmine (Dec. 1911)		25·00	8·00
a.	Top right corner damaged (Pl. D4, R. 1/3)		60·00				
b.	Deformed tablet (Pl. D4, R. 5/9)		£250 £150	4) Grey-green and bright carmine (11 Mar. 1912)		10·00 ✓	6·00 ✓
c.	Major bottom tablet frame break (Pl. D4, R. 13/7) ..		50·00				
d.	Bottom right tablet corner raised (retouched state) (Pl. D4, R. 3/12)		50·00				
e.	Frame damaged at bottom left (state 1) (Pl. H4, R. 2/5)		60·00	—✓	*h.* Top shade line of tablet broken and joined to "2" (Pl. D4, R. 10/1)		55·00
f.	As last, state 2		60·00				
g.	Damage below POS (Pl. H4, R. 10/4)		50·00	*s.* "Specimen", Type 22 ..		—†

The green shades are all deeper and duller than those of De La Rue. The carmine colour on Nos. (3) and (4) shows noticeably on the backs of the stamps.

There are a very large number of minor flaws on the 2d. value (see *The GB Journal*, October 1977, p. 105).

†No. M13*s* exists from NPM archive sales.

M13*a*

M13*c*

M13*e*

M13*f*

M13*g*

Perforation 14

Types V1 V1A

Plate Descriptions

Official Pl. No.	S.G. Pl. No.	Features

Head Plates (Inner Line)

Official Pl. No.	S.G. Pl. No.	Features
1/101	H1	Continuous rules. Cut under 2nd. Used only by De La Rue
2/104	H2	Continuous rules. No cuts. Used only by De La Rue
3/106	H3	Continuous rules. Cut under 1st. Used only by De La Rue
4/264	H4	Coextensive rules. No cuts. Used by De La Rue and Somerset House
5/278	H5	Coextensive rules. Used only by Somerset House

(Duty Plates) (Outer Line)

3	D3	Short bar rules.	Used by De La Rue and in part by Somerset House
4	D4	Short bar rules.	Used by De La Rue and Somerset House
5	D5	Coextensive rules.	Used only by Somerset House

Printings

No. of Printing	Date	Plates		Notes
		Left sheet	Right sheet	

De La Rue

Ordinary Paper (No. M11)

1	Mar./Aug. 1902	H3/D4	H1/D3	Shade (1)
2	Feb./Mar. 1903	H3/D4	H1/D3	Shades (2) and (3)
3	Mar./Apr. 1904	H3/D4	H1/D3	Shade (4)
4	Nov./Dec. 1904	H3/D4	H1/D3	Shade (2)

Chalk-surfaced Paper (No. M12)

5	Feb. 1906	H3/D4	H1/D3	Shade (1)
5 cont.	June/July 1906	H2/D4	H1/D3	Shade (1)
6	May/June 1907	H4/D4	H2/D3	Shade (2). Duty plates worn
7	Apr./May 1908	H4/D4	H2/D3	Shade (2). Duty plates repaired
8	Feb./May 1909	H4/D4	H2/D3	Shades (1) and (3)
9	June/July 1910	H4/D4	H2/D3	Shades (1) (3) and (4)
10	Dec. 1910	H4/D4	H2/D3	Shades (1) (3) and (4)

Somerset House

No. of Printing	Date	Plates	Notes

Ordinary Paper (No. M13)

1st	July 1911	H4a/D4	H4a has 2 cuts under 11th and 1 cut under 7th
2nd	Aug. 1911	H4b/D4	H4b has added green dots over and under 12th in top and bottom rows of each pane
3rd	Nov. 1911	H4c/D4, 3	H4c has added diagonal cut under 11th; parts of D3 substituted for D4
4th	Dec. 1911	H4c/D4, 3	More parts of D3 substituted for D4, especially sections 5 and 9
5th	Jan. 1912	H5/D5	H5 has date dots under 12th. Shade (3)
6th	May 1912	H5/D5	New ink, shade (4)

The dates of the Somerset House printings are approximate.

Price Schedule

Plate Combination Head/Duty	Left or Right sheet	Printing Usage	Recognisable Piece	Price per Pair

De La Rue

(a) Ordinary Paper

H1/D3	Right	1 to 4	Corner	75·00
H3/D4	Left	1 to 4	Corner	75·00

(b) Chalk-surfaced Paper

H1/D3	Right	5	S.W. corner	£150
H3/D4	Left	5	S.W. corner	£150
H2/D4	Left	5	S.W. corner	£200
H2/D3	Right	6 to 10	S.W. corner	£120
H4/D4	Left	6 to 10	Any pair with coextensive green rules	60·00

Somerset House

H4a/D4	—	1st	S.E. corner	85·00
H4b/D4	—	2nd	S.E. corner	65·00
H4c/D4, 3	—	3rd	S.E. corner, upper or lower pane	50·00
H4c/D4, 3	—	4th	Left interpane pair, no red side rules nor complete horiz. red rules	£100
H5/D5	—	5th, 6th	Any pair with coextensive red rules	25·00

Prices are quoted for pairs, although single examples are sometimes adequate for identification.

Before attempting to identify recognisable pieces see notes below the Price Schedule for the 1½d. value.

1910. 2d. Tyrian Plum, Type M5

Cat. No.	S.G. No.	Perf.	Paper	Shades	Unused	Used

1910 (MAY). PREPARED FOR USE BUT NOT ISSUED. PERF. 14. DE LA RUE

| M14 | 266a | 14 | Ordinary | Tyrian plum | £12000 | |
| s. | | "Specimen", Type 17 | £3000 | | | |

Although over 100,000 sheets were printed from the Tyrian plum plates and delivered to the Inland Revenue, release to post offices was delayed until current stocks of the bicoloured value had been used up. After the death of the King on 6th May 1910 it was decided not to proceed with this issue. Practically the whole of the stock was destroyed and very few unused examples survived. One example is known on cover postmarked 6th May.

Essays

Submitted to the Inland Revenue on 19th August 1909. On glazed card:

A rejected design with rectangular duty frame, in slate-purple or olive-green .. *From £2250*
A rejected design with an oval duty frame, in deep reddish brown, blue or bottle-green .. .. *From £2250*
The accepted design in steel-blue or purple .. .. *From £2500*

Essays from the De La Rue Archives

Stamp size photographic essay on card pen-cancelled with cross:

Design with oval duty frame in deep reddish brown, inscribed " Aug 19th 09 " and " Dupl/Design subm. Blue" £3250

The other two designs described above with pen-cancelled cross were acquired by the National Postal Museum.

Die Proofs in black on white glazed card:

Endorsed " BEFORE HARDENING 1 DEC 09 " £2750
Endorsed " AFTER HARDENING 2 DEC 09 " £2750

In various colours on white glazed card:
Without marking .. .. *From £2750*

Piece Cut from the Striking Book

Struck on plain paper cut to size
2d. endorsed with Plates 6 to 10 with various dates from Dec 21 to Feb 25 further endorsed " Feb 25th 10 " in red and " Feb 26, 20 leads " and cancelled by red ink line £5500

Colour Trials

On white wove paper watermarked Crown. Perf. 14
In orange, olive, sage-green, dull blue-green, pale blue, deep blue, violet, red-purple, purple, deep red-brown, pale red-brown, brown, deep brown, grey-brown, grey, black or yellow-ochre .. .. *From £2250*

Perforated colour trials on watermarked paper were also taken in the selected Tyrian plum colour but it is now considered that they cannot be positively distinguished from surviving examples from the supply which was printed.

On white paper without watermark. Imperf. with large margins, 3–10 mm.
In red-rose, green, Tyrian plum or pale brown .. .. *From £2250*

On white paper watermarked Crown. Imperf.
In red-rose, green, mauve, Tyrian plum or deep orange-brown .. .. *From £2250*

The significance of the imperf. colour trials is not yet understood. The colours do not correspond with those of the perforated trials of 12th January 1910. Some may have arisen from the submission of the essays on 19th August 1909 but those with large margins probably derive from the Somerset House colour trials of 1911–12. The British Library has a *se-tenant* trial in brown of the Tyrian plum design with a 2d. King George V Downey head with "Cancelled", Type 24.

1901. 2½d. Purple on Blue, Type M6

Cat. No	S.G. No.	Perf.	Paper	Shades	Unused	Used

1901 (DECEMBER). PURPLE ON BLUE. PERF. 14. DE LA RUE

| M15 | — | 14 | Ordinary | Purple on blue | £20000 | |

The Registration sheet of this stamp was taken on 3rd December 1901. Many thousands of sheets were printed and delivered to the Stamping Department, but were destroyed when the authorities changed their minds in favour of the adopted colour. Only a few examples have survived.

1902-11. 2½d. Blue, Type M6

1902 (JANUARY 1). BLUE. PERF. 14. DE LA RUE

M16   230/31   14   Ordinary

			(1) Deep ultramarine	15·00✓	5·00✓
			(2) Ultramarine	5·50	2·50✓
	Block of four	27·00	22·00	(3) Pale ultramarine	4·50✓	2·50✓

	Used on cover	†	10·00			
a.	Watermark inverted ..	£550				
c.	Frame broken at right ..	—	40·00	f.	Cracked plate .. From	12·00	5·00
d.	Minor frame breaks *From*	12·00	5·00	s.	"Specimen" ,Type 15 ..	35·00†
e.	Retouched background (Pl.			t.	"Specimen", Type 17 ..	
	1a, R. 11/12)	—	20·00	u.	"Cancelled", Type 20 ..	

The Registration sheet in the new colour was taken on 16th December, 1901.

†No. M16s exists from NPM archive sales.

M16c   M16e

Shading at top right retouched and
dent in frame of " REVENUE "

Perforation 14
   Types H1   H1A

A   B   C   D

Essays from the De La Rue Archives
Photographic essays in stamp size on card:

Type A, inscribed " June 18th 01 " and " Dupl " in design of the issued ½d.	£2500
Type B, lettered " C "	£2250
Type C, lettered " F "	£2250
Type D, lettered " H "	£2250

Types B to D were submitted to the Postmaster-General on 10 July 1901, together with four other designs which were acquired by the N.P.M. That lettered " B " was the accepted design which was endorsed " Approved/July 19th " and the others are lettered " D ", " E " and " G ".

Die Proofs in black on white glazed card:

Without marking	£600	Endorsed " BEFORE HARD-ENING 28 NOV 01 "	£550
Without marking but with (M/S) initials and date " 7 Sept 01 "	£550	Endorsed " AFTER HARD-ENING 7 DEC 01 "	£550
Endorsed " 7 SEP. 01 AFTER HARDENING "	£550	Endorsed " Working Die No. 19 "	£550

Pieces Cut from the Striking Books
See notes under the ½d. value.
Struck on plain paper cut to size with various endorsements comprising dates, and/or number of leads

2½d. value ..   *From* £350

Plate Proofs.
On thick white paper. No watermark, Imperf.
Ultramarine, violet-blue, deep ultramarine, steel blue   *Each* £350

Colour Trials
9 December, 1901.   Watermark Crown, Perf. 14.
In nine shades of blue, three shades of ultramarine (including issued colour), sky-blue, milky blue, violet-blue, deep blue, greenish blue and dull blue   *From* £500

Cat. No.	S.G. No.	Perf.	Paper	Shades	Unused	Used

1911 (JULY 10). BLUE. PERF. 14. HARRISON

M17	276	14	Ordinary	(1) Deep bright blue	35·00	15·00
				(2) Bright blue	22·00	10·00 ✓
	Block of four	..	.. £110	80·00	(3) Dull blue	25·00	10·00 ✓
	Used on cover	..	.. †	18·00			
a.	Watermark inverted		£400			

Perforation 14
   Types VI VIA

1911 (OCTOBER 14). BLUE. PERF. 15 × 14. HARRISON

M18	283/84	15 × 14	Ordinary

(1) Deep bright blue 25·00 ✓ 9·00 ✓
(2) Bright blue 11·00 ✓ 5·00 ✓
(3) Dull blue 12·00 ✓ 5·00 ✓
~~deep dull blue~~ — ✓

	Block of four	60·00	50·00
	Used on cover	†	12·00
a.	Watermark inverted ..	—	£200
b.	Imperf. between stamp and left margin		
g.	Frame broken at right (Pl. ?, R. 19/12)	75·00	35·00
h.	Frame broken at right ..	85·00	50·00
i.	Frame broken at right (Pl. 2, R. 5/12)	85·00	50·00
j.	Frame broken at right (Pl. ?, R. 5/12)	85·00	50·00
k.	Frame broken at right ..	85·00	50·00
l.	Frame broken at right (Pl. 6, R. 3/12)	85·00	
m.	Do. (Pl. 6, R. 4/12)	85·00	
n.	Do. (Pl. 6, R. 5/12)	85·00	
o.	Do. (Pl. 6, R. 6/12)	85·00	

Shade No. (3) may be found with double gum.

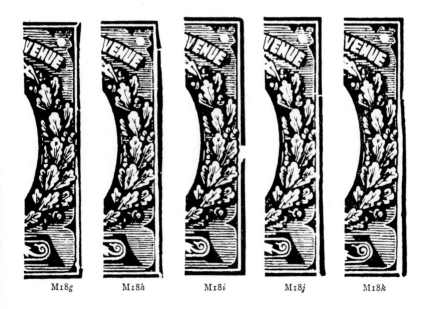

M18g   M18h   M18i   M18j   M18k

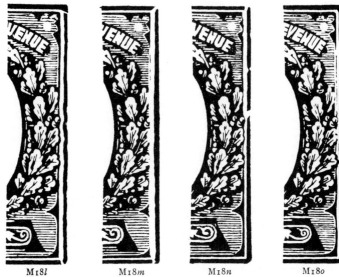

M18*l*   M18*m*   M18*n*   M18*o*

The broken frame varieties *g* to *o* exist in progressive stages of wear.

Perforation 15 × 14
Types V3 V3A

Plate Descriptions

Official Pl. No.	S.G. Pl. No.	Features
1/19	1	Continuous rules. Cut preceded by nick under 2nd. For printing 7 only the plate changed sides with an added cut under ½ of 1st. Used only by De La Rue
2/21	2	Continuous rules. Thin cut between 2 and ½ of 1st. Used by De La Rue and Harrison
5/153	5	Continuous rules. Cut under 2 of 3rd. Used by De La Rue and Harrison, later with cut under 11th
6/155	6	Continuous rules. Cut under ½ of 4th. Used by De La Rue and Harrison
7/157	7	Continuous rules. Diagonal cut and nick under ½ of 1st. Only known used by De La Rue
11/210	11	Coextensive rules. No marking at first, later with thick cut under 2½ of 2nd. Used by De La Rue and Harrison
12/211	12	Coextensive rules. Thin cut under 2 of 1st. Used by De La Rue and Harrison

Plates 3/61 and 4/79 were made but not used as they were faulty. Plate 8/160 with continuous rules seems to have been satisfactory but there is no evidence of its use. Plates 9/189 and 10/190 were sent to Somerset House as reserves but never used.

Printings
De La Rue

No. of Printing	Date	Plates Left sheet	Plates Right sheet	Notes
1	Dec. 1901	2	1	In purple on blue (No. M15)
2	Dec. 1901/Feb. 1902	2	1	In ultramarine (No. M16)
3	Dec. 1902/Apr. 1903	2	1	
		5	6	
4	Nov. 1903/Feb. 1904	2	1	
		5	6	
5	Dec. 1904/Apr. 1905	7	1	
		5?	6?	
6	Sept./Oct. 1905	7	1	
		5?	6?	
7	Nov. 1906	1a	11	Plate 1 changed sides. Added vertical cut under ½ of 1st
		5?	6?	
		7	11a	Added cut under 2nd of Plate 11
8	Oct./Nov. 1907	7	11a	
		5?	6?	
9	Nov./Dec. 1908	7	11a	
		5?	6?	
10	May/Sept. 1910	12	11a	
		5?	6?	

It is believed that Plates 5 and 6 continued in use after the 4th printing but it is not known when they were discontinued.

Harrison
Too little is known about the Harrison printings to prepare a meaningful table of printings.

Price Schedule

Plate No.	Left or Right sheet	Printing Usage	Recognisable Piece	Price
De La Rue				
Perforation 14. Types H1, H1A (No. M16)				
1	Right	2 to 6	S.W. corner pair ..	35·00
2	Left	2 to 4	S.W. corner pair ..	12·00
5*	Left	3, 4	S.W. corner strip of 3	
6*	Right	3, 4	S.W. corner strip of 4	
7	Left	5 to 9	S.W. corner pair ..	35·00
1a	Left	7	S.W. corner pair ..	
11 and 11a	Right	7 to 10	Any corner pair with coextensive rules	18·00
12	Left	10	Any corner pair with coextensive rules	45·00

*These plates could also exist for printings 5 to 10.
No plating pieces are known to exist of the initial printing in purple *on* blue.

Plate No.	Left or Right sheet	Printing Usage	Recognisable Piece	Price
Harrison				
Perforation 14. Types V1, V1A (No. M17)				
2	—	1st	S.W. corner pair ..	60·00
5a	—	1st	S.E. corner with cut under ½ of 11th, S.W. corner strip of 3 or right interpane margin pair with cuts at right	60·00
11a	—	1st	S.W. corner pair ..	60·00
12	—	1st	S.W. corner pair ..	60·00
Perforation 15 × 14. Types V3, V3A (No. M18)				
2	—	2nd	S.W. corner pair ..	40·00
5a	—	2nd	S.E. corner with cut under ½ of 11th, S.W. corner strip of 3 or right interpane margin pair with cuts at right ..	32·00
6	—	2nd	S.W. corner strip of 4	70·00
12	—	2nd	Any marginal pair with coextensive rules	32·00

It is not yet clear whether Harrisons consistently used plates in left and right positions, in the same manner that De La Rue did. Nor is it known at present whether Harrisons made any additional markings on Plates 2, 6, 11a or 12.

Prices quoted are for pairs or strips, although single examples are sometimes adequate for identification.

Before attempting to identify recognisable pieces see notes below the Price Schedule for the 1½d. value.

1902-11.   3d. Purple on Yellow, Type M7

Cat. No.	S.G. No.	Perf.	Paper	Shades	Unused	Used

1902–06. PURPLE ON YELLOW. PERF. 14. DE LA RUE

A. 1902 (MARCH 20). Ordinary Paper

M19   232/32*a*   14   Ordinary   (1) Dull purple on orange-yellow back, yellow front   18·00 ✓   2·50 ✓

Block of four	..	..	£110	25·00
Used on cover	..	..	†	20·00
a.	Watermark inverted	..	
s.	"Specimen", Type 15	..	£100

(2) Deep purple on orange-yellow back, yellow shades front   20·00 ✓   2·50 ✓

B. 1906 (MARCH). Chalk-surfaced paper

M20   232*b*/34   14   Chalky

Block of four ..	..	..	£100	40·00
Used on cover	..	..	†	40·00
b.	Broken scroll (Pl. 5, R. 20/2) ..	..	..	85·00
c.	Broken frame ..	..	..	35·00	15·00
d.	Broken corner	..	..	32·00	15·00
s.	"Specimen", Type 17	..	£200
t.	"Cancelled", Type 20	..	

(1) Pale reddish purple on orange-yellow   70·00   15·00 ✓
(2) Dull purple on orange-yellow   80·00   18·00 ✓
(3) Dull reddish purple on lemon back, yellow front   70·00   28·00 ✓
(4) Pale purple on lemon (1908)   16·00   6·00 ✓
(5) Purple on lemon (1908)   13·00   6·00 ✓

Perforation 14

Types H1 H1A

Die Proofs in black on white glazed card:

Without marking	.. ..	£550
Endorsed " BEFORE HARDENING 21 NOV 01 "	..	£500

Endorsed " AFTER HARDENING 25 NOV 01 " £500

Pieces Cut from the Striking Books

See notes under the ½d. value.

Struck on plain paper cut to size with various endorsements comprising dates and number of leads

3d. value   ..   ..   *From* £300

1911 (SEPTEMBER 12). PURPLE ON YELLOW. PERF. 14. HARRISON

M21   277/*a*   14   Ordinary   (1) Purple on lemon   40·00 ✓   £120

Block of four ..	..	..	£200	£600
Used on cover	..	..	†	£400
b.	Broken scroll (Pl. 5, R. 20/2)	£120	
e.	Frame broken at right (Pl. 4, R. 9/12) ..	..	..	£150
s.	"Specimen", Type 22	..	—†

(2) Greyish purple on lemon   60·00   £120
(3) Grey on lemon   £3750
(4) Dull reddish purple on lemon   40·00   90·00

†No. M21*s* exists from NPM archive sales.

Perforation 14

Types   H2(c)   H2A(c)
        H2(d)   H2A(d)
        V1   V1A

1911 (SEPTEMBER 18). PURPLE ON YELLOW. PERF. 15 × 14. HARRISON

M22   285/85*a*   15 × 14   Ordinary   (1) Purple on lemon   18·00 ✓   3·50 ✓

Block of four ..	..	..	90·00	35·00
Used on cover	..	..	†	15·00
b.	Broken scroll (Pl. 5, R. 20/2)	85·00	20·00
e.	Frame broken at right (Pl. 4, R. 9/12) ..	..	..	85·00	25·00
f.	Frame broken at right (Pl. 5, R. 8/12) ..	..	..	75·00	25·00
g.	Broken crown ..	..	..	75·00	35·00

(2) Greyish purple on lemon   25·00   3·50 ✓
(3) Grey on lemon   £3000
(4) Dull reddish purple on lemon   20·00   3·50 ✓

Variety *c* shows progressive states of wear.
Variety *g* is from the 1st vertical row of the sheet.

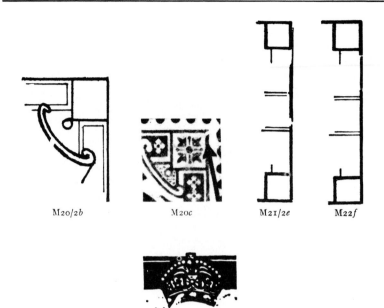

M20/2b   M20c   M21/2e   M22f

M22g

Perforation 15 × 14
Types V3   V3A

Plate Descriptions

Official Pl. No.	S.G. Pl. No.	Features
1/65	1	Continuous rules. Cut under 1st. Used by De La Rue and Harrison
2/67	2	Continuous rules. Cut under 2nd. Used only by De La Rue
3/69	3	Continuous rules. Cut under 3rd. Used only by De La Rue
4/71	4	Continuous rules. Cut under EN of 4th. Used by De La Rue and Harrison
5/78	5	Continuous rules. Cut under VE of 4th. Used by De La Rue and Harrison

Printings

No. of Printing	Date	Plates Left Sheet	Right Sheet	Notes
De La Rue				
Ordinary Paper (No. M19)				
1	1902/6	1	2	No. M19 shades (1) and (2)
		3	4	
Chalk-surfaced Paper (No. M20)				
2	1906	1	2	No. M20 shades (1) to (5)
		3	4	
		3	5	
Harrison				
Ordinary Paper				
Perforation 14 (No. M22)				
1st	Sept. 1911	5	4	No. M21 shades (1) to (4)
Perforation 15 × 14 (No. 23)				
2nd	Sept. 1911	5	4	No. M22 shades (1) to (4)
		5	1	

67

Price Schedule

Plate No.	Left or Right Sheet	Printing Usage	Recognisable Piece	Price

De La Rue

Perforation 14. Types H1, H1A

(a) Ordinary Paper

1	Left	1	S.W. corner pair	60·00
2	Right	1	S.W. corner pair	60·00
3	Left	1	S.W. corner strip of 3	95·00
4	Right	1	S.W. corner strip of 4	£135

(b) Chalk-surfaced Paper

1	Left	2	S.W. corner pair	60·00
2	Right	2	S.W. corner pair	60·00
3	Left	2	S.W. corner strip of 3	90·00
4	Right	2	S.W. corner strip of 4	£120
5	Right	2	S.W. corner strip of 4	£135

Harrison

(a) Perforation 14. Types H2, H2A or V1, V1A

| 4 | Right | 1st | S.W. corner strip of 4 .. .. | £200 |
| 5 | Left | 1st | S.W. corner strip of 4 .. .. | £200 |

(b) Perforation 15 × 14. Types V3, V3A

1	Right	2nd	S.W. corner pair	35·00
4	Right	2nd	S.W. corner strip of 4	60·00
5	Left	2nd	S.W. corner strip of 4	60·00

Prices quoted are for pairs or strips, although single examples are sometimes adequate for identification.

Before attempting to identify recognisable pieces see notes below the Price Schedule for 1½d. value.

1901-06.   4d. Green and Brown, Type M8

Cat. No.	S.G. No.	Perf.	Paper	Shades	Unused	Used

1902-06. GREEN AND BROWN. PERF. 14. DE LA RUE

A. 1902 (MARCH 27). Ordinary Paper

M23   235/36   14   Ordinary

				(1) Green and grey-brown	30·00	11·00 ✓

Block of four .. .. .. £150 85·00
Used on cover .. .. † 50·00

(2) Green and brown   30·00 11·00 ✓
(3) Green and chocolate-brown   30·00 12·00

a. Watermark inverted   ..
c. Damaged 4 (S.W. corner)
    (Pl. ?, R. 3/8) .. .. 50·00
d. Cracked plate .. .. .. 60·00
e. Damaged d   .. ..
f. Cracked plate (N.W. corner)
s. "Specimen", Type 16 .. £100†

Pale yellow green + chocolate brown   ✓   ✓

†No. M23s exists from NPM archive sales.

B. 1906 (JANUARY). Chalk-surfaced paper

M24   237/38   14   Chalky

				(1) Green and chocolate-brown	22·00 ✓	7·00 ✓

Block of four .. .. .. £110 50·00
Used on cover .. .. † 25·00

(2) Deep green and chocolate brown   25·00 8·50 ✓

c. Damaged 4 (S.W. corner
    (Pl. ?, R. 3/8) .. .. .. 50·00

M23/4c   M23d   M23e   M23f

Perforation 14
   Type H1
   A few sheets on chalky paper with Types V2 or V2A

Die Proofs in black on white glazed card. Head Plate only:

Without marking £550
Endorsed " BEFORE HARD-
   ENING 28 NOV 01 " .. £500
Endorsed " AFTER HARDEN-
   ING 28 NOV 01 " .. £500
Cut down and endorsed on back
" Duplicate proof of Head die
for 4d. stamp registered 29
March 1902 " (M/S) £450

Endorsed " AFTER STRIKING
   3 JAN 06 " and initialled .. £500
Endorsed " AFTER STRIKING
   22 JAN 08 " initialled " H.
W. " £500

Pieces Cut from the Striking Books
   For notes see under ½d. value.
Struck on plain paper cut to size with various endorsements comprising dates,
   plate and/or number of leads
      4d. head plates .. .. *From* £300
      4d. duty plate 4 dated "May 8" (1901) £300

Cancelled overprint from the National Postal Museum Archives
   Perforated 14, watermark Type W12
   "Cancelled", Type 18

Plate Descriptions

Official Pl. No.	S G. Pl. No.	Features

Head Plates

The 240 set Outer Line Head Plates each comprise two panes of 120 (10 horizontal rows of 12) and were used only by De La Rue.

In the case of Head Plates 1, 2, 3 and 4 each pane of 120 is made up of 12 sections (8 sections of 3 horizontal rows of 3 across the top and bottom of each pane plus 4 sections of 4 horizontal rows of 3 across the middle of each pane) the positions of which are marked in the case of the 3 continuous margin plates by breaks between the 3rd/4th and 7th/8th rows of stamps in each vertical rule, and by breaks between the 3rd/4th, 6th/7th, and 9th/10th stamps of each horizontal rule. These plates thus comprise 24 such sections—informally numbered 1 to 24 commencing from the NW corner of the upper pane.

In the case of Head Plate 5 each pane of 120 (like the 1s. value) is made up of 6 sections of 20 stamps (5 horizontal rows of 4). The plate thus comprises 12 such sections informally numbered 1 to 12 commencing from the NW corner of the upper pane.

1/77	H1	Continuous rules with all corners cut away. Cut under 2nd stamp bottom row lower pane (a) cut added in the rule under 11th stamp bottom row lower pane
2/82	H2	Continuous rules with all corners (except S.E. corner upper pane) cut away. Cut under 1st stamp and scoops in the top of the rules between the 10th, 11th and 11th/12th stamps of the bottom row lower pane. Towards the end of the life of this plate the rule to the right of rows 19 and 20 disintegrated
3/84	H3	Continuous rules with all corners intact. No plate cut in the bottom row lower pane but a distinctive rule flaw (jagged hole closed at the top) under the 2nd stamp (a) cut added in the rule under the 10th stamp bottom row lower pane
4/250	H4	Coextensive rules. No plate cut but a small scoop under the rule of the 2nd stamp and a large scoop under the rule of the 4th stamp bottom row lower pane. There were also rule scoops to the left of rows 3 and 8 and to the right of rows 4, 7 and 14. Plate 4 has a unique arrangement of the registration rule pieces which show an extra rule break between the 6th and 7th stamps above the upper pane and below the lower pane, and there are also unusual rule breaks over the 5th and 8th stamps of the upper pane. (By contrast plate 5 has perfectly normal Die I registration pieces and no breaks over the 5th and 8th stamps) (a) cut added in the rule under 12th stamp bottom row lower pane
5/279	H5	Coextensive rules. Cut under 11th, very small scoop under the rule of the 2nd, and a full scoop under the rule of the 4th stamp bottom row lower pane. There were also rule scoops to the left of rows 2, 5, 12, 16 and 19, and to the right of rows 2, 9, 12 and 19

Duty Plates

With continuous rules the Inner Line Duty Plates comprise individual 120 set panes in 10 horizontal rows of 12 stamps. The records show that 12 such 120 set electros were made from, apparently, a master plate. The pairings of the Duty Plates with the appropriate Head Plate usage present difficulties, but the allocations which follow reflect the latest stage of research applied to the material available for examination.

—	D1 to D12	Continuous rules without plate cuts

Printings

No. of Printing	Date	Plates (480 set) Left Sheet Right Sheet		Notes

De La Rue

Ordinary Paper (No. M23)

		Left Sheet	Right Sheet	
1 & 2	March 1902	H2/D3D4*	H1/D1D2	Shades (1) to (3)
3	Jan. 1904	H2/D3D6	H1/D1D5	
4	Sept. 1904	H2/D8D6	H1/D7D5	
		H3/D8D6	H1/D7D5	

Chalk-surfaced Paper (No. M24)

5	Jan. 1906	H3/D8D6	H1/D7D5	Shades (1) and (2)
6	1906/07	H3a/D8D6	H1a/D7D5	Rule cut added to both Head Plates
		H3a/D7D5	H1a/D8D6	
7	late 1907	H4/D7D5	H1a/D8D6	
8	Aug. 1908	H5/D11D12	H4a/D9D10	Rule cut added to Head Plate 4

*In each case the first numbered Duty Plate comprised the upper pane of the plate and the second the lower pane.

The plate and printing details are based on research by Michael Astley and Tony Wiseman. For more detailed information reference should be made to their original paper in *The Philatelic Journal of Great Britain* for December 1978, p. 95.

Price Schedule

Plate Combination Head/Duty	Left or Right Sheet	Printing Usage	Recognisable Piece	Price per Pair
(a) Ordinary Paper				
H2/D3D4	Left	1 & 2	S.W. or S.E. corner pair	£120
H1/D1D2	Right	1 & 2	S.W. corner pair	£120
H2/D3D6	Left	3	S.W. or S.E. corner pair	£120
H1/D1D5	Right	3	S.W. corner pair	£120
H2/D8D6	Left	4	S.W. or S.E. corner pair	£120
H1/D7D5	Right	4	S.W. corner pair	£120
H3/D8D6	Left	4	S.W. corner pair	£120
(b) Chalk-surfaced Paper				
H3/D8D6	Left	5	S.W. corner pair	90·00
H1/D7D5	Right	5	S.W. corner pair	90·00
H3a/D8D6	Left	6	S.W. corner pair or S.E. corner strip of 3	90·00
H1a/D7D5	Right	6	S.W. or S.E. corner pair	90·00
H3a/D7D5	Left	6	S.W. corner pair or S.E. corner strip of 3	90·00
H1a/D8D6	Right	6 & 7	S.W. or S.E. corner pair	90·00
H4/D7D5	Left	7	S.W. or S.E. corner pair	90·00
H5/D11D12	Left	8	S.W. or S.E. corner pair	90·00
H4a/D9D10	Right	8	S.W. or S.E. corner pair	90·00

Prices quoted are for pairs, although single examples are sometimes adequate for identification.

Before attempting to identify recognisable pieces see note below the Price Schedule for 1½d. value.

1909-11.   4d. Orange, Type M8

Cat. No.	S.G. No.	Perf.	Paper	Shades	Unused	Used

1909 (NOVEMBER 1). ORANGE. PERF. 14. DE LA RUE

M25   239/41   14   Ordinary

(1) Brown-orange ... £140 ✓ 80·00
(2) Pale orange (Dec. 1909) 7·50 ✓ 6·50 ✓
(3) Orange-red (Dec. 1909) 9·00 ✓ 7·00 ✓

Block of four	..	.. 50·00	50·00
Used on cover	..	†	20·00
s.	"Specimen", Type 17	.. £200	
t.	"Cancelled", Type 20	..	

Perforation 14

Type H1 only

Die Proofs in black on white glazed card:—

Endorsed " BEFORE HARD-
ENING 30 AUG 09 " .. £500
Endorsed " AFTER HARDEN-
ING 2 SEP 09 " £500
Uncleared and cut down from
working die and issued 1 Nov.
1909 and initialled .. £250

Endorsed " BEFORE STRIK-
ING " £500
Endorsed " After striking 8
OCT 09 " £500

Die Proof from the De La Rue Archives

On card unmounted with traces of gum or paper on back:

Cut down (56 × 40 mm) with uncleared surround, initialled £550

Piece Cut from the Striking Book

See notes under the ½d. value.

Struck on plain paper from the monocoloured die and cut to size
4d. plates 6 to 10 with Sept. and Oct. dates (1909) and "20 leads for repairs" £300

4d. Die Proofs tend to have an irregular black surround to the design as they were flat when finished instead of being slightly raised. The same applies to the 7d. value.

Plate Proof. In orange on poor quality buff paper .. .. 25·00

Colour Trials

See the notes under "Colour Trials" for the 1½d. value.
The following were submitted to the Inland Revenue on 19th March 1909:—
All perforated 14

On white paper. Watermark Crown
In carmine-lake, carmine, orange, orange-yellow sage-green, dull blue-green, deep blue,
violet, purple, Tyrian plum, brown, deep brown, slate .. .. .. *From £850*

On yellow paper. Watermark Crown
In scarlet, green, four shades of purple .. .. *From £850*

On tinted paper. No watermark
In red on blue; two shades of purple on pink; two shades of purple on orange; two shades of
purple on blue; black on pink; black on orange .. .. .. *From £550*

Following complaints about the issued colour of the monocoloured 4d., the
following colour trials were submitted on 12th April 1910:—

On white paper. Watermark Crown
In yellow-orange, yellow, olive-yellow .. .. *From £850*

On tinted paper. No watermark
In red on blue; purple on orange; deep purple on blue .. .. *From £850*

The 1910 colour trials were printed from the monocoloured plate while those of 1909
were from the bicoloured plates which can be differentiated by the value circles which are
larger, measuring about 6 mm. in diameter on the monocoloured plate compared with
about 5½ mm.

1911 (JULY 13). ORANGE. PERF. 14. HARRISON

M26   278   14   Ordinary

(1) Bright orange 45·00 ✓ 40·00 3 ⊙
(2) Deep bright orange 50·00 40·00

Block of four	..	.. £250	£275
Used on cover	..	†	£100
s.	" Specimen " Type 22	.. —†	

†No. M26s exists from NPM archive sales.

Perforation 14

Types   H2(c)   H2A(c)   V1   V1A
        H2(d)   H2A(d)

Cat. No.	S.G. No.	Perf.	Paper	Shades		Unused	Used
1911 (NOVEMBER 11). ORANGE. PERF. 15 × 14. HARRISON							
M27	286	15 × 14	Ordinary	(1)	Bright orange	13·00 ✓	6·00 ✓ ✓
				(2)	Deep bright orange	15·00	6·00 ✓
				(3)	Very deep orange	40·00	15·00
	Block of four	..	.. 65·00	60·00			
	Used on cover	..	.. †	40·00			

Perforation 15 × 14
  Types V3   V3A

Plate Descriptions

Official Pl. No.	S.G. Pl. No.	Features
6/301	6	Coextensive rules. No marking. Used by De La Rue and Harrison (a) added fine ½ cut under 2nd
7/302	7	Coextensive rules. No marking. Used by De La Rue and Harrison (a) added fine ½ cut under 1st
8/303	8	Coextensive rules. Fine ½ cut under 4th. Used by De La Rue and (reportedly)* by Harrison
9/304	—	This plate was not used
10/305	10	Coextensive rules. Fine ½ cut under 3rd. Used only by De La Rue

Printings
De La Rue

No. of Printing	Date	Plates Left sheet	Right sheet	Notes
9 & 10	1909/11	7	6	No. M25 shades (1) to (3)
		7a	6a	Rule cut added to both plates
		10	8	

Harrison
Perforation 14

1st	July 1911	6a		No. M26 shades (1) and (2)
		7a		

Perforation 15 × 14

2nd	Nov. 1911	6a		No. M27 shades (1) to (3)
		7a		
		8*		

*Although the use by Harrison of plate 8 perforated 15 × 14 has long been recorded, several specialist collectors report that no piece has been seen by them. Accordingly the publishers would welcome confirmation of any existing plate cut strip of 4 with V3 perforation.

Price Schedule

Plate No.	Left or Right sheet	Printing Usage	Recognisable Piece	Price
De La Rue				
Perforation 14. Type H1				
6	Right	9 & 10	S.W. corner pair	—
7	Left	9 & 10	S.W. corner pair	—
6a	Right	9 & 10	S.W. corner pair	20·00
7a	Left	9 & 10	S.W. corner pair	20·00
8	Right	9 & 10	S.W. corner strip of 4	40·00
10	Left	9 & 10	S.W. corner strip of 3	30·00
Harrison				
Perforation 14. Types H2, H2A or V1, V1A				
6a	—	1st	S.W. corner pair	£100
7a	—	1st	S.W. corner pair	£100
Perforation 15 × 14. Types V3, V3A				
6a	—	2nd	S.W. corner pair	30·00
7a	—	2nd	S.W. corner pair	30·00
8	—	2nd	S.W. corner strip of 4	55·00

Prices quoted are for pairs or strips, although single examples are sometimes adequate for identification.
  Before attempting to identify recognisable pieces see notes below the Price Schedule for 1½d. value.

1902-11.   5d. Purple and Blue, Type M9

Cat. No.   S.G. No.   Perf.   Paper   Shades   Unused   Used
1902-06. PURPLE AND BLUE.   PERF. 14. DE LA RUE
A. 1902 (MAY 14).   Ordinary paper

M28   242   14   Ordinary   (1) Dull purple and ultra-
                                               marine   20·00   6·00 ✓
   Block of four .. .. .. 90·00   30·00   (2) Slate-purple and ultra-
   Used on cover   .. .. †   30·00   marine   20·00   6·00 ✓
 b. Broken frame at right (Pl.
   H1, R. 15/8) .. .. .. 60·00
 c. Damaged R.H. duty tablet
   (Pl. D3, R. 12/10) .. .. 50·00   *f.* Break over lion's tail (Pl.
 d. Damaged L.H. duty tablet   H2, R. 20/8) .. .. .. 50·00
   (Pl. D4, R. 11/4) .. .. 45·00   *g.* Broken cross on Crown (Pl.
 e. Thin VENUE (Pl. H2, R.   H3, R. 1/12) £100
   12/9) .. .. 70·00   *s.* "Specimen", Type 16 .. £100

B. 1906 (MAY).   Chalk-surfaced paper

M29   243/44   14   Chalky   (1) Dull purple and ultra-
                                               marine   25·00   8·00 ✓
   Block of four .. .. .. £100   40·00   (2) Slate-purple and ultra-
   Used on cover   .. .. †   38·00   marine   20·00   8·00 ✓
 a. Watermark inverted .. £500
 b. Broken cross on Crown (Pl.
   H3, R. 1/12) .. .. .. 90·00   (v) *Damage to both duty tablets* £90 ✓
 c. Damaged R.H. duty tablet   *h.* Break over lion's tail (Pl.
   (Pl. D3, R. 12/10) .. .. 60·00   H2, R. 20/8) .. :. .. 55·00
 d. Damaged head plate .. 85·00   *i.* Flaws on PO and A (Pl. H2,
 e. Damaged L.H. duty tablet 55·00   R. 11/1) .. .. .. 85·00
 f. Damaged L.H. duty tablet   *s.* "Specimen", Type 17 .. £200
   (Pl. D4, R. 11/4) .. .. 65·00   *t.* "Cancelled", Type 19 .. —†
 g. Thin VENUE (Pl. H2, R.   *u.* "Cancelled", Type 20 ..
   12/9) (less marked) .. .. 65·00

The value tablets vary from pale to deep ultramarine.
†No. M29*t* exists from NPM archive sales.

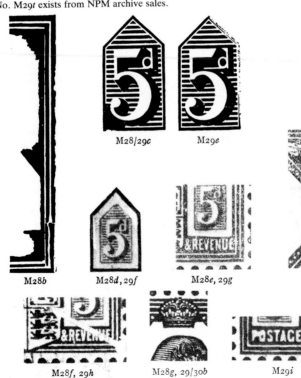

M28/29*c*   M29*e*

M28*b*   M28*d*, 29*f*   M28*e*, 29*g*   M29*d*

M28*f*, 29*h*   M28*g*, 29/30*b*   M29*i*

Perforation 14
  Types H1   H1A

Die Proofs in black on white glazed card:—
  Head plate only

Without marking	£600
Endorsed " BEFORE HARD- ENING 20 DEC 01 " ..	£550
Cut down and endorsed on back " Duplicate proof of Head die for 5d stamp registered 3 May 1902 " (M/S)	£450

Endorsed " AFTER HARDEN-
ING " and (M/S) " 27 Dec 01 " £550

Pieces Cut from the Striking Books
  For notes see under ½d. value.
Struck on plain paper cut to size with various endorsements comprising dates,
  plates and/or number of leads
  5d. head plates   ..   ..   *From* £350

Plate Proofs. In issued colours on poor quality buff paper   ..   .. 22·00

Cat. No.	S.G. No.	Perf.	Paper		Shades		Unused	Used
1911 (AUGUST 7). PURPLE AND BLUE. PERF. 14. SOMERSET HOUSE								
M30	293/94	14	Ordinary		(1) Dull reddish purple and cobalt blue		11·00	4·75 ✓
	Block of four		60·00	40·00	(2) Dull reddish purple and bright blue		15·00	4·75
	Used on cover		†	50·00				
b.	Broken cross on Crown (Pl. H3, R. 1/12)			75·00	(3) Deep dull reddish purple and bright blue		11·00 ✓	4·75 ✓
c.	Thin lion (Pl. H4, R. 7/3) ..			35·00				
d.	2nd and 3rd harp strings broken (Pl. H4, R. 14/5) ..			35·00	(4) Deep plum and cobalt-blue		15·00	5·50 ✓
e.	1st and 2nd harp strings broken (Pl. H4, R. 20/11) ..			30·00				
f.	Damaged shield (Pl. H4, R. 18/2)			35·00				
g.	Damaged R.H. duty tablet (Pl. D5, R. 20/12 *et al.*) ..			30·00				
h.	E of POSTAGE with top strokes joined (Pl. 44, R. 1/1)			35·00				

The value tablets became considerably worn and many minor varieties of breaks and missing lines
may be found on both De La Rue and Somerset House printings. The two composite illustrations
below show examples of typical breaks:

Damaged value tablets

The Somerset House printings are clearly distinguishable by colour. The purple shades all show a distinctive reddish hue when placed side by side with the De La Rue printings. The deep plum shade is the nearest approach to the De La Rue slate-purple colour, and difficulty is encountered with classification as this was a later printing with a fine impression. The cobalt-blue of the value tablet is, however, quite different from the ultramarine of the De La Rue printing.

M30c

M30d

M30e
Several states

M30f

M30h

Perforation 14
   Types V1   V1A

Plate Descriptions

Official Pl. No.	S.G. Pl. No.	Features
Head Plates (Inner Line)		
1/111	H1	Continuous rules. Cut under 2nd. Used only by De La Rue
2/113	H2	Continuous rules. Cut under 1st. Used only by De La Rue
3/115	H3	Continuous rules. No marking. Used by De La Rue and Somerset House
4/248	H4	Coextensive rules. No cuts but square purple dots in interpane margin. Used by De La Rue and Somerset House
Duty Plates (Outer Line)		
3	D3	Short bar rules. Used only by De La Rue
4	D4	Short bar rules, especially short left and right of upper pane. Used only by De La Rue
5	D5	Continuous rules, with breaks in horiz. rules every 3rd stamp. Upward bulge under 2nd. Used by De La Rue and Somerset House
6	D6	Continuous rules, with breaks in horiz. rules every 3rd stamp. Used only by De La Rue

Printings
De La Rue

No. of Printing	Date	Plates Left sheet	Right sheet	Notes
Ordinary Paper (No. M28)				
1	May/Aug. 1902	H2/D4	H1/D3	Head plate is in deeper purple in Printings
2	Apr./May 1903	H2/D4	H1/D3	1 and 2 compared with 3 and 4
3	Feb./Mar. 1904	H2/D4	H1/D3	Plate H1 very worn
4	Feb./Mar. 1905	H2/D4	H3/D3	
Chalk-surfaced Paper (No. M29)				
5	Feb./Mar. 1906	H2/D4	H3/D3	
6	Apr./May 1907	H2/D4	H3/D3	Poor quality chalky paper
7	Mar./Apr. 1908	H2/D4	H3/D3	
8	June/Sept. 1910	H4/D4	H3/D3	
9	May/Sept. 1910	H3/D6	H2/D5	Plate H2 moved to right sheet and H3 to left sheet

Somerset House

No. of Printing	Date	Plates	Notes
Ordinary Paper (No. M30)			
1st	July 1911	H3a/D5	H3a has added 2 cuts under 11th and 1 under 7th bottom pane and purple dots above and below 12th, both panes
2nd	Dec. 1911?	H4a/D5	H4a has 2 cuts under 11th, both panes and purple dots as H3a
3rd	Feb. 1912	H4b/D5	H4b has date cuts under 11th filled up, both panes and 2 cuts added under 12th bottom pane only
4th	Nov. 1912	H4c/D5	H4c has purple dots above and below 12th both panes removed
5th	1913	H4d/D5	H4d has white dot added to right of 12th, bottom pane

For the 4th printing the plate was repaired and the flaws on it were removed.

Shades (1) and (2) came from the 1st and 2nd printings. During the 3rd printing the ink was changed, was sometimes fluorescent and close to shade (4) but usually produced shade (3). The final printings were in shade (4).

Price Schedule

Plate Combination Head/Duty	Left or Right sheet	Printing Usage	Recognisable Piece	Price per Pair
De La Rue				
(a) Ordinary Paper				
H1/D3	Right	1 to 3	S.W. corner pair, lower pane	£150
H2/D4	Left	1 to 4	Corner	90·00
H3/D3	Right	4	S.W. corner pair, lower pane	£150
(b) Chalk-surfaced Paper				
H3/D3	Right	5 to 8	Corner pair with short bar blue rules ..	£120
H2/D4	Left	5 to 7	Corner pair with short bar blue rules and continuous purple rules	£110
H4/D4	Left	8	Pair with coextensive purple rules ..	£110
H2/D5	Right	9	Corner pair with continuous blue rules ..	90·00
H3/D6	Left	9	Corner pair with continuous blue rules ..	90·00
Somerset House				
H3a/D5	—	1st	S.E. corner and any pair with continuous purple rules	35·00
H4a/D5	—	2nd	S.E. corner	60·00
H4b/D5	—	3rd	S.E. corner	55·00
H4c/D5	—	4th	S.E. corner	45·00
H4d/D5	—	5th	S.E. corner	60·00
H4/D5	—	2nd to 5th	Any pair with coextensive purple rules ..	30·00

Prices quoted are for pairs, although single examples are sometimes adequate for identification.

Before attempting to identify recognisable pieces see notes below the Price Schedule for 1½d. value.

1902-13. 6d. Purple, Type M10

Cat. No.   S.G. No.   Perf.   Paper   Shades   Unused   Used

1902-05. PURPLE. PERF. 14. DE LA RUE

A. 1902 (JANUARY 1). Ordinary Paper

M31   245/46   14   Ordinary   (1) Pale dull purple   15·00   4·00
                                        (2) Slate-purple   15·00   4·00

Block of four .. .. 75·00	30·00
Used on cover .. .. †	30·00
s. "Specimen", Type 15 .. £100†	

†No. M31s exists from NPM archive sales.

B. 1906 (JANUARY). Chalk-surfaced paper

M32   247/48   14   Chalky   (1) Pale dull purple   22·00   4·00
                                        (2) Dull purple   18·00   4·00
                                        (3) Slate-purple   24·00   4·00

Block of four .. .. 90·00	40·00
Used on cover .. .. †	50·00
a. Watermark inverted .. —	£1100
b. Frame broken at right .. —	35·00

s. "Specimen", Type 17 .. £200

Perforation 14

Types H1   H1A

Die Proofs in black on white glazed card :—

Without marking £600	Endorsed " 29 APR. 04 AFTER	
Endorsed "28 AUG 01 BEFORE	STRIKING "	£550
HARDENING " £550	Endorsed " Working Die No. 18 "	£550
Endorsed " 7 SEP 01 AFTER	Endorsed "Registered 3.12.1901	
HARDENING " £550	AFTER HARDENING Work-	
	ing Die No. 18" in M/s ..	£550

Pieces Cut from the Striking Books

See notes under the ½d. value.

Struck on plain paper cut to size with various endorsements comprising dates, plates and/or number of leads

6d. value .. .. *From* £350

See under 1½d. value for piece which includes 6d. plate.

Plate Proofs

In grey-black on thick soft white paper ruled on both front and back within
lines 10 mm. apart .. ..   60·00
In black on thin white card .. ..   60·00

Colour Trials

Watermark Crown. Imperf. on very thin paper

In buff, blue, dull purple, grey, slate, green, orange, carmine and bright rose .. *From*   £650

Chalky paper. No watermark

In deep red, red, purple, reddish purple, pale grey, grey, grey-black and black   *From*   £550

These were made on the selvedge of a British Colonial ½d. stamp on chalky paper. They show the green rule along the perforated edge either at top or bottom of the stamp; the other three sides are imperf.

1911-13. PURPLE. PERF. 14. SOMERSET HOUSE

A. 1911 (OCTOBER 31). Ordinary paper

M33   295, 297/300   14   Ordinary   (1) Royal purple (F) (31
                                              Oct. 1911)   35·00   40·00
                                          (2) Reddish purple (F)
                                              (Nov. 1911)   18·00   8·00
                                          (3) Very deep reddish
                                              purple (F) (Nov. 1911) 38·00   18·00
                                          (4) Dull purple (F)   18·00   6·00
                                          (5) Dark purple   18·00   15·00
                                          (6) Pale dull purple   18·00   10·00
                                          (7) Pale reddish purple   18·00   8·00
                                          (8) Dull lilac (F)   90·00   40·00

Block of four .. .. .. 90·00	50·00
Used on cover .. .. †	60·00
ba. Frame broken at bottom	
right (Pl. 2a, R. 11/12) .. 85·00	60·00
bb. Frame repaired (Pl. 2b, R.	
11/12) £100	60·00
c. Frame broken at top right .. —	50·00
d. No cross on crown (Pl. 9, R.	
11/11) £250	
e. Flaw below N of PENCE	
(Pl. 9, R. 20/6) .. .. 45·00	20·00
f. " J " flaw (Pl. 9, R. 10/12) .. 35·00	18·00
s. "Specimen", Type 22 .. £100	

Shades (2) and (4) exist from later printings without the fluorescent property in the ink.
Shades (6) and (7) are very fine impressions on rather thinner plate glazed paper.

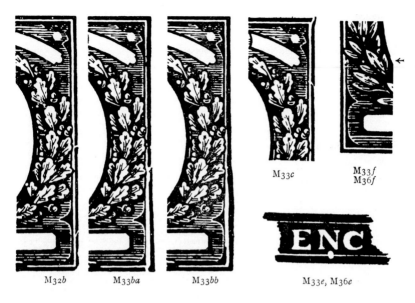

M33*c*

M33*f*
M36*f*

M33*e*, M36*e*

M32*b*   M33*ba*   M33*bb*

Cat. No.	S.G. No.	Perf.	Paper	Shades	Unused	Used
B. 1913 (MARCH).		**"Dickinson" coated paper**				
M34	301	14	Coated	(1) Dull purple	£110	80·00
				(2) Dull reddish purple	£100	75·00
	Block of four	..	..	£500		
	Used on cover	..	..	†	£200	

This paper, although coated, does not respond to the silver point test. Its use was experimental and some experience is needed to identify it.

The surface has the smooth glossy appearance associated with chalk-surfaced paper and an aid to its identification is the dead white appearance of the back of the stamp. Possibly the paper was coated both sides. As the paper is rather thick the watermark is not immediately visible. Printings on this paper were from Plates 10 and 11.

Specimen overprint from the National Postal Museum Archives

Perforated 14, watermark Type W12

"Specimen", Type 26

C. 1911 (OCTOBER 31).   Chalk-surfaced paper

M35	296	14	Chalky	Bright magenta		£2250	
s.	"Specimen", Type 22	..	£950				
M36	303	14	Chalky	Deep plum (July 1913)		14·00	35·00
	Block of four	..	..	70·00	£225		
	Used on cover	..	..	†	75·00		
d.	No cross on crown (Pl. 9, R. 11/11)	..	..	..	£300		
e.	Flaw below N of PENCE (Pl. 9, R. 20/6)	..	..	40·00	28·00		
f.	"J" flaw (Pl. 9, R. 10/12) ..		50·00	25·00			

The ink used for M35 reacted with the chalky surface of the paper and caused a variation in the colour, and the paper itself fluoresces bright lemon under ultra violet light. It was withdrawn on the day after issue. Thereafter the 6d. stamps were issued on ordinary paper (M33) until the "Dickinson" coated paper was introduced in March 1913 (M34).

This was considered to be unsatisfactory and De La Rue were contracted to gum, plate-glaze and apply the chalk-surface coating to the paper which Somerset House used for M36. The gum is thick and yellowish. The impressions are very clear and normally lack the rubbed appearance of the earlier De La Rue printings.

Perforation 14

Types Vı   VıA

Specimen overprint from the National Postal Museum Archives

Perforated 14, watermark Type W12

"Specimen", Type 26

Plate Descriptions

Official Pl. No.	S.G. Pl. No.	Features
1/20	1	Continuous rules. Cut under P of 1st, and a purple dot both to the left and right of the interpane margin (a) added cut under P of 4th Used only by De La Rue
2/22	2	Continuous rules. Cut under P of 2nd (a) date cuts added under EN of 12th, purple dots added over and under the 12th stamp in the top and bottom rows of each pane, two circular scoops containing purple dots cutting into the last two pillars of the interpane margin, and a white dot in the margin rule to the right of the 19th row denoting (initially) ink MB 10394D/24816 (b) as before but the purple dots above and below the 12th stamps and in the circular scoops have been removed, the white dot to the right of the 19th row is filled, and a fresh white dot made in the rule to the right of the 18th row denoting (initially) ink MB 25598 Used by De La Rue and Somerset House—the only plate used by the latter whilst in continuous rule form
3/62	–	This plate was not used
4/80	–	This plate was not used
5/161	5	Continuous rules. Cut under XP of 3rd, and a purple dot both to the left and right of the interpane margin (a) added cut under P of 4th Used only by De La Rue
6/162	6	Continuous rules. Cut under PE of 1st Used only by De La Rue
7/163	7	Continuous rules. A ¾ cut (base) under P of 2nd, and a scoop in the rule below the 9th stamp. One printing is known on ordinary paper with a red dot added in the bottom margin under the 12th stamp (a) added ½ cut (base) under EN of 4th Used only by De La Rue
8/164	8	Continuous rules. Cut under P of 3rd, and scoops in the rules below the 4th and 9th stamps. (There is no purple dot adjoining either of the interpane margins) (a) added white dot under XP of 2nd (b) added cut (pyramidal) under PE of 2nd Used only by De La Rue
9/165	9	Continuous rules. A ¾ cut (base) under PE of 3rd. (There is no purple dot adjoining either of the interpane margins) **Coextensive rules. (a) the plate was converted to one with coextensive rules by cutting up and dividing the original continuous rules—and believed unique in this respect. The cut under the 3rd stamp is filled and a fresh cut made under (P)E of 1st, date cuts added under (P)E of 12th,** purple dots added over and under the 12th stamp in the top and bottom rows of each pane, two circular scoops containing purple dots made cutting into the last pillar (lower scoop touching the 4th pillar bar) of the interpane margin and above which the rule (below R.10/12) received a ¾ cut (base)—probably accidental—under (C)E (The major differences between this plate in its coextensive form and all other plates of this value with coextensive rules are that the S.W. corner rule of the lower pane is joined to the vertical rule to the left of the 20th row; there is no white dot in the registration piece under R.20/6 and 7; and the gaps between the registration piece and the adjoining rules are, unusually, of equal width) (b) as before but a white dot made in the margin rule to the right of the 20th row denoting (initially) ink MB 24655 (c) as before but the white dot in the rule to the right of the 20th row is filled and a fresh white dot made in the rule to the right of the 19th row denoting (initially) ink MB 10394D/24816 (d) as before but the purple dots above and below the 12th stamps and in the circular scoops have been removed, the white dot to the right of the 19th row is filled, and a fresh white dot made in the rule to the right of the 18th row denoting (initially) ink MB 25598. The cut below R.10/12 is now filled (e) the cut under (P)E of 1st is filled Used by De La Rue and Somerset House

Plate Descriptions

Official Pl. No.	S G. Pl. No.	Features
10/191	10	Die I coextensive rules. Date cuts under and just to the left of P of 12th, also a white margin dot in the rule to the right of the 18th row denoting (initially) ink MB 25598. (This plate never received purple margin dots or interpane scoops but in comparison with plate 11, the rule to the right of the interpane gutter is relatively thin) Used only by Somerset House
11/192	11	Die I coextensive rules. Date cuts under and just to the right of P of 12th, also a white margin dot in the rule to the right of the 18th row denoting (initially) ink MB 25598. There is a scoop in the rule below the 9th stamp. (This plate never received purple margin dots or interpane scoops but in comparison with plate 10, the rule to the right of the interpane gutter is relatively thick) Used only by Somerset House
12/226		This plate was a reserve at Somerset House and not used
13/227	13	Die II coextensive rules. Cuts under (P)E of 2nd and PE of 4th (a) Date cuts added under CE of 11th, purple dots added over and under the 12th stamps in the top and bottom rows of each pane, two circular scoops containing purple dots made cutting into the last two pillars of the interpane margin, and a purple dot to the right of the interpane margin (b) as before but the cut under the 4th stamp and the date cuts under the 11th are filled. Fresh date cuts made under EN of 12th which are far from clear and in many instances barely perceptible (c) as before but the date cuts re-made under P of 12th, and a white margin dot made in the rule to the right of the 20th row denoting (initially) ink MB 24655. (In the course of these printings the fillings of the original date cuts fell out giving rise to the variety "date cuts under both 11th and 12th stamps") (d) as before but the white dot in the rule to the right of the 20th row is filled and a fresh white dot made in the rule to the right of the 19th row denoting (initially) ink MB 10394D/24816 Used by De La Rue and Somerset House
14/299	14	Die II coextensive rules. Cut under X of 1st (a) date cuts added under EN of 11th, purple dots added over and under the 12th stamps in the top and bottom rows of each pane, two circular scoops containing purple dots made cutting into the last pillar (lower scoop touching the 3rd pillar bar) of the interpane margin, and there is now a purple dot to the left of the interpane margin Used by De La Rue and Somerset House
15/300	–	This plate was not used

Printings

De La Rue

No. of Printing	Date	Plates Left sheet	Right sheet	Notes
Ordinary Paper (No. M31)				
1	1902/5	1	1a	Shades (1) and (2)
		6	2	
		8	7	
		(pairings unknown)		
Chalk-surfaced Paper (No. M32)				
2 & 3	1906/10	5	1a	Shades (1) (2) and (3)
		6	5a	
		8	7 & 7a	
		9	8a & 8b	
		14	13	
		(pairings unknown)		

Somerset House

No. of Printing	Date	Plates		Paper	Notes
Printings made during 1911 have date cuts under the 11th stamps					
1st	Oct. 1911	14a	13a	Chalky	No. M35 in bright magenta
		14a	13a	Ordinary	No. M33 shade (1) (F)
	Nov. 1911	14a	13a	Ordinary	No. M33 shades (2) (3) and (4) all (F)

Somerset House continued

Printings made during 1912/13 have date cuts under the 12th stamps

2nd	March 1912	9a	13b	Ordinary	No. M33 (8) dull lilac (F) peculiar to this issue
3rd	May 1912	9b	13c	Ordinary	The plates have a white dot 20th row denoting ink MB 24655—in the shade of M33 (4) but not (F)
4th	May/June 1912	9c	13d	Ordinary	The plates have a white dot 19th row denoting
		9c	2a	Ordinary	ink MB 10394D/24816 believed to be M33 (5). Other shades occur including M33 (4) but not (F)
5th	Oct 1912	2b	9d	Ordinary	The plates have a white dot 18th row denoting ink MB 25598—in the shade of M33 (2) but not (F)
6th	Nov. 1912	10	11	Ordinary	The new plates also have a white dot 18th row denoting ink MB 25598. Other shades occur including M33 (4) but not (F)

The 18th row white dots on plates 9, 10 and 11 remained for all later printings

7th	March 1913	11	10	Coated	No. M34 (1) and (2)
8th	June 1913	10	9d	Plate-glazed	Shades of M33 (6) and (7)
9th	July 1913	11	9e	Chalky	No. M36 in deep plum

Price Schedule

Pl. No. and Sheet Side	Printing Usage	Date	Recognisable Piece			Price
De La Rue						
1 left	1	1902/05	S.W. strip of 4	..	..	£120
1a right	1		S.W. strip of 4		..	£120
2 right	1		S.W. corner pair H1 perf.		..	60·00
6 left	1		S.W. corner pair	..	..	60·00
7 right	1		S.W. corner pair		..	60·00
8 left	1		S.W. strip of 3	..	..	90·00
1a right	2 & 3	1906/10	S.W. strip of 4	..	..	£150
5 left	2 & 3		S.W. strip of 4	..	..	£150
5a right	2 & 3		S.W. strip of 4	..	..	£150
6 left	2 & 3		S.W. corner pair	..	..	70·00
7 right	2 & 3		S.W. strip of 4	..	..	£150
7a right	2 & 3		S.W. strip of 4	..	..	£150
8 left	2 & 3		S.W. strip of 3	..	..	£110
8a right	2 & 3		S.W. corner pair	..	..	—
8b right	2 & 3		S.W. corner pair	..	..	—
9 left	2 & 3		S.W. strip 3 H1 perf.		..	—
13 right	2 & 3		S.W. strip of 4	..	..	£150
14 left	2 & 3		S.W. corner pair	..	..	70·00
Somerset House						
13a right	1st	Oct. 1911	No. M35 S.E. corner pair..		..	£3000
14a left	1st		No. M35 S.E. corner pair..		..	—
13a right 14a left	1st		No. M33 (1) S.E. corner pair		..	80·00
13a right 14a left	1st	Nov. 1911	No. M33 (2) & (4) S.E. corner pair			45·00
13a right 14a left	1st		No. M33 (3) S.E. corner pair		..	80·00
9a left 13b right	2nd	March 1912	No.M33 (8) S.E. corner pair			—
9b left 13c right	3rd	May 1912	S.E. corner pair	..	..	—
9c left	4th	May/June 1912	S.E. corner block of 4	..	..	95·00
13d right	4th		S.E. corner block of 4	..	..	95·00
2a right	4th		S.E. corner block of 4	..	..	95·00
2b left 9d right	5th		S.E. corner block of 6	..	..	£150
10 left 11 right	6th	Oct 1912	S.E. corner pair	..	..	45·00
11 left 10 right	7th	Nov. 1912	No. M34 corner pair	..	..	£250
10 left 9d right	8th	March 1913	No. M33 (6) & (7) S.E corner pair			45·00
11 left 9e right	9th	June 1913 / July 1913	No. M36 S.E. corner pair..		..	55·00

Prices quoted are for pairs or strips, although single examples are sometimes adequate for identification.

Before attempting to identify recognisable pieces see notes below the Price Schedule for 1½d. value.

1910-13. 7d. Grey-Black, Type M11

Cat. No.	S.G. No.	Perf.	Paper	Shades	Unused	Used

1910 (MAY 4). GREY-BLACK. PERF. 14. DE LA RUE

M37   249/49*a*   14   Ordinary   (1) Grey-black   3·50 ✓ 6·00 ✓
                                      (2) Deep grey-black   60·00   60·00

Block of four .. .. .. 16·00   30·00
Used on cover   .. .. †   £120
b. Raised crown in watermark
    (corner block of 4) (Pl. 1, R.
    19/2) £300
s. "Specimen", Type 17   .. £200
t. "Cancelled", Type 20   ..
u. "Cancelled", Type 25   ..

Perforation 14

Type H1 only

Essays

    1   2   3   4

Submitted 5th March 1909 on very highly glazed paper

Type 1 in slate £800
Type 2 in carmine-lake £800
Type 3 in brown £800

Type 1 was selected but with larger value tablets as in Type 2.

Submitted 15th July 1909 on very highly glazed paper

Type 4 in grey-green £800
Type 5 as Type 4 but with fringe added round design (card inscribed "5"). In grey-green £800

Essays from the De La Rue Archives

Stamp-size photographic essays on card, pen-cancelled with cross:

Type 4 in grey-green £950
Type 5, as Type 4 but with fringe added round design. In grey-green £950

Types 1, 2 and 3 as described above pen-cancelled with cross were acquired by the N.P.M.

Die Proofs in black on white glazed card :—

Endorsed "Die No. 86"	£600		Endorsed "Die No. 89"	£550

Endorsed " BEFORE HARD-
ENING 7 SEP 09 " .. £550
Endorsed "AFTER HARDEN-
ING 12 SEP 09 " £550
This die was faulty and defaced

Endorsed " BEFORE HARD-
ENING 7 DEC 09 " £550
Without marking but black
surround whited out £550
Endorsed " AFTER STRIKING
12 MAR 10 " £550

As was the case for the 4d. orange, the 7d. Die Proofs tend to have an irregular black surround to the design as they were flat when finished instead of being slightly raised.

Die Proofs from the De La Rue Archives

On card unmounted with traces of gum or paper on the back:

Cut down (83 × 47 mm), with uncleared surround. Stamped " 7 DEC 09 " and
    " BEFORE HARDENING " £750
As last but with surround painted out and without markings £750

Piece Cut from the Striking Book

See notes under the ½d. value.
Struck on plain paper cut to size with various endorsements comprising dates, plates 1 to 3 and leads

7d. value £950

Colour Trials

Submitted on 24th February 1910 to the Inland Revenue

On white paper. Watermark Crown

In yellow-olive, olive, sage-green, dull blue-green, pale blue, deep blue, violet, slate-purple, purple, red-purple, deep red-brown, pale red-brown, brown, grey-brown, grey, black ..   ..   *From £800*

The grey colour was chosen from the colour trials, this having been selected from the essays. The grey-brown colour trial was submitted in duplicate.

1912 (AUGUST 1).   GREY-BLACK.   PERF. 14.   SOMERSET HOUSE

M38	305	14	Ordinary	(1) Deep slate-grey	75·00	35·00	
				(2) Slate-grey	5·00	8·50	
Block of four	..	.. 25·00	60·00	(3) Pale grey (May 1913)	12·00	10·00	
Used on cover	..	.. †	85·00				
s.	" Specimen ", Type 26	.. —†					
t.	" Cancelled ", Type 25	.. £150†					

M38(1) is on poorly surfaced paper which produced a coarse impression. The later printings, M38(2) and M38(3), are on finely calendered paper, and it is difficult to distinguish between these and the De La Rue printings.

All the Somerset House issues show a trace of olive in the grey, some more so than others. The olive is always apparent to the keen eye and is even more noticeable under a quartz lamp.

†Nos. M38s and M38t exist from NPM archive sales.

Perforation 14

Types V1   V1A

Plate Descriptions

Official Pl. No.	S.G. Pl. No.	Features
1/314	1	Coextensive rules. Cut under 2nd (a) date cuts added under & R of 12th and scoop in the interpane gutter cutting the pillars under and between the 6th and 7th stamps Used by De La Rue and Somerset House
2/315	2	Coextensive rules. Cut under 1st (a) date cuts added under RE of 12th Used by De La Rue and Somerset House
3/319	3	Coextensive rules. No cuts under 1st or 2nd, date cuts under & of 12th Used only by Somerset House—plate not proofed until November 1912

Printings

De La Rue

No. of Printing	Date	Plates Left sheet	Right sheet	Notes
Ordinary Paper (No. M37)				
1	1910	2	1	Shade (1) or rarely (2)

Somerset House

No. of Printing	Date	Plates Left sheet	Right sheet	Notes
Ordinary Paper (No. M38)				
1st	Aug. 1912	1a		Shade (1) rare on coarse unsurfaced paper
2nd	1912	1a		Shade (2)
3rd	Dec. 1912	2a		Shade (2)
4th	May 1913	3		Shade (3)

Price Schedule

Plate No.	Left or Right sheet	Printing Usage	Recognisable Piece						Price per pair
De La Rue									
1	Right	1	S.W. corner pair lower pane H1 perf.	..	..	..			8·00
2	Left	1	S.W. corner pair lower pane H1 perf.	..	..	..			8·00
Somerset House									
With date cuts under 12th stamps lower pane only									
1a	—	1st	S.E. corner pair	..	..	..	..	..	£150
1a	—	2nd	S.E. corner pair	..	..	..	..	..	12·00
2a	—	3rd	S.E. corner pair	..	..	..	..	..	12·00
3	—	4th	S.E. corner pair	..	..	..	..	..	12·00

In the 1st Somerset House printing the impressions are very coarse.

Prices quoted are for pairs, although single examples are sometimes adequate for identification.

Before attempting to identify recognisable pieces see notes below the Price Schedule for the 1½d. value.

1902-13.   9d. Purple and Blue, Type M12

Cat. No.	S.G. No.	Perf.	Paper	Shades	Unused	Used

1902-05.   PURPLE AND BLUE.   PERF. 14.   DE LA RUE

A. 1902 (APRIL 7).   Ordinary paper

M39   250/51   14   Ordinary   (1) Dull purple and ultra-marine   40·00   24·00 ✓

Block of four	.. ..	£175	£125
Used on cover	.. ..	†	£120
s.	"Specimen", Type 16 ..	£100	

(2) Slate-purple and ultra-marine   40·00 ✓ 24·00 ✓

(3) Slate-purple and deep ultramarine   50·00   28·00

brek i SE corner ✓

B. 1905 (JUNE).   Chalk-surfaced paper

M40   252/53   14   Chalky   (1) Dull purple and ultra-marine   45·00   30·00

	Block of four	£200	£140
	Used on cover	†	£130
a.	Watermark inverted ..	—	£750
b.	Two breaks in S.W. frame (Pl. H2, Pane D, R. 1/5) ..	90·00	30·00
c.	Left frame cracked (Pl. D (1), Pane B, R. 1/1) ..	90·00	30·00
d.	T in POSTAGE appears as 7 (Pl. H1, Pane B, R. 4/2) ..	90·00	30·00
s.	"Specimen", Type 17 ..	£200	
t.	"Cancelled", Type 18 ..	—†	
u.	"Cancelled", Type 20 ..	£400	

(2) Slate-purple and pale ultramarine   45·00   30·00

(3) Slate-purple and ultra-marine   45·00   30·00 ✓

(4) Slate-purple and deep ultramarine   60·00   35·00

†No. M40t exists from NPM archive sales.

M40b

M40c

M40d

Perforation 14
   Type H1 only

Die Proofs in black on white glazed card :—

Head plate only		Endorsed "BEFORE HARD- ENING 10 DEC 01" ..	£550
Without marking	£650	Endorsed "AFTER HARDEN- ING 10 DEC 01"	£550
Endorsed "BEFORE HARD- ENING 28 NOV 01" ..	£550		
Cut down and endorsed on back "Duplicate proof of Head die for for 9d stamp registered 5 April 1902" (M/S)	£400		

Piece Cut from the Striking Book
   See notes under the ½d. value.

Struck on plain paper cut to size with various endorsements comprising dates, plates 1 to 3 and leads

9d. head plate £800

Cat. No.	S.G. No.	Perf.	Paper	Shades	Unused	Used

1911 (JULY 24). PURPLE AND BLUE. PERF. 14. SOMERSET HOUSE

M 41	306/08	14	Ordinary	(1) Reddish purple and light blue	50·00	30·00 ✔
	Block of four £175 £170			(2) Deep dull reddish purple and deep bright blue (Sept. 1911)	60·00	32·00 ✔
	Used on cover .. .. † 85·00					
b.	Irregular S.W. frame (Pl. H2, Pane G, R. 1/4) .. £100 50·00			(3) Dull reddish purple and blue (Oct. 1911)	40·00	22·00 ✔
c.	Major frame breaks (Pl. H1, Pane G, R. 2/4) .. .. £100 50·00					
d.	Damaged S.E. corner (Pl. H2, Pane D, R. 1/2) .. £100 50·00			(4) Slate-purple and cobalt blue (F) (March 1912)	70·00	35·00 ✔
e.	Damaged upper right corner (Pl. H2, Pane D, R. 2/2) £100			(5) Deep plum and blue (July 1913)	40·00	30·00 ✔
f.	Break in base of upper right value tablet (Pl. D(3), Pane H, R. 1/1) £100					
s.	"Specimen", Type 22 .. £130					

Shades in the 7th Somerset House printing vary from reddish purple, almost indistinguishable from (1) to plum (5).

M41b

M41f

M41c

M41d and M41e

Perforation 14
Types V1 V1A

Plate Descriptions

Official Pl. No.	S.G. Pl. No.	Features
Head Plates.		All the Outer Line head plates have continuous marginal rules
1/94	H1	Cut under 1st pane G and over 1st pane A. Used only by De La Rue except for panes substituted by Somerset House
2/96	H2	Cut under 2nd pane G and over 2nd pane A. Used by De La Rue and Somerset House
3/99	H3	Thin date cuts under 5th panes D and H. Used only by Somerset House

The registration sheet of Plate 1/94 has no De La Rue marks. It is possible that this plate and Plate 2/96 may exist in collectors' hands without markings and, if found, may be recognised by the side of the mill sheet from which they came.

Duty Plates

(1)	D(1)	Nick in left frame of 1st top row pane A and small crack left of 1st top and 4th rows pane B. Used by De La Rue and Somerset House
(2)	D(2)	No marking. Used only by De La Rue
(3)	D(3)	Used only by Somerset House

There were no complete Inner Line duty plates for the 9d. value. Each plate combination included eight duty plates for the eight panes of 20.

Plate (1) comprised official Plates 17, 19, 20, 23, 24, 25, 27 and 36 but their positions in the plate layout are not known. They did not vary and always appeared on left sheets when printed by De La Rue. However Plate 39 was used to substitute the B pane in the 6th Somerset House printing.

Plate (2) comprised official Plates 28 to 35 and are always found in the same but unknown positions on right sheets.

Plate (3) comprised official Plates 40 to 46 and 48. Except for Plate 48, all had been used for Queen Victoria printings and show flaws.

Printings

De La Rue

No. of Printing	Date	Plates Left sheet	Right sheet
Ordinary Paper (No. M39)			
1 to 3	1902–May 1904	H1/D(1)	H2/D(2)
Chalk-surfaced Paper (No. M40)			
4 to 7	1905–Nov. 1909	H1/D(1)	H2/D(2)

Somerset House

No. of Printing	Date	Plates	Notes
Ordinary Paper (No. M41)			
1st	June 1911	H2/D(1)	No added cuts. Only 1 ream of sheets printed
2nd	Aug. 1911?	H2a/D(1)	H2a has purple date dots added under 4th of panes D and H. Being inconsistent in position no definite guidance can be given to distinguish the two panes
3rd	Sep. 1911?	H2b/D(1)	H2b has date dots removed and 2 cuts added under 4th of panes D and H, those in H pane more to right and closer than those in D pane
4th	Feb. 1912	H2c/D(1)	H2c has date cuts filled up and fine cuts added under 5th panes D and H, those in H pane being broader and more to right than those in D pane. S.E. corner of pane E severely damaged
5th	Aug. 1912	H2c, H1/D(1)	Pane A from H1 with cut over 1st unfilled substituted for pane E. F and G panes have substantial flaws. Head plate stack of short lined blocks between E and F panes were replaced inverted
6th	Oct. 1912	H2c, H1/D(1)	As 5th printing but pane G of H1 substituted for pane G of H2c and duty plate 39 substituted for pane B of D(1). Extremely rare printing
7th	Nov. 1912	H3/D(3)	Thin date cuts under 5th of panes D and H differing from those of printings 4 to 6 in being serrated. Head plate stacks of short lined blocks between C and D panes and G and H panes were inverted compared with earlier printings, while those of duty plates between E and F panes and G and H panes were also inverted

This is a complicated value and further guidance for distinguishing the printings is contained in an article by Michael Astley published in the February 1975 issue of *The GB Journal.*

Price Schedule

Plate Combination Head/Duty	Left or Right sheet	Printing Usage	Recognisable Piece	Price per Pair

De La Rue

Perforation 14.   Type H1

(a) Ordinary Paper

H1/D(1)	Left	1 to 3	Corner of sheet	90·00
H2/D(2)	Right	1 to 3	Corner of sheet	£100

(b) Chalk-surfaced Paper

H1/D(1)	Left	4 to 7	Corner of sheet	90·00
H2/D(2)	Right	4 to 7	Corner of sheet	£100

Somerset House

H2/D(1)	—	1st	S.E. corner, panes D or H	95·00
H2a/D(1)	—	2nd	S.E. corner, panes D or H	90·00
H2b/D(1)	—	3rd	S.E. corner, panes D or H	90·00
H2c/D(1)	—	4th	S.E. corner, panes D or H	90·00
H2c, H1/D(1)	—	5th	N.W. corner, panes E or F	90·00
H2c, H1/D(1)	—	6th	S.W. corner, pane G with cut under 1st. Single (pairs not known)	—
H3/D(3)	—	7th	S.E. corner, panes D or H, S.W. corner, pane G or N.W. corner, pane A	85·00

With one exception prices quoted are for pairs, although single examples are sometimes adequate for identification.

Before attempting to identify recognisable pieces see notes below the Price Schedule for the 1½d. value and reference should also be made to the lay-out of the plates for the 9d. value in the General Notes under " PLATES ".

1902-12. 10d. Purple and Red, Type M13

Cat. No. S.G. No.   Perf.   Paper   Shades   Unused   Used

1902-05. PURPLE AND RED. PERF. 14. DE LA RUE

A. 1902 (JULY 3). Ordinary paper

							Unused	Used
M42	254	14	Ordinary			(1) Dull purple and carmine	40·00	18·00
	Block of four..	..	..	£250	90·00	(2) Slate-purple and carmine	50·00 ✔	18·00
	Used on cover	..	..	†	£120			
b.	No cross on Crown	..	..	£225	£100	(3) Slate-purple and carmine-pink	£250	50·00
g.	Break in frame at back of head	..	..	..	£200	75·00		
s.	"Specimen", Type 16	..	£100					

B. 1906 (SEPTEMBER). Chalk-surfaced paper

							Unused	Used
M43	255/6	14	Chalky			(1) Dull purple and carmine	40·00	24·00
	Block of four..	..	..	£200	£150	(2) Slate-purple and carmine	40·00	28·00 ✔
	Used on cover	..	..	†	£130			
b.	No cross on Crown. Shade (2)	£200	90·00	(3) Slate-purple and deep carmine	£200	60·00
c.	No cross on Crown. Shade (4)	£1500				
d.	No cross on Crown. Shade (5)	£190 ✔	80·00 ✔	(4) Slate-purple and deep (glossy) carmine	£1100	£400
g.	Break in frame at back of head	..	..	£150	50·00	(5) Dull purple and scarlet (Sept. 1910)	45·00	35·00 ✔
s.	"Specimen", Type 17	..	£200					
t.	"Cancelled", Type 18	..	—†					
u.	"Cancelled", Type 20	..	£400					

The glossy carmine colour of M43(4) gives the appearance of being enamelled.
M43b/d occurs in various positions but is not fully constant, being due to faulty make ready.
†No. M43t exists from NPM archive sales.

Quoin flaw*   M42g, M43g

*Head plate flaws approximating to the above exist on Nos. M43/4.   They were caused by overtightening quoins between the sub-electros.   They are sometimes found in Rows 1 and 4 between stamps 4 and 5 and also 8 and 9.

Perforation 14

Type H1 only

Die Proofs in black on white glazed card:—

Head plate only

Without marking	.. ..	£650
Endorsed "BEFORE HARDENING 27 NOV 01 "	..	£550
Cut down and endorsed on back "Duplicate proof of Head die for 10d stamp registered 28 June 1902 " (M/S)	.. ..	£400

Endorsed "AFTER HARDENING 28 NOV 01 " £550

Die Proof from the De La Rue Archives
On card unmounted with traces of gum or paper on the back:
Head plate only, without markings £800

Pieces Cut from the Striking Books
See notes under the ½d. value.
Struck on plain paper cut to size with various endorsements comprising dates,
plates and/or leads
10d. head plate £750
10d. duty plate £750

Plate Proof in issued colours on poor quality buff paper .. .. .. 28·00

Cat. No.	S.G. No.	Perf.	Paper	Shades	Unused	Used

1911 (OCTOBER 9). PURPLE AND RED. PERF. 14. SOMERSET HOUSE

M44	309/11	14	Ordinary	(1) Dull reddish purple and scarlet	80·00	40·00 ✓
	Block of four £150 £100			(2) Dull purple and scarlet	45·00	25·00 ✓
	Used on cover .. .. .. † 85·00			(3) Deep dull purple and scarlet	45·00	32·00
h.	Repaired S.W. corner (shade 8) (Pl. D(1), Pane W, R. 2/2) — 55·00			(4) Dull purple and deep scarlet	£140	60·00
i.	Mark after E of REVENUE 65·00 35·00			(5) Dull reddish purple and aniline pink (F)	£175	£110
j.	Cracked duty plate (Pl. D(1), Pane X, R. 4/12) £100			(6) Dull reddish purple and carmine (May 1912)	35·00	20·00 ✓
k.	No cross on Crown (shade 5) £650			(7) Deep dull purple and carmine	45·00	25·00
l.	No cross on Crown (shade like (6)) £500			(8) Dark plum and carmine	45·00	25·00
s.	"Specimen" Type 22.. .. £100†					

†No. M44s exists from NPM archive sales.

M44h M44i M44j

No. M44h consists of a nick in the diagonal white line and only 9 dots instead of 12.

Perforation 14
Types VI VIA

Plate Descriptions

Official Pl. No.	S.G. Pl. No.	Features

Head Plates

With continuous Outer Line marginal rules for each of the four panes of 48 except that each was made up of three sections of 16 (4 × 4) so that each horizontal head plate rule is broken after the fourth and eighth stamps.

| 1/72 | H1 | Cut under 2nd, bottom row pane Z. Used only by De La Rue on right sheets |
| 2/74 | H2 | Cut under 1st, bottom row pane Z. Used only by De La Rue on left sheets only and by Somerset House |

Duty Plates

With continuous Inner Line, marginal rules for each of the four panes of 48. There were no complete duty plates for the 10d. value. Each combination included four duty plates for the panes of 48. Plate (1) comprises duty plates 1 to 4 and Plate (2) comprises duty plates 5 to 8. These were probably arranged in that order from the top downwards.

| (1) | D(1) | No marking. Used by De La Rue on right sheets and by Somerset House |
| (2) | D(2) | No marking. Used only by De La Rue on left sheets |

Head plate 3/76 was also made but never used and duty plates 9 to 12 (of which there is a proof in the N.P.M.) were also made but never used.

Printings

De La Rue

No. of Printing	Date	Plates Left sheet	Right sheet	Notes
(a) Ordinary Paper (No. M42)				
1 to 4	June 1902–Apr. 1905	H2/D(2)	H1/D(1)	
(b) Chalk-surfaced Paper (No. M43)				
5 to 8	July 1906–Sep. 1909	H2/D(2)	H1/D(1)	Purple and carmine shades
9	Sept. 1910	H2/D(2)	H1/D(1)	Dull purple and scarlet

Somerset House

No. of Printing	Date	Plates	Notes
Ordinary Paper (No. M44)			
1st	Aug. 1911	H2a/D(1a)	Date cut added under 8th and 2 cuts under 11th of panes X and Z. The latter cuts are very similar for both panes but normally the right hand cut of pane Z is closed at the bottom by a very thin line of ink. Red dots under 12th of panes X and Z and over 12th of panes W and Y
2nd	May 1912	H2b/D(1a)	Cuts under 8th and 11th filled up and new cuts added under 12th of panes X and Z; those in the X pane being almost central and those in the Z pane are well to the left of centre

Price Schedule

Plate Combination Head/Duty	Left or Right sheet	Printing Usage	Recognisable Piece						Price per pair
De La Rue									
Perforation 14. Type H1									
(a) Ordinary Paper									
H1/D(1)	Right	1 to 4	Corner of sheet	..	..	..	..	..	90·00
H2/D(2)	Left	1 to 4	Corner of sheet	..	..	..	..	..	90·00
(b) Chalk-surfaced Paper									
H1/D(1)	Right	5 to 8	Corner of sheet	..	..	..	..	..	90·00
H2/D(2)	Left	5 to 8	Corner of sheet	..	..	..	..	..	90·00
H1/D(1)	Right	9	Corner of sheet	..	..	..	..	..	90·00
H2/D(2)	Left	9	Corner of sheet	..	..	..	..	..	90·00
Somerset House									
Perforation 14. Types V1, V1A									
H2a/D(1a)	—	1st	S.E. corner pair panes X or Z	..	..	..	80·00
H2b/D1a)	—	2nd	S.E. corner pair panes X or Z	..	..	..	80·00

Prices quoted are for pairs, although single examples are sometimes adequate for identification. Before attempting to identify recognisable pieces see notes below the Price Schedule for 1½d. value.

1902-12.   1s. Green and Red, Type M14

Cat. No.   S.G. No.   Perf.   Paper   Shades   Unused   Used

1902-05.   GREEN AND RED.   PERF. 14.   DE LA RUE

A. 1902 (MARCH 24).   Ordinary paper

M45   257   14   Ordinary   (1) Dull green and carmine 35·00   8·50 ✓
                                                    (2) Dull green and bright
  Block of four ..   ..   ..   £150   45·00   carmine   35·00   8·50 ✓
  Used on cover ..   ..   ..   †   80·00
  e. Frame broken at left (Pl. B3,
      R. 19/1) £120
  f. Frame broken at left (Pl. B2,
      R. 12/1) £180
  s. "Specimen", Type 16   ..   £100

B. 1905 (SEPTEMBER).   Chalk-surfaced paper

M46   258/59   14   Chalky   (1) Dull green and carmine 40·00   12·00 ✓
                                                    (2) Dull green and pale
  Block of four ..   ..   ..   £175   60·00   carmine   60·00   12·00 ✓
  Used on cover ..   ..   ..   †   £100   (3) Dull green and scarlet
  d. "Full beard" to portrait ..   £1500   (Sept. 1910)   40·00   20·00 ✓
  e. Frame broken at left (Pl. B3,   (4) Deep dull green and
      R. 19/1) ..   ..   £150   scarlet   55·00   20·00 ✓
  f. Frame broken at left (Pl. B2,
      R. 12/1) £200
  s. "Specimen", Type 17   ..   £200
  t. "Cancelled", Type 18   ..   —†
  u. "Cancelled", Type 20   ..   £400

†No. M46t exists from NPM archive sales.

M45e, M46e

M45f, M46f

Perforation 14
   Type H1 only

Die Proofs.   In black on white glazed card.   Head and duty plate only:
   Without marking (cleared)   ..   £650   As last but also endorsed "A.C.
   Without marking (uncleared)   ..   £650   10 Dec. 01" £550
   Endorsed " BEFORE HARDEN-   Cut down, with " Duplicate proof
      ING 4 DEC 01 "   ..   ..   £550   of Head die & duty die for 1/–
   Endorsed " AFTER HARDEN-   stamp registered 25 Feb 1902 "
      ING 10 DEC 01 "   ..   ..   £550   annotated on back in M/S   ..   £400

Die Proof from the De La Rue Archives.   On card unmounted with traces of gum or paper
on the back:
   Head plate only with uncleared surround, without markings £950

Pieces Cut from the Striking Books
   See notes under the ½d. value.
Struck on plain paper cut to size with various endorsements comprising dates,
   plates and/or leads
      1s. head plate..   ..   ..   £450
      1s. duty plate..   ..   ..   £450

1911 (JULY 13). GREEN AND RED. PERF 14. SOMERSET HOUSE

M47	312/14	14	Ordinary

	Block of four	£120	50·00
	Used on cover	†	85·00
a.	No watermark	£750	
b.	Watermark inverted ..	90·00	
c.	Watermark inverted and part of the word POSTAGE	£150	
d.	Vertical scratch at back of ear (Pl. H2a) and bottom frame broken (Pl. B5, R. 20/11). No date cuts in marginal rule	£125	
da.	Do. but with date cuts added (Pls. H2b/B5) ..	85·00	
db.	As da but frame break repaired (Pls. H2b/B5a) ..	85·00	
dc.	As db but date cuts removed (Pls. H2c or H2d/B5a or B5b)	70·00	
s.	"Specimen", Type 22 ..	£100	
t.	"Specimen", Type 23 ..		
u.	"Specimen", Type 26 ..	—†	

(1)	Dark green and scarlet	60·00	25·00	
(2)	Deep green and scarlet (9 Oct. 1911)	45·00	9·00	✔
(3)	Green and bright scarlet	42·00 ✔	9·00 ✔	
(4)	Green and scarlet	42·00	9·00 ✔	
(5)	Green and carmine (15 April 1912)	28·00	8·00 ✔	

Prices for M47d, M47da, M47db and M47dc are for singles with selvedge attached.
†No. M47u exists from NPM archive sales.

M47d, M47da

Perforation 14
  Types V1 V1A

Plate Descriptions

Head (incorporating Duty) Plates

With continuous rules (cut away at the corners) the 240 set Outer Line Head Plates each comprise two panes of 120 stamps (10 horizontal rows of 12). Each pane of 120 is made up of 6 sections of 20 stamps (5 horizontal rows of 4) the positions of which are marked by a break in the mid-point of each vertical rule and by breaks between the 4th/5th and 8th/9th stamps of each horizontal rule. The plate thus comprised 12 such sections —informally numbered 1 to 12 commencing from the N.W. corner of the upper pane— and akin to the diagram on page 14 which illustrates the 16 section layout of the 1½d., 2d. and 5d., Outer Line Plates. At least one substitution of a section is known for the 1s. value when section 10 (the S.W. corner lower pane) of Head Plate 1/86 was substituted in that same position in Head Plate 2/89 for the final issue. Other substitutions are probable but not yet proven due to the scarcity of the relevant material.

Official Pl. No.	S.G. Pl. No.	Features
1/86	H1	Cut under 2nd stamp bottom row lower pane. Used only by De La Rue
2/89	H2	Cut under 1st stamp bottom row lower pane, and a highly distinctive constant rule flaw under the 7th stamp bottom row lower pane
		(a) cut added in the rule under the 6th stamp of the lower pane
		(b) the cut under the 6th stamp is filled and a wide date cuts added under the 11th stamps of the bottom rows of the upper and lower panes
		(c) the cut under the 1st stamp is filled, the date cuts under the 11th stamps are filled, and fresh narrow date cuts added under the 12th stamps of the bottom rows of the upper and lower panes
		(d) as before but the S.W. lower pane corner section of 20 stamps (5 rows of 4) is removed and the corresponding section from Head Plate 1/86 substituted—including its rule cut under the 2nd stamp of the bottom row. Used by De La Rue and Somerset House

Border Plates

With continuous rules the Inner Line "frame plates" comprise two panes each of 120 stamps in 10 rows of 12 for each 240 set plate. Some of the Border Plates are believed to have been used previously for the bi-coloured 1s. value of the Queen Victoria "Jubilee" issue.

2	B2	Rule corners cut away and a cut under the 2nd stamp bottom row lower pane. Used only by De La Rue
3	B3	Rule corners cut away (apart from a thin semi-circular line on some printings joining the lower pane S.W. corner) and a cut under the 1st stamp bottom row lower pane. Used only by De La Rue
4	B4	Continuous rule corners with crack in the S.W. corner of the lower pane, no plate cut. Used only by De La Rue
5	B5	Continuous rule corners, no plate cut
		(a) red dots added in the margins above and below the 12th vertical rows of upper and lower panes
		(b) red dots of state (a) removed
		Used by De La Rue and Somerset House

Printings

De La Rue printed 480 set

No. of Printing	Date	Plates Left sheet	Plates Right sheet	Notes
Ordinary Paper (No. M45)				
1	1902/04	H2/B3	H1/B2	Shades (1) and (2)
Chalk-surfaced Paper (No. M46)				
2	1905/09	H2/B4	H1/B2	
		H2/B4	H1/B5	Shades (1) and (2)
3	1910	H2/B4	H1/B5	Shades (3) and (4)

Somerset House printed 240 set

No. of Printing	Date	Plates	Notes
Ordinary Paper (No. M47) Without date cuts			
1st	July 1911	H2a/B5	Shade (1)
With date cuts under the 11th stamps			
2nd	October 1911	H2b/B5	Shades (1) and (2)
3rd	late 1911	H2b/B5a	Shades (3) and (4)
With date cuts under the 12th stamps			
4th	April 1912	H2c/B5a	Shade (5)
5th	October 1912	H2d/B5b	Shade (5)

Price Schedule

Plate Combination Head/Border	Left or Right sheet	Printing Usage	Colour	Recognisable Piece	Price
De La Rue					
(a) Ordinary Paper					
H1/B2	Right	1	Carmine	S.W. corner pair	80·00
H2/B3	Left	1	Carmine	S.W. corner pair	80·00
(b) Chalk-surfaced Paper					
H1/B2	Right	2	Carmine	S.W. corner pair	90·00
H2/B4	Left	2	Carmine	S.W. corner pair	90·00
H1/B5	Right	2	Carmine	S.W. corner pair	90·00
H1/B5	Right	3	Scarlet	S.W. corner pair	£100
H2/B4	Left	3	Scarlet	S.W. corner pair	£100

Somerset House

Ordinary Paper

						Top Pane	Bottom Pane
H2a/B5	—	1st	Scarlet	S.E. corner pair	. .	—	—*
H2b/B5	—	2nd	Scarlet	S.E. corner pair	. .	95·00	£200*
H2b/B5a	—	3rd	Scarlet	S.E. corner pair	. .	95·00	£200*
H2c/B5a	—	4th	Carmine	S.E. corner pair	. .	65·00	£150*
H2d/B5b	—	5th	Carmine	S.E. corner pair	. .	65·00	£150*

*The five bottom pane pairs contain, respectively, and from 1st printing; M47d, M47da, M47db and M47dc in 4th and 5th printings.

Prices quoted are for pairs, although single examples are sometimes adequate for identification.

Before attempting to identify recognisable pieces see notes below the Price Schedule for 1½d. value.

1902-13.   2s. 6d. Purple, Type M15

Cat. No.	S.G. No.	Perf.	Paper	Shades	Unused	Used

1902-05. PURPLE. PERF. 14. DE LA RUE
A. 1902 (APRIL 5). Ordinary paper

M48	260	14	Ordinary	(1) Lilac	£150	45·00 ✓
				(2) Slate-purple	£150	40·00

	Block of four	.. ..	£650	£275
	Used on cover	.. ..	†	£500
b.	Watermark inverted	..	£800	£500
s.	" Specimen ", Type 15	..	£130	
t.	" Specimen ", Type 16	..	£120	

B. 1905 (OCTOBER 7). Chalk-surfaced paper

M49	261/62	14	Chalky	(1) Pale dull purple	£150	80·00
				(2) Dull purple **25o**	£160	55·00 ✓
				(3) Slate-purple	£175	60·00

	Block of four	.. ..	£600	£300
	Used on cover	.. ..	†	£600
b.	Watermark inverted	..	£800	£500
s.	" Specimen ". Type 17	..		

Perforation 14
Type H1 only

Essay from the De La Rue Archives. Photographic essay in stamp size on card:
In approved design, submitted to the Controller on 14 May 1901 ..   ..

Die Proofs. In black on white glazed card:

Without marking	£650	
Endorsed " BEFORE HARDEN- ING 8 NOV 01 "	£750	As last but also endorsed in M/S " AC. 12 Nov. 01 " £750
Endorsed " AFTER HARDEN- ING 12 NOV 01 "	£750	Stamped " AFTER STRIKING 15 NOV 01 " and endorsed in M/S " AC. 15 Nov 01 " .. .. ..

Uncleared Die Proof

Die Proofs from the De La Rue Archives. On card unmounted with traces of gum or paper on the back:

Cut down (86 × 54 mm) with head in oval and partially uncleared surround to head and background £1500
Cut down (68 × 51 mm) with solid dark ground in front of head, lettered " A." and annotated " CANCELLED " in M/S   ..   £1500

Cut down (68 × 51 mm) with lightened background, lettered " B." and annotated " Cancelled " in M/S £1500

Piece Cut from the Striking Book
See notes under the ½d. value.
Struck on plain paper cut to size with various endorsements comprising dates, plates 1 and 2 and leads
2s. 6d. value £650

Plate Proof in issued colour on poor quality buff paper ..   ..   ..   50·00
As above, double impression   ..   ..   60·00

1911 (SEPTEMBER 27). PURPLE. PERF. 14. SOMERSET HOUSE

M50	315/17	14	Ordinary			

(1) Dull greyish purple (F) £250 £150
(2) Dull reddish purple
     (Oct. 1911) £135 45·00 ✓
(3) Dark purple £135 50·00 ✓
(4) Pale dull reddish purple
     (18 Mar. 1913) **275** £125 ✓ 45·00

Block of four	.. .. £550	£275	
Used on cover	.. †	£500	
s.	" Specimen ", Type 22	.. £130†	
t.	" Cancelled ", Type 24	.. —†	

†Nos. M50s and M50t exist from NPM archive sales.

Perforation 14
Types V1   V1A

Plate Descriptions

Official Pl. No.	S.G. Pl. No.	Features

The 112 set plate comprises two panes each of 56 stamps (7 horizontal rows of 8).

1/51	1	No marking

(a) coloured dots added in the margins above and below the last vertical rows in each pane. Cuts added under the 7th stamp bottom row of both panes, those in the lower pane being thicker and broader
(b) cuts under 7th stamps filled up and cuts added under 8th stamp bottom row of both panes
(c) added white dot in the marginal rule at right of corner stamp both panes

Printings and Price Schedule

Series	Date	Plate	Paper	Position				Price	
								Top pane	Bottom pane
De La Rue									
1	1902	1	Ordinary	S.E. corner pair	..		..	£325	£325
2	1905	1	Chalky	S.E. corner pair	..	..	..	£325	£325
Somerset House									
	With 1911 date cuts under 7th stamp								
1st	1911	1a	Ordinary	S.E. corner pair					
				Dull greyish purple (F)	..			£550	£550
				Dull reddish purple		..	..	£275	£275
	With 1912 date cuts under 8th stamp								
2nd	1912	1b	Ordinary	S.E. corner pair	..	..		£275	£275
3rd	1913	1c	Plate glazed	S.E. corner pair	..	..	..	£275	£275

1902-12. 5s. Red, Type M16

Cat. No.	S.G. No.	Perf.	Paper	Shades	Unused	Used
1902 (APRIL 5). RED. PERF. 14. DE LA RUE						
M51	263/64	14	Ordinary	(1) Bright carmine	£200	55·00 ✓
				(2) Deep bright carmine	£200	55·00 ✓

	Block of four	.. ..	£850	£275
	Used on cover	..	†	£500
a.	Watermark inverted	..	—	£750
s.	" Specimen ", Type 16	..	£130	
t.	" Specimen ", Type 17	..		

Perforation 14

Type H1 only

Essay from the De La Rue Archives. Photographic essay in stamp size on card:

In approved design, submitted to the Controller on 14 May 1901 .. .. £450

Die Proofs in black on white glazed card :—

Endorsed " BEFORE HARD-ENING 22 NOV 01 " ..	£850				
Endorsed " AFTER HARDEN-ING 25 NOV 01 "	£850	With initials and (M/S) " 25.11.01 "	£850

Piece Cut from the Striking Books

See notes under ½d. value.

Struck on plain paper cut to size with various endorsements comprising dates, plates 1 and 2 and leads

5s. value £650

Plate Proof in issued colour on poor quality buff paper .. .. .. 50·00

1912 (FEBRUARY 29). RED. PERF. 14. SOMERSET HOUSE						
M52	318	14	Ordinary	(1) Carmine-red	£200	55·00 ✓
				(2) Carmine	£200	55·00

	Block of four	.. ..	£850	£275
	Used on cover	..	†	£500
s.	"Specimen", Type 26	..		

An aid to identification in this difficult value is the back of the stamp. The ink used by De la Rue had a permeating quality which gives the appearance of an offset of the design on the back. No. (2) is the later printing with fine impression. A small printing of No. (1) exists in fluorescent ink.

Perforation 14

Types V1   V1A

Specimen overprint from the National Postal Museum Archives

Perforated 14, watermark Type W9

"Specimen", Type 26

Plate Descriptions

Official Pl. No.	S.G. Pl. No.	Features
		The 112 set plate comprises two panes each of 56 stamps (7 horizontal rows of 8).
1/68	1	No marking
		(a) added small carmine dots in the margins above and below the last vertical rows of both panes. Date cuts added under the 7th stamp in the bottom row of both panes. Top pane cuts very fine and small, lower pane cuts thicker and broader
		(b) date cuts in state (a) filled up and cuts made under the 8th stamp in the bottom row of both panes

Printings and Price Schedule

Series	Date	Plate	Position				Price	
De La Rue								
							Top pane	Bottom pane
1	1902/10	1	S.E. corner pair	..	..	..	£450	£450
Somerset House								
With 1911 date cuts under 7th stamp								
1st	Feb. 1912	1a	S.E. corner pair	..	..	..	£450	£450
With 1912 date cuts under 8th stamp								
2nd	Oct. 1912	1b	S.E corner pair		..	..	£450	£450

1902-12. 10s. Blue, Type M17

Cat. No.	S.G. No.	Perf.	Paper	Shades	Unused	Used

1902 (APRIL 5). BLUE. PERF. 14. DE LA RUE

M53	265	14	Ordinary	(1) Ultramarine	£475	£200
				(2) Deep ultramarine	£475	£200

Block of four £2000   £1000
s. "Specimen ", Type 16 .. £200
t. "Specimen ", Type 17 .. £750
Imprimatur: £6500

Perforation 14
Type H1 only

Essay from the De La Rue Archives. Photographic essay in stamp size on card:
In approved design, submitted to the Controller on 14 May 1901   ..   ..   ..   £650

Die Proofs in black on white glazed card :

Without marking £1100	Endorsed " AFTER STRIKING " and in M/S " AC. 4 DEC 01 " ..	£1000
Endorsed " BEFORE HARD-ENING 22 NOV 01 " .. £950	As last but additional M/S " HW. 25.11.01 "	£1000
Endorsed "AFTER HARDEN-ING 25 NOV 01 " £950		

Piece Cut from the Striking Book
See notes under ½d. value.
Struck on plain paper cut to size with various endorsements comprising dates, plates 1 and 2 and leads
10s. value £750

Plate Proof in issued colour on poor quality buff paper £200

1912 (JANUARY 14). BLUE. PERF. 14. SOMERSET HOUSE

M54	319	14	Ordinary	(1) Bright blue	£500	£200
				(2) Blue	£475	£200 ✓
Block of four £2000	£1000			(3) Deep blue	£475	£200

Perforation 14
Types V1   V1A

Plate Descriptions

Official Pl. No.	S.G. Pl. No.	Features

The 112 set plate comprises two panes each of 56 stamps (7 horizontal rows of 8).

1/73   1   No marking
(a) blue dots added in the margins above and below the last vertical row in each pane. Upper pane with very fine cuts added under the gutter between the 7th and 8th stamps, in the bottom row (sometimes almost entirely removed during perforation). Lower pane cuts are larger and appear under the corner square of the 7th stamp bottom row
(b) cuts in state (a) filled up and cuts made under the last stamp in the bottom row of both panes

Printings and Price Schedule

Series	Date	Plate	Position			Price	
De La Rue						Top pane	Bottom pane
1	1902/10	1	S.E. corner pair	..	..	£950	£950
Somerset House							
With 1911 date cuts under 7th stamp							
1st	Jan. 1912	1a	S.E. corner pair	..	..	..	—	—
With 1912 date cuts under 8th stamp							
2nd	July 1912	1b	S.E. corner pair	..	..	..	£950	£950

1902-11. £1 Green, Type M18

Cat. No.	S.G. No.	Perf.	Paper	Shades	Unused	Used

1902 (JULY 16). GREEN. PERF. 14. DE LA RUE

M55	266	14	Ordinary	(1) Dull blue-green	£1100	£300

	Block of four	£4500
a.	Watermark inverted ..	£15000
s.	"Specimen", Type 16 ..	£400
t.	"Specimen", Type 17 ..	£1000

Imprimatur: £6500

Perforation 14
Type H1 only

Essays from the De La Rue Archives. Photographic essays in stamp size on card:

As illustrated above, submitted to the Controller on 14 May 1901 .. .. £1200
In approved design, submitted to the Controller on 23 May 1901 .. .. £750

Die Proofs in black on white glazed card :—

Without marking	£1300	
Endorsed " BEFORE HARD-ENING 16 DEC 01 " ..	£1100	As last but additional M/S " AC. 19 DEC 01 " £1100
Endorsed " AFTER HARDEN-ING 19 DEC 01 "	£1100	Endorsed "AFTER HARDEN-ING 13 MAR 02 " £1100

Piece Cut from the Striking Book

For notes see under ½d. value.

Struck on plain paper cut to size with various endorsements comprising dates,
plates 1 and 2 and leads

£1 value £850

1911 (SEPTEMBER 3). GREEN. PERF. 14. SOMERSET HOUSE

M56	320	14	Ordinary	(1) Deep green	£1100	£275

	Block of four	£4500
a.	Imperf.	
s.	" Specimen ", Type 22 ..	£600

Perforation 14
Types H2 (f or g) H2A (f or g)

Plate Descriptions

Official Pl. No.	S.G. Pl. No.	Features

The 80 set plate comprises two panes each of 40 stamps (10 horizontal rows of 4).

1/106	1	No marking
		(a) date cuts added under the 4th stamp bottom row of both panes
		(b) cuts in state (a) filled up and a white dot made in the rules above and below the last stamp in the 4th vertical rows of both panes.

Somerset House did not add marginal dots for this value.

Printings and Price Schedule

Series	Date	Plate	Position			Top pane	Bottom pane
De La Rue						Price	
I	1902/10	I	S.E. corner single	↔	••	£1100	£1100
Somerset House							
With 1911 date cuts under 4th stamp							
1st	Sept. 1911	1a	S.E. corner single	••	••	••	£1100	£1100
With 1912 date dot under 4th stamp							
2nd	April 1912	1b	S.E. or N.E. corner single	••		••	£1100	£1100

£1 GREEN, THE "LOWDEN" FORGERY

Produced by photo lithography, and usually found affixed to brown paper with a forged Channel Islands postmark. The watermark was impressed on the surface of the paper, therefore it washes off when the brown paper is soaked off. The stamp is a good imitation of the Somerset House shade, but the impression is coarser than that of the original and the lines of shading are faint and broken. Price £500.

£5 (Unissued)

Essay from the De La Rue Archives.   Photographic essay in stamp size on card:

As illustrated above, submitted to the Controller on 14 May 1901   ••   ••   ••   ••   £1500

Die Proofs in black on white glazed card:—

Endorsed " BEFORE HARDENING 11 MAR 02 "   ••   ••   ••   •• £2500

Endorsed " AFTER HARDENING 13 MAR 1902 "   ••   ••   •• £2500

Endorsed in M/S " Proof of Die prepared but not registered as it was resolved to discontinue the £5 stamp/1902 "   ••   ••   ••   ••   ••   •• £2500

Piece Cut from the Striking Book

For notes see under ½d. value.

Struck on plain paper cut to size in design similar to 1882 issue but with King Edward VII portrait surmounted by Crown

£5 value endorsed in red " After this die was made the G.P.O. decided not to issue a £5 Duty/Charged Mar 12th 02 " and ruled through in red and stamped " 13 MAR 02 "   •• £2000

SECTION MB

Departmental Official Issues (1902-04)

INTRODUCTION. These stamps are overprinted with the name of a Department and in most cases, the word "OFFICIAL". They were for the sole use of essentially autonomous Government Departments. The only stamps which had general use were those overprinted "Government Parcels" which were supplied to, and used by, all Departments.

Certain offices in London, Edinburgh and Dublin were designated Department Head Offices. They enjoyed essentially free use of letter post by right and did not have to use postage stamps on outgoing mail with most incoming mail similarly allowed to pass free. Since there was no weight limit on letter post—heavy packets caused the Post Office severe problems over many years. When Parcel Post was introduced in 1883 these were mitigated by the free issue of Government Parcels overprints. All Government Offices received them free whether Head Office, or "Local". Mail from Head Offices had to be certified externally on each item that it was on Departmental business. At first this was done by manuscript, handstamped or even printed facsimile signatures, but those were phased-out from the 1850's until, by 1900, practically all Departments used handstamped "cachets", certifying or franking stamps. Some of the larger Departments had branch offices outside the three capital cities which had to purchase postage stamps for their mail with cash from post offices.

In 1882 the Inland Revenue was allowed to have its own "I.R. OFFICIAL" overprinted stamps subject only to quarterly returns of the numbers and value of those used. This meant a loss of P.O. cash receipts and set a precedent which effectively blocked the use of overprints by other Departments for many years. In 1896 the Army and the Office of Works (a very small Department) were allowed to use their own stamps, but only on cash payment at the time of issue from Somerset House to the using Department. This prevented a direct loss of cash flow and set a new precedent which was followed in 1902 and 1903 by the Board of Education and the Navy.

None of these Departmental overprints were supposed to be sold, or otherwise made available, to the public in unused condition. The Inland Revenue and the Army did, however, employ non-civil servants to carry out some of their business and the definition of who was entitled to obtain official stamps by Act was impossible. No civil servant who released unused Departmental overprints to the public was deemed to be guilty of any legal offence. So there was a traffic in such overprints, especially those widely used like the Government Parcels stamps. In addition certain philatelists probably received regular supplies of the Inland Revenue overprints. No other mechanism can account for the numbers of such stamps as the mint £1 Official on Orbs paper (SG O12) around today. This practice came to the knowledge of the then Chairman of the Board of Inland Revenue and in 1896 he formulated specific regulations for his staff which were intended to prevent the trade. The effect of these measures was to drive it underground where it continued, although on a reduced scale. In 1903 a series of events led to this trade being terminated. In September of that year W. Richards, a senior Inland Revenue employee, and A. B. Creeke, the well-known philatelist, were convicted of a technical offence in connection with the supply of I.R. Official overprints and imprisoned.

Events in the Inland Revenue did not necessarily reflect the situation in other Departments since they were all effectively autonomous. The Treasury was concerned by the premium over face value of unused overprints offered by stamp dealers and they wished to rectify the situation. A Committee was set up and it recommended the immediate withdrawal of all Departmental overprints. The official date was 13 May 1904, but because so many are dated May 14, that day is generally regarded by collectors as the last day of general authorised usage. For purely administrative reasons some usage after 13 May was tolerated. This tolerance ended in mid-July; any examples used after then must be regarded with the utmost suspicion.

Direct revenue to the Post Office substantially increased in spite of an incentive to all Departments in the form of a 25% discount on purchases of postage stamps. In the meantime, the Inland Revenue had secured use of printed "Official Paid" franks, later Official/crown/paid "logos". Gradually more Inland Revenue local offices began to use them and direct revenue was again lost by local post offices. New social legislation—Labour Exchanges, National Insurance and so on—produced a whole new series of local offices with enormous demands on the post. They were authorised to use the same system of franks and from then on nothing could stop their spread to all Departments who wished to use them.

By 1914 a virtually uniform official mail existed across all Departments at great loss of direct revenue to the Post Office. This system of official mail lasted until very recent times, when its inefficiencies were at last realised. Now, Government mail is little if any different from that of any other large user. Proper postage budgets are needed and the Post Office is fully re-imbursed for its services.

All the stamps listed were printed and overprinted by Thomas De La Rue on ordinary paper. Types **L1**, **L6a** and **L10** were derived from die-struck leads and the other overprints were probably printed from electros developed by repeating rows of hand-set type. All stamps were perforated 14. The ½d. to 1s. have watermark **W12** (Crown); 2s. 6d., 5s., and 10s. have watermark **W9** (Anchor). The £1 has three Crown watermarks on each stamp.

WARNING. Many of the Official stamps may be found with forged overprints and collectors should be on their guard when buying. Some of the forgeries are easy to detect but to determine the genuineness of the overprint requires the use of modern highly sophisticated equipment. It is therefore recommended that these stamps should be purchased only when supported by R.P.S. or B.P.F. certificates dated subsequent to 1973.

Inland Revenue

These stamps were used by revenue officials in the provinces, mail to and from Head Office passing without a stamp. The London office used these stamps only for foreign mail. A Post Office Circular dated 26 September 1882, contained the following notice: "The Postmaster-General has approved of the use, on and after 1st October next, of stamps overprinted I.R. Official, for denoting the Postage and Registration Fees on letters transmitted by certain officers of Inland Revenue, stationed outside the metropolis . . ."

Many of the dates of issue are from Wright and Creeke or from the contemporary philatelic press. Unlike the postage stamps these issues for Departments were not generally available to the public.

I.R.   I. R.

OFFICIAL   OFFICIAL
·L1   L2

Cat. No.	S.G. No.	Date		Stamp optd.	Description	Unused	Used

1902-04. STAMPS OF 1902 OVERPRINTED WITH TYPE L1 (½d. to 1s.) or TYPE L2 (5s., 10s., £1).

MO1	O20	4.2.1902		M1	½d. Blue-green	15·00 ✓	1·50 ✓
	Block of four	.. .. 75·00	15·00				
	Used on cover	.. .. †	40·00				
s.	"Specimen", Type 15 ..	£225†					
MO2	O21	4.2.1902		M5	1d. Scarlet	10·00 ✓	70 ✓
	Block of four	.. .. 50·00	15·00				
	Used on cover	.. .. †	40·00				
s.	"Specimen", Type 15 ..	£225†					
MO3	O22	19.2.1902		M16	2½d. Ultramarine	£400	60·00
	Block of four	.. .. £3000	£350				
s.	"Specimen", Type 15 ..	£325					
t.	"Specimen", Type 16 ..	£275†					
MO4	O23	14.3.1904		M31	6d. Dull purple	£85000	£65000
s.	"Specimen", Type 16 ..	£9000					
MO5	O24	29.4.1902		M45	1s. Green and carmine	£500	65·00
	Block of four	.. .. £3000	£400				
s.	"Specimen", Type 16 ..	£400†					
MO6	O25	29.4.1902		M51	5s. Carmine	£4000	£1300
a.	Raised stop after "R" ..	£4500	£1500				
s.	"Specimen", Type 16 ..	£1200†					
MO7	O26	29.4.1902		M53	10s. Ultramarine	£15000	£9500
a.	Raised stop after "R" ..	£17000	£11000				
s.	"Specimen", Type 16 ..	£3250†					
MO8	O27	29.4.1902		M55	£1 Dull blue-green	£12000	£6000
s.	"Specimen", Type 16 ..	£2750†					

†Nos. MO1s, MO2s, MO3t, MO5s, MO6s, MO7s and MO8s exist from NPM archive sales.

No. MO4. Instructions were issued within the Inland Revenue Department that used copies of No. MO4 were to be so heavily cancelled that they would be worthless to collectors with the result that practically all used copies of this stamp, which are in any case very rare indeed, are of very poor quality.

Controls

½d. Continuous A	75·00
½d. Continuous B	75·00
1d. Continuous A	60·00
1d. Continuous B	60·00

Plates used

½d. A control plate 65 (left), 3 (right), B control 13 (left), 67 (right)
1d. A control plate 5 and 17 (left), 6 and 68a (right), B control 3b (left), 10 (right)

Cancelled overprints from the National Postal Museum Archives

Perforated 14, watermark Type W12. Overprint as Type L1

6d. value (No. MO4) overprinted "Cancelled", Type 18

Perforated 14, watermark Type W9. Overprint as Type L2

5s. value (No. MO6) overprinted "Cancelled", Type 18
10s. value (No. MO7) overprinted "Cancelled", Type 18

Perforated 14, watermark three Crowns as Type W12. Overprint as Type L2

£1 value (No. MO8) overprinted "Cancelled", Type 18

Government Parcels

Government Parcels overprints were created by the Post Office to encourage all Departments to send parcels by parcel post and not letter post which for many of them was free. In consequence these stamps also were provided free. They were originally intended to be used on parcels between 3 lbs (pounds) and 7 lbs, but by the reign of King Edward VII these limits were ignored, although they were never formally changed.

These overprints had no connection with the calculation of the proportion of money raised by parcel post due to the Railways. That was found by "sampling" which automatically took into account the proportion of Government parcels.

Use ceased on 14 May 1904 when surplus stocks were called in. Fine used examples are difficult to find as the majority of those used were cancelled with the normal heavy rubber parcel post marks.

GOVᵀ
PARCELS
L3

Cat. No.	S.G. No.	Date		Stamp optd.	Description	Unused	Used

1902. STAMPS OF 1902 OVERPRINTED WITH TYPE L3

Cat. No.	S.G. No.	Date			Stamp optd.	Description	Unused	Used
MO9	O74	30.10.1902			M5	1d. Scarlet	15·00	5·00
	Block of four ..	..	..	90·00	50·00			
a.	Open top loop to "S"		..					
b.	Thick "VT" ..	..	..					
c.	Large "C" ..	..	..					
d.	"PA" close ..	..	..					
s.	"Specimen", Type 16		..	75·00†				
MO10	O75	29.4.1902			M11	2d. Green and carmine	65·00	15·00
	Block of four ..	..	..	£400	£120			
a.	Open top loop to "S"		..					
b.	Thick "VT" ..	..	..					
c.	Large "C" ..	..	..					
d.	"PA" close ..	..	..					
s.	"Specimen", Type 16		..	75·00†				
MO11	O76	19.2.1902			M31	6d. Dull purple	£100	15·00 ✔
	Block of four ..	..	..	£600	£120			
a.	Open top loop to "S"		..					
b.	Thick "VT" ..	..	..					
c.	Large "C" ..	..	..					
d.	"PA" close ..	..	..					
e.	Overprint double, one albino							
s.	"Specimen", Type 15		..	£100				
t.	"Specimen", Type 16		..	£130				
MO12	O77	28.8.1902			M39	9d. Purple and ultramarine	£225	50·00 ✔
	Block of four ..	..	..	£1500	£350			
a.	Open top loop to "S"		..					
s.	"Specimen", Type 16		..	£225†				
MO13	O78	17.12.1902			M45	1s. Green and carmine	£350	85·00
	Block of four ..	..	..	£2000	£600			
s.	"Specimen", Type 16		..	£225†				

†Nos. MO9*s*, MO10*s*, MO12*s* and MO13*s* exist from NPM archive sales.

Control
1d. Continuous A   £300

S	**Vᴛ**	**RCE**	**PA**
Var. *a*	Var. *b*	Var. *c*	Var. *d*
(R. 19/8)	(R. 15/12)	(R. 20/3)	(R. 20/8)

Variety *a* is also found on the 9d. (MO12), R. 2/1 every pane.

Office of Works

"O.W. Official" overprints on the 1887 ½d. and the 1881 1d. were first issued on 24 March 1896 with King Edward VII ½d. and 1d. stamps being overprinted in February 1902. Overprints were issued to Head and Branch (local) offices in London and to Branch (local) offices at Birmingham, Bristol, Edinburgh, Glasgow, Leeds, Liverpool and Manchester. About 95% of all genuine used overprints (of the ½d. and 1d.) bear postmarks from those cities. Used copies from other places, including Southampton, are less common and many bear forged overprints. No genuine example showing Covent Garden c.d.s. has yet been seen.

The overprints on stamps of value 2d. and upwards were created later in 1902, the 2d. for registration fees and the rest for overseas mail. Since the King Edward VII 5d. and 10d. stamps had not been created when requests for those values came in, the overprints were made on the corresponding Queen Victoria stamps.

O. W.

OFFICIAL

L4

PRICES FOR STAMPS IN USED CONDITION
For well-centred lightly used examples of Nos. MO14/18, add **25%** to each of the used prices.

1902-03. STAMPS OF 1902 OVERPRINTED WITH TYPE L4.

MO14	O36	11.2.1902		M1	½d. Blue-green	£350	80·00
Block of four		..	..	£1600	£475			
Used on cover	..	..	†	£850				
s.	" Specimen ", Type 15	..	£225†					
MO15	O37	11.2.1902		M5	1d. Scarlet	£350	80·00 ✓
Block of four		..	£1600	£475				
Used on cover	..	..	†	£150				
s.	" Specimen ", Type 15	..	£225†					
MO16	O38	29.4.1902		M11	2d. Green and carmine	£600	75·00
Block of four	..		—	†				
Used on cover	..	..	†	£1100				
a.	" C.W." for " O.W."	..	£650	£350				
s.	" Specimen ", Type 16	..	£400					
MO17	O39	29.4.1902		M16	2½d. Ultramarine	£700	£200
Block of four	..			†				
a.	" C.W." for " O.W."	..	£2000	£450				
s.	" Specimen ", Type 16	..	£475					
MO18	O40	28.5.1903		M42	10d. Purple and carmine	£5000	£1500
Block of four		..	—	†				
s.	" Specimen ", Type 16	..	£1800					
t.	" Cancelled ", Type 18	..	£2500					

†Nos. MO14s and MO15s exist from NPM archive sales.

C. W.

MO16a, MO17a (R. 10/3 and 20/3)

Controls

½d. Continuous	A	£1100
½d. Continuous	B	£1100
1d. Continuous	A	£1100
1d. Continuous	B	£1100

Plates used

½d. A and B plate 67, 1d. A plates 11 (left) and 75 (right), B plates U109 (left)* 87 (right)
*U109 is a rare plate which has not yet been assigned a plate number by researchers. It may be a state of an already known plate or it may be a totally new one.

Army

"Army Official" overprints were first issued on 1 September 1896 for use by District and Station Paymasters nationwide including Cox and Co, the Army Agents, who were Paymasters to the Household Division. In due course usage spread to other Army establishments. A considerable trade developed in mint Army Official stamps which was largely suppressed by mid-1902.

ARMY	ARMY
OFFICIAL	OFFICIAL
L5	**L6a**

Cat. No.	S.G. No.	Date	Stamp optd.	Description	Unused	Used

1902. STAMPS OF 1902 OVERPRINTED WITH TYPE L5.

Cat. No.	S.G. No.	Date	Stamp optd.	Description	Unused	Used
MO19	O48	11.2.1902		M1	½d. Blue-green	1·75 ✓	65 ✓
	Block of four		11·00	10·00		
	Used on cover		†	50·00		
e.	Long left leg to "A" in "ARMY"		10·00	5·00		
f.	Very short left leg to "A" in "ARMY"		10·00	5·00		
h.	Splayed "Y"		10·00	5·00		
j.	Long top to second "F" ..		10·00	5·00		
m.	Tall "L"		10·00	5·00		
q.	"C" for "O"					
r.	Short "Y"			✓		
s.	"Specimen", Type 15 ..		£110†			
MO20	O49	11.2.1902		M5	1d. Scarlet	1·25	55 ✓
	Block of four		7·50 ✓	10·00		
	Used on cover		†	50·00		
a.	"ARMY" omitted					
f.	Very short left leg to "A" in "ARMY"		10·00	5·00		
h.	Splayed "Y"		10·00	5·00 ✓		
j.	Long top to second "F" ..		10·00	5·00		
m.	Tall "L"		10·00	5·00		
p.	Shaved top to "ARM" ..		10·00	5·00		
q.	"C" for "O"					
r.	Short "Y"			✓		
s.	"Specimen", Type 15 ..		£120†			
MO21	O50	23.8.1902		M31	6d. Dull purple ✓	60·00	30·00 ✓
	Block of four		£600	£400		
e.	Long left leg to "A" in "ARMY"		85·00	50·00		
f.	Very short left leg to "A" in "ARMY"		85·00	50·00		
h.	Splayed "Y"		85·00	50·00		
j.	Long top to second "F" ..		85·00	50·00		
m.	Tall "L"		85·00	50·00		
s.	"Specimen", Type 16 ..		£150†			

†Nos. MO19*s*, MO20*s* and MO21*s* exist from NPM archive sales.

AR	ARM	Y	FF	L	ARM
Var. *e*	Var. *f*	Var. *h*	Var. *j*	Var. *m*	Var. *p*
(R. 14/4)	(R. 14/4)	(R. 2/3)	(R. 20/11)	(R. 10/2)	(R. 4/12)

CF	ARMY
Var. *q*	Var. *r*
(R. 10/10)	(R. 10/11)

King Edward VII stamps were overprinted from an overprint plate known as "forme 2" which by 1903 had become very worn. A new plate, known as "forme 4", made from a die was created and used to overprint the 6d. in 1903, but overprints were withdrawn before it could be used for the two low values.

During February 1902 "forme 2" was overhauled and a number of varieties, including variety *e* (R. 14/4), were removed from it. Some sheets of the ½d. had, however, already been overprinted. The forme was corrected to variety *f*. Varieties *j* and *m* were on the original plate, but were not removed. Variety *p* arose later, as did many others. Variety *q*, C for O (R. 10/10), occurred during the 17th overprinting in September 1902 and was reported in the 31 July 1903 issue of the *Gibbons Monthly Journal*. It was corrected for the 18th, and last, overprinting from "forme 2". Variety *r* is L 36*i*/38*i* on the Queen Victoria stamps ("short" Y—actually tall ARM), and also occurs on all three "forme 2" King Edward VII overprints.

Controls

½d. Continuous	A	50·00	
½d. Continuous	B	75·00	
1d. Continuous	A	50·00	
1d. Continuous	B	75·00	

Plates used

½d. A control—4(R*), 5(L* and R), 65(L), 66(L), 67(R), 69(L). B control—2a(R), 9(L).
1d. A control—1(L and R), 2a(L), 5(L), 6(R), 11(L and R), 14(L), 16(R), 68(R), 69(L), 70(R), 73(R), 79(L), 80(L and R), 88a(L).
*R = right sheet, L = left sheet.

1903 (SEPTEMBER). STAMP OF 1902 OVERPRINTED WITH TYPE L6a.

MO22	O52	—.12.1903	M31	6d. Dull purple		£850	£275

Block of four ..	..	..	£7000	

Die Proof. In black on white glazed card:
Type L6a endorsed "23 Mar 03"   £900

Board of Education

First issued in the reign of King Edward VII, stamps overprinted for the Board of Education were available on 19 February 1902. Since the 5d. and 1s. showing King Edward VII were not ready, stamps bearing Queen Victoria's portrait were used. These two stamps are listed in Volume 1 of this Catalogue.

BOARD

OF

EDUCATION

L7

Cat. No.	S.G. No.	Date	Stamp optd.	Description	Unused	Used
1902-04.	**STAMPS OF 1902 OVERPRINTED WITH TYPE L7.**					
MO23	O83	19.2.1902	M1	½d. Blue-green	16·00	7·00
	Block of four .. .. £100 30·00					
	Used on cover .. .. † £175					
	s. " Specimen ", Type 15 .. £130					
MO24	O84	19.2.1902	M5	1d. Scarlet	16·00	6·00 ✓
	Block of four .. .. £100 30·00					
	Used on cover .. .. † £125					
	s. " Specimen ", Type 15 .. £130					
MO25	O85	19.2.1902	M16	2½d. Ultramarine	£500	50·00 ✓
	Block of four £3500					450
	s. " Specimen ", Type 15 .. £130					
MO26	O86	6.2.1904	M28	5d. Purple and blue	£2000	£950
	s. " Specimen ", Type 16 .. £325					
	t. " Cancelled " Type 18 .. £500					
MO27	O87	23.12.1902	M45	1s. Green and carmine	£25000	£15000 ✓
	s. " Specimen ", Type 16 .. £3250					

Controls

½d. Continuous A   £200
1d. Continuous A

Cancelled overprint from the National Postal Museum Archives

Perforated 14, watermark Type W12. Overprint as Type L7

1s. value (No. MO27) overprinted " Cancelled ", Type 18

Royal Household

Only the ½d. and 1d. King Edward VII issue were overprinted in 1902. These were for the use of Heads of the Royal Households in the various Royal Palaces. They were overprinted in black by De La Rue.

R.H.

OFFICIAL
L8

Cat. No.	S.G. No.	Date		Stamp optd.	Description	Unused	Used
1902.	**STAMPS**	**OF 1902 OVERPRINTED WITH TYPE L8.**					
MO28	O91	29.4.1902		M1	½d. Blue-green	£150	95·00
	Block of four	.. .. £1200					
	Used on cover	.. .. †	£400				
	s. "Specimen", Type 16 ..	£450					
MO29	O92	19.2.1902		M5	1d. Scarlet	£130	85·00 ✓
	Block of four	.. .. £1100					
	Used on cover	.. .. †	£300				
	s. "Specimen", Type 15 ..	£450†					

†No. MO29*s* exists from NPM archive sales.

Controls

½d. Continuous A   £750
1d. Continuous A   £700

Admiralty

These were for use in the various Admiralty Departments throughout the country and they were overprinted in black by De La Rue. The first overprint was made in 1903 (Type **L9**) but soon after it was found that this electro was damaged and it was remade using a thicker type in a slightly narrower setting (Type **L10**).

ADMIRALTY   ADMIRALTY

OFFICIAL   OFFICIAL
L9   L10

1902 (MARCH 3). STAMPS OF 1902 OVERPRINTED WITH TYPE L9.

Cat. No.	S.G. No.	Date			Stamp optd.	Description	Unused	Used
MO30	O101	3.3.1903			M1	½d. Blue-green	9·00 ✓	3·00 ✓
	Block of four	.. .. 40·00	20·00					
	Used on cover	.. .. †	£225					
	s. "Specimen", Type 16 ..	£130						
MO31	O102	3.3.1903			M5	1d. Scarlet	5·00 ✓	2·50 ✓
	Block of four	.. .. 35·00	15·00					
	Used on cover	.. .. †	50·00					
	s. "Specimen", Type 16 ..	£130						
MO32	O103	3.3.1903			M8	1½d. Purple and green	60·00	40·00 ✓
	Block of four	.. .. £550	£500					
	s. "Specimen", Type 16 ..	£150						

MO33   O104   3.3.1903   M11   2d. Green and carmine   £100   50·00 ✓
  Block of four £800   £500
s. " Specimen ", Type 16 ..   £150†

MO34   O105   3.3.1903   M16   2½d. Ultramarine   £120   40·00
  Block of four £950   £400
s. " Specimen ", Type 16 ..   £150

MO35   O106   3.3.1903   M19   3d. Purple on yellow   £100   35·00
  Block of four £1250   £350
s. " Specimen ", Type 16 ..   £150

†No. MO33s exists from NPM archive sales.

Controls

½d. Continuous A*
½d. Continuous B   £100
1d. Continuous A*
1d. Continuous B   80·00

   * The existence of these Controls has been previously reported but has not been confirmed during recent research. The Editor would be grateful to receive any evidence of their existence.

Cat. No.	S.G. No.	Date	Stamp optd.	Description	Unused	Used

1903-04. STAMPS OF 1902 OVERPRINTED WITH TYPE L10.

MO36   O107   –.9.1903   M1   ½d. Blue-green   7·00 ✓   4·00 ✓
  Block of four   ..   ..   45·00   25·00
  Used on cover   ..   ..   †   £250
s. " Specimen ", Type 16 ..   £130

MO37   O108   –.11.1903   M5   1d. Scarlet   6·50   3·50 ✓
  Block of four   ..   ..   40·00   22·00
  Used on cover   ..   ..   †   50·00
s. " Specimen ", Type 16 ..   £130

MO38   O109   –.2.1904   M8   1½d. Purple and green   £175   50·00
  Block of four £1850   £750

MO39   O110   –.3.1904   M11   2d. Green and carmine   £400   £100
  Block of four £3000   £700
s. " Specimen ", Type 16 ..   £225†

MO40   O111   –.3.1904   M16   2½d. Ultramarine   £450   £225
  Block of four £4000

MO41   O112   –.2.1904   M19   3d. Purple on yellow   £350   85·00
  Block of four £2750   £400
s. " Specimen ", Type 16 ..   £200†

†Nos. MO39s and MO41s exist from NPM archive sales.

Controls

½d. Continuous B   85·00
1d. Continuous B   70·00

Die Proof. In black on white glazed card:
  Type L10 endorsed "27 MAR 03"   £750

Specimen overprint from the National Postal Museum Archives

  Perforated 14, watermark Type W12. Overprint as Type L10
  2½d. value (No. MO40) overprinted " Specimen ", Type 16

Board of Trade

This Department was the first to use official stamps. Instead of overprinting current stamps they were perforated with a " Crown " over the letters " B.T.". Unfortunately insufficient information or records exist to make a complete listing but all values from ½d. to 1s. were so perforated. Collectors should be warned that no less than ten different forgeries have been recorded of this " perforated " variety.

Stationery Office

Following the Board of Trade's practice in perforating current postage stamps for departmental mail, the Stationery Office perforated their supplies of postage stamps with a " Crown " over the letters " S.O.". Similarly no official records have been seen to give complete details.

" C.A. " Overprints

In 1903 the 1d. Scarlet was overprinted in black with the letters " C.A." (4·5 mm. high 10·5 mm. long); later the 6d. Dull Purple also appeared with this overprint. A cover is also known bearing a 1d. Downey Head Die 1B stamp bearing this overprint and post-marked " 11 JAN 12". It had been generally assumed that these initials referred to the Crown Agents but they denied ever having issued stamps with this overprint. It is now established that the overprints were made at Australia House as receipt stamps and refer to "Commonwealth of Australia".

No. M5 1d. scarlet overprinted "C.A." *price £50* unused.

For other overprints see Appendix 5 in this Catalogue.

The King George V Issues

General Notes on the Typographed Issues

INTRODUCTION. King George V came to the throne on 6 May, 1910, and late in June the Postmaster General invited designs for a new series of stamps. Those selected were by two artists who worked from a three-quarter face photograph of the King by W. & D. Downey, the Court photographers. This series was discontinued after 18 months.

A second series of stamps was prepared with the King's head in full profile. The issue of stamps in this series was not completed until August 1913, and these designs remained basically unaltered for the rest of the reign.

ARRANGEMENT. The typographed issues of King George V are arranged as follows:

The Downey Head issue (1911–12)	Section NA
The Profile Head Issue, Wmk Royal Cypher (1912–22)	Section NB
The Profile Head Issue, Wmk Block Cypher (1924–26)	Section NC
Postal Union Congress Commemoratives, ½d., 1d., 1½d., 2½d. (1929)	in Section NF

PRINTERS. Harrison & Sons held the contract for printing the typographed stamps until 1924, and from 1924 until 1933 these stamps were printed by Waterlow and Sons.

Harrison & Sons, who regained the contract in 1934, were to have produced a new set of stamps by the photogravure process. They were, however, unable to get this process under way in time to supply the new stamps before the existing stock of typographed stamps would have become exhausted. In consequence Harrison's made provisional printings by typography, aided in the initial stages by Waterlow.

Preliminary printings of most values were made at Somerset House during 1912-13, and the government printers also were solely responsible for supplies of the 6d. value from 1913-33.

PLATES AND PRINTING. The plates were electrotyped as described in the General Notes on the King Edward VII issues. Initially they were produced by the Royal Mint, the first plates being steel-faced but later they were nickel-faced to combat wear. Eventually Harrison & Sons produced their own plates.

Almost every plate, at some time during its use, carried a marking either deliberately or accidentally made in the marginal rule. These marks were made by the operators for their own guidance for various purposes and serve in plate identification. They consist of cuts and dots made in the marginal rules and examples of these are shown in the General Notes on the King Edward VII issues under "Plate Markings". Reference should be made to these notes in order to follow the descriptions used for the King George V issues.

The research work initiated by the late Lt.-Col. Stanton is chronicled as an appendix to the *Stamps of Great Britain, Part IV*, published by the Royal Philatelic Society. The listings in this catalogue incorporate the result of many years' study of new discoveries by the Great Britain Philatelic Society.

This has entailed much regrouping and re-numbering, but as far as possible the lists keep to the same arbitrary plate numbers as were first laid down in the R.P.S. book. New discoveries are still being made, and the listings are being amplified or amended with each new edition.

SHEET LAYOUT

Harrison 1911 contract. Each sheet consisted of 240 stamps arranged in two panes of 120; the panes contained 10 horizontal rows of 12 stamps, and were separated horizontally from one another by an interpane gutter containing "pillars".

The ½d. and 1d. plates of 1911-12 (Dies 1 and 2) and a few 2d. Die 1 plates had marginal rules as for the K.E.VII ½d. and 1d.; that, is co-extensive, with breaks at top above the 6th and 7th stamps and at bottom below the 6th and 7th stamps, with no break between them.

The issues of 1912-22 had coextensive lines all round the panes.

Waterlow 1924 contract. Each plate contained 240 stamps in 20 rows of 12, with no divisions between the halves.   There was an arrow in each side margin between the 10th and 11th rows.

When Waterlow took over the contract in 1924 they used several of the Harrison plates modified so as to conform with the new layout.   The interpane gutter was removed, and the two halves of the plate brought together.

Somerset House 6d.   Until 1924 the arrangement was the same as for the Harrison 1911 contract.   In 1925 this was changed to conform with the arrangement used by Waterlow.

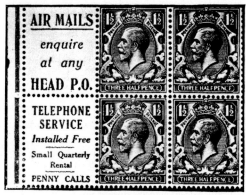

Advertisement Pane

Booklet Panes. The same arrangement as given for King Edward VII.   For the advertisement panes, a special plate was made having two vertical blanks on the binding edge of each pane.   The advertisements were printed at a separate operation.

PAPER. The Crown watermark paper continued to be made by R. D. Turner & Co. Paper with the Simple Cypher watermark was made by William Joynson and that with the Multiple Cypher watermark by Basted Mills.   All these papers were gummed by Samuel Jones and from about the end of 1912 they were plate-glazed as well, which greatly improved the quality of the printing. Reference should be made to the General Notes on the King Edward VII issues under "Types of Paper: Post January 1911 paper".

This good standard of paper continued in use up to 1916. During and after the War period from 1917 to about 1921 the quality varied and, as a result of poorer calendry, the printings assumed a coarser and duller appearance. In 1922 the general appearance of the stamps returned to the earlier high standards.

In 1911 an experimental printing of the 1d. stamp was made on chalk-surfaced paper. Chalk-surfaced paper was used for the 6d. value up to 1925 and again in 1936, for a short period in the Harrison printings.

No. 7.

INTRODUCTION OF

GEORGE V. POSTAGE STAMPS

SALE OF LETTER CARDS, THIN POST-CARDS AND BOOKS OF STAMPS AT FACE VALUE.

REDUCTION IN PRICES OF EMBOSSED ENVELOPES & WRAPPERS

Halfpenny and Penny adhesive Postage Stamps of new design bearing the effigy of His Majesty King George, and registered letter envelopes and thin post-cards bearing impressed stamps with the same effigy, will be placed on sale on the 22nd of June, the day of His Majesty's Coronation, at all Post Offices open on that day. At other Post Offices they will first be sold on the 23rd of June, or, at Offices which are closed on that day also, on the 24th of June. New adhesive stamps of other denominations and other articles of stationery bearing impressed stamps of new design will be issued as soon as possible afterwards.

Adhesive postage stamps and stamped stationery of the present issue will also be on sale at Post Offices until the remaining stocks are exhausted. All Edward VII. postage stamps and all stamps of previous issues which are at present available in payment of postage will still be available.

The following reductions in the prices of the principal articles of stamped stationery, WHICH WILL APPLY TO ARTICLES BOTH OF THE PRESENT AND THE NEW ISSUES, will take effect on Coronation Day:

POST-CARDS.—Thin post-cards bearing ½d. stamp ½d. each. (Stout post-cards will continue to be sold at 6d. a packet of 11, or ¼d. for a single card).

LETTER CARDS bearing 1d. stamp 1d. each.

BOOKS OF STAMPS. Books containing eighteen 1d. and twelve ½d. stamps of George V. design will be issued at an early date price 2s. each. Pending their issue the present books, containing eighteen 1d. and eleven ½d. stamps of Edward VII. design, will, on and after the 22nd of June, be sold for 1s. 11½d. instead of 2s. as at present.

EMBOSSED ENVELOPES.
Court size (bearing 1d. stamp) 1s. a packet of 11.
Commercial size (bearing 1d. stamp) 2s. a packet of 23.
Foolscap size (bearing ½d. stamp)—1s. a packet of 21.
Commercial size (bearing ½d. stamp) 1s. a packet of 22.

NEWSPAPER WRAPPERS. (Bearing ½d. stamp)—1s. a packet of 22. (Bearing 1d. stamp) 2s. a packet of 23.

All cards, envelopes and wrappers are sold in any quantities less than a complete packet at proportionate prices. Full tables of these prices will appear in the Post Office Guide issued on the 1st of July.

GENERAL POST OFFICE,
20th June, 1911.   **By Command of the Postmaster General.**

[1126]   Printed for His Majesty's Stationery Office by W. P. Griffith & Sons Ld., Prujean Square, Old Bailey, E.C.   6/11

Postal Notice Announcing King George V Stamps
to be issued on Coronation Day

(Illustration greatly reduced)

WATERMARKS. The watermarks used for the typographed issues of King George V are as follows *and are shown as seen from the front of the stamp:*

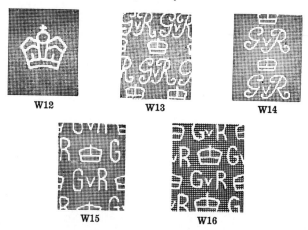

W12   W13   W14

W15   W16

Wmk W12. The Crown watermark used for the King Edward VII issues. The marginal watermarks also remain unchanged (*see under* "Recognising the Halves of the Mill Sheet" in the General Notes on the King Edward VII issues).

Wmk W13. The Multiple Cypher watermark, used for a short time with the ½d. and 1d. Downey Head Die 2 issues. In 1913, stocks of this paper were used for making up vertical rolls of ½d. and 1d. stamps for sale in slot machines (N15 and N17). Subsequently a sheet or part sheet of each value was found; blocks of four are known of both values.

Wmk W14. The Simple Cypher watermark. This is found with the three variations illustrated below.

Type I was used for the issues of 1912-13.

Type II was formerly thought to have been first introduced for the Profile Head stamps but has now been recorded on the ½d. of the Downey Head issue (N5) with Control B 13. It was in general use until 1917 and reappeared as the general watermark in the later issues from 1922 to 1924, but was also used occasionally between 1918 and 1921.

Type III was in general use from 1917 to 1922 and occasionally afterwards.

It seems probable that Types II and III are associated with the quality of paper. For example, the 8d. stamp on ordinary yellow paper is always Type II and the poorer quality granite paper, which appeared in 1917, is always Type III.

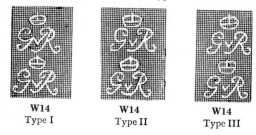

W14   W14   W14
Type I   Type II   Type III

The best method of collecting these watermark types is to obtain specimens from either the top or bottom margin of the sheet. The watermarks can then be seen more clearly.

It is not practical to quote prices for these watermark types but in Section NB details are given in footnotes of those known to exist.

In watermark **W14**, "POSTAGE" appears in the margins on both sides of each pane, as in the King Edward VII issues. Occasionally sheets were incorrectly fed into the printing press, resulting in the word "POSTAGE" appearing on five stamps of the first or the twelfth vertical rows. The remaining five stamps were either without watermark or showed a line.

Where they occur these misplaced watermarks are listed and priced either as single stamps showing letters from "POSTAGE" or as vertical strips sufficient to show the complete "POSTAGE" watermark.

Broken dandy roll varieties also occur on **W14** and prices quoted for these are for unused single stamps in the cheapest shade and with watermark upright.

Wmk W15. The Block Cypher watermark, used solely by Waterlow and Harrison (1934 contract).

Wmk W16. A variant of **W15** used with an experimental paper by Waterlow in 1924–25.

"Royal Cypher" Watermark. This term is used for convenience in the heading to Section NB and is taken to embrace both the Simple Cypher watermark (**W14**) and the Multiple Cypher watermark (**W13**).

Watermark Varieties. The following six illustrations show watermark varieties *as seen from the back of the stamp* and taking **W13** as an example:

Upright

Inverted

Reversed

Inverted and Reversed

Sideways

Sideways-inverted

Note that the watermarks on booklet stamps appeared upright or inverted in equal quantities. The prices quoted in this catalogue for N2a, N3b, N8a, N9a, N10b, N14c, N16b, N18b, N19b, N20b, N33a, N34b and N35c are for booklet stamps. The same stamps *from sheets* with watermark inverted command a substantial premium over these prices, but as evidence of their origin they need to have sheet margins attached or to be in a block or strip larger than 3 × 2 or of a different shape.

No Watermark. The 1½d. and 5d. 1912–22, and 2d. and 2½d., 1924–26, are from *whole* sheets completely without watermark. Similar varieties due to *watermark misplacement* are listed as, "Without watermark".

PERFORATION. All stamps in this section are comb-perforated 15 × 14 on the Grover machines, unless otherwise stated.

SHADES. The series of stamps issued during the years 1912–23 is notable for the wide range of colours and shades. In fact it is probable that no other series of stamps ever issued exhibits such an array.

The stamps issued in these years are treated as one issue, although ideally they should be separated into three groups.

    (a)   Issues of 1912–14
    (b)   The war period 1915–19
    (c)   Issues of 1920–24

The collection sorted in this manner reveals that the shades in groups (a) and (c) are fairly constant, and those in group (b) show great contrasts. However, for practical purposes the series has to be treated as one unit, as the colours of the three periods overlap and sharp lines of division cannot be drawn. The chief reason for the startling variations from the normal in group (b) is the fact that the World War of 1914–18 interrupted the supply of aniline dyes from Germany.

Early in 1916 experiments were carried out with British dyes, and printings of the ½d. and 1d. stamps are known in various shades of green and red overprinted "cancelled".

The compilation of the check-list has been a job of the utmost difficulty, particularly with the naming of the colours. In general we have adhered to the terms most familiar to philatelists, and wherever possible have described the colours in such a manner as to make them self-evident. We have not attempted to list every known shade and some of those given should be regarded as covering a range of intensity.

The controls give an indication of the time of printing. The figure refers to the year, and the letter to the first or second half of the year, i.e. K 18 indicates use during the first six months of 1918 and L 18 indicates use in the second half of 1918.

Due to the length of time this issue was at press, it is only possible to list the shades in colour groups. The rarer shades, because of their brief appearances, are more precise and distinctive, but the basic shades that traversed the span of twelve years will show minor variations of hue in the published descriptions.

Wherever possible, a rough indication of the year or years when the shade was in use has been noted. This has been made possible by a study of the controls, which indicate the year the plate was at press. Where no dates are given, it must be taken that the colour group is generally spread over the entire issue.

FUGITIVE INKS. Experiments with fugitive inks seem to have been made during 1919 and 1920. Many of the values change their appearance when immersed in water, and used specimens of a diffused hue are usually from these printings. The ½d. olive-green of 1916 is also highly fugitive, and produces a bright yellow-green after immersion in water.

COLOUR VARNISH. Printings in a heavy thick glossy ink are known on some ½d., 1d., 5d. and 1s. values. These varieties are listed as " varnish ink ", and are probably caused by inadequate mixing of the pigments by the printer. Other values in " varnish ink " are known, but until more information is known they are not listed here.

PROVISIONAL PRINTINGS. These are the printings made by both Waterlow and Harrison just prior to the issue of the photogravure stamps. For further information see *King George V. A Study of the Provisional Issues of 1934 and 1935* by J. B. M. Stanton and K. G. Rushworth.

COIL STAMPS. The experiments in the use of coil machines for selling stamps took place in the reign of King Edward VII and information about these is given in the General Notes there. By 1912 many machines had been installed using coils made up from sheets by their promoters. In 1913 the Post Office began issuing rolls of stamps manufactured by the printers. At first they were all made up from sheets with joins on the back at every tenth stamp in the case of vertical delivery rolls and every twelfth stamp for horizontal delivery rolls. As pairs with coil joins can easily be identified they are listed under the basic stamps.

In the Profile Head issue there was one experiment in making continuous rolls of the 1d. with the Simple Cypher watermark but in 1924 it was more common for the stamps with the Block Cypher watermark to be in continuous rolls. As these are more difficult to identify they are not individually listed. However we record details of all the coils issued, stating their code identification (as printed on the leader), the earliest known date of issue, number of stamps, total face value and method of delivery.

The price of the roll was stated on the coil leader and at first it was the practice to make a handling charge for rolls sold over the counter: 1d. for coils of 500 and 2d. for coils of 1000, but the charge varied from time to time so that sometimes a coil was reissued at a different price. Moreover, those used in the Kermode post office machines did not have any premium expressed and were generally labelled "KERMODE". From 1 September 1927 the charges were dropped and all coils were sold at face value. As this information is only of interest to specialists who collect coil leaders we record only the actual face value of the rolls, not the prices at which they were sold.

All the typographed coils normally have the watermark upright but obviously if sheets with inverted or reversed watermarks happened to be used in coil manufacture, inverted and reversed watermarks may be found on coil stamps but no attempt has been made to list these. Similarly plate varieties which occur on sheets may be found on coil stamps.

There are no precise dates of issue for coil stamps as a rule, particularly in the case of the early issues. It is assumed that in each case the first coil stamps were released about the same time as the relative sheet stamps (except where otherwise stated), and approximate dates are given for later issues.

CONTROLS. The system of controls was now extended to all values from $\frac{1}{2}$d. to 1s. As before, the control was screwed into the margin before printing, and removed when printing had ceased. The Somerset House controls all had a stop after the letter which enable these printings to be distinguished.

The controls are listed and priced after their respective values in the catalogue.

Position. The Control appears below the 2nd stamp in the bottom row, except for the 1d. value where it is beneath the 11th stamp.

Prices. Control pieces in Section NA are classified according to the perforation type. Therefore, as in the King Edward VII issues, they are priced for unused *corner pairs* with side and bottom selvedge intact.

Controls in Sections NB and NC (and Controls of the 1929 P.U.C. low values) are not at present classified according to perforation type, although this may be possible in a future edition. The priced lists are merely sub-divided into Controls with *imperforate* selvedge (abbreviated to "*I*".) and those with the selvedge *perforated through* (abbreviated to "*P*."). Partially perforated margins are regarded as imperforate.

Prices quoted are for *single* unused examples with Control attached, *unless otherwise stated*. For corner pairs or strips of these the "normal" prices for the additional stamps must be added.

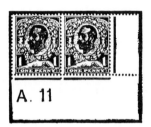 

Somerset House Controls with imperforate bottom margins with single extension hole.

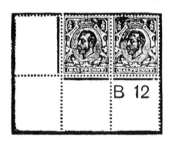

Harrison Control with bottom margins perforated through

Letters and figures with serifs. Used from L 18 onwards.

Small thick letters and figures, with serifs. Used with Block Cypher wmk.

CHECKLIST OF KING GEORGE V ISSUES

Description	Spec. Cat. Nos.	S.G. Nos.	Page
1911-12 Downey Head Issues			
½d. Die 1A	N1	321–23	135
½d. Die 1B	N2, N3	324–26, 334–35	137
½d. Die 2	N4, N5, N6	338–40, 344, 346–8	139
1d. Die 1A	N7	327–28	144
1d. Die 1B	N8, N9, N10	329–33, 336–7	148
1d. Die 2	N11, N12, N13	341–3, 345, 349–50	151
1912-22 Profile Head Issues, Wmk Simple Cypher			
½d.	N14	351–56	162
1d.	N16	357–61	168
1d. exptal. ptg.	N17A	—	176
1½d.	N18	362–65	177
2d. Die I	N19	366–69	181
2d. Die II	N20	370	184
2½d.	N21	371–73	186
3d.	N22	374–77	188
4d.	N23	378–80	191
5d.	N25	381–83	194
6d.	N26	384–86	197
7d.	N27	387–89	199
8d.	N28	390–91	202
9d. agate	N29	392–93	205
9d. olive-green	N30	393a–93b	206
10d.	N31	394	207
1s.	N32	395–96	209
1913-34 "Seahorse" High Values			
2s. 6d. Waterlow	N63	399–400	269
2s. 6d. De La Rue	N64	405–408	270
2s. 6d. B.W.	N65	413a–415a	272
2s. 6d. re-engraved	N73	450	277
5s. Waterlow	N66	401	274
5s. De La Rue	N67	409–410	274
5s. B.W.	N68	416	274
5s. re-engraved	N74	451	277
10s. Waterlow	N69	402	275
10s. De La Rue	N70	411–413	275
10s. B.W.	N71	417	275
10s. re-engraved	N75	452	277
£1	N72	403–404	276
1913 Profile Head Issue, Wmk Multiple Cypher			
½d.	N15	397	167
1d.	N17	398	176
1924-26 Profile Head Issue, Wmk Block Cypher			
½d.	N33	418	211
1d.	N34	419	215
1½d.	N35	420	218
2d. Die II	N36	421	225
2½d.	N37	422	227
3d.	N38	423	229
4d.	N39	424	231
5d.	N40	425	232
6d. chalky paper	N41	426	233
6d. ord. paper	N42	426a	234
9d.	N43	427	235
10d.	N44	428	236
1s.	N45	429	238
1924 British Empire Exhibition			
1d.	NCom1	430	278
1½d.	NCom2	431	278
1925 British Empire Exhibition			
1d.	NCom3	432	279
1½d.	NCom4	433	279
1929 Postal Union Congress			
½d.	NCom5	434	280
1d.	NCom6	435	280
1½d.	NCom7	436	280
2½d.	NCom8	437	280
£1	NCom9	438	286

Description	_Spec. Cat. Nos._	_S.G. Nos._	_Page_
	1934-36 Photogravure Issue		
½d. intermediate format	N46	—	244
½d. small format	N47	439	245
1d. large format	N48	—	247
1d. intermediate format	N49	—	247
1d. small format	N50	440	248
1½d. large format	N51	—	250
1½d. intermediate format	N52	—	251
1½d. small format	N53	441	253
2d. intermediate format	N54	—	256
2d. small format	N55	442	256
2½d.	N56	443	258
3d.	N57	444	259
4d.	N58	445	260
5d.	N59	446	261
6d. (unissued)	—	—	243
9d.	N60	447	261
10d.	N61	448	262
1s.	N62	449	262
	1935 Silver Jubilee Issue		
½d.	NCom10	453	288
1d.	NCom11	454	288
1½d.	NCom12	455	288
2½d. blue	NCom13	456	288
2½d. Prussian blue	NCom14	456a	288

CHECKLIST OF KING GEORGE V BOOKLET PANES

Spec. Cat. Nos.	Description	From Booklets Nos.	Listed Below Cat. No.	Page
Downey Head Issue				
NB1, NB1a	6 × ½d. Die 1B, wmk Crown	BB1–2	N2	137
NB2, NB2a	6 × ½d. Die 1B, wmk Simple Cypher	BB3–5	N3	139
NB3, NB3a	6 × 1d. carmine Die 1B, wmk Crown	BB1–2 (part)	N8	149
NB4, NB4a	6 × 1d. scarlet Die 1B wmk Crown	BB1–2 (part)	N9	150
NB4b, NB4c	6 × 1d. aniline scarlet Die 1B, wmk Crown	BB1–2 (part)	N9	150
NB5, NB5a	6 × 1d. scarlet Die 1B	BB3–5	N10	150
Profile Head Issue, Wmk Simple Cypher				
NB6, NB6a	6 × ½d.	BB6–11, BB18–19, BB22, BB31–32	N14	164
NB7, NB7a	6 × 1d.	BB6–11, BB18–19, BB22, BB30–32	N16	170
NB8, NB8a	6 × 1½d.	BB11, BB18–19, BB22–23, BB31–32	N18	178
NB9, NB9a	4 × 1½d. and two printed labels	BB11	N18	179
NB10, NB10a	6 × 2d. Die I	BB20, BB30–31, BB32 (part)	N19	182
NB11, NB11a	6 × 2d. Die II	BB21, BB32 (part)	N20	184
Profile Head Issue, Wmk Block Cypher				
NB12, NB12a	6 × ½d.	BB12, BB14, BB24, BB26, BB33–35	N33	212
NB13, NB13a	6 × 1d.	BB12, BB14, BB24, BB26, BB33–35	N34	215
NB14, NB14a	6 × 1½d.	BB12, BB14, BB24, BB26, BB33–35	N35	219
NB15, NB15a	4 × 1½d. and two printed labels	BB12, BB14, BB33–35	N35	219
Photogravure Issue				
NB20, NB20a	6 × ½d. intermediate format	BB15, BB27, BB36	N46	244
NB21, NB21a	6 × ½d. small format	BB17, BB29, BB37	N47	246
NB22, NB22a	6 × 1d. intermediate format	BB15, BB27, BB36	N48	247
NB23, NB23a	6 × 1d. small format	BB17, BB29, BB37	N50	248
NB24, NB24a	6 × 1½d. intermediate format	BB15, BB27, BB36	N52	251
NB25, NB25a	4 × 1½d. intermediate format and two printed labels	BB15, BB36	N52	252
NB26, NB26a	6 × 1½d. small format	BB17, BB29, BB37	N53	254
NB27, NB27a	4 × 1½d. small format and two printed labels	BB17, BB37	N53	254
Postal Union Congress Issue				
NComB1, NComB1a	6 × ½d.	BB13, BB25	NCom8	281
NComB2, NComB2a	6 × 1d.	BB13, BB25	NCom8	282
NComB3, NComB3a	6 × 1½d.	BB13, BB25	NCom8	282
NComB4, NComB4a	4 × 1½d. and two printed labels	BB13	NCom8	282
Silver Jubilee Issue				
NComB5, NComB5a	4 × ½d.	BB16, BB28	NCom14	290
NComB6, NComB6a	4 × 1d.	BB16, BB28	NCom14	290
NComB7, NComB7a	4 × 1½d.	BB16, BB28	NCom14	290

Essays

Artists. After consultation with the President of the Royal Academy invitations were sent to G. W. Eve, A. Garth Jones and C. W. Sherborn on 1 July and they each submitted three designs. Later Bertram Mackennal was brought in at the King's suggestion as he was designing the coinage for the Mint, but he objected to taking part in a competiton but then agreed to submit a design for a fee. Eventually it was the Eve and Mackennal designs which were accepted, subject to modifications. The Royal Mint also submitted some hand-painted essays which were shown to the King but were not approved. Most of this material, together with a number of designs submitted by members of the public, exists only in the National Postal Museum or the Royal Collection. However, some of Mackennal's and J. A. C. Harrison's pen and ink drawings are in private hands as indeed are certain essays among which are the following:

De La Rue. In a bid to retain the printing contract, which was due to expire at the end of the year, De La Rue were very quick off the mark in submitting the above designs to the Inland Revenue on 26 May 1910. They were produced by the Miller & Motley Printex Process, a photographic method. They used a head similar to that later employed for the Newfoundland 2 c. Coronation issue and the Union of South Africa 2½d. but the Crowns were placed at the side as the King had previously informed them that he did not like the Crown suspended above the head.

½d. design in green	£1350
Two 1d. designs in carmine .. .. *Each*	£900

Type A   Type B (shown
                          actual size)

Perkins, Bacon. Perkins, Bacon also used the Printex method to produce essays in the above designs by unknown artists.

Type A on wove paper in carmine-pink (there were 32 in the sheet) .. .. *Each*	£100
Type B on glazed paper in red, green, blue, violet or black .. .. .. *From*	£150
As Type B but head in blue and frame in light green	
As Type B but stamp size toned photographic proof	

Waterlow. It is believed that Waterlow & Sons also produced some essays.

The Downey Head Issue (1911–12)

INTRODUCTION. The first issue of stamps of King George V was the work of two artists: Mr. Bertram Mackennal (later Sir Bertram) and Mr. G. W. Eve. The head was copied from a photograph of the King in Admiral's uniform by W. & D. Downey, the Court Photographers. Mr. J.A. C. Harrison, a freelance engraver who was contracted to the Royal Mint, engraved the dies.

The first two values of the intended series, ½d. and 1d., were issued on Coronation Day, 22 June, 1911, and they were greeted with a storm of criticism on artistic and other grounds. The head, having been copied from a photograph, was unsuited for the typographic process, and the majority of printed impressions were blotchy (Die 1A). In an effort to improve the appearance, the die was deepened and fresh plates were made in August 1911 (Die 1B), but the results were still not satisfactory. A new die (Die 2) was then produced from Die 1A, and the stamps from this improved die were placed on sale on 1 January, 1912. During this whole period the remaining values of the intended series (1½d. to 1s.) were in various stages of production but further issues were abandoned owing to a change of plan to issue stamps having a full Profile Head (Die 3). Thus only the ½d. and 1d. in the Downey series were put on sale.

The Original Downey Photograph

Upon reflection the Downey Head issue can be said to have failed for a number of reasons. In the first place the public was not used to a three-quarter face head and, as we have stated, the use of a photograph was not compatible with the typographic process. Moreover, the Royal Mint, which had been asked to make the dies and plates, had no facilities for doing so, and also no experience, and had to send to the United States for certain pieces of equipment. Mackennal, the designer, had never designed a stamp before and was primarily a sculptor, but he had been asked by the King to undertake this because of the very poor trial drawings that had been submitted by other artists.

It has also been said that J. A. C. Harrison was partly responsible as this was his first effort at engraving for typography. However, in July 1911 the Royal Mint used the Harrison master die of the head only to make a duplicate which was sent to De La Rue for printing Post Office Savings Bank stamps which were bi-coloured. We illustrate a die proof of the head and frame plate together with a copy of the actual stamp to show that De La Rue were capable of producing a clear and acceptable portrait from it. However, because of their low quotation, the printing contract had gone to Harrison & Sons despite their lack of experience in printing stamps and use of fugitive inks.

Head and frame De La Rue Die Proof using J. A. C. Harrison Head

Issued Post Office Savings Bank Stamp

PRINTERS. Except for the preliminary Somerset House printings (distinguishable only by the stop Controls), all the stamps in Section NA were printed by Harrison & Sons.

PERFORATION TYPES. For these, see the priced lists of Control pieces.

ARRANGEMENT. The Downey Head series is listed as follows:

Downey Head Dies

J. A. C. Harrison's first engraved head die is known in four primary stages, one intermediate and the accepted final stage.

Stage 1a

Stage 1b

Stage 1c

Stage **1a.**   Circular clearing around design.   Shading of circumference of design in solid colour and showing blurred lines of colour; moustache partly shaded; lobe of ear in solid colour; parting of hair light and distinct.

Stage **1b.**   Circle of solid colour replaced by even shading except at lower left; moustache more detailed with fine lines of shading; ear lobe shaded; hair parting slightly darkened.

Stage **1c.**   Circumference now completely shaded through; ear lobe more detailed; white spot at tip of King's nose.   Proofed at the Royal Mint and submitted to the King.

Stage 1d. As stage 1c, but outer circle mostly cleared and added detail to moustache and beard. Proofed in November 1910.

Stage 2   *Stage 3*

Stage 2. Die now part cleared into square. As stage 1d except for very slight highlight on bridge of King's nose. Used by Hentschel & Co. to insert in Mackennal's sketch die frame and used for making blocks to print the colour essays.

Stage 3. Head completely cleared in a 13½ mm. circle of shading; shading of moustache now perfectly detailed. Proofed in January 1911 at the Royal Mint and accepted for making working dies.

Die Proofs

Stage 1a.   On fine wove paper
    In black, dull blue-green or red   ..   .. *From* £650
Stage 1b.   On fine wove paper
    In black, dull green or dull red   ..   .. *From* £500
Stage 1c.   On fine wove paper
    In black, deep blue, purple or bright red   ..   .. *From* £500
Stage 1d. On fine wove paper
    In black or red   ..   ..
Stage 2.   On fine wove paper
    In black, blue, green or red   ..   .. *From* £500
Stage 3.   On glazed card
    In black, blue, green or red   ..   .. *From* £650
    Proofs are known of other heads prepared for use on Postal Stationery, Postal Orders and Savings Bank stamps. (*Price from* £300.)

Perkins, Bacon Die Proofs

Perkins, Bacon produced a die from a three-quarter face head. The first proof illustrated was typographed and shows an uncleared oval shaded frame. It also exists partly cleared in a thick black oval. The second illustration is a negative version of this so that the wells print out in recess or intaglio form. This may have been intended for a dummy stamp. (*Price from* £400.)

W. & D. Downey Die Proof

(a)   (b)

Upset that the court photograph was partly blamed for the poor likeness of the King on the Die 1A stamps, W. & D. Downey themselves commissioned an engraver to produce a die from their photograph.

Uncleared proof in red (a)	£1100
Cleared proof in green (b)	£1100

A photographic proof of Downey's large King's head (b) was affixed to the firm's publicity card. In vertical format, this has the W. & D. Downey imprint, coat-of-arms and their Ebury Street address at foot. Two other publicity cards exist which were probably prepared at the same time. These show the original issue (die 1a), improved issue (die II) and a paste-up of die 1a frame with W. & D. Downey cleared head in blue-green for ½d. and carmine for 1d.

Essays for Colour Only

Quite early in the new reign the Postmaster General rashly committed himself to issuing as many as possible of the new stamps by Coronation Day, 22 June 1911. Rather than wait until all the dies had been prepared and approved, Mr. Seymour Bennett, Inspector of Stamping at the Inland Revenue, offered to supply colour trials for the whole series of values using ordinary printing blocks made from photographs. These would be rather rough in execution but would serve as colour trials.

The offer was accepted, and in the event three methods of production were employed. They were printed on pieces of paper with the ink manufacturer's reference numbers stamped or occasionally handwritten alongside:— " M.B. " (Manders Bros.); " S.P. " (Slater and Palmer); " W. " (Winston); or just showing the colour maker's number only. On a few occasions there are no references at all. " S.D. "=Stamping Department at Somerset House.

Hentschel Zinc Block Essays

These essays were made in late November 1910 employing zinc line-blocks made by Hentschel & Co. They were made from photographs of the original Eve and Mackennal designs combined with a Stage 2 proof of the Downey head which had been completed on 14 November. As die proofs were preferred for colour essays the Hentschel blocks up to the 3d. value ceased to be used after the Autumn of 1911.

First Proof

The first proof in black consisted of the ½d., 1d., 1½d., 2d., 2½d. and 3d. printed as a block together on white paper annotated "1st proof" in pencil. The designs, with wide figures of value, differ from those shown below. On the ½d. and 1½d. "Postage" and "Revenue" is in white on black background; 1d. and 2½d. have tall "Postage" and "Revenue" in the upper scrolls and the 2d. and 3d. show the lower scrolls blank and "Postage" and "Revenue" in the upper scrolls either side of the crown. (*Price* £6000.)

Second Proof

A. All six values printed together as block of six in black on piece £5000

B. On white unwatermarked paper unless otherwise stated

½d.	In various shades of green	*From* £350
1d.	In various shades of red	*From* £400
1½d.	In various colours	*From* £350
2d.	In various colours on white or tinted paper	*From* £350
2½d.	In various shades of blue and one in green	*From* £350
3d.	In various colours on white or tinted paper	*From* £350

For details of the frame bromide used for the 1d. and 2½d. values see page 158.

Eve carried out a long series of modifications to his "wreath" and "pillar" designs to match the frames to the new Mackennal full profile head dies so Hentschel colour essays of the values from 4d. to 1s. continued to be used until early 1912.

On white unwatermarked paper unless otherwise stated

4d.	In various colours	*From* 95·00
5d.	In various colours	*From* 95·00
6d.	In various colours	*From* 95·00
7d.	In various colours on white or coloured paper	*From* 95·00
8d.	In various colours	*From* 95·00
	In black on various green papers	*From* 95·00
	In various colours with shading around head removed	*From* 95·00
9d.	In various colours	*From* 95·00
	In black on various shades of yellow paper	*From* 95·00
	In red with shading around head removed	95·00
10d.	In various colours	*From* 95·00
	In black on various coloured papers	*From* 95·00
1s.	In various colours	*From* 95·00
	In black on various coloured papers	*From* 95·00

Half Tone Essays

On 14 December 1910 essays of the 3d. and 7d. were sent to the Post Office from half tone blocks (also obtained from Hentschel). These were made from the original Eve "wreath" and "pillar" designs of the frames into which a photograph of the Downey head had been pasted. They were produced by the new "Printex" method invented by A. H. Motley and C. A. Miller which was patented the following year. It is a primitive form of photogravure since the image is made up of a screen of dots.

They were produced in two sizes but the 7d. in the large format was not submitted to the Post Office.

On white unwatermarked paper unless otherwise stated

Small Format		
3d.	In various colours on white or yellow paper	*From* 75·00
7d.	In various colours	*From* 75·00
Large Format		
3d.	In various colours on white, also purple on yellow paper	*From* 75·00
	In black on white paper with Crown watermark	£200
7d.	In various colours	*From* 75·00
	In black	95·00

Some of the essays are known in multiple pieces comprising two or three different values on the same piece and these are rare, especially the ½d. to 3d. values.

Edward VII Colour Trials

In 1911 colour trials were made at Somerset House using King Edward VII die proofs. Three sets of trials were produced (a) using the King Edward colours on ungummed paper; (b) using proposed King George colours on gummed paper and (c) *se-tenant* pairs comprising King Edward die proofs and King George Hentschel zinc block essays in the proposed King George colours on gummed paper for the purposes of comparison. However this comparison was misleading since the quality of reproduction of the zinc blocks could not compare with that of the die proofs.

Typical *se-tenant* Colour Trial

Imperforate, without watermark

(a) In the K.E. VII Colours

Ungummed paper

½d. green	4d. orange
1d. scarlet	6d. dull purple
2½d. ultramarine	7d. slate-grey
3d. purple on yellow	

(b) In the proposed K.G. V Colours

Gummed paper

½d. bright green	4d. sage-green
1d. rose-red	6d. violet
2½d. indigo	7d. pale blue
3d. bright orange	

Edwardian trials in Edwardian colours	From	£950
Edwardian trials in proposed Georgian colours	From	£1250
Se-tenant pairs of K.E. VII and K.G. V in Edwardian colours (spaced 30 mm apart)		£4000
Se-tenant pairs of K.E. VII and K.G. V in proposed Georgian colours (spaced 12 mm apart)	From	£4000

The colour makers' reference numbers were as follows:

King Edward colours: ½d. SD11, 1d. SD1, 2½d. W5, 3d. SP4 (on yellow paper), 4d. W20, 6d. MB39 7d. SP6.

Proposed Georgian colours: ½d. SD3, 1d. SD2, 2½d. SD6, 3d. SD7, 4d. SD8, 6d. SD15, 7d. SD10.

1912.   King Edward VII 1d.   Watermark Royal Cypher

(a)	Imperforate		
	In orange-red, rose-carmine or rose-red	From	£2000
(b)	Perf. 15 × 14. With gum		
	In scarlet		£4000

Engraver's Sketch Dies for the Unissued Values

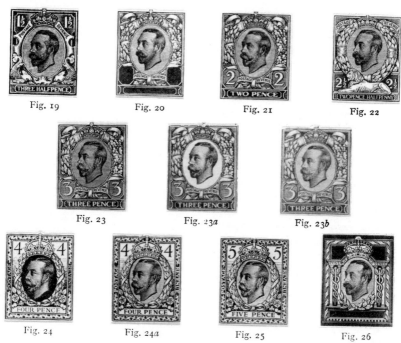

Fig. 19   Fig. 20   Fig. 21   Fig. 22

Fig. 23   Fig. 23a   Fig. 23b

Fig. 24   Fig. 24a   Fig. 25   Fig. 26

Engraved at the Royal Mint by H. P. Hugill (4d.) or J. A. C. Harrison (others)

Fig. 19 was produced from the original ½d./1½d. master die with the value engraved later. Fig. 22 was produced from the original 1d./2½d. master die with the value engraved later. Figs. 20, 21 and 23b are Mackennal's wreath design. Figs. 24/25 are Eve's wreath design. Fig. 26 is Eve's pillar design which was initially for the 8d. to 1s. values.

The early Royal Mint engravings had the Die 1 Downey Head. This head was rolled out on to pieces of die steel which then had the appropriate frames engraved around them. The head was re-engraved and this new style was incorporated in the design.

Although there was only one Die 1 head, there are several slightly differing Die 2 heads. For instance the head on the ½d. Die 2 is not the same as that on the 1d. Die 2.

1½d. Fig. 19. Die proofs

Die 1 head, uncleared. On thick glazed paper in grey-black	£800
Die 2 head. On card in brown, yellow-brown, orange, chocolate-brown, turquoise-green, purple or violet .. .. *From*	£800
As above but on thin wove paper in red-brown, chocolate-brown or magenta .. *From*	£800

2d. Fig. 20 (without value). Master die for 2d. Die 1 head, uncleared (numbered "6C" above design)*

On paper without watermark in black or pink .. .. *From*	£750
On paper watermarked Crown in rose-red or ochre-brown .. .. .. *From*	£750

2d. Fig. 21 (with value)

Die proof, uncleared, on white glazed card in black	£800
Die proof, fully cleared, on wove paper in black	£800
Colour trials from printing plate. Die 2 head. Wmk. Crown. Perf. 15×14, in bistre	£1250

2½d. Fig. 22

Die 1 or Die 2 head. Four stages, differing in the lettering of the value. On thin card in black .. .. *From*	£1350
Colour trials from printing plate. Die 2 head. Wmk. Crown. Perf. 15×14, in indigo-blue	£1250

3d. Fig. 20 (without value). Master die for 3d. Die 1 head, uncleared (numbered " 7C " above design)*

    On paper watermarked Crown in slate-blue £800

3d. Fig. 23. Shaded background to head with upper corners shaded. Die 2 head
    Uncleared die proofs on thick white paper in red or black   ..   ..   ..   *From*   £900
    Cleared die proof on thick white glazed paper in black £300
    Plate proofs cut close on card in pale red-brown or yellowish-brown   ..   ..   ..
    Plate proofs on gummed paper in pale violet, orange or claret   ..   ..   ..

    Fig. 23*a*. White background to head with upper corners shaded.
    Cut down die proofs used as colour trials on thick white paper in rose, orange, green, grey, pale
      purple, blue geranium (carmine-lake) or brown   ..   ..   *From*   £900
    Uncleared die proof on proof paper in rose-red   ..   ..

    Fig. 23*b*. Shaded background to head with upper corners solid. Die 2 head
    Uncleared die proofs on thick white paper in various colours including yellow and slate-grey
       ..   ..   *From*   £900
    Plate proofs cut close on paper watermarked Crown (upright or sideways), in various colours
      including orange, pale brown, chocolate-brown, grey-green, pale violet, maroon, blue
      geranium (carmine-lake), and grey ..   ..   *From*   £900

4d. Fig. 24. Die 2 head on solid background
    Uncleared die proof on proof paper in black £1350

    Fig. 24*a*. Die 2 head with shaded background
    Uncleared die proof on proof paper in black £1350
    As last but in orange £900
    On paper watermarked Crown in bright orange £900

5d. Fig. 25. Die 2 head
    Uncleared die proof on card in black £800
    As last but in light blue £900
    Die proofs used as colour trials on white proof paper in various colours, including
      light blue   ..   ..   *From*   £900
    On paper watermarked Crown in light blue £900

8d. Fig. 26 (without value)
    Uncleared die proofs on paper watermarked Crown with gum in black or purple ..   *From*   £900

*Complete die proofs containing the die number above are worth at least twice the prices quoted.

1911-12.   ½d. Green

N1

Dies 1A and 1B

Ornament above P of HALFPENNY
has two thin lines of colour; beard
is undefined

N2

Die 2

Ornament has one thick line;
beard well defined

Die 1A. The three upper scales on the body
of the right hand dolphin form a triangle.
The centre jewel of the cross inside the crown
is suggested by a comma.

Die 1B. The three upper scales are incomplete.
The centre jewel is suggested by a crescent.

Die 1A   **Die 1B**

Cat. No. S.G. No.	Watermark	Die	Shades		Unused	Used

1911 (JUNE 22).   GREEN, TYPE N1, WMK. CROWN.   DIE 1A

N1	321/23	W12	1A	(1) Green	2·25 ✓	75 ✓
a. Watermark inverted	..	—	£500	(2) Pale green	3·25 ✓	85 ✓
b. Perforation 14. Shade (1) ..		—	£250	(3) Deep green	6·00	3·50 ✓
c. White blob right of left ½ (Pl. 8, R. 20/2 Control A 11)		85·00		(4) Bluish green	£375	£125 ✓
d. White spot at top of fore- head (Pl. 8, R.19/3)	..	75·00		(5) Yellow-green	4·00	85 ✓
e. White spot under ear (Pl. 9, R.20/3)		75·00				
s. "Specimen", Type 22 ..						

N1c   N1d   N1e

Controls.   Prices are for unused corner pairs.

Control			Perf. Type		
Perf. 15 × 14	1A	2	2A	2(c)	3
A 11 (w)	5·00	6·00	6·00	25·00	90·00

Perf. 14	V1A
A 11 (w)	—

An example of Control A11(c) was reported but confirmation is required for listing. Excess pressure and overinking
can make the normal "wide" spacing appear as the "close" type. The perf. 14 stamps were perforated on an old
machine used by Harrison to perforate King Edward VII stamps and giving Type V1A. One single Control example
is known from plate 7 (official plate no. 5/5).

Die Proofs of the Accepted Design

Without value with reversed " 2 " above design

On thick card in green	£1000
Ditto, in rose-pink or deep red-brown	Each £500
On proof paper in bright pink or deep carmine	Each £500
On proof paper with small dot after " 2 ", in pink	£500

Finished die with reversed " 5A " above design

On thin card in dull green	£1000
On paper watermarked Imperial Crown in pale yellowish green	£1000
Ditto, but in lake-brown (intended for 1½d. value)	£1500
Cut close as colour trials in three different shades of green, including issued colour	Each £1250

Plate Proofs

Imperf. on thick paper in black	£180
Perf. 14 on thick paper in bluish green	£800

Imprimatur

Die IA. Imperforate. Wmk. Crown on gummed paper in issued colour
The imprimatur is rare and should have a certificate stating provenance.

Colour Essays. See under General Notes.

Plate Markings

The listing of these ½d. Die 1A plates has been revised according to recent research. Seven plates were put to press, and our numbering follows the official numbers.

Plate	Marking
2	No marking. (Official plate 2/2) (left sheet)
4	No marking. (Official plate 4/4) (right sheet)
5	Dot (breaking left) 18th right side, 13.5 mm.; slight scoop (outer) 12th right side. (Official plate 5/5) (right sheet)
6	Half dot (inner) 17th right side, 13.5 mm. (Official plate 6/6) (left sheet)
7a	Scoop (outer) 2nd right side, 14 mm. (Official plate 7/7) (right sheet)
7b	Added cut 20th right side, 11 mm. (right sheet)
7c	Added cut 18th right side, 10.5 mm. (right sheet)
8	Cut 19th right side, 11.5 mm. (Official plate 8/8) (left and right sheets-plate changed sides in press)
9	Cut 19th right side, 8.75 mm. (Official plate 9/9) (left sheet)

Two different states of "no marking" are known, one of which is probably an early state of a marked plate.

Control Schedule

Control A11(w) was used with all these plates. Confirmation is required of the use of Control A11(c) on this issue.

Cat. No.	S.G. No.	Watermark	Die

1911. As last, but DIE 1B

N2	324/26	W12	1B	
a.	Watermark inverted (ex bklt. panes)		6·00	2·50
b.	Watermark sideways ..		—	£1700
c.	Cracked plate (Pl. 3, R. 20/2)	£110		
d.	Gash in Crown (R. 1/1 of booklet pane)	£150		
e.	Varnish ink. Shade (6) ..	£1850		
f.	Broken left frame by dolphin's tail (Pl. 7, R. 19/1)	90·00		
g.	Blob above E of POSTAGE and white flaw in corner (Pl. 8, R. 19/2)	75·00		
h.	White spot right of left "½" (Pl 10b, R. 20/3)	75·00		
s.	"Specimen", Type 22 ..			

Shades	Unused	Used
(1) Bright green	3·75	50 ✓
(2) Pale bright green	5·00	50 ✓
(3) Yellow-green	5·00	50 ✓
(4) Bright yellow-green	15·00	6·00
(5) Green	5·00	1·00 ✓
(6) Deep green	9·00	4·00 ✓
(7) Very deep green	£180	50·00
(8) Bluish green	£200	70·00

N2c   N2d

N2f   N2g   N2h

Controls. Prices are for unused corner pairs.

Control		Perf. Type					
		1	1A	2	2A	2(c)	3
A 11 (w)		30·00	15·00	18·00	22·00	25·00	75·00
A 11 (c)		30·00	15·00	15·00	18·00	†	75·00

(c) "close" and (w) "wide" refer to the space between the figures at foot (1½ mm. and 2 mm. respectively).

The following watermark variety is known:
Wmk inverted: A 11(w) Perf. Type 2

Booklet Panes of Six

From Booklets BB1/2

NB1	**½d. Green (shades),**	
	Watermark upright	35·00
s.	"Specimen", Type 22 ..	
t.	Cancelled "London Chief Office, E.C.", Type E ..	25·00
u.	Cancelled "London (Chief) Office E.C.", Type F ..	35·00
v.	Cancelled "London, E.C.", Type G	25·00
w.	Cancelled "London, E.C.", Type H	25·00

NB1a	**½d. Green (shades),**	
	Watermark inverted	35·00
as.	"Specimen", Type 22 ..	
at.	Cancelled "London Chief Office, E.C.", Type E ..	25·00
au.	Cancelled "London (Chief) Office E.C.", Type F ..	35·00
av.	Cancelled "London, E.C.", Type G	25·00
aw.	Cancelled "London, E.C.", Type H	25·00

Die Proof

On thick paper in green £1250

Plate Proofs

On thick paper in black £200
Imperf. trial on paper watermarked Multiple Cypher, with gum, in green from Control A11(c)   £300

Plate Markings

Two minute nicks either side, 19th left side, 8 mm. is a master plate flaw.

1a   Cut 20th left side, 12¾ mm., cut 20th right side, 11¾ mm.; minute dot at left under 3rd
1b   Added cut 18th right side, 10¼ mm.; cut 19th right side, 17½ mm.
1c   Added cut 17th left side, 13½ mm.; cut 17th right side, 14 mm.
2   Cut 18th left side, 14½ mm.; cut 20th left side, 12¼ mm.; cut 20th right side, 12½ mm.
3   Cut 17th left side, 11½ mm.
4   Cut 20th right side, 8¼ mm.
5a   Cut 17th right side, 10¼ mm. 3rd rule bulges up under FP
5b   Added cut under PE of 12th
5c   Added double cut 17th left side
6   Cut 17th left side, 12½ mm.; cut 17th right side, 14½ mm.; cut 19th right side, 13 mm.; slight depression (inner) 20th left side, 12½-5 mm.
7   Cut under FP of 11th; cut 20th right side, 10¾ mm.
8a   No marking
8b   Added cut 18th left side, 11¾ mm.; slight depression (inner) 20th left side, 2½ mm.

9a   Cut 19th left side, 13 mm.; cut 20th left side, 12 mm.; cut 19th right side, 12½ mm.; cut right side, 12½ mm.
9b   Added cut 18th left side, 14½ mm.
10a   Cut under P of 11th
10b   Added cut 19th left side, 10½ mm.; cut 19th right side, 12 mm.
11a   Cut under FP of 12th. Rule under 2nd thinner at right
11b   Added cut 17th right side
12   Cut under HA of 12th; cut 20th right side, 12½ mm.
13   Cut 18th left side, 14½ mm.
14   Oval cut 18th right side, 10½ mm.
15   Cut 20th right side, 11½ mm.; cut 19th right side, 17½ mm.; oval cut 18th right side, 10½ mm.
16   Cut 20th right side, 10 mm.
17   Notch out of 2nd at right
18   Cut 17th left side; double cut 18th left side; cut 20th left side
19   Cut 18th right side, 10½ mm.; cut 20th right side, 8½ mm.
20   Cut 17th right side, 10½ mm.; cut 20th right side, 10 mm.

Index to Plate Markings

Bottom Margin, Stamp Numbers

Stamp No.	Plate
2	11a, 11b, 17
3	1a, 1b, 5a, 5b, 5c

Stamp No.	Plate
11	7, 10a, 10b, 11a, 11b
12	5a, 5b, 11a, 11b, 12

Left Margin, row numbers

Row No.	Plate
17	1b, 3, 5c, 6, 18
18	2, 8b, 9b, 13, 18

Row. No	Plate
19	9a, 9b, 10b
20	1a, 1b, 2, 6, 8b, 9a, 9b, 18

Right Margin, row numbers

Row No.	Plate
17	1c, 5a, 5b, 5c, 6, 11b, 20
18	1b, 1c, 14, 15, 19
No marking	8a

Row	Plate
19	1b, 1c, 6, 9a, 9b, 10b, 15
20	1a, 1b, 2, 4, 7, 9a, 9b, 12, 15, 16, 19, 20

Control A11 was used with all these plates.

Cat. No. S.G. No.	Watermark	Die	Shades	Unused	Used
1912 (AUGUST). As last, but WMK. SIMPLE CYPHER (Booklets only)					
N3 334/35	W14	1B	(1) Green	28·00	22·00 ✓
a. Without watermark ..			(2) Pale green	28·00	22·00 ✓
b. Watermark inverted ..	28·00	20·00 ✓ 1,2 ✓	(3) Deep green	40·00	25·00
c. Watermark reversed ..	£275				
d. Watermark inverted and reversed	£300		s. "Specimen", Type 22 ..	£120	
e. Varnish ink. Shade (3) ..	£1850		t. "Specimen", Type 26 ..		
f. White flaw after Y (R.2/2 of booklet pane, with wmk upright)	£150				

N3*f*

Booklet Panes of Six

From Booklets BB3/5

NB2	**½d. Green (shades),**	
	watermark upright	£125
s.	"Specimen", Type 22 ..	£750
t.	Cancelled "London E.C.",	
	Type H	50·00
u.	"Specimen", Type 26 ..	
v.	Cancelled " London E.C.",	
	Type 1	50·00

NB2a	**½d. Green (shades),**	
	watermark inverted	£125
as.	"Specimen", Type 22 ..	£750
at.	Cancelled "London E.C."	
	Type H	50·00
au.	"Specimen", Type 26 ..	

1912 (JANUARY 1). GREEN, TYPE N2, WMK. CROWN. DIE 2

N4	338/40	W12	2
a.	Watermark inverted	£250	
b.	No cross on Crown	60·00	12·00
c.	No cross on Crown and		
	broken frame..	90·00	22·00
d.	No cross on Crown shade (5)		
da.	Do. with broken frame ..		
e.	Part double printing (lower		
	portion)*	£250	
f.	White spot in oval below E of		
	POSTAGE (Pl. ?, R. 1/11)		
g.	Coil join (vert. pair) (8.12) ..		
s.	"Specimen", Type 26 ..	£150	

(1)	Green	2·50 ✓	50 ✓
(2)	Pale green	5·00 ✓	50 ✓
(3)	Deep green	7·00 ✓	3·00
(4)	Myrtle-green	50·00	7·50 ✓
(5)	Bluish green	50·00	10·00
(6)	Yellow-green	2·50	50 ✓
(7)	Bright yellow-green	10·00	5·00 ✓

A similar variety to No. N4*c* occurs in N5 attributed to plate wear.

*In No. N4*e* a small part of the sheet has made extra contact with the plate and the variety can be described as a " kiss " print.

N4*f*

Plates.   19 Plates were used.

Controls.   Prices are for unused corner pairs.

Control				Perf. Type				
				1	1A	2	2A	3
B 11	..	..	..	†	†	6·00	6·50	†
B 12 (c)	..	..	..	—	22·00	5·50	5·50	50·00
B 12 (w)	..	..	..	†	†	9·00	8·50	†
None*	..	..	..	†	†	50·00	†	†

*The missing control is an error and the price is for a corner pair.
(c) "close" and (w) "wide" refer to the space between the "B" and the serif of the "1" (4½ mm. and 6 mm. respectively).
Control B. 12 Perf. Type 2A is believed to exist but confirmation is needed. This control was used for Somerset House printings.

Coils

Vertical delivery made up from sheets with joins every 10th stamp

Code No.	Issued	Number in roll	Face value	
C	Aug. 1912	1000	£2.1. 8	Top delivery
D	Aug. 1912	1000	£2.1. 8	Bottom delivery
G	Aug. 1912	500	£1.0.10	Top delivery
H	Aug. 1912	500	£1.0.10	Bottom delivery

Die Proofs

Transitional stages leading to Die 2 frame

All the following have a Die 2 head and are on thin card

Stage 1

Stage 2

Stage 1. Die 1A frame

    Two lines of colour in background of dolphins; one line of colour in dolphins'
foreheads; two lines in central ornament with lines of shading at sides;
" H " of " HALFPENNY " open at top and bottom

      In emerald-green £1500

Stage 2. Proofed 6 August 1911

    As Stage 1 but background of dolphins solid and no shading at sides of
central ornament; " H " solid at top and bottom

      In light chestnut £1500

Stage 3

Stage 4

Stage 3. Proofed 6 October 1911

    As Stage 2 but foreheads of dolphins cut away and solid line at left of
central ornament

      In green on proof paper £1500

Stage 4. Die 1B frame. Proofed 20 October 1911

    As Stage 3 but some lines of shading added to dolphins' foreheads

      In green on proof paper £1500

Stage 5

Stage 5. The accepted Die 2.   Proofed 28 October 1911
As Stage 4 but shading added in dolphins' heads and above them as well
as at sides of central ornament

    In grey-black £1500

The Stage 3 die was used for the colour trials that follow and working dies were prepared from it
for striking leads.

Plate Proofs

    On thick paper, in black or green   ..   .. *From* £300
    In green on paper, Wmk. Crown (upright or sideways) £500

Colour Trials

No watermark.   Imperf.

    In various colours from the accepted die ..   .. *From* £350

Watermark Crown (upright or sideways).   Imperf. With gum

    In green, cerise, azure, deep claret, and bluish green from the accepted die ..   .. *From* £350

Cat. No.	S.G. No.	Watermark	Die	Shades	Unused	Used
1912 (AUGUST). As last, but WMK. SIMPLE CYPHER						
N5	344	W14	2	(1) Green	3·00 ✓	60 ✓
a.	Without watermark £200			(2) Pale green	2·00 ✓	50 ✓
b.	Watermark inverted .. .. 50·00		15·00	(3) Deep green	4·00 ✓	75 ✓
c.	Watermark reversed .. .. 40·00		15·00	(4) Yellow-green	5·00	75 ✓
d.	Watermark inverted and reversed .. .. 5·00		2·00	*Bluish-green*		✓
e.	No cross on Crown .. .. 65·00		15·00	h. Wmk. "POSTAGE", (vert. block of 10 (2 × 5))		
ed.	Do. watermark inverted and reversed £110			i. White spot in oval below E of POSTAGE (Pl. ?, R. 1/11) ..		
f.	No cross on Crown and broken frame*			s. "Specimen", Type 26 ..	£250	
g.	Coil join (vert. pair)			t. "Cancelled", Type 24 ..	£125†	

*Examples of No. N5f vary in appearance due to progressive plate wear. The cross on the crown
and most of the frame at left is omitted.
    No. N5h is similar to No. N6j but may be distinguished by the cypher watermark.
    For illustration of No. N5i see No. N4f.
    †No. N5t exists from NPM archive sales.
    No. N5s came from control B12(w).

N5f

Plates.   18 Plates were used.

Controls.   Prices are for unused corner pairs.

Control				Perf. Type	
				2	2A
B 12 (c)	..	..	..	4·50	4·75
B 12 (w)	..	..	..	4·50	4·75
B 13	..	..	..	4·50	4·75

(c) "close" and (w) "wide" refer to the space between the "B" and the serif of the "1" (4½ mm. and 6 mm. respectively).

The following watermark varieties are known:
Wmk inverted, Type I: B 12 (c) Type 2; B 13 Type 2A
Wmk reversed, Type I: B 12 (w) Type 2; B 13 Type 2A
Wmk inverted and reversed, Type I: B 12 (c) Type 2; B 12 (w) Types 2 and 2A; B 13 Types 2 and 2A
Wmk upright, Type II: B 13 Types 2 and 2A

Coils

Vertical delivery made up from sheets with joins every 10th stamp

Code No.	Issued	Number in roll	Face value	
C	Aug. 1912	1000	£2.1. 8	Top delivery
D	Aug. 1912	1000	£2.1. 8	Bottom delivery
G	Aug. 1912	500	£1.0.10	Top delivery
H	Aug. 1912	500	£1.0.10	Bottom delivery

Cat. No.	S.G. No.	Watermark	Die	Shades		Unused	Used

1912 (OCTOBER).   As last, but WMK. MULTIPLE CYPHER

N6	346/8	W13	2	(1) Green	5·00 ✓ 3·00 ✓
a.	Watermark inverted ..	4·00	2·75	(2) Pale green	5·00 2·50 ✓
b.	Watermark reversed ..	4·00	2·75	(3) Deep green	7·00 ✓ 3·25 ✓
c.	Watermark inverted and re-			(4) Yellow-green	5·00 ✓ 3·75 ✓
	versed	100 18·00 ✓	100	Bluish - green	
d.	Watermark sideways ..	†	£800	j. Dark blob on Y (coil stamp	
e.	Crown missing in watermark	£100		with join at bottom) ..	85·00
f.	Imperforate	£110		k. Wmk. "POSTAGE", (vert	
g.	Printed on gummed side ..	—	†	block of 10 (2 × 5)) ..	
h.	No cross on Crown	65·00	20·00		
i.	Coil join (vert pair) ..				

An additional marginal rule has been seen at the bottom of a right-hand corner pair from Plate 13 (see notes after Controls of No. N8).

A single example of No. N6g is known.

N6j
This may not be a plate flaw
but a number of copies are known

Plates.   10 Plates were used.

Controls.   Prices are for unused corner pairs.

Control				Perf. Type	
				2	2A
B. 12	..	..	..	£650	£650
B 12 (c)	..	..	..	6·50	8·00
B 12 (w)	..	..	..	7·00	7·00

(c) "close" and (w) "wide" refer to the space between the "B" and the serif of the "1" (4½ mm. and 6 mm. respectively).
Control B. 12 was used for Somerset House printings.

The following watermark varieties are known:
Wmk inverted: B 12 (c) Types 2 and 2A; B 12 (w) Types 2 and 2A
Wmk reversed: B 12 (c) Types 2 and 2A; B 12 (w) Types 2 and 2A
Wmk inverted and reversed: B 12 (c) Type 2

Coils

Vertical delivery made up from sheets with joins every 10th stamp

Code No.	Issued	Number in roll	Face value	
C	Oct. 1912	1000	£2.1. 8	Top delivery
D	Oct. 1912	1000	£2.1. 8	Bottom delivery
G	Oct. 1912	500	£1.0.10	Top delivery
H	Oct. 1912	500	£1.0.10	Bottom delivery

Plate Markings

Plate	Marking
1a	Small dot under P of 5th
1b	Added dot under E of 12th
2	Small dot under LF of 6th; gap under 7th narrower
3	Big double dot under (N)N of 7th
4	Pear dot under FP of 8th; rule broken under E of 10th in later printings with B12(c) (Crown wmk.)
5	Small dot under FP of 9th; tiny dot (top) ½ mm. from left under 6th
6	Small dot under P of 10th; base of 20th left side completely bevelled off
7	Small dot under F of 11th
8	Small dot (base) under FP of 12th (sometimes showing as a ½ dot (base))
9	Minute dot 20th left side, 6 mm.
10a	Big dot under F of 5th
10b	Added single fine diagonal cut 20th left side, 5 mm. (Sometimes showing as a fine 'V' cut)
11	Big dot under HA of 6th; fine 'X' cut in 20th left side, 5½ mm.
12a	Big dot under AL of 7th

Plate	Marking
12b	Added horizontal 'V' cut in 20th left side 6½ mm.
13	Big oval dot (top) under FP of 8th; two fine diagonal cuts 20th left side, 5 mm. forming an open 'V'
14	Small dot under PE of 9th; base of 20th left side partly bevelled off
15	Minute nick under NY of 9th; dot (base) under PE of 11th (sometimes showing as a ½ dot (base)
16a	Dot under FP of 1st, horizontal dash under HALFP of 2nd; dot under NN of 12th
16b	Added cut under A of 12th
17	½ cut (base) and dot under N(N)Y of 12th
18	Long dot under HA of 12th; S.E. corner missing on 8th rule
19	20th left side bent
20	¾ cut (base) under PE of 9th
21	½ cut (base) under N(N) of 10th
22	Small dot (top) under F of 12th; fine diagonal ½ cut 19th left side
23	Dot under PE of 12th
24	No marking

Index to Plate Markings

Bottom Margin, Stamp Numbers

Stamp No.	Plate
1 ..	16a, 16b
2 ..	16a, 16b
5 ..	1a, 1b, 10a, 10b
6 ..	2, 5, 11
7 ..	2, 3, 12a, 12b

Stamp No.	Plate
8 ..	4, 13, 18
9 ..	5, 14, 15, 20
10 ..	4, 6, 21
11 ..	7, 15
12 ..	1b, 8, 16a, 16b, 17, 18, 22, 23

Left Margin, Row Number

Row No.	Plate
19 ..	22

Row No.	Plate
20 ..	6, 9, 10b, 11, 12b, 13, 14, 19

No Marking: Plate 24

Control Schedule

All Wmk. Crown unless marked (s) Simple Cypher or (m) Multiple Cypher

Control	Plate with which it was used
B 11	1a, 2, 3, 4, 5, 6, 7, 8, 22
B 12(c)	1a, 2, 3, 4, 5, 6, 7, 10a, 10b, 11, 12, 13, 14, 15, 16a, 17, 18
B 12(w)	10b, 12, 13, 16a
B 12(c)(s)	4, 11, 12, 13, 15, 16b, 18
B 12(w)(s)	8, 10b, 11, 12, 13, 17, 19, 20, 21, 22, 23

Control	Plate with which it was used
B.12(m)	9
B 12(c)(m)	11, 12, 13, 15, 16a, 16b, 18
B 12(w)(m)	10b, 12, 13
B 13(s)	1b, 4, 5, 8, 13, 16b, 17, 19, 20, 21, 22, 23, 24
None	17

As stated below the Control listing for No. N4 confirmation is required for B. 12 on Crown watermarked paper.
Somerset House control B. 12(m) was used with a plate other than Plate 9 which has not yet been identified.

1911-12. 1d. Red

N3
Dies 1A and 1B
Lion unshaded

N4
Die 2
Lion shaded

Die 1A   Die 1B

Die 1A. The second line of shading on the ribbon to the right of the crown extends right across the wreath. The line nearest to the crown on the right-hand ribbon shows as a short line at the bottom of the ribbon.
Die 1B. The second line of shading is broken in the middle. The first line is little more than a dot.

Cat. No.	S.G. No.	Watermark	Die	Shades	Unused	Used

1911 (JUNE 22). RED, TYPE N3, WMK. CROWN. DIE 1A

N7	327/8	W12	1A	(1) Carmine-red	2·00 ✓	90 ✓
a.	Experimental printing, un-watermarked chalk-surfaced paper (Pl. 1a) ..		£225	(2) Pale carmine-red	3·00	75 ✓
b.	Without watermark		£950	(3) Deep carmine-red	15·00	6·00 ✓
c.	Watermark inverted ..		£750	£350	(4) Carmine	5·50 ✓	2·75
d.	Watermark sideways ..		†	—	(5) Pale carmine	10·00	1·00 ✓
e.	Perforation 14		—	—	(6) Rose-pink	50·00	18·00
f.	No cross on Crown		£350	£150			
g.	Varnish ink. Shade (3) ..		£1850				
h.	White fleur-de-lis (Pl. 4, R. 16/1)		£125				
i.	Flaw between E and P (Pl. 9, R. 20/11)		90·00				
j.	Gash under crown (Pl. 13b/13c, R. 19/11)		90·00				
s.	"Specimen", Type 22 ..		£225				

The flaw N7i may be connected with the marking in the marginal rule.

Under ultra-violet light Somerset House printings generally fluoresce dark plum and Harrison printings fluoresce pink.

N7h

N7i

N7j

Controls. Prices are for unused corner pairs.

Control				I	1A	Perf. Type 2	2A	2(c)
A. 11	..	..	..	£120	40·00	40·00	50·00	†
A 11 (w)	..	..	..	†	5·00	5·50	9·00	25·00
A 11 (c)	..	..	..	†	†	11·00	45·00	—

(c) "close" and (w) "wide" refer to the space between the figures at foot (1½ mm. and 2 mm. respectively).

Control A. 11 was used for Somerset House printings and No. N7a is known with this control.

Control A 11 (w) may exist with Perf. Type 3.

Die Proofs

Early Stage   Completed Die
The very first Die engraved by J. A. C. Harrison

The design differs from the issued Die 1A stamps and is very similar to the Hentschel essays for colour only.

Cleared die proofs on card

Early stage of engraving, outline of lion and part of wreath only. In black £1800
Completed die. In red £1800

The die was discarded in favour of the following transitional stages leading to Die 1A. All have a Die 1 head (as Downey Head Stage 3).

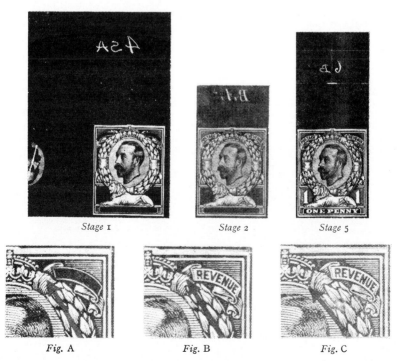

Stage 1   Stage 2   Stage 5

Fig. A   Fig. B   Fig. C

Stage 1.   Proofed 23 February 1911
No inscription or value.   Ribbon at right with fourth line of shading broken (*Fig.* A)
> In scarlet on proof paper with " 4SA " engraved in reverse £750

Stage 2.   Proofed 2 March 1911
As Stage 1 but with " POSTAGE " and " REVENUE " added and lighter shading around lion
> In pale rose-red on thick glazed card engraved " B.1 " in reverse £1500

Stage 3.   Proofed 3 March 1911
As Stage 2 but fourth line of shading now completed (*Fig.* B)
> In pale rose-red on thick glazed card..   ..   .. £900

Stage 4.   Proofed 23 March 1911
As Stage 3 but additional colour at bottom right of Crown leaving only one lower line of shading in upper right part of ribbon instead of two lines (*Fig.* C)
> In pale rose-red on thick glazed card £900

Stage 5.   Proofed 31 March 1911.   The accepted Die 1A
As Stage 4 but value added and shading deepened, especially on the lion, but finer lines of shading removed.   Uncleared
> In deep grey on proof card engraved " 6 B " in reverse £1500
> In scarlet on paper watermarked Crown pasted on thick card, proofed early April 1911 (usually cut close to margins) £1250

Colour Trial

Watermark Crown (upright only). Perf. 13.75 × 14. With gum
> In scarlet ..

Two examples, formerly a pair, are known. For similar perforated trials see below No. N11, Die 2, perf. 14.8 × 14.

Plate Proofs
> In carmine on white paper. No watermark, imperf. £200
> In red on white paper. Watermark Crown, imperf. £200

Colour Essays.   See under General Notes.

Plate Markings

Plate	Marking
1	Dot 19th right side, 11 mm.; cut under EP of 2nd; cut under NN of 7th
2a	Cut under P of 1st
2b	Added cut 20th right, 13.5mm.
3a	Dot 20th right side, 12¾ mm.; fine diagonal cut through 19th left side, 18 mm.; rule broken under EP of 11th in later printings
3b	Added cut under (P)E of 9th; dot 20th right side enlarged
4a	Small 'U' mark under (N)E of 3rd
4b	Added ½ dot (inner) 19th right side, 10½ mm.; dot 19th left side, 12½ mm.; small nick (lower) under (N)E of 9th
4c	Added cut under (P)E of 11th
5	Deleted. Now part of Plate 13
6	Dot 17th right side, 19½ mm.; rule broken under NN of 2nd in later printings
7	Deleted.. Now part of Plate 2
8	Deleted. Now part of Plate 4
9	½ dot (outer) 20th right side, 10 mm.; small dot (breaking inner) 20th left side, 8¾ mm.; rule broken under (N)E of 11th in later printings
10	Cut 19th right side, 10½ mm.; left of 11th rule cut away
11	Deleted. Now part of Plate 3
12	Deleted. Now part of Plate 4
13a	Dot 18th right side, 10½ mm.; small nick (outer) 20th right side, 13 mm.
13b	Added dot 18th left side, 12½ mm.
13c	Added cut under (P)E of 10th

Index to Plate Markings
Bottom Margin, Stamp Numbers

Stamp No.	Plate
1	2a, 2b
2	1, 6
3	4a, 4b, 4c
7	1

Stamp No.	Plate
9	3b, 4b, 4c,
10	**13c**
11	3a, 3b, 4c, 9, 10

Left Margin, Row Number

Row No.	Plate
18	13b, 13c
19	3a, 3b, 4b, 4c

Row No.	Plate
20	9

Right Margin, Row Number

Row	Plate
17	6
18	13a, 13b, 13c

Row	Plate
19	1, 4b, 4c, 10
20	2, 3a, 3b, 9, 13a, 13b, 13c

Control Schedule
   Control A. 11 was used with Plates 1 and 2a, A11 (w) with all plates (including Plates 1 and 2a) and A 11 (c) with Plates 2b, 13b and 13c.

Cat. No.	S.G. No.	Watermark	Die	Shades	Unused	Used

1911. As last, but DIE 1B

N8   329/31   W12   1B

	Shades	Unused	Used
(1)	Carmine	2·50 ✔	90 ✔
(2)	Pale carmine	2·75	90 ✔
(3)	Deep carmine	8·00	1·00 ✔
(4)	Bright carmine	5·00 ✔	1·00 ✔
(5)	Deep bright carmine	25·00	5·00 ✔
(6)	Carmine-red	4·00	75 ✔
(7)	Pale carmine-red	4·00	90 ✔
(8)	Rose-pink	70·00	18·00 ✔

a. Watermark inverted .. 6·00 2·25 ✔✔
b. No cross on Crown £450 £250
c. Varnish ink. Shade (1) .. £1850
d. White spot left of O, and white dot above T of POSTAGE (Pl. 14, R. 20/11 control A11 (c)) .. .. 80·00
e. Frame break over EP (Pl. 3b/3c, R. 19/11) .. .. 60·00
f. Small white spot on forehead (Pl. 4, R. 20/11) .. 60·00
g. Scratch to right of left figure "1" (Pl. 6a/6b, R. 20/11) .. 60·00
h. Broken ribbon under last E of REVENUE (Pl. 16, R. 20/10) .. .. .. 60·00

i. White scratch to left of lion's face, (Pl. 16, R. 20/11) .. 40·00
j. Broken left frame (R. 1/2 of booklet pane) £125
k. Pale lion (Pl. 12, R. 19/12)..
s. "Specimen", Type 22 ..

Under ultra-violet light Somerset House printings generally fluoresce dark plum and Harrison fluoresce pink.

N8d   N8e

N8f   N8g   N8h

N8i   N8j   N8k

Controls.   Prices are for unused corner pairs.

Control					Perf. Type				
				1	1A	2	2A	2(c)	3
A. 11	..	..	..	†	†	8·00	8·00	†	†
A 11 (w)	..	..	..	†	†	20·00	90·00	—	†
A 11 (c)	..	..	..	£125	8·00	5·50	5·50	22·00	40·00

(c) "close" and (w) "wide" refer to the spaces between the figures (1½ mm. and 2 mm. respectively).

Control A. 11 was used for Somerset House printings.

Additional marginal rules are known below the control A. 11 for Plates 9a and 15 printed by Somerset House. They exist as one, two or three rules, the latter at the very bottom of widely trimmed sheets. It is believed that three rules were normally printed, the number showing depending upon the width of the trim. They are thought to have been used to prevent the fraudulent use of unwatermarked paper. Other stamps are reported to have been treated in this way.

Booklet Panes of Six

From Booklets BB1/2 (part)

NB3	1d. Carmine (shades), water- mark upright	40·00		**NB3a**	1d. Carmine (shades), watermark inverted	40·00
s.	Cancelled "London Chief Office, E.C.", Type E ..	25·00		*as.*	Cancelled "London Chief Office, E.C.", Type E ..	25·00
t.	Cancelled "London (Chief) E.C.", Type F	35·00		*at.*	Cancelled "London (Chief) Office E.C.", Type F ..	35·00
u.	Cancelled "London E.C.", Type G	25·00		*au.*	Cancelled "London, E.C.". Type G	25·00

Die Proofs

In carmine or rose-red on thick paper. Uncleared and cut close   ..   .. *Each* £1000
In carmine-pink on paper with Crown watermark. Two impressions on one piece   .. £2250
As last in carmine, but single impression from working die £1000

Plate Proofs. From master Die 1B

In carmine or rose-red, cleared and on ordinary proof paper £1700
In carmine on special chalk-surfaced paper. No watermark, imperf., with gum   .. £150
In pale carmine or black on thick paper. No watermark or gum ..   ..   ..

The plate proof on chalk-surfaced paper fluoresces bright lemon under ultra violet light; those in pale carmine or black do not.

Plate Markings

Plate	Marking		Plate	Marking

Minute nick, 19th right side, 8½ mm. is a master plate flaw.

Plate	Marking
1	No marking
2	Cut 20th right side, 9 mm.
3a	No marking
3b	Added cut 20th right side, 11½ mm.
3c	Added cut 17th right side, 11 mm.
4	Cut 20th right side, 14½ mm.; cut 17th right side, 12 mm. and fine cut, 20 mm.; damage (outer) to 15th right side, 5 mm.
5	Cut 20th right side, 13½ mm.; right of 12th thicker at base
6a	No marking
6b	Added ½ dot (outer) 20th right side, 12 mm.
7	Cut under PE of 12th; cut 20th right side, 10 mm.; damage under NY of 11th; fine cut 20th left side, 10½ mm.
8a	½ cut (base) under (N)E of 11th; cut 19th right side, 13¾ mm.; large break 18th left side, 13½ mm.; very fine cut 19th left side, 17 mm.

Plate	Marking
8b	Added cut 20th right side, 11¾ mm.
9a	Minute nick at top 1 mm. from left under 11th; scoops in 3rd and 4th pillars of 12th in inter-pane gutter
9b	Nick has disappeared; added cut 19th right side, 15¾ mm.
10a	No marking
10b	Added cut 19th right side, 11½ mm.
11	Cut 19th right side, 9 mm.
12	Cut 19th right side, 8 mm.
13	Deleted. Now part of Plate 15
14	Cut 17th right side, 9 mm.; 12th split at right
15a	Minute dot under (P)E of 9th
15b	Dot has disappeared; added cut 18th right side, 14½ mm.
16	Cut 17th left side, 16 mm.

Index to Plate Markings

Bottom Margin, Stamp Numbers

Stamp No.	Plate		Stamp No.	Plate
9 ..	15a, 15b		12 ..	5, 7, 9a, 9b, 14
11 ..	7, 8a, 8b, 9a			

Left Margin, Row Numbers

Row No.	Plate		Row No.	Plate
17 ..	16		19 ..	8a, 8b
18 ..	8a, 8b		20 ..	7

Right Margin, Row Numbers

Row No.	Plate		Row No.	Plate
17 ..	3c, 14		19 ..	8a, 8b, 9b, 10b, 11, 12
18 ..	15b		20 ..	2, 3b, 3c, 4, 5, 6b, 7, 8b

No Marking: Plates 1, 3a, 6a, 10a

Control Schedule

Control A. 11 was used with Plates 3, 9a and 15a, A 11 (c) with all the rest and A 11 (w) with at least Plates 7 and 8a.

Cat. No.	S.G. No.	Watermark	Die	Shades	Unused	Used

1912 (JUNE).   As last, but SCARLET (Booklets only)

N9	332/3	W12	1B	(1) Scarlet	13·00	9·00 ✓
a.	Watermark inverted	.. 15·00	6·00	(2) Pale scarlet	15·00	6·00
s.	"Specimen", Type 22	..		(3) Bright scarlet	13·00	9·00 ✓
				(4) Aniline scarlet	£120	55·00

Booklet Panes of Six

From Booklets BB1/2 (part)

NB4   1d. Scarlet, watermark
          upright   85·00
  s.   "Specimen", Type 22   ..
NB4b   1d. Aniline scarlet   £700

NB4a   1d. Scarlet, watermark
               inverted   85·00
  as.   "Specimen", Type 22   ..
NB4c   1d. Aniline scarlet,
          watermark inverted £700

1912 (AUGUST).   As last, but WMK. SIMPLE CYPHER (Booklets only)

N10	336/7	W14	1B	(1) Scarlet	15·00	12·00
a.	Without watermark £750			(2) Pale scarlet	15·00	10·00 ✓
b.	Watermark inverted .. 15·00		12·00 ✓	(3) Bright scarlet	15·00	12·00 ✓
c.	Watermark reversed .. £275			(4) Deep bright scarlet	30·00	15·00 ✓
d.	Wmk. inverted and reversed £350		75·00			
e.	Varnish ink. Shade (3) .. £1850					
f.	White flaw above right value					
	(No. 4 of booklet pane, with					
	wmk inverted) £125					
s.	"Specimen", Type 22 .. £100					
t.	"Specimen", Type 26 ..					

N10f

Booklet Panes of Six

From Booklets BB3/5

NB5   1d. Scarlet (shades),
          watermark upright 80·00
  s.   "Specimen", Type 22   ..   £600
  t.   Cancelled "London, E.C.".
          Type H ..   ..   ..   45·00
  u.   "Specimen", Type 26   ..
  v.   Cancelled "London E.C.",
          Type 1 ..   ..   ..   45·00

NB5a   1d. Scarlet (shades),
               watermark inverted 80·00
  as.   "Specimen", Type 22   ..   £600
  at.   Cancelled "London, E.C.",
               Type H ..   ..   ..   45·00
  au.   "Specimen", Type 26   ..

Cat. No.	S.G. No.	Watermark	Die	Shades	Unused	Used

1912 (JANUARY 1). SCARLET, TYPE N4. WMK. CROWN. DIE 2

N11   341/3   W12   2   (1) Scarlet   1·00 ✓   35 ✓

				(2) Bright scarlet	1·00 ✓	40 ✓
a.	Watermark inverted	..	£140 90·00	(3) Deep bright scarlet	1·90 ✓	1·00 ✓
ab.	Without watermark			(4) Very deep bright scarlet	60·00	18·00
b.	No cross on Crown		45·00 12·00 ✓✓	(5) Aniline scarlet	£120	55·00
ba.	Do. wmk. inverted		£150	(6) Scarlet-vermilion		
c.	No cross on Crown and			(7) ~~Carmine~~		
	broken frame		75·00	*h.* Wmk. "POSTAGE"		
d.	No cross on Crown shade (5)		£750	(inverted), strip of 4 from		
da.	Do. with broken frame ..		£900	top row		
e.	Coloured blot on O of ONE			*j.* Varnish ink		
	(Pl. 5b, 4. 20/10) ..		65·00	*s.* "Cancelled", Type 24 ..	£120	
f.	Printed double, one albino		£125	*t.* "Cancelled", Type 25 ..	£250	
g.	Coil join (vert. pair) (8.12)					

Our prices for the aniline scarlet 1d. stamps listed above, are for specimens in which the colour is suffused on the surface of the stamp and shows through clearly on the back.   The correct aniline reaction is a bright golden emission on both sides of the stamp.   Specimens without these characteristics, but which show orange " aniline " reactions under the quartz lamp are relatively common.

No. N11*ab* came from a sheet with an inverted watermark. Examples can only be distinguished from No. N12*a* by attached selvedge showing the inverted Crown.

Shade (6) is known with control B 11.

N11*e*

Examples of this variety also show a disturbance to the left of " 1 " above the variety

Controls.   Prices are for unused corner pairs

Control									Perf. Type			
								1	1A	2	2A	3
B. 11	..	..	..	..	..	..	..	†	†	5·00	5·00	†
B 11	..	..	..	..	..	..	..	16·00	2·50	2·00	2·00	40·00
B. 12	..	..	..	..	..	..	..	†	†	5·00	5·00	†
B 12 (c) ..	..	..	..	..	..	..	..	†	2·00	2·25	2·00	40·00
B 12 (w) ..	..	..	..	..	..	..	..	†	†	2·00	2·00	†

(c) "close" and (w) "wide," refer to the space between "B" and the serif of "1" (4½ mm. and 6 mm. respectively).

The inverted watermark occurs with control B 12 (c) but confirmation of perforation types is needed. Controls B. 11 and B. 12 were used for Somerset House printings.

Coils

Vertical delivery made up from sheets with joins every 10th stamp

Code No.	Issued	Number in roll	Face value	
A	Aug. 1912	1000	£4·3·4	Top delivery
B	Aug. 1912	1000	£4·3·4	Bottom delivery
E	Aug. 1912	500	£2·1·8	Top delivery
F	Aug. 1912	500	£2·1·8	Bottom delivery

Die Proofs

The following have a Die 2 head (but different from ½d. Die 2 head)

Stage 1a   Stage 1b

Stage 1a.   Proofed 6 October 1911

More lines of shading on lion's back but white patches left on fore paws and haunches
In dull grey or pale orange on proof paper, uncleared £1500

Stage 1b.   The accepted Die 2.   Proofed about 30 October 1911

Lion almost completely shaded
In grey-black or carmine on proof paper, uncleared £1500
In blue-geranium, cleared and cut down on Crown watermarked paper, with gum   .. £1250

Colour Trials

From Stage 1b (accepted Die 2)

Taken at various stages of completion of the die and showing minor differences of detail to right-hand ribbon and shading of leaves to wreath (previously known as the amended or modified die)

Imperf.   No watermark
In issued colour, carmine, royal scarlet or yellow ..   .. *From* £700

Taken between 20 October and 29 November 1911
Watermark Crown (upright).   Imperf.   With gum
In blue £750
In pink, carmine or royal scarlet   ..   .. *From* £650
As above and pale blue-green but watermark sideways   ..   .. *From* £750

From plates used for printing
Watermark Crown (upright only).   Perf. 14·8 × 14. With gum
In vermilion, carmine, brownish carmine, royal scarlet, brilliant scarlet, blood-red, rose-carmine, magenta-rose or violet-rose ..   .. *From* £400

Paper Trials.   No watermark.   Imperf.
On Austrian enamelled paper
In carmine or scarlet (F)   ..   .. *Each* 75·00
On wove paper
(a) In carmine on John Dickinson extra superfine very white paper   ..   ..   .. 45·00
(b) In carmine on John Allen special finish very thin paper   ..   .. 45·00
(c) Ditto Plate glazed on face only ..   .. 45·00
(d) Ditto Plate glazed both sides   ..   .. 45·00
(e) In scarlet on John Allen special finish paper ..   .. 45·00
(f) Ditto but machine finish (face only)   ..   .. 45·00
(g) Ditto but thinner paper ..   .. 45·00
(h) Ditto on gummed paper ..   .. 45·00

Cat. No.	S.G. No.	Watermark	Die	Shades	Unused	Used
1912 (AUGUST). As last, but WMK. SIMPLE CYPHER						
N12	345	W14	2	(1) Scarlet	1·50	40
a. Without watermark ..		£200		(2) Bright scarlet	1·10	20
b. Watermark inverted ..		10·00	4·50	(3) Deep bright scarlet	15·00	5·00
c. Watermark reversed ..		20·00	6·00	(4) Carmine		
d. Watermark inverted and reversed		10·00	4·00			
e. No cross on Crown ..		55·00	13·00			
eb. Do. watermark inverted ..		£130				
ec. Do. watermark reversed ..		£160				
ed. Do. watermark inverted and reversed		£130				
f. No cross on Crown and broken frame		90·00	20·00			
g. Coil join (vert. pair) ..						
h. Watermark " POSTAGE " (vert. strip of 5)						
s. "Cancelled", Type 24 ..		£150				

No. N12*h* was from a sheet on which the watermark was reversed.

Controls.   Prices are for unused corner pairs

Control						Perf. Type	
						2	2A
B 12 (w) ..	..	..	..	..	..	1·20	1·20
B 13	..	..	..	..	..	2·00	2·00

The notes below the Controls of N8 about additional marginal rules also apply to the above and one additional marginal rule is known to exist with Controls B 12 (w) (Plates 12, 13 and 16a) and B 13 (Plates 15 and 16b).

The following watermark varieties are known:

Wmk inverted: B 12 (w) (perf. Types need confirmation)
Wmk reversed: B 12 (w) Types 2 and 2A
Wmk inverted and reversed: B 12 (w) Types 2 and 2A

Coils

Vertical delivery made up from sheets with joins every 10th stamp

Code No.	Issued	Number in roll	Face value	
A	Aug. 1912	1000	£4.3.4	Top delivery
B	Aug. 1912	1000	£4.3.4	Bottom delivery
E	Aug. 1912	500	£2.1.8	Top delivery
F	Aug. 1912	500	£2.1.8	Bottom delivery

1912 (OCTOBER).   As last, but WMK. MULTIPLE CYPHER

N13	349/50	W13	2

a.	Watermark inverted	..	8·00
b.	Watermark reversed	..	8·00
c.	Watermark inverted and reversed	..	£250	£100
d.	Watermark sideways	..	£110	75·00
e.	Imperforate	..	85·00
f.	No cross on Crown	..	70·00	16·00 ✓
fa.	Do. watermark inverted	..	£110
fb.	Do. watermark reversed	..	£110

(1) Scarlet   6·50 ✓   3·00 ✓
(2) Bright scarlet   6·50 ✓   4·00 ✓
(3) Deep bright scarlet   30·00   8·00

fd.	Do. watermark sideways	..	£550
g.	No cross on Crown and broken frame	..	£110	25·00
h.	Crown missing in watermark	85·00
i.	Coil join (vert. pair)	..	

Controls.   Prices are for unused corner pairs

Control						Perf. Type	
						2	2A
B. 12 ..	..	..	..	..	..	£750	£750
B 12 (w)	..	..	..	..	..	11·00	11·00
B 12 (w) wmk sideways	..	..	..	£600	£600

Control B. 12 was used for Somerset House printings.

The following watermark varieties are known:

Wmk inverted: B 12 (w) Types 2 and 2A
Wmk reversed: B 12 (w) Types 2 and 2A
Wmk inverted and reversed: B 12 (w) (perf. Types need confirmation)

Coils

Vertical delivery made up from sheets with joins every 10th stamp

Code No.	Issued	Number in roll	Face value	
A	Oct. 1912	1000	£4.3.4	Top delivery
B	Oct. 1912	1000	£4.3.4	Bottom delivery
E	Oct. 1912	500	£2.1.8	Top delivery
F	Oct. 1912	500	£2.1.8	Bottom delivery

Plate Markings

Minute dot at left under 1st is a master plate flaw.

Plate	Marking
1a	No marking
1b	Added dot under EP of 5th
1c	Added cut under right serif of P of 11th
2a	Break 19th right side, 13½ mm.
2b	Added dot under NE of 6th
3a	No marking
3b	Added dot under NN of 7th
4a	Scoop (base) under right of 8th; disturbance (base) under right of 11th; also small dash just below rule of 11th under (N)E; S.W. corner off 20th left side
4b	Added dot under N(E) of 8th
5a	Small dash just below rule of 11th under EN; base of 11th extends to right
5b	Added dot under P(E) of 9th
6a	Dot above 1st in top row
6b	Added dot under PE of 1st; added dot under EP of 10th
7a	Small shreds breaking off (base) of 11th under (P)E and at right
7b	Added dot under E(P) of 11th
8a	Nick above 2nd in top row; minute dot 19th right side, 15 mm.

Plate	Marking
8b	Dot has disappeared; added dot under EP of 12th
9a	Dash under PE of 11th
9b	Added dot under EP of 11th
10a	Dash under PE of 12th; 11th rule thin and irregular
10b	Added dot under (N)E of 12th
11	Cut under PE of 9th
12	½ cut under PE of 10th
13	Cut under P of 11th
14	Cut under (P)E of 12th; ½ dot (outer) 16th left side, 20 mm.
15	Small dot 19th right side, 9¼ mm.; minute dot under PE of 11th
16a	Two small dots 20th right side, 10½, 16 mm.; rule broken under EP of 11th in later printings on Crown paper
16b	Added dot under P of 12th
17	Dot under P of 9th
18	Dot under PE of 10th
19a	Small patch of pale colour between 11th and 12th rules
19b	Added ½ dot under (P)E of 11th

Index to Marginal Markings

Top Margin, Stamp Numbers

Stamp No.	Plate
1	6a, 6b
2	8a, 8b

Bottom Margin, Stamp Numbers

Stamp No.	Plate
1	6b
5	1b, 1c
6	2b
7	3b
8	4a, 4b
9	5b, 11, 17
10	6b, 12, 18
11	1c, 4a, 4b, 5a, 5b, 7a, 7b, 9a, 9b, 10a, 10b, 13, 15, 16a, 16b, 19a, 19b
12	8b, 10a, 10b, 14, 16b, 19a, 19b

Left Margin, Row Numbers

Row No.	Plate
16	14

Right Margin, Row Numbers

Row No.	Plate
19	2a, 2b, 8a, 15
20	4a, 4b
20	16a, 16b

No Marking: Plates 1a, 3a

Control Schedule

All Wmk. Crown unless marked (s) Simple Cypher or (m) Multiple Cypher

Control	Plate with which it was used
B. 11	6a, 8a
B 11	1a, 1b, 2b, 3a, 3b, 4a, 4b, 5a, 5b, 6b, 7a, 7b, 8b
B. 12	2a, 6a, 8a
B 12(c)	1c(?), 2b, 3b, 4b, 5b, 6b, 7b, 8b, 9a, 9b, 10a, 10b, 19a, 19b
B 12(w)	11, 12, 13, 14, 15, 16a
B 12(s)	11, 12, 13, 16a
B.12(m)	2a, 8a
B 12(m)	11, 12, 13, 16a
B 13(s)	11, 12, 15, 16b, 17, 18

The Profile Head Issue, Wmk Royal Cypher (1912–22)

INTRODUCTION. The Profile Head issue replaced the Downey Head issue in the second half of 1912, though some of the values were not issued until August, 1913.

The design for this issue was based on the " coinage " and " medal " profile heads of the King, which were the work of Mr. Bertram Mackennal. The " coinage " head was used as the basis for the designs of the ½d., 1½d. 2d., 3d. and 4d. values, the large " medal " head for the 1d. and 2½d., whilst an intermediate version of this was used for the 5d. to 1s. denominations and an even smaller head was employed for fiscal stamps.

Bertram Mackennal was also responsible for designing the frames of the ½d. to 4d. and G. W. Eve designed the frames for the 5d. to 8d. " pillar " design and 9d. to 1s. " wreath " design.

PRINTERS. The stamps in Section NB were printed by Harrison & Sons, except for the 6d. printed at Somerset House by the Stamping Department of the Board of Inland Revenue, where printings of other values were also made (distinguishable only by the stop Controls).

PERFORATION. Types 2 or 2A were used throughout the issue (*see* Appendix 1). In addition, the variety Type 2(c) is known on the ½d., 1d., 1½d., 2d., 2½d., 4d., 6d. and 1s. values and Types 3 and 3A are known on the ½d., 1d., 2d. and 6d. values.

Imperforate stamps of this issue exist but may be wartime colour trials.

CONTROLS. Prices quoted are for *single* unused examples with Control attached. The priced lists are merely sub-divided into Controls with *imperforate* selvedge (abbreviated to "*I.*") and those with the selvedge *perforated through* (abbreviated to "*P.*"). Partially perforated margins are regarded as imperforate.

Position. The Control appears below the 2nd stamp in the bottom row, except for the 1d. value where it is beneath the 11th stamp.

Bromide of George V Head

BROMIDES. The use of photography as an aid to designers, engravers and others connected with stamp production was well founded by 1910. The process enabled heads and frames to be enlarged or reduced at will and simple artistic changes could be carried out and an immediate impression produced. Photography was invaluable as a time-saving device.

In some cases today the only known example extant of a particular artwork may be a photograph or bromide. The word 'bromide' is used because the term was employed at the time and referred, of course, to the type of printing paper. Bromide prints tend to be in shades of sepia. It is now known that most bromides were made at the Royal Mint.

PRINTEX TRIALS. Bromide prints should be distinguished from Printex trials which are also photographic but produced by a sophisticated 'step and repeat' process. This was invented by A. H. Motley and C. A. Miller and patented in 1911, having been used earlier for the 3d. and 7d. Downey Head essays listed in Section NA.

Furthermore Printex photographic trials (which were produced as singles) should be distinguished from a Printex printing, which came from a small printing plate, usually with four images, that was photo-etched from the original photographic trial. Some Printex photographic trials have been seen with a distinct impression around the design of the camera lens itself.

COINAGE HEAD DIES. Mackennal was evidently influenced by the A. G. Wyon head found on the pattern crown piece of 1910.   In February 1911 a composite photograph of the head of King George V was produced, probably by W. & D. Downey, and a bromide of this, superimposed on a penny piece, sepia toned, was used by Mackennal as a model for the coinage head.   The King was pleased with this and asked Mackennal to prepare a sketch of a design for use on the postage stamps.

A. G. Wyon Head

Mackennal's Coinage Head

Bromide of Mackennal's
Bas-relief Plaque

J. A. C. Harrison's Sketch

A bromide of the original bas-relief plaque sculpted by Meckannal was given to J. A. C. Harrison to produce his original coinage head. This bears the initials BM in the truncation.

From this, Harrison made a sketch and then began engraving the die during January 1912. The first proofs were taken towards the end of January but there were seven progressive states of the head die taken during February and proofed either by Harrison or the Royal Mint.   The first and final stages are shown overleaf and a full description will be found in *The GB Journal* of January 1975 in an article by Alain de Cadenet.   This was reprinted in the March 1978 issue of Gibbons *Stamp Monthly*.

1st Stage (2 February 1912)   Final Stage (21 February 1912)

Die Proofs

In various states, uncleared

In blue on proof paper	£1350
In shades of red or pink, green or black on proof paper .. .. *From*	£800
In black on card	£750

In final accepted state, uncleared

(a) On proof paper
In scarlet, green or black   .. .. *From* £750

(b) On thin card
In scarlet, green or black   .. .. *From* £750

(c) On paper watermarked Imperial Crown
In scarlet, green or black   .. .. *From* £1350

These proofs are sometimes found cut down and inserted into cardboard bevelled frames which are usually dated 28 February 1912 (*Prices from* £1000).

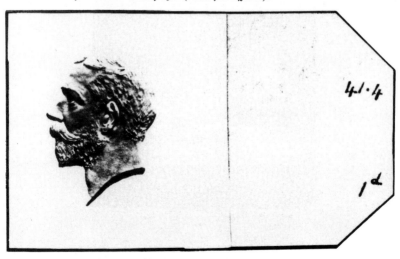

Bromide of Mackennal's Bas-relief Plaque

157

Bromides

Mid 1912.   Bromides of coinage heads in different sizes from Mackennal's bas-relief plaque for insertion into frames to give different percentage widths overall.   No initials in truncation.

(a) Head image 30·7 mm. wide = 41·4% of total width
of frame for 1d. and 2d. values   ..   .. *Each*
(b) Head image 29·5 mm. wide = 39·4% of total width
of frame for 1d. and 2d. values   ..   .. *Each*

November 1912.   Reproduced from Harrison's line sketch illustrated on previous page and dated "**2.11.12**".

36·1 mm. wide = 47·4% of total width of frame   ..

A coinage head bromide, inscribed "47.4", was later discovered combined with a Downey Head frame for the 1d. and unissued 2½d. values.

(a) Frame (75 × 90 mm.) of the 1d. and 2½d. Downey Head
with coinage head inserted   ..   ..
(b) A similar bromide essay reduced to stamp size but
without "Twopence Halfpenny" value tablet inscribed
"47.4" in M/S   ..   ..

MEDAL HEAD DIES

The "large" medal as used in the 1d./2½d. master design

Coinage Head

Mackennal sculptured the design in clay and included the already adopted full profile coinage head.   A photograph was sent to the King and this was approved on 21 February. The head used was small and had the initials B M Sc in the truncation.

Medal Head

Soon afterwards it was decided to use the adaptation of the Mackennal head, which had been employed for the 1911 Coronation Medal, for the 1d. and 2½d. values. A composite photograph was made of the new head, inserted into the Mackennal frame. This head was larger and the details differ from the original coinage head.

J. A. C. Harrison's Sketch

J. A. C. Harrison produced a pen and ink sketch of the head and from this engraved the die ready for proofing early in April 1912.

159

Die Proofs

Stage 1a   Stage 2

Stage 1a.   Proofed by J. A. C. Harrison in early April 1912.
Uncleared and without background shading.   Undated
In black on proof paper £2250

Stage 1b.   As last but with background shading to head in an oval
In black on proof paper £2000

Stage 2.   As last, with basic outline of frame engraved around head
In black on proof paper £2000

Stage 3

Stage 3.   As last, with more of the frame engraved, including POSTAGE
In rose-pink or scarlet on proof paper   ..   .. *From* £2000

160

Stage 4.   Master Die

Stage 4.   Master Die for 1d. and 2½d. values.   On proof paper, dated 15 May **1912**
    In brown-carmine, pale rose-red or deep rose-red .. .. *Each* £900
    In deep turquoise-blue, dull royal blue or slate-blue .. .. .. *Each* £2500
    In black £400

This die was proofed at the Royal Mint on 16 May 1912 and a roller impression was taken up.   On 22 May the Royal Mint proofed a die which was rolled out from this roller.   This secondary die was sent to Harrison for him to engrave the figures and words for the 1d. value.   On 16 July 1912 an identical master die was sent to Harrison for him to engrave the 2½d. on.

The smaller version of the head was used for the 5d. to 1s. values.

Bromide

November 1912.   Large bromide (120 × 165 mm.) reproduced from Harrison's
    sketch of April 1912 (*shown on page* 159) and dated "2.11.12"
    34·5 mm. wide = 46% of total width of frame .. ..

N5

N6

N7

N8

N9

Cat. No.	S.G. No.	Wmk.				Shades	Unused	Used

1913 (JANUARY). ½d. GREEN, TYPE N6. WMK. SIMPLE CYPHER

N14	351/56	W.14 Simple Cypher			

			Unused	Used
a.	Doubly printed	£9500		
b.	Without watermark	55·00		
c.	Watermark inverted	75	25 ✓	
d.	Watermark reversed	9·00	5·00	
e.	Watermark inverted and reversed	2·25	1·50	
f.	"New Moon" flaw (R. 1/3 of booklet pane from Booklet No. BB22)	£250	£110	
g.	Cracked plate (R. 9 or 19/1 and vert. coil)	90·00		
h.	"Ruffled Hair" (Pl. 28, R. 20/1)	£400		
i.	Broken left frame (R. 1/1 of booklet pane with wmk inverted)	£125		
j.	Stop after "HALFPENNY" (Pl. 16c, R. 19/3)	40·00		
k.	Coloured mark on right dolphin's forehead (Pl. 43, R. 20/2)	25·00		
l.	White spot in hair (Pl. 52a, R. 19/3)			
m.	Deformed "E" in "HALFPENNY" (Pl. 49b, R. 20/2)			
n.	Solid shading to left of "HALFPENNY" (Pl. 36b, R. 20/1)	30·00		
o.	White spot above right dolphin's mouth (Pl. 46b, R. 20/3)	30·00		
p.	Broken line below "LF" (Pl. 72, R. 10/7)	50·00		
r.	Printed double, one albino with C13 control .. Strip of 3	£500		

		Unused	Used
(1)	Green	40	12 ✓
(2)	Deep green	2·25	90 ✓
(3)	Pale green	4·50	20 ✓
(4)	Very pale green (1919)	£110	25·00
(5)	Very deep green (1919)	£100	35·00 ✓
(6)	Bright green	40	15 ✓
(7)	Deep bright green	4·50	45 ✓
(8)	Yellow-green	5·00	1·25 ✓
(9)	Dull yellow- (" apple ") green (1915)	13·00	7·00 ✓
(10)	Very yellow- (" Cyprus ") green (1914)	£2500	
(11)	Bright yellow-green	50·00	7·50 ✓
(12)	Olive-green (1916)	40·00	
(13)	Pale olive-green (1916)	30·00	
(14)	Blue-green (1913 & 1918)	32·00	12·00
(15)	Deep blue- (" Myrtle ") green	£150	32·00
(16)	Deep myrtle-green	£450	80·00
(17)	Cobalt-green (1922) ..	13·00	4·00
(18)	Deep cobalt-green (1922)	£175	32·00

r.	Coil join (vert. pair)		
ra.	Coil join (horiz. pair.) (9.20)..		
s.	"Specimen", Type 23	25·00	
t.	"Specimen", Type 26	75·00	
u.	Do. Imperf.	50·00	
v.	"Cancelled", Type 24	15·00	
w.	"Cancelled", Type 28	75·00	

Shades (12) and (13) are highly fugitive.

Six specimens are known of variety a showing partial double prints in the lower portions of the stamp (control G15).

Var. h is only found with control I 16. Printings with the J 17 control being from the rechromed plate.

Var. j. is found on late printings with control G 15 and all printings with control H 16.

No. N14r shows the (unprinted) albino impression on the gummed side particularly on the control margin.

For variety v. in grey-green see "Colour Trials". No. N14w is probably a colour trial printed as an experiment in 1916.

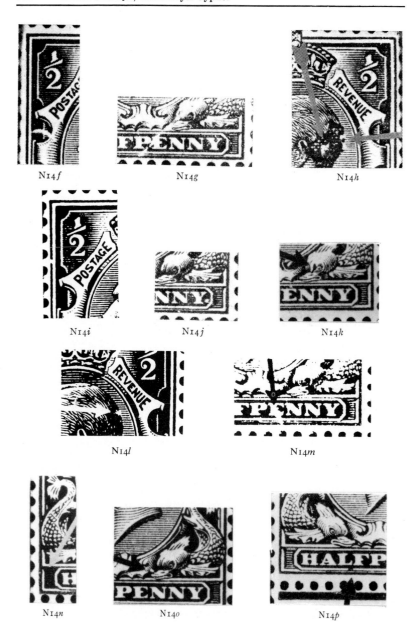

N14*f*

N14*g*

N14*h*

N14*i*

N14*j*

N14*k*

N14*l*

N14*m*

N14*n*

N14*o*

N14*p*

Watermark Varieties.   The following have been recorded:

Wmk upright: Types I, II, III
Wmk inverted: Types I, II, III
Wmk reversed: Types I, II, III
Wmk inverted and reversed: Types I, II, III

Misplaced Watermarks

ya. Single stamp showing letters from " POSTAGE."   3·00

yb. Vertical strip sufficient to show complete " POS-TAGE " watermark   ..   60·00

Broken Dandy Roll Varieties

za.	Missing Crown	.. ..	15·00
zb.	Missing G	.. ..	7·00
zc.	Missing v	.. .. ..	4·50
zd.	Missing R	.. ..	9·00
ze.	Missing Gv	..	6·00

zf.	Missing vR	.. .. ..	9·00
zg.	Missing Crown vR	..	9·00
zi.	Missing left side to R	..	7·00
zj.	Missing tail to R (" GvP ")	3·50
zk.	Long tail to G	.. ..	9·00

Controls. Prices are for unused singles.

Somerset House Printings:

	I.	P.
B. 13	75 ✓	£150

Watermark varieties known:
Wmk upright, Type I ; wmk inverted, Type I ; wmk reversed, Type I ; wmk inverted and reversed, Type I ; wmk upright, Type II.

Harrison Printings:

	I.	P.			I.	P.			I.	P.
C 13	.. ..	60 ✓	60 ✓	K 18	.. ..	1·00 ✓	1·00 ✓	R 21	.. ..	60 ✓	60 ✓
C 14	.. ..	2·50 ✓	2·50 ✓	L 18	..	1·25	1·25 ✓	S 21	.. ..	2·75 ✓	2·75 ✓
D 14	.. ..	60 ✓	60 ✓	M 18	..	2·50 ✓	2·50 ✓	S 22	.. ..	3·75 ✓	3·75 ✓
E 14	.. ..	60 ✓	60 ✓	M 19	..	75 ✓	75 ✓	T 22	.. ..	75	75 ✓
F 15	.. ..	60	60 ✓	N 19	..	75 ✓	75 ✓	U 22	.. ..	1·00	1·00 ✓
G 15	.. ..	60 ✓	60 ✓	O 19	..	2·00	2·00 ✓	U 23	.. ..	80	80 ✓
H 16	.. ..	60 ✓	1·00	O 20	..	1·50 ✓	1·50 ✓	V 23	.. ..	60 ✓	60
I 16	.. ..	60 ✓	60 ✓	P 20	..	75 ✓	75 ✓	W 23	..	5·00	5·00
J 17	.. ..	60 ✓	60 ✓	Q 20	..	2·25 ✓	2·25 ✓	W 24	..	75·00	75·00
K 17	.. ..	1·50 ✓	1·50 ✓	Q 21	..	75 ✓	75 ✓				

Watermark varieties known:
Wmk upright, Type I : C 13, D 14.
Wmk upright, Type II : C 13, C 14, D 14, E 14, F 15, G 15, H 16, I 16, J 17, K 17, K 18, N 19, O 19, O 20, P 20, Q 21, R 21, T 22, U 22, U 23, V 23, W 23, W 24.
Wmk inverted, Type II : C 13, C 14, D 14, E 14, F 15, G 15, H 16, I 16, U 23, V 23, W 23, W 24.
Wmk reversed, Type II : C 13, C 14, F 15, G 15, H 16.
Wmk inverted and reversed, Type II : C 13, C 14, D 14, E 14, F 15, G 15, H 16, I 16, U 23, V 23.
Wmk upright, Type III : J 17, K 17, K 18, L 18, M 18, M 19, N 19, O 19, O 20, P 20, Q 20, Q 21, R 21, S 21, S 22, T 22, U 22, U 23, V 23, W 23.
Wmk inverted, Type III : J 17, K 17, K 18, L 18, M 18, M 19, N 19, O 19, O 20, P 20, Q 20, Q 21, R 21, S 21, T 22.
Wmk reversed, Type III : J 17, K 17, L 18, M 19, P 20, S 21, T 22.
Wmk inverted and reversed, Type III : J 17, K 17 K 18, L 18, M 18, M 19, N 19, O 19, O 20, P 20, Q 20, Q 21, R 21, S 22, T 22, U 22.

Booklet Panes of Six

From Booklets BB6/11, BB18/19, BB22 and BB31/32

NB6   Watermark upright   5·00

s.	" Specimen ", Type 23	..	£400
t.	" Cancelled ", Type 24	..	£100
u.	Cancelled " London E.C.", Type H	.. .. ..	35·00
v.	Cancelled " London E.C.", Type I	.. .. ..	35·00

NB6a   Watermark inverted   5·00

as.	" Specimen ", Type 23	..	£400
at.	" Cancelled ", Type 24	..	£100
au	Cancelled " London E.C.", Type H	.. ..	35·00
av.	Cancelled " London E.C.", Type I	.. .. ..	35·00

Coils

Vertical delivery made up from sheets with joins every 10th stamp

Code No.	Issued	Number in roll	Face value	
C	1913	1000	£2.1. 8	Top delivery
D	1913	1000	£2.1. 8	Bottom delivery
G	1913	500	£1.0.10	Top delivery
H	1913	500	£1.0.10	Bottom delivery
KERMODE	Mid 1920	1000	£2.1. 8	Top delivery

Sideways delivery made up from sheets with joins every 12th stamp

P	Sept. 1920	480	£1.0. 0	Left side delivery

Die Proofs

Approved die, uncleared (Sept. 1912)

In green on proof paper	£2250
As last but cut close	£1250
In green on paper watermarked Simple Cypher (cut close only)	£1350

Cleared for working purposes (Nov. 1912)

In black on card	£1750

Colour Trials

Perforated 15 × 14. Watermark Simple Cypher

In grey-green (1916) overprinted "Cancelled", Type 24	£325

The colour trial listed here was one of three shades which exist perforated and overprinted "CANCELLED", type 24. The other two are close to issued shades although neither was accepted and they only exist with the "CANCELLED" overprint.

Imprimaturs from the National Postal Museum Archives

Booklet pane of six. Imperforate, watermark Type W14

Two panes as No. NB6 arranged horizontally *tête-bêche* and marginal pillars at right

Plate Markings

Plate	Marking
1a	Dot above 1st in upper and lower panes; minute dot under H of 2nd
1b	Dots above first filled in; added cut under N(N) of 1st
2a	Dot above 2nd in upper and lower panes; indents at base of 1st and 12th
2b	Dots above 2nd filled in; added large dot bulging (sometimes breaking) base under FP of 3rd
2c	Added dot under E of 3rd
3a	Dot above 3rd in upper and lower panes
3b	Dots above 3rd filled in; added small dot 17th left side, 11 mm.
3c	Added big cut under P of 1st
4a	Dot above 4th in upper and lower panes
4b	Dots above 4th filled in; added sloping cut (base) under FP of 4th; small dot 18th left side, 12½ mm.
5	Dot (top) under H of 1st
6a	Dot (top) under PE of 1st; indent (top) under EN of 3rd; ½ cut (top) to left of H of 6th
6b	Added dot under N(N) of 1st
7a	½ cut (base) under LF of 1st; small dot 20th left side, 13¾ mm.
7b	Added dot under PE of 2nd
8	½ cut (top) under LF of 2nd
9a	Irregular cut under E of 3rd
9b	Added ½ nick 20th left side (slanting down to outer edge) 22–21½ mm.
9c	Added 2 dots 20th left side, 10, 12 mm.
10a	Small dot 19th left side, 10½ mm.
10b	Added small dot under A of 1st
11a	Cut within rule at left of 9th
11b	Added cut 20th left side, 12¾ mm.
12a	Dash at right of 2nd. Scoop (top) above 1st top row
12b	Added dot under PE of 3rd
12c	Added sloping cut under FP of 3rd
13a	Dot under FP of 1st
13b	Added dot under PE of 1st
13c	Added dot (inner) 20th left side, 9¾ mm.
13d	Added dot under PE of 2nd
14a	Dot under P of 2nd
14b	Added dot (top) under EN of 2nd
14c	Added dot under LF of 3rd; added dot at left above 1st top row; ½ dot (outer) 18th left side, 12½ mm.
14d	Added ½ dot (top) under P of 3rd; added nick and ½ dot (inner) 18th left side, 6½, 10 mm.
15	Dot under PE of 1st
16a	Dot under PE of 2nd
16b	Added 2 dots 19th left side, 11, 14 mm.
16c	Added cut under N(N) of 1st
17	Dot (top) under P of 3rd
18	Dot under FP of 4th
19	3 dots (left dot minute) under LFPE of 2nd
20a	3 dots (centre dot minute) under LFP of 3rd
20b	Added dot under A of 1st
21a	2 dots (top/base) under FPE of 4th
21b	Added cut under LF of 3rd
22	2 dots (base/top) under FPE of 4th
23a	Dot under H of 1st
23b	Added cut under HA of 4th
24	Dot under H of 2nd
25	Dot under H of 3rd
26	Dot under H of 4th
27	2 dots under NN of 1st
28a	2 small dots under PEN of 2nd
28b	Added dot under P of 1st
29	2 dots under ALF of 3rd
30	2 dots under HALF of 4th
31a	Double ½ cut (top/base) under HA of 2nd
31b	Added dot covering base of above cut
32a	Tiny dot under P of 1st
32b	Added fine double cut under PE of 3rd; small dot 17th right side, 16 mm.
33	Tiny dot under PE of 3rd
34a	Cut under PE of 1st
34b	Added dot under NN of 9th
35	Cut under E of 2nd
36a	Cut under P of 3rd
36b	Added 3 dots under HALFP of 3rd
37	Cut under F of 4th; minute ½ cut (outer) 20th right side, 6 mm.
38a	4 dots from left to under right of F of 4th
38b	Added dot (breaking base) under PE of 1st; dot 20th left side, 11½ mm; 2 dots 17th left side, 7, 11¾ mm.
39	Withdrawn
40	Small, slightly ovoid dot (central) under PE of 1st
41	Dot, barely bulging top, under P of 2nd; right of rule under 3rd has small downward projection
42	Dot (breaking base) under FP of 1st. Scoop (outer) 2nd left side.
43a	Very fine ½ cut (base) under (N)N of 3rd
43b	Added ½ dot (top) under E of 10th
44	Small oval dot (bulging and during later stages with Control K18, breaking base) under right serif of P of 2nd

Plate	Marking

45a Large dot 19th right side, 7¼ mm.
45b Added small dot 20th left side, 11½ mm.
46a Cut under N(N) of 1st
46b Added cut 20th right side, 11½ mm; large dot (breaking outer) 18th right side, 11 mm.
47 Dot (central) under right serif of P of 2nd; 2 dots 19th left side, both breaking outer, 4½, 8½ mm.
48 Large oval dot (breaking base) under PE of 1st. Two minute dots under LF, NN of 2nd; two minute dots under A, N(N) of 5th. Base 20th left side damaged (outer).
49a Dot (breaking top) under PE of 9th
49b Added small, slightly ovoid dot (base) under right serif of P of 2nd
50 Nearly round dot (bulging—later breaking base) under right serif of P of 2nd
51a Large dot 17th right side, 9 mm.
51b Added dot under PE of 1st
52a Large dot under E of 9th
52b Added small dot 20th left side, 14 mm.
53a Small dot 17th right side, 4½ mm.
53b Added slanting cut 19th right side, 4 mm.
54a Dot 19th left side, 10 mm.
54b Added dot (top) under FP of 2nd
54c Added dot under E of 2nd
55 Dot (base) under F of 1st
56 Small dot (central) 18th right side, 11½ mm; small dot (inner) 17th right side, 10 mm.
57a Large dot (later breaking inner) 17th right side, 11 mm.
57b Added ½ dot (top) under N(N) of 9th
58 Base of 20th right side bevelled off; dot 17th right side, 9½ mm.
59 19th left side scooped out (outer) 8-12 mm. with vertical dash to right of it
60a Dot under F of 10th
60b Added 4 dots under AL, FP, and 2 touching each other under E of 3rd
61a Nick (outer) 19th right side, 14½ mm; ½ dot (outer) 19th left side, 6¾ mm.

61b Added dot (top) under FP of 9th
61c Added 4 dots from left end to left of F of 4th
63a Large dot (breaking outer) 18th right side, 10 mm; dot (breaking inner) 3rd right side, 11½ mm.
63b Added small dot (central) 17th right side, 10 mm.
64 3 dots breaking inner 19th right side, 5½, 7½, 10½ mm.
65a Small double dot 18th right side, 11½ mm.
65b Added dot, breaking base, under PE of 10th
65c Added dot 19th left side, 9 mm.
66a Small dot (central) 19th left side, 9½ mm. Dot (breaking inner) 2nd left side, 10½ mm.
66b Added 2 fine cuts 19th left side, 11¾, 13½ mm.
67 Small dot inner 18th right side, 11 mm.
68 Dot 1st left side, 11½ mm. Dot inner 20th left side, 11½ mm.
69 **2 cuts 19th left side, 7, 9¼ mm.**
70 ½ dot (base) under P and nick under NY both of 4th
71 Large oval dot breaking top and bottom under PE of 2nd; 20th left side thins towards base
72 Oval dot under FP of 3rd; base of 19th right side bevelled off
73 No marking
74 Oval dot (widely breaking top) to right of P of 2nd; ½ dot (inner) 17th right side, 12 mm.
75 Large oval dot either bulging or just breaking top, under PE of 2nd
76 Small dot (outer) 18th left side, 11 mm.
77 2 large dots 19th left side, 11, 13½ mm.
78 5 cuts under HALF of 12th; minute fine nick (outer) 19th left side, 8¼ mm.
79 Base of 2nd rule cut away from under ENNY to right end; 4 large dots 19th right side
80 Large dot (central) 19th left side, 9½ mm.
81 ½ cut and ½ dot (outer) 19th left side, 11 13½ mm; cut 18th left side, 13½ mm.
82 Small dot (outer) 20th left side, 11½ mm.
83 2 small cuts under NN of 11th

Index to Marginal Markings

Top Margin, Stamp Number

Control Schedule

Control	Plate with which it was used	Control	Plate with which it was used
B 13 ..	1a, 2a, 3a, 4a	L 18 ..	43b, 45a, 45b, 46b, 52a, 54a
C 13 ..	1b, 2b, 3b, 3c, 4b, 5, 6a, 7a, 8, 9a, 9b, 10a, 11a	M 18 ..	42, 43b, 45b, 46b, 51a, 52a, 53a, 54a, 63a, 65a
C 14 ..	1b, 2b, 3c, 4b, 5, 6a, 7a, 8, 9b, 10a, 11a, 11b, 12a	M 19 ..	42, 46b, 49b, 51b, 52b, 53b, 54a, 54b 55, 56, 57b, 59, 60a, 61a, 61b, 63a, 65b
D 14 ..	1b, 2b, 3c, 4b, 5, 7a, 7b, 8, 10a, 11b, 12a, 12b, 13a, 14a	N 19 ..	42, 51b, 52b, 53b, 54a, 54b, 54c, 55, 56, 59, 60b, 61c, 63b, 65c
E 14 ..	2c, 6b, 9c, 12b, 12c, 13a, 13b, 13c, 13d, 14a, 14b, 15, 16a, 16b, 17, 18, 19, 20a, 21a, 22	O 19 ..	55, 56, 58, 59, 65c, 66a
		O 20 ..	59, 66a, 67
F 15 ..	6b, 10b, 13d, 14b, 14c, 15, 16b, 17, 18, 19, 20a, 21a, 22, 23a, 24, 25, 26	P 20 ..	55, 56, 59, 61c, 65c, 66a, 66b, 67, 68
		Q 20 ..	55, 61c, 65c, 68, 69
G 15 ..	6b, 10b, 14d, 16c, 19, 20a, 21a, 23a, 23b, 24, 25, 26, 27, 28a, 29, 30, 31a	Q 21 ..	48, 55, 58, 61c, 65c, 66b, 69, 70, 71, 72, 71
		R 21 ..	47, 68, 70, 71, 72, 74, 75
H 16 ..	16c, 23b, 25, 27, 28a, 29, 30, 31a, 32a, 32b, 33, 34a, 35, 36a, 37	S 21 ..	68, 70, 71, 72, 76
		S 22 ..	68, 70, 71, 72
I 16 ..	27, 28a, 30a, 31a, 32b, 33, 34a, 35, 36b, 37, 38a	T 22 ..	48, 66b, 68, 70, 71, 72, 74, 75, 76
		U 22 ..	48, 58, 66b, 68, 70, 72, 74, 75, 77
J 17 ..	28a, 28b, 29, 31a, 31b, 32b, 33, 34b, 35, 36b, 38a, 38b, 40, 41, 42, 43a, 45a, 46a, 46b, 47, 49a, 50, 57a	U 23 ..	48, 64, 66b, 68, 71, 74, 75, 77, 78, 79, 80, 81
		V 23 ..	71, 72, 73, 74, 77, 78, 79, 80, 81, 82, 83
K 17 ..	42, 43a, 43b, 44, 45a, 46b, 49b, 51a, 52a	W 23 ..	78, 81, 83
		W 24 ..	78, 81
K 18 ..	42, 43b, 44, 45a, 46b, 49b, 50, 51a, 57a	? ..	20b, 21b

Cat. No.	S.G. No.	Wmk.	Shades	Unused	Used

1913 (AUGUST). ½d. GREEN, TYPE N6. WMK. MULTIPLE CYPHER

Cat. No.	S.G. No.	Wmk.	Shades	Unused	Used
N15	397	W13 Multiple Cypher	(1) Bright green	75·00	90·00
			(2) Green	75·00	90·00
a.	Block of four	.. £500			
b.	Coil join (vert. pair)	.. £150			
c.	Watermark inverted	.. £275			
d.	Crown missing in wmk.	.. £250			

Originally issued in vertical rolls of 500 stamps. Subsequently sheets or part sheets were found, so that horizontal pairs, blocks and three control pairs are known.

Control. Wmk. Multiple Cypher

	I.	P.
C 13 ..	—	—

Coil

Vertical delivery made up from sheets with joins every 10th stamp

Code No.	Issued	Number in roll	Face value	
G	Aug. 1913	500	£1.0.10	Top delivery

| Cat. No. | S.G. No. | Wmk. | | | Shades | Unused | Used |

1912 (28 SEPTEMBER). 1d. RED, TYPE N5. WMK. SIMPLE CYPHER

N16   357/61   W.14 Simple Cypher

		Unused	Used
a.	Without watermark	55·00	
b.	Watermark inverted	75	25✓
c.	Watermark reversed	9·00	5·00
d.	Watermark inverted and reversed	1·75	50
e.	Tête-bêche (pair)	—	†
f.	Printed on the back*	£200	
fb.	Printed double, one albino with C13 control.. *Strip of 3*	£400	
g.	Varnish ink (controls C.13, G 15)	£1500	
h.	Q for O (Control E 14, R. 1/4)	£200	75·00
i.	Q for O (Control T 22, R. 4/11)†	£350	£100
j.	Reversed Q for O (Pl. 96, Control T 22, R. 15/9)	£400	£125
k.	Inverted Q for O (Pl. 114b, Control V 23, R. 20/3).. ..	£550	£150
ka.	Inverted and reversed Q for O and spot in centre (R. 2/3 of booklet pane with wmk upright)	£200	
l.	Broken frame (Pl. 17, R. 19/12)	90·00	
m.	Broken corner (Pl. 43, R. 19/10)	90·00	
n.	Spot under eye (Pl. ?, R. 20/12)	75·00	
o.	Ragged beard (Pl. ?, R. 1/12)	75·00	
p.	Large blob over ear (Pl. 67a, Control J17, R. 19/11).. ..	£150	

	Shades	Unused	Used
(1)	Bright scarlet	25 ✓	15
(2)	Deep bright scarlet	8·00	1·25
(3)	Scarlet	25	15
(4)	Deep scarlet	2·50	25
(5)	Brick-red	3·75	25
(6)	Deep brick-red	25·00	4·00
(7)	Vermilion	1·50	60
(8)	Pale red	7·50	1·25
(9)	Pale rose-red	6·00✓	40 ↙
(10)	Pink	£225	
(11)	Carmine-red	7·00✓	2·25
(12)	Bright carmine-red	10·00	85
(13)	Deep carmine-red	£250	35·00
(14)	Scarlet-vermilion (1913 & 1918)	70·00	20·00
(15)	Orange-vermilion (1917-19)	£120	25·00
(16)	Deep orange-vermilion (1918)	£225	45·00

		Unused	Used
q.	Two white dots below "POSTAGE" (Pl. 33, R. 19/11)	90·00	
r.	Coil join (vert. pair)		✓
ra.	Coil join (horiz. pr.) (9.20) ..		
s.	"Specimen", Type 23	50·00	
t.	"Specimen", Type 26	75·00	✓
u.	Do. Imperf.	35·00	✓
w.	"Cancelled", Type 24	15·00	✓
x.	Do. Imperf.	30·00	

*The impression on variety *f* is set sideways, and is very pale.

No. N16fb is similar to the same variety listed under N14 and is best collected as a control strip of 3.

†There are two versions of variety *i* as illustrated but it is not known if they occur in different positions or whether one is a second state of the other.

N16*i*

N16*i*

N16*j*

N16*h*

N16*k*

PENNY 1

N16*l*

N16*ka*

N16*m*

N16*n*   N16*o*

N16*p*

N16*q*

Watermark Varieties. The following have been recorded:

Wmk upright: Types I, II, III
Wmk inverted: Types I, II, III
Wmk reversed: Types I, II, III
Wmk inverted and reversed: Types I, II, III

Misplaced Watermarks

ya.	Single stamp showing letters from "POSTAGE"	3·00	
yb.	Vertical strip sufficient to show complete "POSTAGE" watermark	..	40·00

Broken Dandy Roll Varieties

za.	Missing Crown	.. ..	15·00
zb.	Missing G ..	.. ..	7·00
zc.	Missing v ..	.. ..	4·50
zd.	Missing R ..	.. ..	6·50
zf.	Missing vR ..	.. ..	7·00
zg.	Missing Crown vR	..	9·00
zh.	Missing Crown GvR	..	25·00
zi.	Missing left side to R	..	—
zj.	Missing tail to R ("GvP")		3·50
zk.	Long tail to G	.. ..	9·00

Perforation

Normally Types 2 or 2A, but Type 2(c) with controls D14 and T22 also Type 3 with control G15 are known.

Controls. Prices are for unused singles.

Harrison Printings:

			I.	P.				I.	P.				I.	P.
C 12	..	..	60✔	60	K 18	..	..	60✔	60	Q 21	..	..	3·00✔	3·00
C 13	..	..	50	50✔	L 18	..	..	60	60	R 21	..	..	1·75✔	1·75
C 14	..	..	2·00	2·00	M 18	..	..	3·00	3·00	S 21	..	..	1·75✔	1·75
D 14	..	..	50✔	50	M only ("18" omitted)		..	£1500		S 22	..	..	1·50	1·50
E 14	..	..	50	50✔						T 22	..	..	50	50
F 15	..	..	50✔	50✔	M 19	..	..	50✔	50	U 22	..	..	1·75	1·75
G 15	..	..	50✔	50✔	N 19	..	..	50	50	U 23	..	..	1·75	1·75
H 16	..	..	50✔	50	O 19	..	..	90	90	V 23	..	..	50	50
I 16	..	..	60	60	O 20	..	..	3·00✔	3·00	W 23	..	..	1·50	1·25✔
J 17	..	..	50✔	50✔	P 20	..	..	50	50✔	W 24	..	..	8·00	8·00
K 17	..	..	50	50✔	Q 20	..	..	50	50					

Watermark varieties known:
Wmk upright, Type I: C 12, C 13.
Wmk inverted, Type I: C 12.
Wmk reversed, Type I: C 12.
Wmk inverted and reversed, Type I: C 12.
Wmk upright, Type II: C 13, C 14, D 14, E 14, F 15, G 15, H 16, I 16, J 17, K 17, K 18, N 19, O 19, O 20, P 20, Q 21, R 21, S 22, T 22, U 22, U 23, V 23, W 23, W 24.
Wmk inverted, Type II: C 13, D 14, E 14, F 15, G 15, I 16, U 23, V 23, W 23, W 24.
Wmk reversed, Type II: D 14, G 15, H 16, I 16.
Wmk inverted and reversed, Type II: C 14, D 14, E 14, F 15, G 15, H 16, I 16, U 23, V 23, W 23, W 24.
Wmk upright, Type III: J 17, K 17, K 18, L 18, M 18, M only, M 19, N 19, O 19, O 20, P 20, Q 20, Q 21, R 21, S 21, S 22, T 22, U 22, U 23, V 23, W 23, W 24.
Wmk inverted, Type III: J 17, K 17, K 18, L 18, N 19, O 19, O 20, P 20, Q 20, Q 21, R 21, S 21, S 22, T 22.
Wmk reversed, Type III: K 17, L 18, M 19, P 20, Q 20, R 21, S 21, T 22.
Wmk, inverted and reversed, Type III: J 17, K 17, K 18, L 18, M 18, M 19, N 19, O 19, O 20, P 20, Q 20, Q 21, R 21, S 22, S 23, T 22.

Booklet Panes of Six

From Booklets BB6/11, BB18/19, BB22 and BB30/32

NB7 Watermark upright 5·00	NB7a Watermark inverted 5·00
b. Do. Watermark reversed ..	*ba.* Do. Watermark reversed..
s. " Specimen ", Type 23 .. £500	*as.* " Specimen ", Type 23 .. £500
t. " Cancelled ", Type 24 .. £100	*at.* " Cancelled ", Type 24 .. £100
u. Cancelled " London E.C.",	*au.* Cancelled " London E.C.",
Type H .. .. .. 35·00	Type H .. .. 35·00
v. Cancelled " London, E.C.",	*av.* Cancelled " London E.C.",
Type I .. .. .. 35·00	Type I .. .. .. 35·00

Coils

Vertical delivery made up from sheets with joins every 10th stamp

Code No.	Issued	Number in roll	Face value	
A	1913	1000	£4.3.4	Top delivery
B	1913	1000	£4.3.4	Bottom delivery
E	1913	500	£2.1.8	Top delivery
F	1913	500	£2.1.8	Bottom delivery
KERMODE	Mid 1920	1000	£4.3.4	Top delivery

Experimental coils from continuous reels with vertical delivery

E	1923	500	£2.1.8	Top delivery

Sideways delivery made up from sheets with joins every 12th stamp

O	Sept. 1920	480	£2.0.0	**Left side delivery**

In 1915 1d. stamps were printed on paper of better quality, known as "currency" paper made by William Joynson & Son. This was an imperforate printing and the watermark employed was Simple Cypher. It is understood that plate 28a was used, but there was no control number. The paper needed more ink than normal, to give a good print, and the sheets were eventually perforated, made into coils and sold through automatic vending machines.

Die Proofs

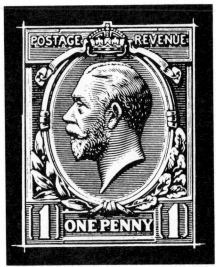

Stage 5

Stage 5.   Completed by 30 May 1912 but subsequently slightly amended and hardened for working purposes about the end of June.   On proof paper or card.   Uncleared

In deep rose-red, bright scarlet, ultramarine or black   ..   ..   *From* £2250

Colour Trials

In die proof form but cut close to margins
  On thick paper or thin card
    In four shades of red including geranium blue, also in blue .. .. .. *From* £1000
  On paper watermarked Imperial Crown (vertical or sideways). Imperf.
    In four shades of red including geranium blue, also in blue .. .. .. *From* £1100

Perforated 15 × 14. Watermark Simple Cypher
  In brown-red (1916) overprinted "Cancelled", Type 24 .. .. £275

   In 1916 experiments were carried out using inks described as Monolite Fast Scarlet, Monolite Red and Monolite Fast Red (Paranitraniline Red). The latter is brown-red and is listed above but the others were close to issued shades (see No. N16w).

Imprimaturs from the National Postal Museum Archives

  Booklet pane of six. Imperforate, watermark Type W14

  Two panes as No. NB7 arranged horizontally *tête-bêche* and marginal pillars at right

1d. Advertisement Trials

   About 1922 the Post Office prepared trial advertisements on the back of the issued 1d. stamps with "Specimen" overprint.
   Different advertisements were used on the same sheet and we illustrate one of these. The project was not proceeded with and so the stamps were never issued.

On No. N16 optd "Specimen" Type 23

  With various advertisements on back, in red .. .. *Each from* £120

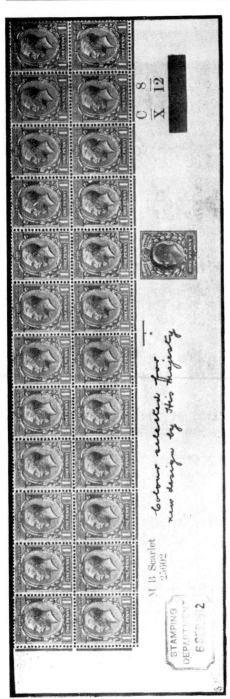

1d. Colour Trials, 1912

Colour trials were made in **eight different shades of red** on paper with Simple Cypher watermark, perforated 15 × 14.

They were printed from 1d. plate no. 1/199, 240 set, with Control $\frac{C}{X}\frac{8}{12}$ in the bottom margin together with a One Penny stamp of King Edward VII which was left imperforate.

As with the colour essays of the 1911 issue some were marked with the colour makers' reference numbers as shown below. The colours in the second column are as we would describe them.

Inscribed	Shade
A M/B Scarlet 25568	Pale scarlet-vermilion
B M/B Scarlet 25569	Scarlet-vermilion
C S.P Scarlet 1	Deep scarlet-vermilion
D M/B Scarlet 25612	Scarlet
E M/B Scarlet 25602	Bright Scarlet
F S.E. Scarlet 3181	Rose-red (present colour)
G Scarlet 1182	Deep rose-red
H Blue Geranium	Carmine-lake

The colour makers were Mander Bros. (A,B,D,E); Slater & Palmer (C) and Shackell Edwards & Co. (F,G,H,).

As far as is known only two sheets of each were prepared, one of which is in the Royal Collection.

In carmine-lake (" Blue
Geranium ") £275
In the other seven shades
From £150
Block of twelve (6 × 2) from
right of sheet similar to that
illustrated

Plate Markings

Plate	Marking

1   No marking
2a   Dot under left serif of P of 1st
2b   Added $\frac{1}{2}$ dot (inner) and dot 20th left side, 8 mm.
3a   Dot under E(N) of 2nd
3b   Added two dots under O(N)E of 3rd
3c   Added dot and $\frac{1}{2}$ dot (outer) 20th left side, 10$\frac{1}{2}$ mm.
4a   Small dot under P of 3rd
4b   Added minute dot at left, under 3rd
5a   Dot under P of 4th
5b   Added dot under N(N) of 4th
5c   Added dot under N(E) of 1st
6a   Dot under PE of 1st
6b   Added dot under N(E) of 1st. Dot 18th right side, 10 mm. Rule under 11th thin
7   Dot under P of 3rd. $\frac{1}{2}$ dot (inner) 17th left side, 12$\frac{1}{2}$ mm. Dot 17th right side, 10 mm. Nick left base of 12th. Rule under 11th thin
8a   Slanting internal cut under PE of 1st
8b   Added small dot under (P)E of 5th
8c   Added $\frac{1}{2}$ dot (inner) and dot bulging (inner) 20th left side, 8$\frac{1}{2}$, 7 mm.
9   Dot 20th left side, 13$\frac{1}{2}$ mm.
10a   2 big dots under (O)N, E(N) of 2nd
10b   Added long dot under EP of 2nd
11a   Dot (breaking right) 18th right side, 10 mm.
11b   Added small dot 18th right side, 4$\frac{3}{4}$ mm., the original dot now bulging right
12   Dot (central) 18th right side, 10 mm.
13   Long dot (breaking right) 19th left side, 8 mm.
14a   Dot 19th left side, 12 mm.   Two internal cuts to left of O and under O of 2nd
14b   Added two internal cuts under NE and P of 2nd
15   Dot 17th right side, 8$\frac{3}{4}$ mm.
16   Small dot 20th left side, 7$\frac{3}{4}$ mm. Dot 18th right side, 11 mm. Top 19th left side bevelled
17   **Triangular dot under E(N) of 2nd**
18   **Triangular dot under P of 3rd**
19   Irregular dot, which is large and sometimes plain, but at other times hardly visible (top) under EN of 4th. Small dot above 11th upper pane
20   Small dot 18th right side, 11 mm.   Rule thinner at top
21   Dot 18th right side, 7$\frac{1}{2}$ mm.
22   Dot (bulging right) 17th right side, 11 mm.
23   $\frac{1}{2}$ cut (base) and $\frac{1}{2}$ dot (top) under (N)N of 1st
24   2 small dots under ONE of 2nd
25   Two small dots at left and under PE of 4th
26   Dot breaking left 18th right side, 11$\frac{3}{4}$ mm.
27   Small dot 18th right side, 12 mm.
28   Dot (right) 18th right side, 11 mm.
29a   Dot (left) 20th left side, 12$\frac{1}{2}$ mm.
29b   Added cut to left of O of 1st.   Added large dot to left of O of 4th
30   Flat oval dot under EN of 1st
31   Dot (breaking base) under EP of 2nd
32a $\frac{3}{4}$ dot (base) left of O of 3rd
32b   Added large dot 20th left side, 10 mm.
33   Dot under O of 4th. Dot 18th right side, 12$\frac{1}{2}$ mm. Base of 10th damaged at right
34   Dot 18th right side, 8$\frac{1}{2}$ mm.
35   Minute nick under NY of 11th; dot 17th right side, 10 mm. (Smaller and more regular than Pl. 7)
36   Curved dot under PEN of 1st (breaking base)
37a   Dot 20th left side, 8$\frac{3}{4}$ mm. Right end of rule under 3rd damaged
37b   Added slanting $\frac{3}{4}$ cut (base) under PE of 3rd
37c   Added wide $\frac{3}{4}$ cut (base) under PEN of 2nd
38a   Curved dot under PE of 3rd
38b   Added dot 19th left side, 11 mm.
39a   Curved dot under E(P) of 3rd
39b   Added curved dot under PE of 4th

40a   Dot under (N)E of 3rd; dot under P of 7th; dot 18th left side, 13 mm. Dot 19th left side, 11 mm. (breaking inner)
40b   Added dot 17th left side, 11$\frac{1}{4}$ mm.
41   Dot under N(E) of 4th.   Dot under P of 8th $\frac{1}{2}$ dot (inner) 17th left side, 12 mm.
42a   Dot under P of 6th
42b   Added dot under EN of 1st and under EN of 2nd
43   Horizontal gash (base) under PE of 1st
44   Dot under P of 1st.   Dot under P of 5th Dot 20th left side, 10$\frac{1}{2}$ mm.   Dot 17th left side, 14 mm.
45   Large dot breaking base under EN of 2nd. Dot 20th left side, 10 mm. Dot 19th left side, 12$\frac{1}{2}$ mm.
46a   Curved dot under NE of 3rd
46b   Added large irregular curved dot under EPE of 1st
47   Small dot under P of 2nd
48   Dot under N(N) of 2nd. Dot under NE of 3rd which later became larger oval dot (breaking base)
49   Dot under NE of 2nd; minute dot under ON of 12th. X cut 20th left side, 12–14 mm.
50   Large $\frac{1}{2}$ dot (base) under PE of 2nd. Dot 19th left side, 10 mm.
51   $\frac{1}{2}$ dot (top) under PE of 3rd
52   Dot under PE of 1st
53a   Large dot (breaking top) under EP of 3rd. Long dot 19th left side, 11 mm. Cut 15th left side, 12$\frac{1}{2}$ mm. Rules at sides thick.
53b   Added large dot (breaking base) under EN of 1st
54   Indent (base) under ON of 5th. Dot (breaking inner) 19th left side, 10 mm.
55   Dot 20th left side, 11$\frac{1}{4}$ mm.   The rule is 23 mm. high (see Plate 119)
56a   Small oval dot under PE of 1st. Base (outer) 20th left side rounded
56b   Added dot (top) under (N)E of 3rd
57   Dash under EN and dot under (N)N of 1st. Dot and irregular $\frac{1}{2}$ cut (base) under EP of 2nd. Dot (base) under NE of 3rd. 4 cuts 19th left side, 9$\frac{1}{2}$–11 mm.
58   Large dot (breaking top) under PEN of 2nd
59   Oval cut under EP of 2nd. Nick (base) at right end of 10th
60   Dot under P of 2nd. 2 oval cuts under PE of 3rd
61a   Dot and oval dot under EPE of 2nd. Large dot (breaking top) under NE of 4th
61b   Added large dot (top) under N(N) of 4th
62   Irregular dot with spur breaking base under E(P) of 4th
63   Dot under EP and dash to the right of Y of 4th.   Nick (outer) 20th left side, 10 mm. Dot 17th left side, 15$\frac{1}{4}$ mm. Base 20th left side bevelled. $\frac{1}{2}$ dot (top) above 1st top row to right of rule
64   Inverted V cut (base) under (P)E of 2nd
65a   Indent (base) under NN of 11th
65b   Added diagonal cut with internal nick below it 18th right side, 10 mm., 9$\frac{1}{2}$ mm.
66   X cut 17th right side, 14$\frac{1}{2}$ mm.   X cut and straight cut 18th right side, 13$\frac{1}{2}$, 12$\frac{1}{2}$ mm.
67a   2 dots over 2 cuts 19th right side, 9, 13 mm. Rule under 11th thinner. Dot (top) under P of 3rd
67b   Added X cut 17th right side, 10 mm.   X cut 18th right side, 10$\frac{1}{2}$ mm.
68a   Dot (breaking base) under P of 1st
68b   Added half dot (breaking base) under NE of 2nd
68c   Added 3 dots under PE, NN to right of Y of 11th

Plate	Marking
69a	Dot (base) under PE of 1st
69b	Added dot 20th left side, 13¾ mm.
70a	Dot under EN of 2nd
70b	Added two irregular dots breaking top and base under (P)E of 3rd
71	½ dot (top) under PE of 10th; small dot 18th right side, 6 mm.
72	Nick (base) at right end of 11th
73a	Dot 18th right side, 9½ mm.
73b	Added dot under (N)N of 1st; added ½ dot (inner) 20th left side, 9¼ mm.
74	Dot (base) under EP of 2nd. Dot (central) 19th left side, 14 mm.
75a	Dot (sometimes breaking base) to left of P of 10th. 2 dots, left of O and under (N)E of 2nd
75b	Added slanting ½ cut 18th right side (inner)
76	Diagonal cut 19th right side, 14–13 mm. Thin tapering cut, 13 mm. (forming a rudimentary V)
77a	Dot under (P)E of 1st. ½ dot (inner) 20th left side, 11¾ mm.
77b	Added dot (outer) 19th left side, 13¼ mm.
78	Cut at right of 1st
79	Dot under EP of 1st
80a	Dot under EN of 2nd; dot 19th left side, 10½ mm.
80b	Added four dots under EN, NY of 11th
81	Dot under (N)E of 10th
82	Dot (top) under EP of 2nd
83	Dot 20th left side breaking outer, 10½ mm. Rule 20th left bevelled at base. Tiny nick (base) under EP of 4th
84	½ dot (base) at extreme left of 11th
85	Dot 19th left side, 10½ mm.
86	Cut under (P)E of 2nd. Two tall dots 2nd left side, 10, 14½ mm.
87a	Dot (breaking inner) 20th right side, 12 mm.
87b	Added dot under PE of 10th
88a	Dot 17th right side, 3 mm.
88b	Added dot 19th left side, 7 mm.
89	Dot (inner) 18th right side, 9¾ mm.
90	Tall dot 17th right side, 12½ mm.
91	Dot 18th right side 9½ mm. minute nick 19th right side, 12¾ mm.
92	3 cuts 20th right side, 8, 12½, 17 mm. Small dot 17th right side, 5½ mm. Minute dot 20th left side, 6½ mm.
93	4 half cuts (outer) 20th right side, 5, 8¾, 12¼, 15½ mm.
94	Tiny dot (inner) 20th left side, 12 mm.
95	Large dot (breaking left) 18th right side, 11½ mm.
96	Left of 12th thinner
97a	½ dot (base) under (P)E of 1st
97b	Added dot joined to tiny dot, 20th left side, 9½ mm.
98	Vacant
99	Tall dot 20th right side, 12 mm. (Waterlow Plate 3)
100	Dot 20th left side, 13½ mm.; two small cuts left of O and under O of 3rd
101	Fine tall dot 19th left side, 8¼ mm. (Waterlow Plate 5)
102	Thick irregular cut 19th right side, 14¼–13 mm., thin tapering cut, 13 mm. (Rather similar to Plate 76, but the upper cut is thicker and longer)
103	Dot 18th right side 10 mm.; fine diagonal cut 19th right side with outer part of rule indented, 10 mm.
104	Thin X cut over diagonal cut 17th right side, 7 mm. Internal crescent cut 20th left side, 11 mm.
105	Dot breaking top under right serif of P of 9th
106	Large oval ½ dot (top) under PE of 9th
107	Dot (base) under EP of 9th
108	Dot (base) under P of 9th (bulging base). Rules at sides, particularly the left, very irregular
109	Cut 15th left side, 12½ mm. Rules at sides thinner than Plate 53
110	Cut 16th left side, 12 mm.
111	Tiny dot under PE of 3rd. Rule 19th left side very thick. Rule 20th left side tapers slightly at base
112	Small dot (inner) 18th left side, 11 mm. Small dot under P of 2nd. Dot under PE of 3rd. Nick (inner) 18th right side, 21 mm.
113	Minute nick 19th right side, 16 mm. Tall ot (breaking left) 18th right side, 12 mm.
114a	Cut with central dot under O of 3rd. Tiny dot above 5th top row
114b	Added two cuts with central dots, 20th left side, 13, 17½ mm. (Waterlow Plate 1)
115	Small dot 18th right side, 16 mm.
116	Dot 18th right side, 10 mm.
117	Dot 17th right side, 12 mm.; dot 18th right side, 14 mm. ½ dot (top) above 1st top row to left of rule
118	Tiny ½ dot (outer) 20th right side, 5½ mm. Large irregular dot 19th left side, 10¾ mm. (Waterlow Plate 4)
119	Dot (breaking inner) 20th left side, 11½ mm. The rule is 22¾ mm. high (to distinguish from plate 55)
120	Minute nick (outer) 20th left side, 2½ mm. (Waterlow Plate 6)
121	Small dot 20th left side, 11¾ mm. Rule damaged 15th right side. Tiny dot above 3rd top row

Index to Marginal Markings

Top Margin, Stamp Number

Stamp No.		Plate
1	..	63, 117
3	..	121
5	..	114a, 114b
11	..	19

Bottom Margin, Stamp Number

Stamp No.		Plate
1	..	2a, 2b, 5c, 6a, 6b, 8a, 8b, 8c, 23, 29b, 30, 36, 42b, 43, 44, 46b, 52, 53b, 56a, 56b, 57, 68a, 68b, 68c, 69a, 69b, 73b, 77a, 77b, 78, 79, 97a, 97b
2	..	3a, 3b, 10a, 10b, 14a, 14b, 17, 24, 31 37c, 42b, 45, 47, 48, 49, 50, 57, 58, 59, 60, 61a, 61b. 64. 68b, 68c, 70a, 70b, 74, 75a, 75b, 80a, 80b, 82, 86, 112
3	..	3b, 4a, 4b, 7, 18, 32a, 32b, 37a, 37b, 37c, 38a, 38b, 39a, 39b, 40a, 40b, 46a, 46b, 48, 51, 53a, 53b, 56b, 57, 60, 67a, 67b, 70b, 100, 111, 112. 114a, 114b
4	..	5a, 5b, 5c, 19, 25, 29b, 33, 39b, 41, 61a, 61b, 62, 63, 83
5	..	8b, 8c, 44, 54
6	..	42a, 42b
7	..	40a, 40b
8	..	41
9	..	105, 106, 107, 108
10	..	33, 59, 71, 75a, 75b, 81, 87b
11	..	6b, 7, 35, 65a, 65b, 67a, 67b, 68c, 72, 80b, 84
12	..	7, 49, 96

Left Margin, Row Number

Row No.	Plate
2 ..	86
15 ..	53a, 53b, 109
16 ..	110
17 ..	7, 40b, 41, 44, 63
18 ..	40a, 40b, 112

Right Margin, Row Number

15 ..	121
17 ..	7, 15, 22, 35, 66, 67b, 88a, 88b, 90, 92, 104, 117
18 ..	6b, 11a, 11b, 12, 16, 20, 21, 26, 27, 28, 33, 34, 65b, 66, 67b, 71, 73a, 73b, 75b, 89, 91, 95, 103, 112, 113, 115, 116, 117

No Marking: Plate 1

Row No.	Plate
19 ..	13, 14a, 14b, 16, 38b, 40a, 40b, 45, 50, 54, 74, 77b, 80a, 80b, 85, 88b, 101, 111, 118
20 ..	2b, 3c, 8c, 9, 16, 29a, 29b, 32b, 37a, 37b, 37c, 44, 45, 49, 55, 56a, 56b, 63, 69b, 73b, 77a, 77b, 83, 92, 94, 97b, 100, 104, 111, 114b, 119, 120, 121
19 ..	53a, 53b, 57, 67a, 67b, 76, 91, 102, 103, 113
20 ..	87a, 87b, 92, 93, 99, 118

Control Schedule

Control	Plates with which it was used
C 12 ..	2a, 3a, 4a, 5a, 6a, 6b, 7
C 13 ..	2a, 2b, 3a, 3b, 3c, 4a, 4b, 5a, 5b, 5c, 6b, 7, 8a, 8b, 8c, 9, 10a, 11a, 11b, 12, 15, 16, 25
C 14 ..	4b, 5c, 8c, 12, 13, 14a, 15, 19, 43
D 14 ..	9, 12, 13, 14a, 15, 16, 17, 18, 19, 20, 21, 22, 25, 43
E 14 ..	10b, 12, 14b, 15, 16, 17, 18, 19, 22, 23, 24, 25, 26. 27, 28, 29a, 37a
F 15 ..	16, 29b, 30, 31, 32a, 33, 34, 35, 37a, 52
G 15 ..	29b, 32b, 33, 35, 36, 37a, 37b, 37c, 38a, 39a, 39b, 40a, 41, 42a, 42b, 44, 52, 55, 64
H 16 ..	30, 31, 36, 37c, 38a, 39b, 40a, 40b, 41, 42b, 44, 45, 46a, 55, 110
I 16 ..	38a, 38b, 40b, 41, 46b, 47, 48, 49, 50, 51, 53a, 54, 55, 109
J 17 ..	49, 51, 53a, 53b, 55, 56a, 56b, 57, 58, 59, 60, 61a, 61b, 62, 63, 65a, 66, 67a, 67b, 69a, 73a, 76, 102, 104, 111
K 17 ..	49, 63, 65a, 66, 67b, 68a, 69b, 70a, 71 72, 73a, 76, 104, 105, 112

Control	Plates with which it was used
K 18 ..	63, 65a, 65b, 68b, 70b, 71, 72, 74, 75a, 76, 77a, 80a, 104, 105, 107
L 18 ..	70b, 74, 75a, 77a, 103, 104, 105, 107
M 18 ..	69b, 70b, 71, 74, 103, 104
M 19 ..	70b, 71, 73a, 77b, 78, 80a, 105
N 19 ..	68c, 73b, 75a, 78, 79, 80a, 80b, 81, 82, 84, 108
O 19 ..	75a, 78, 79
O 20 ..	75b, 90, 119
P 20 ..	68a, 73b, 80b, 85, 87a, 88a, 95
Q 20 ..	85, 87a
Q 21 ..	87a, 88b, 113
R 21 ..	72, 75b, 87a, 87b, 89, 113
S 21 ..	75b, 87b, 96, 106
S 22 ..	83. 86, 87b, 91, 94, 96, 97b, 114a
T 22 ..	86, 87b, 91, 92, 93, 94, 96, 106
U 22 ..	87b, 91, 92, 93, 97b, 116
U 23 ..	91, 92, 93, 97b
V 23 ..	92, 93, 101, 114b, 117, 118, 121
W 23 ..	86, 99, 101, 115, 118
W 24 ..	99, 101, 117, 120
? ..	1, 97a, 100

Cat. No. S.G. No.	Wmk.	Shades	Unused	Used

1913 (AUGUST). 1d. RED, TYPE N5. WMK. MULTIPLE CYPHER

N17	398	W.13 Multiple Cypher	(1) Scarlet	£150	£130
			(2) Dull scarlet	£150	£130

a. Block of four £900
b. Coil join (vert. pair) .. £300
c. Watermark inverted .. £300
d. Crown missing in wmk. .. £350

Originally issued in vertical rolls of 500 stamps. Subsequently sheets or part sheets were found, so that horizontal pairs, blocks and three control pairs are known.

Control. Wmk. Multiple Cypher

	I.	*P.*
C 13 ..	—	†

Coil
Vertical delivery made up from sheets with joins every 10th stamp

Code No.	Issued	Number in roll	Face value	
E	Aug. 1913	500	£2.1.8	Top delivery

1924. 1d. RED, TYPE N5. WMK. SIMPLE CYPHER. SOMERSET HOUSE EXPERIMENTAL PRINTING

N17A	—	W.14 Simple Cypher	Pale scarlet	£200

b. Coil join (vert. pair) £450
s. "Specimen", Type 30 .. .. £200

This was from an experimental coil printing made by Somerset House on Simple Cypher watermarked paper using a plate supplied by the Royal Mint about the end of 1923. It is distinguishable from No. N16 in pale red by its very coarse impression, whilst the paper is also rougher and of a different texture. Possibly it had not been plate-glazed.

The wording on the coil leaders has been reset and lacks Harrison's name. The leader and tail joins were crudely made using coarse white paper but more often brown or red paper, quite different from the Harrison joins. The trailers were invariably blank but some of the Harrison trailers were stamped with " JOINED BY . . ." and " DATE . . ." for record purposes and the paper was usually yellow. The earliest recorded purchase of this item was in May 1924.

Coil
Vertical delivery printed in continuous reels

Code No.	Issued	Number in roll	Face value	
E	1924	500	£2.1.8	Top delivery

| Cat. No | S.G. No. | | Wmk. | | | Shades | Unused | Used |

1912 (OCTOBER).   1½d. RED-BROWN, TYPE N6

N18 362/65 W.14 Simple Cypher

a.	No watermark	£120
b.	Watermark inverted ..	1·50 / 65 /
c.	Watermark reversed ..	7·50 3·00
d.	Watermark inverted and reversed	4·50 2·25
e.	PENCF variety (Pl. 12, R. 15/12)	£225 90·00
f.	PENCF variety (Pl. 29, R. 15/12)	£110 50·00
fa.	Do. Wmk. inverted and reversed	£750
g.	PENCE repaired (Pl. 12, R. 15/12)	£450
h.	PENCE repaired (Pl. 29, R. 15/12)	£350
ha.	Do. No watermark	
i.	Blurred beard (Pl. ?, R. ?/12)	£300
j.	Gash behind head (Pl. ?, R. 1/2)	95·00
k.	White spot top right corner (vert. coil)	35·00
l.	CE damaged (Pl. ?, R. ?/12)	30·00
m.	Final E of PENCE damaged (Pl. ?, R. ?/10)	30·00
n.	Frame damaged (Pl. 15b. Control N 19, R. 20/2) ..	£150
q.	Coil join (vert pair) (8.18)	
r.	Coil join (horiz. pr.) (5.20) .	

(1)	Red-brown	80 /	15 /
(2)	Pale red-brown	3·75	1·10 /
(3)	Deep red-brown	2·00 /	55 /
(4)	Very deep red-brown (1922)	£150	30·00
(5)	Chocolate-brown	1·00 /	35 /
(6)	Deep chocolate-brown (1918-19)	30·00	4·00 /
(7)	Chocolate (1919)	£150	12·00 /
(8)	Brown (1918)	£250	£100
(9)	Pale brown (1918)	£300	£100
(10)	Yellow-brown (1916-18)	15·00	9·00
(11)	Deep yellow-brown (1916)	25·00	5·00
(12)	Bright yellow-brown (1920-21)	15·00	4·00 /
(13)	Chestnut	1·25 /	25 /
(14)	Bright chestnut (1922-23)	30·00 /	6·50 /
(15)	Orange-brown (1919-20)	3·50	45 /
(16)	Bright orange-brown (1920)	30·00	6·50 /

s.	" Specimen ", Type 23	..	15·00
t.	" Specimen ", Type 26	..	35·00
u.	" Cancelled ", Type 24	..	15·00

N18e/f

N18g/h "Pence" repaired

The PENCF variety and corrected versions from plate 12 (thin rule) and plate 29 (thick rule)

N18i

N18j

N18k

Nos. N18i/j are not plate flaws, nevertheless a number of examples are known

N18l

N18m

N18n

177

Watermark Varieties. The following have been recorded:

Wmk upright: Types I, II, III
Wmk inverted: Types II, III
Wmk reversed: Types II, III
Wmk inverted and reversed: Types I, II, III

Misplaced Watermarks

ya. Single stamp showing letters from " POSTAGE " .. 5·50	*yb.* Vertical strip sufficient to show complete " POSTAGE " watermark .. 75·00

Broken Dandy Roll Varieties

za. Missing Crown	.. ..	15·00
zb. Missing G	.. ..	7·00
zc. Missing v	.. ..	5·00
zd. Missing R	.. ..	6·50
ze. Missing Gv	..	7·00

zf. Missing vR ..	.. ..	9·00
zg. Missing Crown vR ..	..	9·00
zj. Missing tail to R (" GvP ")		4·00
zk. Long tail to G	.. ..	15·00

Perforation

Variety Type 2C is known with controls C13 and J17 .. .. *Strip of 3, each* 25·00

Controls

Somerset House Printings:

	I.	P.
A. 12 (w)	2·00	75·00
A. 12 (c)	2·00	

(w) " wide " and (c) " close " refer to the spacing between the " A " and the serif of the " 1 " (4 mm and 1¾ mm respectively).
Watermark varieties known:
Wmk upright, Type I: A. 12 (w), A. 12 (c).
Wmk inverted and reversed, Type I: A. 12 (w).

Harrison Printings:

	I.	P.			I.	P.			I.	P.
C 13	1·00	1·00	L 18	80	80	Q 21 ..	..	2·50	3·00
D 14	1·00	1·00	M 18	1·00	1·00	T 22 ..	..	1·00	1·00
F 15	2·50	1·75	M 19	1·00	1·00	U 22 ..	..	1·00	1·00
G 15	1·00	1·00	19 only [M omitted] ..	£1500	£1500	U 23 ..	..	1·00	1·00
H 16	1·50	1·25	N 19	1·00	1·00	V 23 ..	..	1·00	1·00
J 17	3·00	2·50	O 19	1·00	1·00	W 23 ..	..	1·50	1·50
K 18	3·00	3·00	O 20	1·00	1·00	W 24 ..	..	60·00	60·00
18 only [K omitted] ..	£750	£750	Q 20	3·50	3·50				

Watermark varieties known:
Wmk upright, Type I: C 13.
Wmk upright, Type II: C 13, D 14, F 15, G 15, H 16, J 17, K 18, L 18, N 19, O 19, O 20, Q 21, U 22, U 23, V 23, W 23, W 24.
Wmk inverted, Type II: U 22, U 23, V 23.
Wmk reversed, Type II: U 22, U 23.
Wmk inverted and reversed, Type II: C 13, D 14, F 15, G 15, U 22, U 23, V 23, W 23.
Wmk upright, Type III: J 17, K 18, 18 only, L 18, M 18, M 19, 19 only, N 19, O 19, O 20, Q 20, Q 21, T 22, U 22, U 23, V 23, W 23.
Wmk inverted, Type III: L 18, M 18, M 19, N 19, O 19, O 20, Q 21, T 22.
Wmk reversed, Type III: L 18, N 19, Q 21, T 22.
Wmk inverted and reversed, Type III: L 18, M 18, M 19, N 19, O 19, O 20, Q 20, Q 21, T 22.

Booklet Panes of Six

From Booklets BB11, BB18/19, BB22/23 and BB31/32

NB8 Watermark upright 12·00
s. " Specimen ", Type 23 ..	£250
t. " Cancelled ", Type 24 ..	£100
u. Cancelled " London E.C.", Type H	35·00
v. Cancelled " London E.C.", Type I	35·00

NB8a Watermark inverted 12·00
as. " Specimen ", Type 23 ..	£250
at. " Cancelled ", Type 24 ..	£100
au. Cancelled " London E.C.", Type H	35·00
av. Cancelled " London, E.C.", Type I	35·00

Booklet Panes with Advertising Labels

Panes of six, comprising two labels printed in black and four stamps
From Booklet BB11

NB9 Watermark upright   £225   NB9a Watermark inverted   £225

  a. Cancelled " London E.C.",
    Type 1 ..   ..   ..

			Wmk	*Wmk*
			Upright	*Inverted*
(1)	" Stamp Auctions, Harmer, Rooke, expert advice free/Millennium Oat-Flakes "		£225	£225
(2)	" Millennium Oat-Flakes / Stamp Auctions, Harmer, Rooke, expert advice free "		£225	£225

Coils

Vertical delivery made up from sheets with joins every 10th stamp

Code No.	Issued	Number in roll	Face value	
J	Aug. 1918	1000	£6.5.0	Top delivery
K	Aug. 1918	1000	£6.5.0	Bottom delivery
L	Aug. 1918	500	£3.2.6	Top delivery
M	Aug. 1918	500	£3.2.6	Bottom delivery

Sideways delivery made up from sheets with joins every 12th stamp

| N | May 1920 | 480 | £3.0.0 | Right side delivery |
| N | Late 1920 | 480 | £3.0.0 | Left side delivery |

Die Proofs

Finished die in black on white glazed card ..	..	..	..	..	..	..	£1750
Finished die in brown on wove paper	..	..	..	..	..	..	£1500
Finished die in red or brown on paper, Wmk. W. 14	..	..	..	..	*From*	£1500

Imprimaturs from the National Postal Museum Archives

Booklet pane of six. Imperforate, watermark Type W14

Two panes as No. NB8 arranged horizontally *tête-bêche* and marginal pillars at right

Plate Markings

Plate	Marking
1a	**Dot** above 1st in upper and lower panes
1b	Dots above 1st filled in
2a	**Dot** above 2nd in upper and lower panes; scoop under THR of 10th. 1st right side split **at top**
2b	Dots above 2nd filled in
2c	Added minute dot under L of 1st
2d	Added very fine cut 1st top row. Added dot 20th right side, 11½ mm.
3a	**Dot** above 3rd in upper and lower panes
3b	Dots above 3rd filled in
3c	Added minute dot under L of 2nd. Large internal cut 18th right side, 5–10 mm.
3d	Added very fine cut 2nd top row
3e	Added dot 19th right side, 8½ mm.
4a	**Dot** above 4th in upper and lower panes
4b	Dots above 4th filled in
5a	Dot (base) to left of T of 1st
5b	Added ¼ dot (inner) 19th left side, 6¼ mm.
6a	**Large dot** (breaking base) to left of T of 2nd
6b	Added fine ¼ cut (base) under P of 2nd; added dot under AL of 9th
7	Dot (top) to left of T of 3rd. Nick (outer) 3rd left side, 21 mm.
8a	Dot (base) to left of T of 4th
8b	Added ¼ cut (outer) 19th left side, 9½ mm. Added fine ¼ cut (base) under FP of 2nd
9	**Large dot** (bulging top) under T of 1st
10a	**2 dots** 19th left side, 8¼, 9 mm. Lower dot breaking outer
10b	Added tiny nick (base) under H of 2nd
11	**Dot** 20th left side, 11½ mm. Crack (outer) 11th **right side**
12a	**2 cuts** 20th left side, 5¼, 7 mm. Minute dot under F of 12th
12b	Added dot under A of 9th
13a	**2 cuts** 19th left side, 7, 8 mm. Rules 18th, 19th and 20th left irregular. ¼ dot (base) under F of 11th
13b	Added nick (base) under HA of 2nd
14a	**Cut** 20th left side, 10 mm. Fine cut under H of 1st
14b	Cut under H filled in
15a	¼ cut 17th left side, 7¼ mm. Nick (inner) 20th left side, 14¼ mm.
15b	Added dot under AL of 2nd. Nick (inner) 20th left side 14½ mm.
16a	**Dot** 17th left side, 11¼ mm.
16b	Added small dot under A of 3rd. Added cut 18th right side, 10½ mm.
17	**Large dot** (breaking base) under H(A) of 1st
18	**Large oval dot** under L of 2nd (breaking base). **Tall oval dot** 19th left side, 11½ mm., usually breaking right, sometimes left as well
19	**Nick** (inner) 19th left side, 10½ mm.
20a	**Cut** 20th left side, 6½ mm.
20b	Added ½ cut under TH of 1st
21	**Large ¼ dot** (base) under L of 2nd. Fine ¼ cut (base) under L of 11th
22	**Double dot** under A of 10th

Plate	Marking
23	No marking
24a	Dot (outer) 19th left side, 6½ mm. Double dot under A of 9th
24b	Added nick (base) under EN of 2nd. *Note* Rule at 19th left is thicker and measures 23 mm. See Plate 27
25	Cut 19th left side, 5½ mm.
26	Oval (blurred) cut 20th left side, 15 mm.
27	Small dot (outer) 19th left side, 6¾ mm. *Note* Rule at 19th left measures 22¾ mm. See Plate 24. On late printings from U 23, the rule under 1st is broken at bottom left
28	Small dot under A of 4th
29	½ dot (outer) 20th right side, 21 mm.
30	No marking on lower pane. ½ cut (outer) 3rd right side, 10 mm.
31	½ dot (inner) 19th left side, 12 mm.
32	Dot 17th left side, 11 mm. ½ dot (outer) 20th left side, 9 mm. Lower end of 20th left side thinner. Dot and ½ dot above 1st top row
33	½ dot (outer) 20th left side, 10½ mm.
34	Dot (inner) 20th left side, 13 mm.
35	Small dot 20th left side, 9 mm.
36	Oval cut 17th right side, 9½ mm.

Plate	Marking
37	Small nick (base) to left of T of 2nd
38	Tall dot 19th left side, 10½ mm
39	Dot (outer) 20th left side, 11½ mm. ½ dot (outer) 19th left side, 10 mm.
40	2 cuts 18th right side, 8¾, 10½ mm.
41	½ dot (outer) 20th left side, 5 mm. (Waterlow Plate 10)
42	Outer side of 20th left side damaged 4-5 mm.
43	Small ½ dot (base) under A of 4th. Nick (outer) 7 mm. and tiny dot 11 mm. both 17th left side. (Waterlow Plate 11)
44a	Small dot (inner) 18th left side, 9½ mm.
44b	Added dot under H of 10th; added tiny dots under HR and (E)E of 11th
45	Small ½ dot (inner) 20th right side, 12 mm Tiny dot below EE of 12th
46	Dot (outer) at foot of 1st right side. Small dot 18th right side, 12½ mm. Dot (outer) 20th right side, 7 mm.
47	Dot 19th right side, 12 mm., also internal nick, 10 mm. Tiny dot under A of 10th. Small dot 13th left side, 9 mm. Small ½ dot (outer) 15th left side, 15 mm.

Index to Marginal Markings

Top Margin, Stamp Numbers

Stamp No.	Plate
1 ..	1a, 2d, 32
2 ..	2a, 3d, 3e
3 ..	3a
4 ..	4a

Bottom Margin, Stamp Numbers

Stamp No.	Plate
1 ..	2c, 2d, 5a, 5b, 9, 14a, 17, 20b, 27
2 ..	3c, 3d, 3e, 6a, 6b, 8b, 10b, 13b, 15b, 18. 21, 24b, 37
3 ..	7, 16b
4 ..	8a, 8b, 28, 43
9 ..	6b, 12b, 24a, 24b
10 ..	2a, 2b, 2c, 2d, 22, 44b, 47
11 ..	13a, 13b, 21, 44b
12 ..	12a, 12b, 45

Left Margin, Row Numbers

Row No.	Plate
3 ..	7
13 ..	47
15 ..	47
17 ..	15a, 15b, 16a, 16b, 32, 43
18 ..	13a, 13b, 44a, 44b
19 ..	5b, 8b, 10a, 10b, 13a, 13b, 18, 19, 24a, 24b, 25, 27, 31, 38, 39
20 ..	11, 12a, 12b, 13a, 13b, 14a, 14b, 20a, 20b, 26, 32, 33, 34, 35, 39, 41, 42

Right Margin, Row Numbers

Row No.	Plate
1 ..	2a, 2b, 2c, 2d, 46
3 ..	30
11 ..	11
17 ..	36
18 ..	3c, 3d, 3e, 16b, 40, 46
19 ..	3e, 24b, 47
20 ..	2d, 29, 45, 46

No Marking: Plates 1b, 3b, 4b, 23

Control Schedule

Control	Plates with which it was used
A. 12 ..	1a, 2a, 3a, 4a
C 13 ..	1b, 2b, 3b
D 14 ..	2b, 3b
F 15 ..	2c, 3c
G 15 ..	2c, 3c
H 16 ..	2c, 3d
J 17 ..	2c, 2d, 3e
K 18 ..	2d, 3e, 4b, 5a, 6a, 7, 8a
(K) 18 ..	2c
L 18 ..	2d, 3e, 5a, 6a, 7, 8a, 8b, 9, 10a, 11, 12a, 13a, 16a, 44a
M 18 ..	5a, 6b, 9, 13a, 14a, 19, 23, 44a
M 19 ..	5a, 5b, 6b, 7, 8b, 9, 11, 13a, 14b, 15a, 15b, 16b, 28, 44b
(M) 19 ..	14b
N 19 ..	7, 8b, 10b, 11, 13a, 13b, 14b, 15b, 17, 18, 19, 20a, 21, 30
O 19 ..	12a, 17, 18, 20a, 21, 24a, 25, 26
O 20 ..	17, 18, 21, 24a, 26
Q 20 ..	20a, 21, 25, 40
Q 21 ..	12b, 18, 19, 20a, 21, 24a, 24b, 26, 29
T 22 ..	8b, 12b, 17, 18, 20a, 22, 24b, 25, 26, 27, 31, 32, 33, 34, 35, 36
U 22 ..	20a, 25, 27, 31, 32, 33, 34
U 23 ..	18, 20a, 20b, 25, 27, 31, 32, 33, 34, 39
V 23 ..	17, 18, 20b, 35, 37, 38, 39, 40, 41, 42, 43, 45, 47
W 23 ..	37, 38, 39, 40, 41, 42, 45, 46
W 24 ..	38

DIE I

Inner frame-line at top and sides close to solid of background. *Four* complete lines of shading between top of head and oval frame-line. White line round " TWOPENCE " thin.

DIE II

Inner frame-line farther from solid of background. *Three* lines between top of head and oval. White line round " TWOPENCE " thicker.

Cat. No.	S.G. No.	Wmk.		Shades	Unused	Used

1912 (AUGUST).   2d. ORANGE, TYPE N7.   DIE I

					Unused	Used
N19	366/69	W.14 Simple Cypher		(1) Orange-yellow (1912)	3·00 ✓	1·50 ✓
a.	Without watermark	..	75·00	(2) Reddish orange (1913)	1·00 ✓	35 ✓
b.	Watermark inverted	..	6·50 / 3·00	(3) Deep reddish orange		
c.	Watermark reversed	..	9·00 4·50	(1916)	50·00	10·00 ✓
d.	Watermark inverted and reversed	.. ..	7·00 2·50	(4) Pale orange	2·00 ✓	45 ✓
e.	Frame line double (1)	..	20·00	(5) Orange	90 ✓	35 ✓
f.	Broken frame at left (Pl. 14, R. 19/1)	.. ..	70·00	(6) Brown-orange (1921)	18·00 ✓	4·50 ✓
g.	Damaged left value tablet (Pl. ?, R. 1/4)	.. ..	60·00	(7) Bright orange	1·10 ✓	55 ✓
h.	Coil join (vert. pair) (7.20)			(8) Deep bright orange	3·25 ✓	50 ✓
i.	Coil join (horiz. pr.) (9.20)	..		(9) Intense bright orange	£1500	£425
s.	" Specimen ", Type 26	..	50·00			
t.	" Cancelled ", Type 24	..				

Shade (9) is a printing in fugitive ink, highly suffused, and showing through to the back of the stamp.   Shade (8) is also known printed in fugitive ink.

Variety *e* occurs between the 6th and 7th stamps on some rows of the sheet.

The change of colour from orange-yellow to reddish orange in 1913 was deliberate.

N19f

N19g

Watermark Varieties.   The following have been recorded:

Wmk upright: Type I (*orange-yellow*); Type I (*reddish orange*); Types II, III (*orange*)
Wmk inverted: Type I (*orange-yellow*); Types II, III (*orange*)
Wmk reversed: Type I (*orange-yellow*); Type II (*orange*)
Wmk inverted and reversed: Type I (*orange-yellow*); Type I (*reddish-orange*); Types II, III (*orange*)

Misplaced Watermarks

ya. Single stamp showing letters from " POSTAGE " ..	5·50	*yb.* Vertical strip sufficient to show complete " POST-AGE " watermark ..	95·00

Broken Dandy Roll Varieties

za. Missing Crown	.. ..	15·00	*zf.* Missing vR	14·00
zb. Missing G	.. ..	9·00	*zg.* Missing Crown vR	12·00
zc. Missing v	.. .. ..	6·50	*zh.* Missing Crown GvR ..	45·00
zd. Missing R	.. .. ..	9·00	*zj.* Missing tail to R (" GvP ")	5·00
ze. Missing Gv ..	.. ..	9·00	*zk.* Long tail to G	12·00

Perforation
Normally Types 2 or 2A, but most control pieces from C. 13 show Types 3A or 2C

Controls
Somerset House Printings:

	I.	P.
C. 13	2·00	2·00

Wmk upright, Type I, or inverted and reversed, Type I.

Harrison Printings:

	I.	P.		I.	P.		I.	P.
no control*	35·00	35·00	J 17	1·25	2·00	P 20	1·25	1·25
C 14	2·25	2·00	K 17	1·25	9·00	Q 20	1·25	1·25
D 14	1·25	1·25	L 18	1·25	1·25	Q 21	1·25	1·25
F 15	1·25	1·60	M 19	2·00	3·00	R 21	1·25	1·25
G 15	1·25	1·25	N 19	1·25	3·00	S 21	1·80	1·80
H 16	1·25	£125	O 19	1·40	30·00	S 22	1·80	1·80
I 16	1·25	9·00	O 20	1·25	1·25	T 22	5·00	5·00

* The prices quoted are for bottom left-hand corner pairs with selvedge attached.

Watermark varieties known:
Wmk upright, Type I: no control.
Wmk inverted, Type I: no control.
Wmk reversed, Type I: no control.
Wmk inverted and reversed, Type I: no control.
Wmk upright, Type II: C 14, D 14, F 15, G 15, H 16, I 16, J 17, K 17, N 19, O 19, O 20, P 20, Q 21, R 21, T 22.
Wmk inverted, Type II: H 16, I 16, R 21.
Wmk reversed, Type II: G 15, I 16.
Wmk inverted and reversed, Type II: G 15, H 16, I 16.
Wmk upright, Type III: J 17, K 17, L 18, M 19, N 19, O 19, O 20, P 20, Q 20, Q 21, R 21, S 21, S 22, T 22.
Wmk inverted, Type III: K 17, M 19, N 19, O 20, P 20, Q 20, Q 21, S 21.
Wmk reversed, Type III: P 20.
Wmk inverted and reversed, Type III: L 18, M 19, N 19, O 19, O 20, P 20, Q 20, Q 21, R 21, S 21, T 22.

Booklet Panes of Six
From Booklets BB20, BB30/31 and BB32 (part)

NB10 Watermark upright	30·00		**NB 10a** Watermark inverted	40·00	
s. Cancelled "London E.C.", Type H	40·00		*as.* Cancelled "London E.C.", Type H	40·00	
t. Cancelled "London, E.C.", Type I	40·00		*at.* Cancelled "London, E.C.", Type I	40·00	

Coils
Vertical delivery made up from sheets with joins every 10th stamp

Code No.	Issued	Number in roll	Face value	
Q	July 1920	1000	£8.6.8	Bottom delivery
R	July 1920	500	£4.3.4	Top delivery
R	July 1920	500	£4.3.4	Bottom delivery
KERMODE	Mid 1920	1000	£8.6.8	Top delivery

Sideways delivery made up from sheets with joins every 12th stamp

T	Sep. 1920	480	£4.0.0	Left side delivery

Die Proofs
Head placed too high in frame with solid background, uncleared
In black on white glazed card.. .. .. £1750

Head in normal position with horizontal background shading, uncleared
In black on white glazed card.. .. .. £1850

Plate Proofs
Special plate of four on surfaced paper in black or orange .. .. *Per block* £2000

Colour Trials
Imperf. on gummed paper
In cadmium orange, bright green, magenta or the issued colour .. .. .. *From* £650

Imprimaturs from the National Postal Museum Archives
Booklet pane of six. Imperforate, watermark Type W14

Two panes as No. NB10 arranged horizontally *tête-bêche* and marginal pillars at right

Plate Markings

This value departed from the normal usage in the setting of the marginal rules. The settings are:

A All rules fully co-extensive; rule under 6th vertical row very long (20 mm.). (Plates 1, 2, 3, 4 and 5.)

B Cuts above and below 6th and 7th vertical rows; no cuts between 6th and 7th rows. (Plates 7, 10, 13, 16 and 19.)

C As Setting B but cuts have been filled in. (Plates 9 and 18.)

D As Setting A, but rule under 6th vertical row measures 19½ mm. (Plates 8, 11 and 21.)

E As Setting D, but rule under 6th vertical row measures 19 mm. This setting shows signs of having cuts above and below 6th and 7th vertical rows filled in. (Plate 20.)

The settings of the remaining plates (6, 12, 14, 15 and 17) are not known.

Plate	Marking
1	No marking
2a	Dot above 6th in upper and lower panes; dash under E of 2nd
2b	Dash under E repaired, but traces showing at bottom of rule
2c	Added tall oval dot 19th left side, 12 mm. Later this dot breaks left and right edges of rule
3	Dot above 8th in upper pane only; cut under PE of 1st
4	Cut under WO of 2nd
5a	Dot above 2nd in upper and lower panes. 20th left side shows a slight bulge in the centre and a progressive thickening towards the base
5b	Dots above 2nd filled in
6	Large dot 20th left side bulging rule at right, 12 mm.
7a	Dot 19th left side, 11 mm.
7b	Dot now breaking right side of rule; added dot 19th left side (breaking left), 7½ mm. Dot to right of 4th in top row
8a	Fine dot 20th left side, 13 mm.
8b	18th left side damaged slightly at left; added dot 20th left side, 14 mm.
9a	Nick (inner) 20th left side, 2 mm. Dot 17th right side, 9½ mm.
9b	Added oblique dot 20th left side, 14½ mm.
10	Dot 18th right side, 8 mm.
11	Dot 17th right side, 10½ mm. ½ dot (outer) 18th left side, 11½ mm.
12	Outer base of 19th left side bevelled off. Nick (outer) 20th left side, 10 mm.
13	Tall dot 19th left side, 11½–12 mm., usually breaking rule at left and bulging rule slightly at right
14	Scoop (outer) 19th left side, 8½–11 mm.; outer frame of stamp 19/1 broken opposite left value tablet
15	Elongated dot 19th left side, 11 mm.
16	Nick (base) under W of 1st; nick (outer) 19th left side, 2 mm.
17a	Oval cut 20th left side, 11¾ mm.
17b	Added three tiny dots 1st right side
18a	½ dot (outer) 18th right side, 18 mm.
18b	Added ½ dot (inner) 20th left side, 8 mm.
19	Tall oval dot 19th left side breaking right and usually left, 14½ mm. Dot (inner) 18th right side, 11 mm. Dot 20th right side, 10 mm.
20	Double dot 17th left side, 13½ mm.

Index to Marginal Markings

Top Margin, Stamp Numbers

Stamp No.	Plate
2	5a
4	7b
6	2a, 2b, 2c
8	3

Bottom Margin, Stamp Numbers

Stamp No.	Plate
1	3, 16
2	2a, 2b, 2c, 4

Left Margin, Row Numbers

Row No.	Plate
17	20
18	8b, 11
29	2c, 7a, 7b, 12, 13, 14, 15, 16, 19
10	5a, 5b, 6, 8a, 8b, 9a, 9b, 12, 17a, 17b, 18b

Right Margin, Row Numbers

Row No.	Plate
1	17b
17	9a, 9b, 11
18	10, 18a, 18b, 19
20	19

No Marking: Plate 1

Control Schedule

Control	Plates with which it was used
None	1, 3, 4
C. 13	2a, 5a
C 14	3, 4
D 14	1, 3,
F 15	3, 4
G 15	3, 4
H 16	3, 4
I 16	3, 4
J 17	3, 4, 5b
K 17	3, 4, 5b
L 18	3
M 19	3, 5b
N 19	3, 4, 5b
O 19	3, 4
O 20	2a, 4, 5b, 6, 13, 18a
P 20	2a, 2b, 3, 4, 5b, 6, 7a, 7b, 8a, 8b, 9a, 12, 13, 20
Q 20	2b, 3, 5b, 6, 7b, 8b, 9a, 13
Q 21	2b, 6, 7b, 8b, 9b, 12, 13, 14, 15, 16
R 21	2b, 2c, 8b, 9b, 10, 11, 12, 15, 16, 17a, 18b, 19
S 21	2c, 7b, 8b, 12, 16, 17a, 18b, 19
S 22	6, 9b, 12, 16, 17a, 18b, 19
T 22	9b, 12, 15, 16, 17b, 18b, 19

Cat. No.	S.G. No.	Wmk.		Shades		Unused	Used

1921 (SEPTEMBER). As last, but DIE II

N20	370	W.14 Simple Cypher		(1) Orange		2·50✓	1·75✓
a.	Without watermark	£400		(2) Pale orange		2·50✓	1·75
b.	Watermark inverted	12·00	4·50	(3) Deep orange		4·00	1·50
c.	Watermark inverted and reversed	12·00	4·50	(4) Bright orange		3·00	1·10
d.	Frame break below "N" (Pl. 3, R. 20/2)	30·00					
s.	"Specimen", Type 15 ..						
t.	"Specimen", Type 23 ..						

No. N20 is known with so-called varnish ink but as stated in the General Notes we defer listing.

N20*d*

Watermark Varieties. The following have been recorded:

Wmk upright: Types II, III
Wmk inverted: Types II, III
Wmk inverted and reversed: Types II, III

Misplaced Watermarks

ya. Single stamp showing letters
  from " POSTAGE " .. 18·00

yb. Vertical strip sufficient to
  show complete " POST-
  AGE " watermark .. £200

Broken Dandy Roll Varieties

za. Missing Crown .. .. 22·00

zc. Missing v .. .. .. 12·00

Controls

Harrison Printings:

			I.	*P.*				*I.*	*P.*				*I.*	*P.*
S 21	..	..	6·00	6·00	U 22	..	..	3·00	3·00✓	W.23	..	..	3·00✓	3·00✓
S 22	..	..	3·00	3·00	U 23	..	..	3·00	3·00	W 24	..	..	55·00	55·00
T 22	..	..	3·00	3·00	V 23	..	..	3·00	3·00					

Watermark varieties known:
Wmk upright, Type II: T 22, U 22, U 23, V 23, W 23, W 24.
Wmk inverted, Type II: W 23, W 24.
Wmk inverted and reversed, Type II: W 23, W 24.
Wmk upright, Type III: S 21, S 22, T 22, U 22, U 23, V 23, W 23.
Wmk inverted, Type III: S 22.
Wmk inverted and reversed, Type III: S 21, S 22, T 22, U 23.

Booklet Panes of Six

From Booklets BB21 and BB32 (part)

NB11   Watermark upright 50·00
  s. Cancelled "London E.C.",
    Type I.. .. .. 40·00

NB11a   Watermark inverted 90·00
  s. Cancelled "London E.C.",
    Type I .. .. .. 40·00

Imprimaturs from the National Postal Museum Archives

Imperforate, watermark Type W14

Watermark upright

Booklet pane of six. Imperforate, watermark Type W14

Two panes as No. NB11 arranged horizontally *tête-bêche* and marginal pillars at right

184

Plate Markings

Plate	Marking
1	Oval dot 19th left side, sometimes breaking rule at left and right, 13 mm.
2	Dot (outer) 20th left side, 14½ mm.; ½ dot (base) under P of 1st bottom row
3	Lower part of 20th left side slightly tapered; dot (top) under OP of 9th bottom row; dot (breaking inner) 17th right side, 12¼ mm. (Waterlow Plate 17)

Plate	Marking
4	Dot 20th left side, 13 mm. (Waterlow Plate 4)
5	Dot 19th left side, 12½ mm.; scratch 20th left side (not always visible) (Waterlow Plate 5)
6	Dot under P of 10th bottom row; dot (central) 18th right side, 13 mm. (Waterlow Plate 18)

Control Schedule

Plate		Controls employed
1	..	S 21, S 22, T 22, U 22, U 23, V 23
2	..	S 21, S 22, T 22, U 22, U 23
3	..	S 21, S 22, T 22, V 23, W 23, W 24

Plate		Controls employed
4	..	T 22, U 23, V 23, W 23, W 24
5	..	T 22, U 23, V 23, W 23, W 24
6	..	S 22, T 22

Cat. No.	S.G. No.	Wmk.			Shades	Unused	Used

1912 (OCTOBER).   2½d. BLUE, TYPE N5

N21	371/73	W.14 Simple Cypher		(1)	Cobalt-blue (1912-14)	4·50	1·00
				(2)	Cobalt-violet-blue (1912)	15·00	5·00
a.	Without watermark	..	£700	(3)	French blue (1913-16)	20·00	85
b.	Watermark inverted	..	18·00	5·00	(4)	Bright blue (1914-17)	4·00	1·00
c.	Watermark reversed	..	10·00	3·50	(5)	Deep bright blue	
d.	Watermark inverted and re-					(1915-22)	£225	50·00
	versed	.. .. ..	9·00	4·00	(6)	Milky blue (1917)	15·00	1·40
e.	Watermark double shade (1)			(7)	Pale milky blue (1917)	£800	£100
s.	" Specimen ", Type 15	..		(8)	Powder blue (1918)	8·00	1·25
t.	" Specimen ", Type 23	..	35·00	(9)	Violet-blue (1918)	18·00	4·00
u.	" Specimen ", Type 26	..	50·00	(10)	Blue	4·00	1·00
v.	Imperf. optd. " Cancelled ",			(11)	Pale blue (1917-19)	5·00	85
	Type 24	..	65·00	(12)	Deep blue (1920-22)	7·50	1·00
				(13)	Dull blue (1920)	5·00	1·00
				(14)	Indigo-blue (1920)	£900	£550
				(15)	Indigo-blue (toned	
					paper) (1920)	£3000	
				(16)	Royal blue (1920)	£250	
				(17)	Dull Prussian blue	
					(1921)	£600	£325
				(18)	Dull Prussian blue	
					(toned paper) (1921)	£4500	
				(19)	Ultramarine (1919-23)	8·50	1·00

Shade (7) is from a worn printing of Plate 1 (Control J 17). Shades (14), (15), (16) are printed in fugitive ink; used examples in the correct shades are consequently very rare. Most printings of shade (12) Controls O 20 and P 20 are also fugitive.

Shades (14) and (15) are from Control O 20 and should not be confused with shades (17) and (18) which are Control R 21.

Shade (18) is slightly deeper than (17) and both are unlike the rare Prussian blue shade of the 2½d. Jubilee issue.

Watermark Varieties.   The following have been recorded:

Wmk upright: Types I, II, III
Wmk inverted: Types I, II, III
Wmk reversed: Types II, III
Wmk inverted and reversed: Types I, II, III

Misplaced Watermarks

ya.	Single stamp showing letters from " POSTAGE " ..	25·00	*yb.*	Vertical strip sufficient to show complete " POST-AGE " watermark ..	£500

Broken Dandy Roll Varieties

za.	Missing Crown	..	..	22·00	*zf.*	Missing vR ..	.. ..	14·00
zb.	Missing G	..	..	12·00	*zg.*	Missing Crown vR ..	..	15·00
zc.	Missing v	..	..	9·00	*zi.*	Missing left side to R		15·00
zd.	Missing R	..	..	12·00	*zj.*	Missing tail to R (" GvP ")..		9·00
ze.	Missing Gv	..	..	12·00	*zk.*	Long tail to G	.. ..	15·00

Perforation

Variety Type 2C is known with control C14   .. .. *Strip of 3* 30·00

Controls

Somerset House Printings:

			I.	*P.*
A. 12	..	..	7·00	£300
J. 17	..	..	£175	†

Watermark varieties known:
Wmk upright, Type I: A. 12.
Wmk inverted, Type I: A. 12.
Wmk inverted and reversed, Type I: A. 12.
Wmk upright, Type II: J. 17.

Harrison Printings:

	I.	P.		I.	P.		I.	P.
C 13	5·00	5·00	K 17	6·00	£275	Q 21	9·00	9·00
C 14	6·00	6·00	L 18	5·00	5·00	R 21	7·00	7·00
D 14	12·00	12·00	M 18	8·00	8·00	S 21	6·00	6·00
E 14	5·00	5·00	M 19	8·00	8·00✓	S 22	20·00	20·00
G 15	5·00	5·00	N 19	6·00	6·00	T 22	9·00	9·00
H 16	5·00	5·00	O 19	6·00	6·00	U 23	7·50	6·50
I 16	6·00	7·00	O 20	6·00	6·00	V 23	6·00	6·00
J 17	6·00	6·00	P 20	6·00	6·00			

Watermark varieties known:

Wmk upright, Type II: C 13, C 14, D 14, E 14, G 15, H 16, I 16, J 17, K 17, L 18, M 18, O 20, R 21, U 23, V 23.

Wmk inverted, Type II: C 14, J 17.

Wmk reversed, Type II: G 15.

Wmk inverted and reversed, Type II: C 13, C 14, G 15, H 16.

Wmk upright, Type III: J 17, K 17, L 18, M 18, M 19, N 19, O 19, O 20, P 20, Q 21, R 21, S 21, S 22, T 22.

Wmk inverted, Type III: L 18, O 19, O 20, Q 21, R 21.

Wmk inverted and reversed, Type III: J 17, L 18, M 18, M 19, N 19, O 19, O 20, P 20, R 21, T 22.

Die Proof

The transfer die for the 2½d. was taken from the same roller as the 1d. die and Harrison completed engraving the figures and words of value on 30 July 1912. The die was proofed at the Royal Mint on 20 August 1912.

Uncleared in blue on thick paper £1750

Plate Markings

Plate	Marking
1a	Dot above 1st in upper and lower panes
1b	Dots above 1st filled in
1c	Added nick (outer) 3rd left side
1d	Added oval dot under 2nd bottom row
2a	Dots above 2nd in upper and lower panes
2b	Dots above 2nd filled in
2c	Added oval dot under P of 1st bottom row
3a	Dots above 4th in upper and lower panes
3b	20th left side bent inwards at base. 19th right side damaged (outer)
4a	Dots above 5th in upper and lower panes. 20th right side damaged
4b	Dots above 5th filled in
5	Minute nick at left of 1st bottom row. Tiny nick top right of 2nd bottom row
6	19th right side damaged (inner). Small ½ dot (base) under 12th bottom row. 12th left side bevelled; nick (outer) 14th left side

Plate	Marking
7a	No marking. Tiny nick (top) of 1st bottom row beneath Y. (Hardly visible on M19)
7b	20th left side bevelled at base
8a	1st left side bevelled at top; rule under 7th bottom row thins at right
8b	Added circular dot under P of 1st bottom row (Waterlow Plate 6)
9a	No marking
9b	Added ½ dot (base) under FP of 2nd bottom row
10	Cut under (P)E of 1st bottom row (Waterlow Plate 15)
11a	Base of 12th bottom row worn with nick (central) at top
11b	Added cut under F of 2nd bottom row (Waterlow Plate 4)
12	4th and 9th rules right side bevelled

Control Schedule

Plate	Controls employed	Plate	Controls employed	Plate	Controls employed
1a ..	A. 12	4a ..	A. 12	9a ..	M 18, N 19
1b ..	C 13	4b ..	D 14, E 14, I 16	9b ..	N 19, O 20, Q 21, R 21
1c ..	I 16	5 ..	H 16	10 ..	S 21, T 22, U 23, V 23
1d ..	I 16, J 17	6 ..	C 14, G 15	11a ..	R 21
2a ..	A. 12	7a ..	K 17, L 18, M 18, M 19	11b ..	S 21, S 22, T 22, U23, V 23
2b ..	I 16	7b ..	O 19, O 20, Q 21	12 ..	G 15
2c ..	I 16, J 17	8a ..	J 17, K 17, M 19, N 19		
3a ..	A. 12	8b ..	N 19, O 19, P 20, Q 21, R 21, S 22, T 22		
3b ..	C 13				

Cat. No.	S.G. No.	Wmk.		Shades	Unused	Used

1912 (OCTOBER). 3d. VIOLET, TYPE N7

Bright reddish violet ✓

N22	374/77	W.14 Simple Cypher	
a.	Without watermark	..	£110
b.	Watermark inverted	..	20·00	7·00
c.	Watermark reversed	..	35·00	15·00
d.	Watermark inverted and reversed	.. ..	10·00	6·00
e.	Frame broken (Pl. 4, R.20/2)	25·00
s.	"Specimen", Type 15	..
t.	"Specimen", Type 23	..	65·00
u.	"Cancelled", Type 24	..
v.	"Specimen", Type 26	..	50·00

(1)	Reddish violet (1912-13)	13·00	3·50
(2)	Dull reddish violet (1912-13)	7·00 ✓	1·00 ✓
(3)	Violet	2·00 ✓	55 ✓
(4)	Pale violet (1917-18)	4·00 ✓	90 ✓
(5)	Very pale violet (1916)	£130 ?	20·00
(6)	Bright violet	2·25 ✓	70 ✓
(7)	Bluish violet	2·50 ✓	90 ✓
(8)	Lavender-violet	5·00	70 ✓
(9)	Dull violet (1920)	3·00 ✓	70
(10)	Very deep violet (1922-23)	·50·00 ✓	11·00 ✓
(11)	Heliotrope (1919)	10·00 /	1·25 ✓
(12)	Brownish violet (1921)	15·00 ✓	1·25

Shade (11) heliotrope has a decidedly pinkish tone.   The change of colour **from reddish to** bluish violet was deliberate.

N22e

Watermark Varieties.   The following have been recorded:

Wmk upright: Types I, II (*reddish violet*); Type I (*violet*); Types I, II, III (*bluish violet*)
Wmk inverted: Type II (*reddish violet*); Type I (*violet*); Types II, III (*bluish violet*)
Wmk reversed: Types II, III
Wmk inverted and reversed: Types II, III

Misplaced Watermarks

ya.	Single stamp showing letters from "POSTAGE" ..	10·00

yb. Vertical strip sufficient to show complete "POSTAGE" watermark   ..   £130

Broken Dandy Roll Varieties

za.	Missing Crown	..	..	20·00
zb.	Missing G	..	..	14·00
zc.	Missing v	..	..	9·00
zd.	Missing R	..	..	—
ze.	Missing Gv	..	..	—

zf.	Missing vR ..	..	..	12·00
zg.	Missing Crown vR ..	....	14·00
zi.	Missing left side to R	..	12·00
zj.	Missing tail to R ("GvP")	9·00
zk.	Long tail to G	..	..	15·00

Controls

Somerset House Printings in reddish violet:

		I.	P.
A. 12 (w)..	..	15·00 ✓	£100
A. 12 (c) ..	..	20·00	25·00
B. 13	.. ..	20·00	25·00

(w) "wide" and (c) "close" refer to the spacing between "A" and "1" (4mm and 1¼ mm respectively).
Watermark varieties known:
Wmk upright, Type I: A. 12 (w), A. 12 (c), B. 13.
Wmk inverted, Type I: B. 13.
Wmk inverted and reversed, Type I: A. 12 (w), B. 13.

Somerset House Printings in bluish violet:

		I.	P.
C. 13	..	10·00	25·00

Wmk upright, Type II only.

Harrison Printings in reddish violet:

		I.	P.
C 13	.. ..	12·00	12·00 ✓

Wmk upright, Types I or II.

Harrison Printings in bluish violet shades:

	I.	P.		I.	P.		I.	P.
C 13	3·00	3·00	L 18	3·00✓	3·00	S 22	3·00	3·00
D 14	3·00	3·00	M 18	3·00	4·00	T 22	4·00	4·00
E 14	3·00	3·00	N 19	3·00	3·00	U 22	4·00✓	4·00
F 15	3·00	3·00✓	O 20	3·00	3·00	U 23	4·00	4·00✓
G 15	7·00	3·00	P 20	3·00	3·00	V 23	4·00✓	4·00
H 16	4·00	4·50	Q 21	3·00	3·00	W 23	4·00	4·00
I 16	4·00	4·00	R 21	3·00✓	3·00			
J 17	3·00	4·00✓	S 21	7·00	7·00			

Watermark varieties known:
Wmk upright, Type I: E 14.
Wmk upright, Type II: C 13, D 14, E 14, F 15, G 15, H 16, I 16, J 17, N 19, O 20, R 21, U 22,
   V 23, W 23.
Wmk inverted, Type II: G 15, U 22, U 23, V 23.
Wmk reversed, Type II: I 16.
Wmk inverted and reversed, Type II: C 13, E 14, F 15, G 15, I 16, U 22.
Wmk upright, Type III: J 17, L 18, M 18, N 19, O 20, P 20, Q 21, R 21, S 21, S 22, T 22, U 22, U 23,
   V 12, W 23.
Wmk inverted, Type III: L 18, N 19.
Wmk reversed, Type III: Q 21.
Wmk inverted and reversed, Type III: J 17, L 18, O 20, Q 21, R 21, S 22.

Colour Trial

Produced from a 240 set plate under special control
X. 13 watermarked Simple Cypher, perf. 15 × 14 and
known only in a control block of six

   In shade of violet not selected ..   *Control block of six* £3500
   One example recorded and endorsed "not accepted" in
manuscript.

Plate Markings

Plate	Marking
1a	Dot at left and dot (central) above 1st in upper pane; dot (central) above 1st in lower pane
1b	Dots above 1st filled in
1c	Added dot at right of 1st in upper and lower panes
2a	Dot above 2nd in upper and lower panes. Minute ⅓ dot under right of 5th bottom row
2b	Dots above 2nd filled in
2c	Added cut 20th left side, 12½ mm.
3a	Dot above 3rd in upper and lower panes
3b	Dots above 3rd filled in
4a	Dot above 4th in upper and lower panes
4b	Dots above 4th filled in
4c	Further dot cut above 6th in upper and lower panes
5	Diamond cut under EP of 2nd bottom row. Minute dot under EN of 11th bottom row
6a	No marking
6b	Added cut under E(E) of 1st bottom row
7a	⅓ dot (outer) 14th right side, 3 mm.
7b	Added cut under EP of 2nd bottom row
8a	Base of 20th right side bevelled
8b	Added nick (outer) 19th left side, 5¾ mm.
9	⅓ dot (inner) 20th left side, 12¾ mm.
10	Dot 19th left side, 13 mm. (Waterlow Plate 3)
11	Base 17th right side bevelled. Damage (base) under REEP of 8th bottom row
12a	Rule under 2nd bottom row damaged and broken away at bottom right. Cut above 11th top row
12b	Left of line under 3rd broken at base. Added horizontal dash under PE of 2nd bottom row
13a	Cut above 12th top row
13b	Added large ⅓ dot (base) under EP of 1st bottom row

Control Schedule

Plate	Controls employed	Plate	Controls employed	Plate	Controls employed
1a ..	A. 12 (close)	4b ..	C 13	9 ..	U 22, U 23, V 23, W 23
1b ..	C 13	4c ..	C. 13, F 15, G 15	10 ..	U 22, U 23, V 23, W 23
1c ..	C. 13, F 15, H 16, I 16	5 ..	M 18, N 19, O 20, P 20,	11 ..	S 21, S 22, T 22, U 22,
2a ..	B. 13		Q 21, T 22, U 23, V 23		U 23
2b ..	C 13, D 14	6a ..	Q 21, R 21	12a ..	J 17, L 18
2c ..	E 14, F 15, H 16, I 16	6b ..	R 21	12b ..	M 18, N 19, Q 21
3a ..	A. 12 (close), A. 12	7a ..	Q 21, R 21	13a ..	L 18, M 18
	(wide)	7b ..	R 21	13b ..	M 18, N 19, O 19, O 20
3b ..	F 15, G 15	8a ..	S 21, S 22, T 22		P 20
4a ..	A. 12 (wide)	8b ..	U 22		

Cat. No.	S.G. No.	Wmk.		Shades	Unused	Used

1913 (JANUARY).   4d. GREY-GREEN, TYPE N7 (MACKENNAL'S WREATH DESIGN)

N23	378/80	W.14 Simple Cypher		(1) Grey-green	4·50	60
a.	Without watermark	.. £130		(2) Pale grey-green	9·00	1·75
b.	Watermark inverted	.. 15·00	4·50	(3) Deep grey-green	18·00	3·50
c.	Watermark reversed	.. 20·00	6·00	(4) Slate-green	4·50	50
d.	Watermark inverted and re-versed .. .. .. 18·00	4·50		(5) Pale slate-green	8·00	75
e.	Break above O of FOUR (Pl. 1, R. 19/2) .. .. 30·00			(6) Bluish grey-green (1919)	18·00	1·40
f.	Cracked plate (Pl. 2, R.19/1)	30·00		(7) Deep slate-green (1921)	35·00	1·40
g.	Breaks in bottom frame (R.10/11) .. .. .. 75·00			*s.* "Specimen", Type 15 ..		
h.	Frame breaks at foot (Pl. ?, R. 5/12) .. .. .. 65·00			*t.* "Specimen", Type 23 ..	50·00	
				u. "Cancelled", Type 24 ..	50·00	
				v. "Specimen", Type 26 ..	50·00	

N23e   N23f   N23g

N23h

Watermark Varieties. The following have been recorded:

Wmk upright: Types I, II, III
Wmk inverted: Types I, II, III
Wmk reversed: Type II
Wmk inverted and reversed: Types I, II, III

Misplaced Watermarks

ya. Single stamp showing letters from "POSTAGE" .. 10·00		*yb.* Vertical strip sufficient to show complete "POST-AGE" watermark £130

Broken Dandy Roll Varieties

za.	Missing Crown	.. .. 20·00	*zf.*	Missing vR	15·00
zb.	Missing G ..	.. .. 14·00	*zg.*	Missing Crown vR.. ..	14·00
zc.	Missing v ..	.. .. 9·00	*zi.*	Missing left side to R ..	12·00
zd.	Missing R ..	.. .. —	*zj.*	Missing tail to R ("GvP")	9·00
ze.	Missing Gv ..	.. .. 14·00	*zk.*	Long tail to G	15·00

Perforation

Variety Type 2C is known with control J 17   ..   ..   *Strip of 3*   30·00

Controls

Somerset House Printings:

			I.	P.
B. 13	..	..	7·50	20·00

Watermark varieties known: wmk upright, Type I; wmk inverted, Type I, wmk inverted and reversed, Type I.

Harrison Printings:

			I.	P.				I.	P.				I.	P.
C 13	..	..	5·00	5·00	K 17	..	..	9·00	95·00	S 21	..	..	20·00	25·00
D 14	..	..	5·50	5·50	K 18	..	..	5·00	5·00	S 22	..	..	7·00	20·00
F 15	..	..	5·00	5·00	M 18	..	..	5·00	5·00	T 22	..	..	5·00	5·00
G 15	..	..	5·00	5·00	N 19	..	..	6·00	6·00	U 22	..	..	12·00	15·00
H 16	..	..	5·00	20·00	O 20	..	..	6·00	6·00	U 23	..	..	10·00	8·00
I 16	..	..	5·00	5·00	Q 21	..	..	35·00	35·00	V 23	..	..	6·50	6·50
J 17	..	..	5·00	5·00	R 21	..	..	6·00	6·00					

Watermark varieties known:
Wmk upright, Type I: C 13.
Wmk upright, Type II: C 13, D 14, F 15, G 15, H 16, I 16, J 17, K 17, K 18, O 20, R 21, U 22, U 23, V 23.
Wmk inverted, Type II: G 15.
Wmk reversed, Type II: C 13.
Wmk inverted and reversed, Type II: C 13, G 15, I 16, U 22.
Wmk upright, Type III: J 17, K 17, K18, M 18, N 19, O 20, Q 21, R 21, S 21, S 22, T 22, U 23.
Wmk inverted, Type III: K 17, M 18.
Wmk reversed, Type III: J 17.
Wmk inverted and reversed, Type III: J 17, K 17, M 18, R 21.

Fig. 26a
21·5 mm.

Fig. 26b
22·3 mm.

Bromides of Eve's Wreath Design

Eve's original design in sunken frame, dated 7 May 1912

Original had coinage head pasted in. Value and lettering weak. 21·5 mm. high ..	£350

Similar to above but not in sunken frame, dated on reverse 16 May 1912

Lettering better defined. Lines of shading behind head slope down from left to right. 22·3 mm. high	£175

Large master design (78 × 94 mm.) inscribed on face " 4d. The First Essay.
8:VI:12 " with Harrison's accepted coinage head inserted. Value omitted

Lines of shading behind head slope down from right to left	£500

Similar to Fig. 26a but only 22 mm. high

Mounted on card with M/S noting " Mr. Eve's emmendations ". Lines of shading behind head horizontal	
Lines of shading behind head horizontal	£300
As above but not on card	90·00
On card with M/S " Make plate and submit to Board with colour scheme—F.G. 13 June 1912 "	£350
As above but lines of shading to head slope down from right to left. Dated on reverse 10 June 1912	£175

As Fig. 26b on pale blue card with typed note " Design for 4d. Postage Stamp amended by Mr Eve to correspond with the amended 5d. design. (Motley Process)."

Lines of shading behind head horizontal and graduated from top to bottom	£350

Fig. 27a
22·8 mm.

Fig. 27b
22·5 mm.

Fig. 27c
22 mm.

Fig. 28
22·5 mm.

Trials of Eve's Wreath Design

Figs. 27a/c by Miller and Motley using their Printex machine and used as trials for colour. Large coinage head. Shading at sides of design extends down to P of POSTAGE and last E of REVENUE. The measurements are taken between top and bottom frame lines.

a) Fig. 27a 22·8 mm. high. Left-hand ribbon under head has an ornament in it

    Uncleared die proof with reversed "K"* above design

In black on thin card (but only 22 mm. high)	£750
In purple-brown on thin card	£850
In various colours on thick white ungummed paper taken from plate of four impressions	

Block of four from £1750
    As last but single copies   ..   ..   *From* £400

(b) Fig. 27b. 22·5 mm. Solid colour in left-hand ribbon under head
    In blue on gummed paper watermarked Crown taken from plate of four impressions
    (June 1912) ..   ..   *Block of four* £2000
    As last but single copy £500

(c) Fig. 27c. As (b) but only 22 mm. high
    In various colours on white gummed paper without watermark   ..   ..   *From* £450
    In blue on pink, brown on pink or claret on blue ..   ..   *From* £500

Fig. 28 produced from a die engraved at the Royal Mint by J. A. C. Harrison's assistant, Mr. Lewis. Large coinage head. Shading at sides of the design extends only to the A of POSTAGE and first E of REVENUE. 22·5 mm. high.

Uncleared die proof in pale blue on gummed paper watermarked Simple Cypher, upright or sideways. Uncut	£750
As last but cut close to margin .. .. *From*	£500
Uncleared die proof in red-brown	£750
Cleared die proof in black on card dated "16.9.12"	£600
Cleared die proof in pale blue on paper dated "16.12.12"	£750

*Complete die proofs containing the die number above are worth at least twice the prices quoted.
    For illustration of typical block of four from a special plate see under the 7d. value.

Die Proofs

Uncleared in black on white glazed card	£1750
From cleared working die on gummed paper in grey, pearl-grey and bronze-green on official card dated "10 Dec. 1912"	£2000

Plate Proofs

In pale ultramarine on thick paper	£250
In grey-green on thin gummed paper	£300

Plate Markings

Plate	Marking
1a	Dot above 1st in upper and lower panes
1b	Dots above 1st filled in
1c	Added small dot under RP of 1st bottom row
1d	Dot under RP enlarged
1e	Rule under 3rd bottom row bevelled off at left
2a	Dot above 2nd in upper and lower panes
2b	Dots above 2nd filled in
2c	Added small dot under RP of 2nd bottom row
2d	Dot under RP enlarged (Waterlow Plate 8)
3a	No marking; outer edge left 19th split 8–9 mm.
3b	Added dot under RP of 1st bottom row. Rule under 3rd bottom row not bevelled (Waterlow Plate 4)

Control Schedule

Plate		Controls employed
1a	..	B. 13
1b	..	C 13, D 14
1c	..	F 15, G 15
1d	..	G 15, H 16, I 16
1e	..	I 16, J 17, K 17, K 18, O 20, Q 21, R 21, S 21, S 22, T 22, U 22
2a	..	B. 13
2b	..	C 13, D 14
2c	..	F 15, G 15
2d	..	G 15, H 16, I 16, J 17, K 18, M 18, N 19, O 20, Q 21, R 21, S 21, S 22, T 22, U 22, U 23, V 23
3a	..	I 16, J 17, M 18
3b	..	N 19, R 21, S 21, U 23, V 23

Cat. No.	S.G. No.	Wmk.	Shades	Unused	Used

1913 (JUNE). 5d. BROWN, TYPE N8

N25 381/83 W.14 Simple Cypher

a.	No watermark	£500
b.	Watermark inverted ..	£250	50·00
c.	Watermark inverted and reversed	£110	40·00
d.	Varnish ink (Control H 16)	£1500
e.	Lower left frame break (Pl. ?, R. 20/1 control B.13) ..	80·00
f.	White blotch near "V" of "REVENUE" (Pl. 1c, late ptg. R. 20/2)	40·00
s.	"Specimen", Type 15 ..
t.	"Specimen", Type 23 ..
u.	"Specimen", Type 26 ..	65·00

Shades	Unused	Used
(1) Brown	4·50 ✓	3·00
(2) Reddish brown	6·00	2·25
(3) Yellow-brown	4·50 ✓	2·25 ✓
(4) Ochre-brown (1916)	55·00	15·00 ✓
(5) Ginger-brown (1917)	22·00	7·50 ✓
(6) Bistre-brown	65·00	25·00 ✓

N25*e*

N25*f*

Watermark Varieties. The following have been recorded:

Wmk upright: Types I, II, III
Wmk inverted: Types II, III
Wmk inverted and reversed: Types II, III

Misplaced Watermarks

ya. Single stamp showing letters from "POSTAGE" .. 25·00

yb. Vertical strip sufficient to show complete "POSTAGE" watermark £250

Broken Dandy Roll Varieties

za.	Missing Crown	..	25·00
zc.	Missing G	..	20·00
zc.	Missing v	..	11·00
zd.	Missing R	..	—
zf.	Missing vR	..	15·00

zg.	Msising Crown vR ..	..	15·00
zi.	Missing left side to R ..	..	15·00
zj.	Missing tail to R ("GvP")	..	12·00
zk.	Long tail to G ..	..	15·00

Controls

Somerset House Printings:

	I.	P.
B.13	15·00	15·00

Watermark varieties known: Types I or II, upright only.

Harrison Printings:

	I.	P.		I.	P.		I.	P.
C 14	5·00 ✓	5·00	J 17	5·00	5·00	R 21	5·00	5·00
D 14	5·00	5·00	K 17	5·00	5·50	S 21	5·00	5·00
F 15	5·00	5·00	L 18	5·00	5·00	S 22	6·00	75·00
G 15	5·00	5·50	N 19	5·00	5·00	T 22	5·00	5·00
H 16	5·00	5·00	O 19	5·00	5·00	U 23	5·00	5·00
I 16	8·00	8·00 ✓	Q 21	5·00	5·50	V 23	5·00	5·00

Watermark varieties known:
Wmk upright, Type II: C 14, D14, F 15, G 15, H 16, I 16, K 17, N 19, O 19, Q 21, R 21, U 23, V 23.
Wmk inverted, Type II: H 16.
Wmk inverted and reversed, Type II: D 14.
Wmk upright, Type III: J 17, K 17, L 18, N 19, O 19, Q 21, S 21, S 22, T 22, U 23.
Wmk inverted, Type III: L 18, N 19.
Wmk inverted and reversed, Type III: N 19.

Fig. 28*a*	Fig. 28*a*	Fig. 28*b*	Fig. 28*c*
23 mm.	22·5 mm.	22·5 mm.	22·25 mm.

Bromides of Eve's Wreath Design

There is no evidence of any engraved die with this design used for this value.

Fig. 28*a*. Shading at sides extends down to P of POSTAGE and last E of REVENUE. Large coinage head (12 mm.). Even horizontal lines of shading to background

Dated " 27.6.12 ". 23 mm. high £500
Dated " 2.7.12 ". 22·5 mm. high £500

As Fig. 28*a* on pale blue card with typed note "Embodying Mr. Eve's latest emendations (Motley Process)." ..   ..

Fig. 28*b*. Shading at sides extends only to E of POSTAGE and R of REVENUE

With coinage head and inside of Crown in solid colour. Image completely reversed. Even lines to background of head

Undated £500

With medal head and inside of Crown shaded. A bromide of Eve's artwork 22·5 mm. high. Graduated lines to background of head

Dated " 28.11.1912 " £500

As last but 23 mm. high and endorsed " Photograph taken at The Mint 29 Nov 1912 of Eve's Sketch for an amended Design for 5d. and other Rates " £350

Bromides of Eve's Pillar Design

Fig. 28*c*. With medal head. 22·25 mm. high. Graduated shading to background

Dates " 29.4.13 ". 22·25 mm. high £500
Dated " 29.4.13 ". 22·75 mm. high £500

The last bromide was sent to Harrison who made his own engraving sketch from an enlargement.

Die Proofs from Eve's Pillar Design

Without value in black. Master die for 5d. to 8d. £1750
Fully cleared in black on white glazed card, endorsed "6 May 13" in manuscript £1750
Fully cleared in black on paper watermarked Simple Cypher (sideways), endorsed "2.5.13" in manuscript £1750

Plate Proof

In a block of four with a swatch of colour underneath and used for colour trials

In ochre on paper watermarked Simple Cypher (upright) £2500

Plate Markings

Plate	Marking
1a	Dot above 1st in upper and lower panes
1b	Dots above 1st filled in
1c	Added 1½ sloping cuts under EN of 1st bottom row
2a	Dot above 2nd in upper and lower panes
2b	Dots above 2nd filled in
2c	Added sloping cut under P of 2nd bottom row
3	Tiny diagonal internal cut, 14 mm. 19th right side. (Waterlow Plate 1)

Control Schedule

Plate		Controls employed	Plate		Controls employed
1a	..	B. 13	2b	..	C 14, D 14, F 15, G 15. H 16
1b	..	C 14, D 14, F 15, G 15, H 16	2c	..	H 16, I 16, J 17, K 17, L 18, Q 21, S 21
1c	..	H 16, I 16, J 17, K 17, L 18. N 19, O 19,			S 22
		Q 21 R 21	3	..	Q 21, R 21, S 22, T 22, U 23, V 23
2a	..	B. 13			

Cat. No.	S.G. No.	Wmk.		Shades	Unused	Used

1913 (AUGUST). 6d. PURPLE, TYPE N8. CHALK-SURFACED PAPER

N26	384/86	W.14 Simple Cypher	(1) Dull purple (1913)	14·00	3·00 ✓
a.	Without watermark	£200	(2) Slate-purple (1913)	60·00	15·00
b.	Watermark inverted	14·00 4·75	(3) Reddish purple	7·00	1·00 ✓
c.	Watermark reversed	£400	(4) Pale reddish purple	7·50	45 ✓
d.	Watermark inverted and reversed	18·00 6·00	(5) Deep reddish purple	12·00	1·50 ✓
e.	Perforation 14 (10.20)	60·00 80·00	(6) Purple	8·00	50 ✓
s.	" Specimen ", Type 15		(7) Rosy mauve	6·50	50
t.	" Specimen ", Type 23	45·00	(8) Plum	7·00	75 ✓
u.	" Specimen ", Type 26	65·00			
v.	" Cancelled ", Type 24				
w.	" Cancelled ", Type 28				

Watermark Varieties. The following have been recorded :

Perf 15 × 14 :
  Wmk upright : Types II, III
  Wmk inverted : Types II, III
  Wmk reversed : Types II, III
  Wmk inverted and reversed, Types II, III

Perf 14 :
  Wmk upright : Types II, III
  Wmk inverted : Type III
  Wmk inverted and reversed : Type III

Misplaced Watermarks

ya. Single stamp showing letters from " POSTAGE "   25·00

yb. Vertical strip sufficient to show complete " POST-AGE " watermark ..   £350

Broken Dandy Roll Varieties

za.	Missing Crown		25·00
zab.	Do. Perf 14		£110
zc.	Missing v ..		12·00
zd.	Missing R ..		14·00
zda.	Do. Perf 14		—

zf.	Missing vR		15·00
zg.	Missing Crown vR..		15·00
zi.	Missing left side to R		20·00
zj.	Missing tail to R (" GvP ")		12·00
zka.	Long tail to G (perf 14) ..		—

Perforation

Normally Types 2 or 2A but the following are also known :

									Strip of 3
Type 3	C. 13	Dull purple	..	..	..	..	..	..	80·00
	C. 13	Reddish purple	..	..	..	..	..	..	40·00
Type 3A	C. 13	Dull purple	..	..	..	..	..	..	90·00
Type 2C	C. 13	Reddish purple	..	..	..	..	..	..	75·00
	W. 23	..	..	..	..	..	..	..	75·00
	A. 24	Plum	..	..	..	..	..	..	75·00
	B. 24	Plum	..	..	..	..	..	..	75·00

Controls

Somerset House Printings, Perf 15 × 14 :

	I.	*P.*			*I.*	*P.*			*I.*	*P.*
C. 13 *dull purple*	25·00	30·00	J. 17	..	7·00	†	R. 21	..	7·50	†
C. 13 (*reddish*			K. 17	..	7·00	†	S. 21	..	7·50 ✓	25·00
purple)	10·00	12·00	L. 18	..	7·50	25·00	T. 22	..	9·00 ✓	35·00
D. 14	..	7·00	†	L. 18 [no stop]	..	7·50	†	U. 22	..	7·00	†
E. 14	..	8·00 ✓	8·00	M. 18	..	7·00	£250	V. 23	..	7·00	†
F. 15	..	10·00	£150	N. 19	..	7·00 ✓	35·00	W. 23	..	7·00	†
G. 15	..	7·00	†	O. 19	..	7·00	†	A. 24	..	9·00	†
H. 16	..	7·00	†	P. 20	..	8·00	†	B. 24	..	50·00	†
I. 16	..	7·00 ✓	†	Q. 20	..	8·00 ✓	†				

Watermark varieties known:
Wmk upright, Type II: C. 13 (both shades); D. 14, E. 14, F. 15, G. 15, H. 16, I. 16, J. 17, O. 19, P. 20, Q. 20, S. 21, V. 23, W. 23, A. 24, B. 24.
Wmk inverted, Type II: C. 13 (*reddish purple*), E. 14, H. 16, W. 23, A. 24.
Wmk reversed, Type II: D. 14.
Wmk inverted and reversed, Type II: D. 14, E. 14.
Wmk upright, Type III: J. 17, K. 17, L. 18 (with and without stop), M. 18, N. 19, O. 19, P. 20, Q. 20, R. 21, S. 21, T. 22, U. 22, V. 23, A. 24, B. 24.
Wmk inverted, Type III: L. 18, M. 18, N. 19, O. 19, P. 20, Q. 20, R. 21, S. 21, U. 21, U. 22, V. 23.
Wmk reversed, Type III: O. 19.
Wmk inverted and reversed, Type III: K. 17, N. 19, O. 19, P. 20, T. 22, U. 22.

Somerset House Printings, Perf 14:

	I.	P.
Q. 20	75·00	†
R. 21	85·00	†

Watermark varieties known:
Wmk upright, Type II: Q. 20.
Wmk upright, Type III: Q. 20, R. 21.
Wmk inverted, Type III: R. 21.
Wmk inverted and reversed, Type III: R. 21.

Die Proof

Uncleared in black on white glazed card dated "28.5.1913" £1750

Plate Markings

Plates with interpane margin.

Plate markings such as those used by Harrison and Waterlow were not used at Somerset House, and plating can only be accomplished by the study of fortuitous marks. It seems that the 6d. stamps were printed in pairs of plates and these were marked above the top rows of the panes with a dot above the 1st or 2nd stamps to signify the position in the press.

Plate	Marking
1	Dot above 1st in upper and lower panes
	20th right side thick and mis-shapen
2	Dot above 2nd in upper and lower panes
3a	Dot above 1st in upper and lower panes
	No marking
3b	Small dot below (P)E of 2nd bottom row
4	Dot above 2nd in upper and lower panes
	Base of 20th left side splayed out

Plate	Marking
5	Dot above 1st in upper and lower panes
	Rule under 2nd bottom row **very thick**
6	Dot above 2nd in upper pane (to left of rule)
	Small projection under X of 1st bottom row
7	No marking
	No dots in upper rows

Plate 6 was also used with the Block Cypher watermark.

Control Schedule

Plate	Controls employed
1	C. 13 (dull purple)
2	C. 13 (dull purple)
1	C. 13, D. 14, F. 15, G. 15, H. 16, I. 16
2	C. 13, D. 14, F. 15, G. 15, H. 16
3a	J. 17, K. 17

Plate	Controls employed
3b	L. 18, M. 18, N. 19, O. 19, P. 20, Q. 20
4	I. 16, J. 17, K. 17, Q. 20, R. 21, S. 21
5	L. 18, M. 18, N. 19, O. 19
6	S. 21, T. 22, U. 22, V. 23, W. 23, A. 24, B. 24
7	V. 23, A. 24, B. 24

Cat. No.	S.G. No.	Wmk.		Shades	Unused	Used

1913 (AUGUST). 7d. OLIVE, TYPE N8

N27	387/89	W.14 Simple Cypher		(1) Olive	9·00	3·75
a.	Without watermark	.. £250		(2) Olive-grey	9·00	3·25
b.	Watermark inverted	.. 20·00	6·00	(3) Bronze-green (1915)	50·00	12·00
c.	Watermark inverted and			(4) Sage-green (1917)	25·00	6·00
	reversed	.. £1500				
d.	Watermark reversed ..	..				
s.	"Specimen", Type 26	.. 85·00†				
t.	"Cancelled", Type 24	.. £100				

†No. N27s exists from NPM archive sales.

Watermark Varieties. The following have been recorded:
Wmk upright: Types I, II, III
Wmk inverted: Type III

Misplaced Watermarks

ya. Single stamp showing letters from "POSTAGE" .. 25·00

yb. Vertical strip sufficient to show complete "POSTAGE" watermark £350

Broken Dandy Roll Varieties

za. Missing Crown .. .. 65·00
zc. Missing v .. .. .. 25·00
zj. Missing tail to R ("GvP") 22·00

Perforation

Variety Type 2C is known with control J 17.

Controls

Somerset House Printings:

	I.	P.
C. 13 ..	.. 50·00	—

Wmk upright, Types I and II only.

Harrison Printings:

	I.	P.			I.	P.			I.	P.
C 13 ..	.. 11·00	11·00	G 15 ..	.. 11·00	11·00	L 18 ..	.	14·00	75·00
D 14 ..	.. 11·00	11·00	H 16 ..	.. 11·00	11·00				
F 15 ..	.. 11·00	11·00	J 17 ..	.. 14·00	14·00				

Watermark varieties known:
Wmk upright, Type II: C 13, D 14, F 15, G 15, H 16, J 17.
Wmk upright, Type III: J 17, L 18.
Wmk inverted, Type III: J 17, L 18.

Fig. 29

Fig. 29a.

Fig. 30a

Fig. 30b

Fig. 30c

Typical Example from Special Plate of Four

Trials of Eve's Wreath Design

There is no evidence of any engraved die with this design used for this value.

Trials by Miller and Motley using their Printex machine

Fig. 29.   Large coinage head (12 mm.).   Shading at sides extends down to P of POSTAGE and last E of REVENUE.   Frame 22·5 mm. high

In black on card taken from plate of four impressions .. .. .. *Block of four*	£950
As last but single copy	£140
In bistre-brown, turquoise or magenta on gummed paper without watermark .. *From*	£400
In bistre-brown or magenta on gummed paper without watermark and overprinted "ESSAY" .. .. *From*	£400

Fig. 29a.   Smaller coinage head (10½ mm.).   Shading at sides extends down to P of POSTAGE and last E of REVENUE.   Frame 22 mm. high

In black on light brown card with pencil manuscript by Seymour Bennett and dated "22 October 1912"	£300

Figs. 30a/c.   Smaller coinage head (10½ mm.).   Shading at sides extends only to E of POSTAGE and R of REVENUE.   Three different types of background shading to the head.   Frame 22 mm. high

(a) Fig. 30a.   With background of solid colour

In black on card taken from plate of four impressions .. .. .. *Block of four*	£950
As last but single copy	£140
In bistre-brown, greenish grey, purple-brown, Tyrian red (dated "3 Jan. 1913"), gloriosa-blue or bright yellow-green (lime) on thick paper without watermark and ungummed except for lime shade, taken from plate of four impressions .. *Block of four from*	£1250
As last but single copies .. .. *From*	£250

(b) Fig. 30b.   With background of solid colour from 8 to 12 o'clock

In black on card taken from plate of four impressions .. .. .. *Block of four*	£950
As last but single copy	£140
In bright yellow-green (lime) on thick gummed paper without watermark	£400
In black on light brown card	£180

(c) Fig. 30c.   With background evenly shaded with horizontal lines

In black on card taken from plate of four impressions .. .. .. *Block of four*	£950
As last but single copy	£140
In black on light brown card and endorsed by Seymour Bennett "An Essay by the Printex Process for a new Design for 7d. A copy handed to me 29 Oct 1912 to Mr. Eve" and signed	£250
In sepia on card with background to head hand inked to produce solid colour as Fig. 30a	£300

Die Proof

Uncleared in black on white glazed card dated "5.6.1913"	£1750

Plate Markings

Plate	Marking
1a	Dots above 1st in upper and lower panes
	Dot above 5th in upper and lower panes
1b	Dots filled in

Plate	Marking
1c	Added small dot under (VE)N of 1st bottom row. Thin half cut above 1st top row
2a	No marking
2b	Added small dot under NP of 2nd bottom row

Control Schedule

Both plates (i.e. 1a, 1b and 2a) were at press with controls C. 13, C 13 and D 14, and are not easily distinguishable.

Plate	Controls employed
1c	F 15, G 15, H 16, J 17, L 18

Plate	Controls employed
2b	F 15, G 15, H 16

Cat. No.   S.G. No.   Wmk.   Shades   Unused   Used

1913 (AUGUST). 8d. BLACK ON YELLOW, TYPE N8

N28	390/91	W.14 Simple Cypher		(1) Black on yellow paper	20·00 ✔ 6·50 ✔
a.	Without watermark	..	£800	(2) Black on yellow-buff	
b.	Watermark inverted	..	50·00 22·00	(granite) paper	
c.	Watermark reversed	..	55·00	(1917–18)	20·00 8·00 ✔
d.	Watermark inverted and re-				
	versed	.. .. ..	£1500		
e.	Frame broken lower right				
	side (R.20/10)	.. ..	£150		
f.	Frame broken (R.1–10?/12)	£200			
s.	" Specimen ", Type 26	..	£100†		
t.	" Cancelled ", Type 24	..	£150		

The granite paper is of poorer quality and shows hairs and other particles in the texture.

†No. N28s exists from NPM archive sales.

N28*e*   N28*f*

Watermark Varieties. The following have been recorded:

Wmk upright: Types II, III
Wmk inverted: Type II
Wmk reversed: Type II
Wmk inverted and reversed: Type II

Misplaced Watermarks

ya. Single stamp showing letters
from " POSTAGE "   ..   35·00

yb. Vertical strip sufficient to
show complete " POST-
AGE " watermark £400

Broken Dandy Roll Varieties

zc. Missing v   ..   ..   ..   40·00
zi. Missing left side to R   ..   40·00
zj. Missing tail to R (" GvP ")   30·00

Controls

Somerset House Printings:

               I.   *P.*
C.13   ..   ..   38·00   †
Wmk upright, Type I only.

Harrison Printings:

	I.	*P.*			*I.*	*P.*			*I.*	*P.*
D 14	.. ..	25·00	25·00	H 16	.. ..	25·00	25·00	J 17	.. ..	30·00	30·00
F 15	.. ..	25·00	25·00	I 16	.. ..	25·00	25·00	K 18	.. ..	£150	40·00
G 15	.. ..	25·00	25·00							

Watermark varieties known:
Wmk upright, Type II: D 14, F 15, G 15, H 16, I 16, J 17.
Wmk inverted, Type II: F 15.
Wmk reversed, Type II: G 15, H 16.
Wmk inverted and reversed, Type II: D14.
Wmk upright, Type III (*granite paper*): J 17, K 18.

As Fig. 31 but graduated shading

Bromides of Eve's Pillar Design

As Fig. 31 but with graduated shading around head

    With large margins £200

Bromides with large margins of Eve's original artwork for 8d. value with medal head and graduated background shading

    Dated " 22.11.12 " £120

    Also dated " 22.11.12 " but with chinese white additions to numerals—intended by Eve as a master die for 8d. to 1s. values £200

Large master design (75·5 × 92 mm.) for Figs. 33a etc. with medal head. Background to head completely clear. 6 copies made and distributed in accordance with the instructions given on the reverse by Seymour Bennett

    Dated " 18 Jan. 1913 " £400

    As above but with background to head painted in as Fig. 33a £400

    As above but with background to head painted in as Fig. 33b £400

    As above but with background to head painted in as Fig. 33d £400

Subsequently it was decided to change the position of the " A " in " POST-AGE " and " V " in " REVENUE ":—

With the top of the letters almost level with " GE " and " ENU " respectively

    Dated " 1.1.13 " and intialled " E.W.".   (Eve) £200

With the letters angled differently and slightly lower

    Dated " 9.4.13 .. with M/S " Design Approved by Sir Mathew Nathan " and **G.P.O.** file No. A ER/9413 " £250

    Dated " 12.4.13 " and initialled by Eve with M/S recommendation for adoption of " A " and " Vz " etc. £250

    Enlarged photograph (74 × 90 mm) made at the G.P.O., dated " 9.4.13 " ..   ..

Fig. 31	Fig. 32	Fig. 32	Fig. 33a
22·5 mm.	22·5 mm.	Optd. "ESSAY"	22 mm.

Fig. 33b	Fig. 33c	Fig. 33c	Fig. 33d
22 mm.	22 mm.	Optd. "ESSAY"	22 mm.

203

Trials of Eve's Pillar Design

Trials from an engraved die

Fig. 31.   Large coinage head (12 mm.).   Crown has shading inside it.   Frame 22·5 mm. high

Uncleared die proof in black on proof paper, dated "13.9.12"	£850
Uncleared die proof in brown on proof paper, dated "18.9.12"	£900
Cleared die proof in black on proof paper	£850

Trials by Miller and Motley using their Printex machine

Fig. 32.   Coinage head (11 mm.).   Crown has solid colour inside it.   Even shading to head.   Frame 22·5 mm. high

In black on card taken from a plate of four impressions .. .. .. *Block of four*	£950
As last but single example	£140
In various colours on thin card .. .. *From*	£400
In black on lemon on thick gummed paper	£400
Overprinted " ESSAY " in various colours on white paper .. .. *From*	£400
Overprinted "ESSAY" in black on salmon on gummed white paper without watermark	£400

Figs. 33a/d.   Medal head (11½ mm.).   Crown has shading inside it.   Frame 22 mm. high.   Four different types of background shading to the head

(a) Fig. 33a.   With background of solid colour

In black on card taken from a plate of four impressions .. .. .. *Block of four*	£950
As last but single example	£140
In magenta, red-brown, brown-orange or agate on paper with Simple Cypher watermark, dated "29.1.13" .. .. *Block of four from*	£1250
As last but single examples .. .. *From*	£250
In black on light brown card (16 × 19·5 mm)	£120

(b) Fig. 33b.   With background of solid colour from 8 to 12 o'clock

In black on card taken from a plate of four impressions .. .. .. *Block of four*	£950
As last but single example	£140
In red-brown, orange-brown or agate on paper with Simple Cypher watermark *Block of four from*	£1250
As last but single examples .. .. *From*	£250

(c) Fig. 33c.   With background of graduated shading

In black on card taken from a plate of four impressions, dated "6 Feb. 1913" *Block of four*	£950
As last but single example	£140
In agate on paper with Simple Cypher watermark .. .. *Block of four*	£1250
As last but single example	£250
Overprinted " ESSAY " in sage-green, magenta, orange-brown or bistre on white gummed paper without watermark .. .. *From*	£400
Overprinted " ESSAY ' in pale blue-grey on thick card	£400
In black on light brown card (16 × 19·5 mm)	£120

(d) Fig. 33d.   With background evenly shaded with horizontal lines

In black on card taken from a plate of four impressions .. .. .. *Block of four*	£950
As last but single example	£140
As last but annotated in pencil "Fine lines surround, 19 Mch. 1913" .. .. *Block of four*	
In orange-brown on paper with Simple Cypher watermark	£400

For illustration of typical block of four from a special plate see under the 7d. value.

Die Proof

Uncleared in black on white glazed card dated "5.6.1913"	£1750

Imprimatur from the National Postal Museum Archives

Imperforate, watermark Type W14

Watermark upright

Plate Markings

Plate	Marking	Plate	Marking
1a	Dot above 1st in upper and lower panes	1b	Dots filled in

Control Schedule

Plate	Control employed	Plate	Controls employed
1a	C.13	1b	D 14, F 15, G 15, H 16, I 16, J 17, K 18

Cat. No.	S.G. No.	Wmk.		Shades	Unused	Used

1913 (JUNE). 9d. AGATE, TYPE N9

N29	392/93	W.14 Simple Cypher		(1) Agate	7·00 ✓	2·00
a.	Without watermark	..	£300	(2) Pale agate	11·00	1·90 ✓
b.	Watermark inverted	..	30·00	15·00	(3) Deep agate	12·00	2·75 ✓
c.	Wmk. inverted and reversed	28·00	14·00	(4) Very deep agate	£250	65·00
d.	Frame broken at left (each side of O of POSTAGE) (R. 3/1)	..	..	..	85·00	s. " Specimen ", Type 26	.. £110

N29d

Watermark Varieties. The following have been recorded:

Wmk upright: Types II, III
Wmk inverted, Types II, III
Wmk inverted and reversed: Types II, III

Misplaced Watermarks

ya. Single stamp showing letters from " POSTAGE " .. 35·00

yb. Vertical strip sufficient to show complete " POST-AGE " watermark .. £350

Broken Dandy Roll Varieties

za.	Missing Crown	.. ..	48·00
zb.	Missing G ..	.. ..	28·00
zc.	Missing v ..	.. ..	25·00
zf.	Missing vR ..	.. ..	28·00

zh.	Missing Crown GvR	..	80·00
zj.	Missing tail to R (" GvP ")	22·00
zk.	Long tail to G	..	—

Controls

Somerset House Printings:

	I.	P.
B. 13 ..	.. 12·00	†

Wmk upright or inverted, Type I only.

Harrison Printings:

	I.	P.			I.	P.			I.	P.
E 14	.. ..	† 10·00	K 17	..	.. 10·00 10·00	P 20	..	.. 10·00 10·00
F 15	..	.. 11·00 18·00	K 18	..	.. 11·00 11·00	Q 20	..	.. 20·00 35·00
G 15	..	.. 10·00 10·00	L 18	..	.. 10·00 10·00	R 21	..	.. 10·00 10·00
H 16	..	.. 10·00 10·00	N 19	..	.. 10·00 10·00	S 21	..	.. 10·00 10·00
I 16	..	.. 10·00 16·00	O 19	..	.. 10·00 10·00	S 22	..	.. 15·00 11·00
J 17	..	.. 10·00 10·00	O 20	..	.. 10·00 10·00			

Watermark varieties known:
Wmk upright, Type II: E 14, F 15, G 15, H 16, I 16, J 17, O 20, R 21.
Wmk inverted, Type II: F 15.
Wmk inverted and reversed, Type II: G 15.
Wmk upright, Type III: J 17, K 17, K 18, L 18, N 19, O 19, O 20, P 20, Q 20, R 21, S 21, S 22.
Wmk inverted, Type III: L 18, O 19, P 20, Q 20.
Wmk inverted and reversed, Type III: J 17, O 19, P 20, S 21, S 22.

Die Proofs

In black on white glazed card, fully cleared, endorsed "2.v.1913" in M/S £2250
In black on gummed paper watermarked Simple Cypher (sideways), fully cleared, endorsed "2.v.1913" in M/S £2000

Plate Proof

In black on poor quality buff paper .. .. 90·00

Imprimatur from the National Postal Museum Archives

Imperforate, watermark Type W14

Watermark upright

Plate Markings

Plate	Marking
1a	Dot above 1st in upper and lower panes
1b	Dots above 1st filled in
	Minute dot in rule under PE of 3rd bottom row
1c	Dot under 3rd now filled in. Flaw in base of
	rule under CE of 1st bottom row
1d	Flaw at base of 1st repaired
1e	Added nick top (outer) 20th left side

Plate	Marking
1f	Added dot (top) under EN of 1st bottom row
2a	Dot above 2nd in upper and lower panes
2b	Added tiny nick (outer) 19th left side, 13 mm.
3a	Small internal nick 19th left side, 11–12 mm.
	Small cut under first N of 4th bottom row
3b	Added dot (base) under P of 2nd bottom row

Plates 1f, 2b and 3b were also used for the 9d. olive-green.

Control Schedule

Plate	Controls employed
1a	B. 13
1b	E 14, F 15, G 15, I 16
1c	G 15, H 16, I 16, J 17
1d	J 17, K 17
1e	L 18, N 19
1f	N 19, O 20, S 21

Plate	Controls employed
2a	B. 13, K 17, L 18, N 19, O 19, O 20, P 20
	Q 20
2b	R 21, S 21, S 22
3a	K 18, L 18, N 19
3b	N 19 ,O 19, O 20, P 20, Q 20, R 21, S 21, S 22

Cat. No.	S.G. No.		Wmk.		Shades	Unused	Used
1922 (SEPTEMBER).		**As last, but OLIVE-GREEN**					
N30	393a/b	W.14 Simple Cypher			(1) Olive-green	65·00	14·00 ✓
a.	Watermark inverted	..	£400	£170	(2) Pale olive-green	70·00	14·00 ✓
b.	Watermark inverted and reversed	.. ..	£350	£170	(3) Deep olive-green	80·00	20·00 ✓
s.	"Specimen", Type 15	..					
t.	"Specimen", Type 23	..					

Watermark Varieties. The following have been recorded:

Wmk upright: Types II, III
Wmk inverted: Type II
Wmk inverted and reversed: Type II

Broken Dandy Roll Variety

z. Missing v .. £120

Controls

Harrison Printings:

			I.	P.
T 22	..	..	80·00	80·00
U 23	..	..	80·00	80·00
V 23	..	..	85·00	85·00

Watermark varieties known:
Wmk upright, Type II: U 23, V 23.
Wmk inverted, Type II: U 23.
Wmk inverted and reversed, Type II: U 23.
Wmk upright, Type III: T 22, U 23.

Imprimatur from the National Postal Museum Archives

Imperforate, watermark Type W14

Watermark upright

Plate Markings

Plates 1f, 2b and 3b as used for 9d. Agate, see No. N29.

Control Schedule

Plate	Controls employed
1f	T 22, U 23
2b	T 22, U 23, V 23
3b	T 22, U 23, V 23

Cat. No.	S.G. No.	Wmk.		Shades	Unused	Used

1913 (AUGUST).   10d. TURQUOISE-BLUE, TYPE N9

N31   394/a   W.14 Simple Cypher
- a. Watermark inverted   .. £750   £125
- b. Watermark inverted and reversed   ..   ..   .. 85·00   28·00
- c. Frame broken by E of POSTAGE ..   ..   .. £150   60·00
- s. " Specimen ", Type 15   ..
- t. " Specimen ", Type 23   ..
- u. " Cancelled ", Type 24   .. £120
- v. " Specimen ", Type 26   .. £120

Shades:
- (1) Bright turquoise-blue   18·00   8·00 ✓
- (2) Turquoise-blue   13·00 ✓ 11·00 ✓
- (3) Deep turquoise-blue   30·00   15·00 ✓
- (4) Greenish blue   15·00   8·00 ✓
- (5) Pale greenish blue   15·00   8·00

No. N31 is known with so-called varnish ink but as stated in the General Notes we defer listing.

Watermark Varieties.   The following have been recorded:
Wmk upright: Types I, II, III
Wmk inverted: Types II, III
Wmk inverted and reversed: Types II, III

Misplaced Watermarks

ya. Single stamp showing letters from "POSTAGE" ..   .. 35·00

yb. Vertical strip sufficient to show complete "POSTAGE" watermark £450

Broken Dandy Roll Varieties

za. Missing Crown   ..   .. 48·00
zc. Missing v   ..   ..   .. 28·00

zg. Missing Crown vR ..   .. 30·00
zj. Missing tail to R (" GvP ") 28·00

Controls

Somerset House Printings:

	I.	P.
C. 13	22·00	£250

Wmk upright or inverted and reversed, Type II only.

Harrison Printings:

	I.	P.			I.	P.			I.	P.
D 14	..	.. 15·00	15·00	J 17	..	.. 18·00	15·00	S 21	..	.. 15·00 15·00
F 15	..	.. 15·00	15·00	K 18	..	.. 18·00	15·00	S 22	..	.. 22·00 20·00
G 15	..	.. 15·00	18·00	M 19	..	.. 15·00	15·00	T 22	..	.. 30·00 20·00
H 16	..	.. 15·00	20·00	O 19	..	.. 15·00	15·00	U 23	..	.. 22·00 22·00
I 16	..	.. 15·00	18·00	Q 21	..	.. 22·00	22·00			

Watermark varieties known:
Wmk upright, Type I: F 15.
Wmk upright, Type II: D 14, F 15, G 15, H 16, I 16, J 17, K 18, U 23.
Wmk inverted, Type II: H 16.
Wmk upright, Type III: J 17, K 18, M 19, O 19, Q 21, S 21, S 22, T 22.
Wmk inverted, Type III: M 19.
Wmk inverted and reversed, Type III: O 19, Q 21.

Die Proof
Uncleared in approved design

In black on white glazed card dated "7.6.13" £2250

Plate Markings

Plate	Marking
1a	Base of 20th left side bends inwards; dot above 1st in upper and lower panes
1b	Dots above 1st filled in. Two minute dots under PE of 1st bottom row

Plate	Marking
1c	Added large dot under P of 2nd bottom row
2a	No marking. Base of 16th right side bevelled
2b	Added large dot under PE of 1st bottom row

Plates 1c and 2b were also used for the Block Cypher watermark.

Control Schedule

Plate	Controls employed
1a	C. 13
1b	D 14, F 15, G 15, H 16, I 16, J 17, K 18 M 19

Plate	Controls employed
1c	M 19, Q 21, S 21, S 22
2a	D 14, G 15, K 18, M 19
2b	M 19, O 19, Q 21, S 21, S 22, T 22, U 23

Cat. No.	S.G. No.	Wmk.		Shades	Unused	Used

1913 (AUGUST).   1s. BISTRE-BROWN, TYPE N9

N32 395/96 W.14 Simple Cypher

(1) Bistre		7·50	75
(2) Pale bistre-brown		10·00	75
(3) Deep bistre-brown		11·00	75
(4) Buff-brown		13·00	90
(5) Pale buff-brown		10·00	90
(6) Fawn-brown (1916-17)		65·00	10·00
(7) Bistre-brown		20·00	5·00
(8) Pale bistre		15·00	1·25
(9) Olive-brown (1920)		25·00	2·25
(10) Deep bronze-brown (1920)		£500	

a. Without watermark .. £400
b. Watermark inverted .. 65·00 15·00
c. Watermark inverted and re-versed .. .. .. 30·00 10·00
d. Varnish ink (Controls G 15, I 16, R 21) £1850
s. "Specimen", Type 15 ..
t. "Specimen", Type 23 ..
u. "Cancelled", Type 24 .. £130
v. "Specimen", Type 26 .. £120
w. "Specimen", Type 31 in violet or black .. ..

Shade (10) is from a part sheet on which the impressions were centred low and to the right.

Watermark Varieties. The following have been recorded:
Wmk upright: Types II, III
Wmk inverted: Type III
Wmk inverted and reversed: Types II, III

Misplaced Watermarks

ya. Single stamp showing letters from " POSTAGE " .. 35·00

yb. Vertical strip sufficient to show complete " POST-AGE " watermark £350

Broken Dandy Roll Varieties

za. Missing Crown .. .. 40·00
zc. Missing v .. .. .. 22·00
zd. Missing R .. · .. .. 22·00
ze. Missing Gv .. .. .. —

zf. Missing vR .. .. .. 25·00
zi. Missing left side to R .. 25·00
zj. Missing tail to Ro (" GvP ") 15·00
zk. Long tail to G .. .. 25·00

Perforation

Variety Type 2C is known with control J 17 .. .. *Strip of* 3 50·00

Controls

Somerset House Printings:

	I.	P.
C. 13	16·00	25·00

Wmk upright, Type II only.

Harrison Printings:

	I.	P.			I.	P.			I.	P.
D 14	11·00	11·00	L 18	11·00	11·00	S 21	10·00	10·00
E 14	£175	£175	M 19	15·00	11·00	S 22	10·00	10·00
F 15	11·00	11·00	N 19	22·00	22·00	T 22	10·00	10·00
G 15	10·00	10·00	O 19	11·00	11·00	U 22	22·00	22·00
H 16	11·00	13·00	O 20	13·00	11·00	U 23	10·00	10·00
I 16	10·00	15·00	P 20	18·00	18·00	V 23	22·00	22·00
J 17	10·00	15·00	Q 20	10·00	10·00			
K 17	10·00	35·00	R 21	10·00	10·00			

Watermark varieties known:
Wmk upright, Type II: D 14, E 14, F 15, G 15, H 16, I 16, J 17, K 17, O 20, R 21, U 22, U 23, V 23.
Wmk inverted and reversed, Type II: D 14, F 15, G 15, I 16, U 22.
Wmk upright, Type III: J 17, K 17, L 18, M 19, N 19, O 19, O 20, P 20, Q 20, R 21, S 21, S 22, T 22, U 23.
Wmk inverted, Type III: J 17, K 17, O 19, P 20, Q 20, R 21, S 21.
Wmk inverted and reversed, Type III: L 18, N 19, O 19, P 20, Q 20, S 21.

Die Proof

Uncleared in approved design
In black on white glazed card dated "12th June 1913." £2250

Plate Markings

Plate	Marking
1a	Dots above 1st in upper and lower panes Rule 20th left side thick and rounded outer base corner
1b	20th left side now shows a nick base (outer). Dots above 1st filled in
2a	Dot above 2nd in upper and lower panes Rule 20th left side irregular
2b	Dots above 2nd filled in. Nick 19th right side (outer), 10½ mm.

Plate	Marking
2c	Added cut under S of 2nd bottom row
3	Tiny nick (outer) 19th left side, 4 mm.
4	Cut 19th left side, 18½ mm. (Waterlow Plate 2)
5a	Tiny nick (inner) 19th left side, 14 mm.
5b	Added dash at left of 2nd bottom row
5c	Added cut under S of 1st bottom row (Waterlow Plate 5)
6	No marking

Control Schedule

Plate	Controls employed
1a	C. 13
1b	D 14, E 14, F 15, G 15, H 16, I 16, J 17, M 19, O 19, O 20
2a	C. 13
2b	D 14, E 14, F 15, G 15, H 16, I 16, J 17, M 19
2c	M 19, N 19, O 19, O 20

Plate	Controls employed
3	O 20, P 20, O 20, R 21, S 21, S 22, T 22, U 22, U 23
4	R 21, S 21, S 22, T 22, U 22, U 23, V 23
5a	J 17, K 17, L 18
5b	M 19
5c	M 19, N 19, O 19, O 20, P 20, Q 20, R 21 V 23
6	V 23

The Profile Head Issue, Wmk Block Cypher (1924-26)

WATERMARK. All the stamps in this section have watermark **W15**, except for the varieties on experimental **W16** paper listed under the 1d. and 1½d.

PERFORATION. This is normally Type 2, but the following may be found:

Type 2A	Variety Type 2(c)	Type 3
½d. A 24, B 24, C 25, E 26, H 27, V 34	½d. B 24, E 26, H 27	6d. D 38
1d. A 24, C 25	1d. E 26, P 31	
1½d. F 26, I 28	1½d. B 24, E 26	
2d. B 24, I 28	2d. B 24, P 31	
3d. G 27	3d. B 24	
6d. E. 26, W 35, X 35, B 37, D 38	4d. B 24, E 26	
9d. X 35	6d. B 24, C 25	
1s V 34	9d. P 31	

Type 3A	Type 4
½d. A 24, E 26, F 26, G 27, H 27, L 29, V 34	½d. U 34, V 34
1d. A 24, L 29, V 34	1d. U 34, V 34
1½d. A 24, F 26, H 27, K 29	1½d. U 34, V 34
2d. B 24	2d. V 34
5d. A 24	2½d. V 34
6d. E. 26, I. 28, J. 28, M. 30	3d. V 34
9d. A 24	4d. V 34
10d. A 24	5d. V 34
1s. A 24	6d. V 34, W 35
	9d. V 34
	1s. V 34

CONTROLS. The notes given on controls in Section NB apply here. The perforation type is identified by the four margins of the sheet not merely the control piece. A part imperf. margin with control may show one or two extension holes opposite the marginal rule and these are "I" in the lists but are from perf. types 2 or 3 (single extension hole) and perf. type 4 (two extension holes). Part encroachments in the bottom margin are also regarded as "I". (See page 120, Section N for notes and illustrations).

Cat. No.	S.G. No.			Shades	Unused	Used
1924 (FEBRUARY*).		**½d. GREEN, TYPE N6**				
N33	418			(1) Green	12	12
a.	Watermark inverted	75	30	(2) Pale green	30	10
b.	Watermark sideways (5.24)	7·00	2·50	(3) Deep green	1·00	10
c.	Watermark sideways-inverted			(4) Bright green	15	10
				(5) Deep bright green	1·60	25
d.	Doubly printed		£6500	(6) Yellow-green	15·00	2·00
e.	Imperf. between right side and margin		£2000			
f.	Coil join (horiz. pair)			w. "Cancelled", Type 28	8·00	
s.	"Specimen", Type 15			wa. "Cancelled", Type 28P		
t.	"Specimen", Type 23	8·00		x. "Cancelled", Type 33P	8·00	
u.	"Specimen", Type 30	8·00		y. "Cancelled", Type 33	10·00	
ua.	"Specimen", Type 32			z. "Specimen", Type 32 and		
v.	"Cancelled", Type 24			"Cancelled", Type 34		

* Issued first in 3s. Booklet BB24 edition no. 55 in February. Sheets were first reported in May.

An example of
a double print,
each varies
slightly

N33*d*

Controls

Waterlow Printings:

				I.	P.					I.	P.					I.	P.
A 24	..	..		40	2·00	H 27	..	..		80	10·00	O 31	..	..		40	†
B 24	..	..		40	8·00	I 28	..	..		40	†	P 31	..	..		40	†
C 25	..	..		40	13·00	J 28	..	..		40	†	Q 32	..	..		40	†
D 25	..	..		40	†	K 29	..	..		90	†	R 32	..	..		40	†
E 26	..	..		50	50·00	L 29	..	..		80	10·00	S 33	..	..		40	†
F 26	..	..		40	15·00	M 30	..	..		40	†	T 33	..	..		40	†
G 27	..	..		40	10·00	N 30	..	..		40	†	U 34	..	..		—	†

Watermark varieties known:
Wmk inverted: A 24, B 24, C 25, D 25, E 26, F 26, G 27, H 27, I 28, J 28, K 29, L 29, M 30, N 30, O 31, Q 32, R 32, T 33.

Harrison Printings:

			I.	P.
U 34‡	..	..	80	†
U34[streaky gum]		1·25	†
V34[streaky gum]		50	6·00

‡Known doubly printed.

Watermark variety known:
Wmk inverted: U 34.

Booklet Panes of Six

From Waterlow Booklets BB12, BB24, B33/34 and Harrison Booklets BB14, BB26, BB35

NB12   Watermark upright   5·00
s. " Specimen ", Type 23   ..   50·00
t. " Specimen ", Type 30   ..   50·00
u. " Cancelled ", Type 24   ..
v. " Cancelled ", Type 28   ..   50·00
va. " Cancelled ", Type 28P   ..
w. " Cancelled ", Type 33   ..   70·00
x. " Cancelled ", Type 33P   ..   50·00
y. Cancelled, "London E.C.",
　　 Type I   ..   ..   ..   25·00
z. Cancelled " London Chief
　　 Office E.C.1 ", Type J, in
　　 violet   ..   ..   ..   50·00
za. Cancelled " London Chief
　　 Office E.C.1 ", Type K, in
　　 violet   ..   ..   ..

NB12a   Watermark inverted   8·00
as. " Specimen ", Type 23   ..   50·00
at. " Specimen ", Type 30   ..   50·00
av. " Cancelled ", Type 28   ..   50·00
ava. " Cancelled ", Type 28P   ..
aw. " Cancelled ", Type 33   ..   70·00†
ax. " Cancelled ", Type 33P   ..   50·00
ay. Cancelled, "London E.C.",
　　 Type I   ..   ..   ..   25·00
az. Cancelled " London Chief Of-
　　 fice E.C.1", Type J. in violet
aza. Cancelled " London Chief
　　 Office E.C.1 ", Type K, in
　　 violet   ..   ..   ..

†No. NB12*aw* exists from NPM archive sales.

Coils

Vertical delivery printed in continuous reels

Code No.	Issued	Number in roll	Face value	
D	1924	960	£2.0.0	Bottom delivery
G	1924	480	£1.0.0	Top delivery
KERMODE	1924	960	£2.0.0	Top delivery
KERMODE	Aug. 1927	1920	£4.0.0	Bottom delivery
W	1928	960	£2.0.0	Bottom delivery
Y	1928	1920	£4.0.0	Bottom delivery

Sideways delivery made up from sheets with joins every 12th stamp

P	1924	480	£1.0.0	Left side delivery

Sideways delivery printed in continuous reels with watermark sideways (Crown pointing to left)

P	May 1924	480	£1.0.0	Left side delivery

Imprimaturs from the National Postal Museum Archives

Imperforate, watermark Type W15

Watermark upright
Watermark sideways

Booklet pane of six. Imperforate, watermark Type W15

Two panes as No. NB12 arranged horizontally *tête-bêche* with marginal pillars at right

Specimen and Cancelled overprints form the National Postal Museum Archives

Booklet pane of six. Perf. 15 × 14, watermark Type W15 (inverted)

"Specimen", Type 32 and upper left stamp with punch hole

Plate Markings

Plate	Marking
1	Large dot (top) under N(N) of 3rd
2	Dot (base) under EN of 1st
3	Minute dot (inner) 20th left side, 10½ mm.
4	Tiny dot 19th left side, 8 mm.
5	(a) Dot (base) under PE of 2nd (b) Projection below rule under L of 1st; ½ dot (outer) 19th left side, 13 mm.
6	Base of 2nd rule cut away from under ENNY to right end; 4 large dots 19th right side (as Harrison Plate 79)
7	Large dot (central) 19th left side, 9½ mm. (as Harrison Plate 80)
8	½ dot (top) under E of 3rd
9	Dot (breaking outer) 18th left side, 12 mm.
10	½ dot (top) under F of 4th
11	½ dot and ½ cut (top) under E of 2nd
12	½ dot (top) under PE of 3rd; rule 19th left side damaged (top)
13	Split at right end of rule under 2nd. Dot (inner) 19th left side, 7½ mm.
14	2 large dots under PEN of 3rd
15	Dot (outer) 20th left side, 6½ mm.
16	2 small cuts under NN of 11th (as Harrison Plate 83) with small ½ cut (base) under L of 1st
17	2 dots 19th left side, 10½ mm., 13½ mm.
18	Dot under F of 2nd
19	Large dot (outer) 20th left side, 11 mm. Indent (base) under 11th
20	Dot (base) under FP of 1st
21	Dot under P of 3rd
22	Small dot 20th left side, 11½ mm.
23	Large dot 19th left side, 12 mm. Tiny dots under F of 7th and A of 12th
24	Nick at left of 3rd rule
25	Minute dot at base of 20th left side
26	Indistinct dot 19th left side, 16 mm. Dot (top) under FP of 11th
27	Nick at right of 2nd
28	Dot (central) above 3rd top row. Minute dot 20th left side, 7½ mm.
29	½ dot (outer) 19th left side, 11 mm. Gash below 8th
30	Indents (base) under H and L of 1st
31	Left end of 1st rule very thick and curves upwards. Top of 20th left bevelled (outer)
32	Cut at top of 1st left side with dot halfway down. Dot above 4th top row
33	Very fine cut 19th left side, 13 mm.
34	5 cuts under HALF of 12th; minute fine nick (outer) 19th left side, 8¼ mm. (as Harrison Plate 78)
35	Rule 19th right side has projection at base. 2 internal cuts under F of 12th
36	Dot 19th left side, 13¼ mm.
37	Nick bottom left corner of 9th. Dot 20th right side, 2½ mm.
38	Dot extreme right of rule under 11th
39	Tiny dot 19th right side, 18½ mm.
40	Small dot at top of both 19th and 20th rules at right side
41	Small dot 18th left side, 13 mm.
42	Dot and small dot 3rd left side. Scoop (outer) 4th right side
43	Dot 4th left side. 2 tiny dots 1st right side
44	Tiny dot above 1st top row. Dot (to right) above 3rd top row. Dot (top) 4th right side
45	Large and small dots 3rd left side, 11½ mm. 4th right side damaged
46	Tiny dot under LF of 3rd
47	Dot (breaking top) under P(E) and nick under (N)N of 3rd
48	No marking
49	Small vertical nick at top of 20th right side
50	20th left side ragged and thickens at base. 7th rule thins at left
51	Minute dot 20th right side, 8 mm.
52	3 dots breaking inner 19th right side, 5½, 7½, 10½ mm. (as Harrison Plate 64)
53	Tiny half dot (outer) 17th left side, 8 mm.
54	Small dot 17th left side, 13¼ mm.

Index to Marginal Markings

Top Margin, Stamp Numbers

Stamp No.	Plate
1	..	44
3	..	28, 44

Bottom Margin, Stamp Numbers

1	..	2, 5, 16, 20, 30, 31
2	..	5, 6, 11, 13, 18, 27
3	..	1, 8, 12, 14, 21, 24, 46, 47
4	..	10

Left Margin, Row Numbers

Row No.	Plate
1	..	32
3	..	42, 45
4	..	43
17	..	53, 54

Right Margin, Row Numbers

1	..	43
4	..	42, 44, 45

No Marking: Plate 48

Stamp No.	Plate
4	..	32
7	..	23, 50
8	..	29, 37
11	..	16, 19, 26, 38
12	..	23, 34, 35

Row No.	Plate
18	..	9, 41
19	..	4, 5, 7, 12, 13, 17, 23, 26, 29, 33, 34, 36
20	..	3, 15, 19, 22, 25, 28, 31, 50

19	..	6, 39, 40, 52
20	..	37, 40, 49, 51

Control Schedule

Waterlow Printings, 1924–33

Control	Plates with which it was used
A 24	..	1, 2, 3, 4, 5, 41, 46, 54
B 24	..	1, 3, 5, 6, 7, 9, 35, 41, 54
C 25	..	1, 2, 3, 5, 6, 7, 8, 9, 10
D 25	..	1, 2, 4, 5, 6, 8, 11, 12, 17, 35, 52
E 26	..	4, 5, 6, 8, 11, 13, 34
F 26	..	4, 11, 12, 13, 14, 15, 16, 17, 45, 53
G 27	..	8, 11, 12, 13, 14, 15, 16, 17, 43, 53
H 27	..	4, 12, 13, 14, 15, 42
I 28	..	8, 11, 12, 13, 18, 19, 20, 21, 23, 43
J 28	..	8, 10, 18, 19, 20, 21, 22, 23

Control	Plates with which it was used
K 29	..	8, 10, 18, 19, 20, 21, 22, 23, 36, 47
L 29	..	18, 19, 20, 21, 22, 23, 36
M 30	..	23, 24, 25, 26, 36
N 30	..	19, 22, 23, 24, 25, 26, 28, 44
O 31	..	25, 26
P 31	..	26, 27, 28, 37
Q 32	..	24, 25, 27, 29, 37, 38
R 32	..	27, 29, 39
S 33	..	27, 29
T 33	..	27, 29, 40

Waterlow Provisional Printing, 1934

U 34	..	32, 48, 49

Harrison Provisional Printing, 1934

U 34	..	30, 31, 49, 50
V 34	..	30, 31, 33, 48, 50, 51

Cat. No. S.G. No.

1924 (FEBRUARY*). 1d. RED, TYPE N5

	Shades	Unused	Used

N34   419

						Unused	Used
a.	Experimental paper, Water-mark Type W. 16 (10.24) ..	30·00		(1)	Scarlet	25	25
b.	Watermark inverted ..	75	45	(2)	Pale scarlet	40	10
c.	Watermark sideways (1928)	16·00	10·00	(3)	Scarlet-vermilion	30	20
d.	Inverted Q for O in ONE (Pl. 1, R. 20/3).	£375		(4)	Deep scarlet-vermilion	10·00	1·00
e.	Damaged top. No Cross on Crown	£150		ua.	Do. Wmk. sideways ..	£100	
f.	Gash in Crown (Pl. 7, R. 20/12)	90·00		v.	"Specimen", Type 30 ..	8·00	
s.	"Specimen", Type 15			va.	"Specimen", Type 32		
t.	"Specimen". Type 23 ..	8·00		w.	"Cancelled", Type 24 ..		
u.	Imperf. opt. "Specimen". Type 23	12·00		x.	"Cancelled", Type 28 ..	8·00	
				xa.	"Cancelled", Type 28P ..		
				y.	"Cancelled", Type 33 ..	8·00	
				z.	"Cancelled", Type 33 ..	10·00	
				za.	"Specimen", Type 32 and "Cancelled", Type 34 ..		

*Issued first in 3s. Booklet BB24 edition no. 55 in February. Sheets are believed to have been issued in April.

For illustration of N34d see N16k.

N34e   N34f

Controls

Waterlow Printings:

		I.	P.				I.	P.				I.	P.
A 24	.. ..	65	9·00	H 27	.. ..		50	†	O 31	.. ..		50	—
B 24	.. ..	50	11·00	I 28	.. ..		50	†	P 31	.. ..		50	†
C 25	.. ..	50	5·00	J 28	.. ..		50	†	Q 32	.. ..		50	†
D 25	.. ..	20·00	†	K 29	.. ..		50	†	R 32	.. ..		5·00	†
E 26	.. ..	50	†	L 29	.. ..		50	25·00	S 33	.. ..		50	†
F 26	.. ..	50	†	M 30	.. ..		50	†	T 33	.. ..		50	†
G 27	.. ..	60	†	N 30	.. ..		1·00	†	U 34	.. ..		—	†

Watermark varieties known:

Wmk inverted: A 24, B 24, C 25, D 25, E 26, F 26, G 27, H 27, I 28, J 28, K 29, L 29, M 30, O 31, Q 32, T 33.

Waterlow printing, experimental wmk **W16:**

		I.	P.
B 24	.. ..	95·00	†

Harrison Printings:

		I.	P.
U 34	.. ..	2·00	†
U34[streaky gum]		3·00	†
V34[streaky gum]		2·00	8·00

Watermark variety known:

Wmk inverted: U 34.

Booklet Panes of Six

From Waterlow Booklets BB12, BB24, B33/34 and Harrison Booklets BB14, BB26, BB35

NB13	Watermark upright	4·50
s.	"Specimen", Type 23 ..	50·00
t.	"Specimen", Type 30 ..	50·00
u.	"Cancelled", Type 28 ..	50·00
v.	"Cancelled", Type 28P ..	
w.	"Cancelled", Type 33 ..	70·00
x.	"Cancelled", Type 33P ..	50·00
y.	Cancelled, "London E.C.", Type I	25·00
z.	Cancelled "London Chief Office E.C.1", Type J, in violet	
za.	Cancelled "London Chief Office E.C.1", Type K, in violet	

NB13a	Watermark inverted	4·50
as.	"Specimen", Type 23 ..	50·00
at.	"Specimen", Type 30 ..	50·00
au.	"Cancelled", Type 28 ..	50·00
av.	"Cancelled", Type 28P ..	
aw.	"Cancelled", Type 33 ..	70·00†
ax.	"Cancelled", Type 33P ..	50·00
ay.	Cancelled, "London E.C.", Type I	25·00
az.	Cancelled "London Chief Office E.C.1", Type J, in violet	
aza.	Cancelled "London Chief Office E.C.1", Type K, in violet	

†No. NB13aw exists from NPM archive sales.

Coils

Vertical delivery printed in continuous reels

Code No.	Issued	Number in roll	Face value	
B	1924	960	£4.0.0	Bottom delivery
E	1924	480	£2.0.0	Top delivery
KERMODE	1924	960	£4.0.0	Top delivery
KERMODE	Aug. 1927	1920	£8.0.0	Bottom delivery
X	1928	960	£4.0.0	Bottom delivery
Z	1028	1920	£8.0.0	Bottom delivery

Sideways delivery printed in continuous reels with watermark sideways

O	1928	480	£2.0.0	Left side delivery

Imprimaturs from the National Postal Museum Archives

Imperforate, watermark Type W15

Watermark upright
Watermark sideways

Booklet pane of six. Imperforate, watermark Type W15

Two panes as No. NB13 arranged horizontally *tête-bêche* with marginal pillars at right

Specimen and Cancelled overprints from the National Postal Museum Archives

Booklet pane of six. Perf. 15 × 14, watermark Type W15 (inverted)

"Specimen", Type 32 and upper left stamp with punch hole

Plate Markings

Plate	Marking
1	As for Harrison Plate 114b
2	Small dot at right of 11th
3	Dot (inner) 20th right side, 12 mm. Irregular dot 11–12 mm. 20th left side. Nick (base) under (N)N of 4th. Damage to left base of rule under 11th (Harrison Plate 99)
4	Dot 19th left side, 10¾ mm. Tiny half dot (outer), 20th right side 5½ mm. (Harrison Plate 118)
5	Dot 19th left side, 8¼ mm. (Harrison Plate 101)
6	½ cut (outer) 18th left side, 7½ mm. Nick 20th left side (outer), 2½ mm. Small ½ cut base under left of 9th. Large double dot breaking both sides. 18th right side, 12 mm. (Harrison Plate 120)
7	Large ½ dot (breaking inner) 19th left side, 13 mm. Indent (base) under (N)N of 8th
8	Dot 17th right side, 11 mm.
9	Dot 17th right side, 7½ mm. Rule 15th left side damaged (centre). Cut 20th left side 14½ mm. Nick (top) 6th under P
10	Dot 20th left side, 12 mm. Tiny dot 17th right side, 7½ mm.
11	Rule 19th left side damaged (outer). Minute dot 17th right side, 14 mm.
12	Dot 17th left side, 10½ mm.
13	Dot under EP of 1st
14	Dot 18th left side, 12½ mm. Rule 19th left bevelled at base
15	20th left side severely damaged at left and broken near base
16	Left at 10th broken away at base
17	Horizontal dash at left of 11th
18	Nick 3rd right side, 6¼ mm. Small nick at left base of 6th No other marking on sheet
19	Dot 4th left side, 11½ mm. 20th left side irregular. 12th right side bevelled at base
20	Cut 4th left side, 11 mm. Tiny nick 20th left side, 17½ mm. Scoop 6th right side
21	Minute dot to right of Y of 2nd. No other marking on sheet
22	Tiny dot and double dot 1st left side, 20½, 11 mm. ½ dot at right end of 3rd. Dot over 4th, and ½ dot at right of 5th all top row
23	Nick at left of 11th
24	Base of 20th right side bent in
25	As for Harrison Plate 117
26	Two dots 20th left side, 16 and 17½ mm.; two nicks 19th left side, 12 and 15½ mm.; crescent shaped cut (breaking inner) 1st left side, 19½ and 21 mm.; dot above centre 1st top row

Index to Marginal Markings

Top Row, Stamp Numbers

Stamp No.	Plate	Stamp No.	Plate	Stamp No.	Plate
1 ..	25, 26	4 ..	22	5 ..	1, 22

Bottom Row, Stamp Numbers

Stamp No.	Plate	Stamp No.	Plate	Stamp No.	Plate
1 ..	13	4 ..	3	9 ..	6
2 ..	21	6 ..	9, 18	10 ..	16
3 ..	1, 22	8 ..	7	11 ..	2, 3, 17, 23

Left Margin, Row Numbers

Row No.	Plate	Row No.	Plate	Row No.	Plate
1 ..	22, 26	17 ..	12	19 ..	4, 5, 7, 11, 14, 26,
4 ..	19, 20	18 ..	6, 14	20 ..	1, 3, 6, 9, 10, 15, 19 20, 26
15 ..	9				

Right Margin, Row Numbers

Row No.	Plate	Row No.	Plate	Row No.	Plate
3 ..	18	12 ..	19	18 ..	6, 25
6 ..	20	17 ..	8, 9, 10, 11, 25	20 ..	3, 4, 24

Control Schedule

Waterlow Printings, 1924–33

Plate	Controls	Plate	Controls	Plate	Controls
1	C 25, E 26	9	B 24, C 25	17	Q 32, R 32, S 33, T 33
2	F 26, G 27	10	A 24, B 24	18	K 29
3	F 26, G 27	11	B 24	19	L 29
4	F 26, G 27, H 27	12	B 24, C 25, H 27	20	M 30
5	C 25	13	F 26, G 27	21	J 28
6	C 25, D 25, E 26	14	A 24, B 24	22	?
7	E 26	15	M 30	25	C 25
8	F 26	16	K 29, L 29, M 30, N 30		

Waterlow Provisional Printing, 1934

24	U 34

Harrison Provisional Printings, 1934–35

23	U 34, V 34
26	U 34, V 34

Cat. No.	S.G. No.				Shades	Unused	Used

1924 (FEBRUARY*). 1½d. RED-BROWN, TYPE N6

N35	420				(1) Red-brown	20	20
a.	Tête-bêche (pair)	£375	£500		(2) Deep red-brown	1·00	15
aa.	Do. with gutter margin ..	£400	£325		(3) Pale red-brown	12·00	1·75
b.	Experimental paper, Watermark Type W.16 (10.24) ..	40·00			(4) Chestnut (1924)	1·25	20
ba.	Do. with wmk. inverted ..				(5) Bright chestnut (1926-7)	2·00	20
c.	Watermark inverted ..	60	30		(6) Orange-brown (1925)	2·00	15
d.	Watermark sideways (8.24)	4·25	2·25		(7) Chocolate-brown (1924)	2·50	25
da.	Wmk. sideways-inverted ..				(8) Yellow-brown (1932-34)	40	15
e.	Printed on the gummed side	£425	†		(9) Deep yellow-brown		
f.	Imperf. between right side and margin	£700			(1934)	2·50	20
fa.	Imperf. between left side and margin	£1250			(10) Bright yellow-brown (1934)	3·50	25
g.	Varnish ink (Controls L 29, U 34)	£2500					
h.	Double impression	£4500		*t.*	"Specimen", Type 23 ..	8·00	
i.	Coil join (horiz. pair) ..			*u.*	"Specimen", Type 30 ..	8·00	
j.	Frame broken at left (R.?/11)	75·00		*ua.*	"Specimen", Type 32 ..		
k.	Blob on King's nose ..	£130		*v.*	"Cancelled", Type 24 ..		
l.	Missing top to final E in HALFPENCE (R. ?/10)	£170		*w.*	"Cancelled", Type 28 ..	8·00	
				wa.	"Cancelled", Type 28P ..		
m.	Frame damage (R. 2/1 of Booklet pane of 6)	75·00		*x.*	"Cancelled", Type 33P ..	8·00	
n.	White spot on dolphin (Pl. 34 and Pl. 52, R. 20/3) ..	35·00		*y.*	"Cancelled", Type 33 ..	10·00	
				ya.	Do. Watermark sideways ..		
s.	"Specimen", Type 15 ..			*z.*	"Specimen", Type 32 and "Cancelled", Type 34 ..		

*Issued first in 3s. Booklet no. BB24 edition no. 55 in February. Sheets were reported to have been issued on 4 April.

Variety *e*. One sheet known to exist from Control U34

Variety *i* comes from the Waterlow printings made into continuous coils (Wmk. sideways) on every thirteenth stamp and is scarce.

Variety N35*n* exists from plates 34 and 52. Bottom marginal examples from plate 34 show a white dot in the rule below HA. In plate 52 the rule is undamaged. Non-marginal examples of the variety are identical.

N35*j*   N35*l*   N35*m*   N35*n*

Controls

Somerset House Emergency Printing (during General Strike):

	I.	P.
E. 26	£375	†

Waterlow Printings:

		I.	P.					I.	P.					I.	P.
A	24	50	2·00	H	27	..	..	50	12·00	O	31	..	..	50	†
B	24	50	24·00	I	28	..	..	50	24·00	P	31	..	..	50	†
C	25	50	—	J	28	..	..	50	†	Q	32	..	..	50	†
D	25	50	†	K	29	..	..	50	24·00	R	32	..	..	50	†
E	26	50	†	L	29	..	..	50	†	S	33	..	..	50	†
F	26	50	12·00	M	30	..	..	1·00	†	T	33	..	..	50	†
G	27	75	†	N	30	..	..	50	—	U	34	..	..	1·00	†

Watermark varieties known:

Wmk inverted: A 24, B 24, C 25, D 25, E 26, F 26, G 27, H 27, I 28, J 28, K 29, M 30, N 30, O 31, Q 32.

Waterlow Printings on experimental **W16** *paper:*

				I.	P.
A	24	..	..	£125	†
B	24	..	..	£140	†
D	25	..	..	£125	†

Watermark variety known:
Wmk inverted: D 25.

Harrison Printings:

				I.	P.
U	34	..	..	1·25	†
U	34[streaky gum]‡			1·60	†
V	34[streaky gum]			1·25	—

‡Known printed on the gum.

Booklet Panes of Six

From Waterlow Booklets BB12, BB24, B33/34 and Harrison Booklets BB14, BB26 and BB35

NB14	Watermark upright	5·00		NB14a	Watermark inverted	5·00
s.	" Specimen ", Type 23 ..	50·00		*as.*	" Specimen ", Type 23 ..	50·00
t.	" Specimen ", Type 30 ..	50·00		*at.*	" Specimen ", Type 30 ..	50·00
u.	" Cancelled ", Type 24 ..			*av.*	" Cancelled ", Type 28 ..	50·00
v.	" Cancelled ", Type 28 ..	50·00		*ava.*	" Cancelled ", Type 28P ..	
va.	" Cancelled ", Type 28P ..			*aw.*	" Cancelled ", Type 33 ..	70·00†
w.	" Cancelled ", Type 33 ..	70·00		*ax.*	" Cancelled ", Type 33P ..	50·00
x.	" Cancelled ", Type 33P ..	50·00		*ay.*	Cancelled, " London E.C.", Type I	25·00
y.	Cancelled, " London E.C.", Type I	25·00		*aza.*	Cancelled " London Chief Office E.C.1 ", Type K, in violet	
z.	Cancelled " London Chief Office E.C.1 ", Type J, in violet					
za.	Cancelled " London Chief Office E.C.1 ", Type K, in violet					

†No. NB14*aw* exists from NPM archive sales.

Booklet Panes with Advertising Labels

Panes of six, comprising two labels printed in *black* or *green* (NB15/a (72)) and four stamps From Waterlow Booklets BB12, BB33/34

NB15	Watermark upright	60·00		NB15a	Watermark inverted	60·00
b.	Watermark sideways ..	£2000		*as.*	" Specimen ", Type 23 ..	60·00
s.	" Specimen ", Type 23 ..	60·00		*at.*	" Specimen ", Type 30 ..	60·00
t.	" Specimen ", Type 30 ..	60·00		*av.*	" Cancelled ", Type 28 ..	60·00
u.	" Cancelled ", Type 24 ..			*aw.*	" Cancelled ", Type 33P ..	60·00
v.	" Cancelled ", Type 28 ..	60·00		*ax.*	" Cancelled ", Type 33 ..	80·00†
w.	" Cancelled ", Type 33P ..	60·00		*ay.*	Cancelled, " London E.C.", Type I	40·00
x.	" Cancelled ", Type 33 ..	80·00				
y.	Cancelled, " London E.C.", Type I	40·00				
z.	Cancelled, " London Chief Office ", Type K, in violet..					

†No. NB15*ax* with advertisement (9) exists from NPM archive sales.

Pane Nos. NB15 or NB15a

G.P.O. Adverts:

		Wmk Upright	*Wmk Inverted*
(1)	" Air Mails (enquire) / Cable via Imperial "	60·00	60·00
(1a)	As (1), but text on both labels inverted	75·00	75·00
(2)	" Air Mails (enquire) / Telephone Service "	60·00	60·00
(3)	" Cable via Imperial / Air Mails (enquire) "	60·00	60·00
(4)	" Cable via Imperial / Telephone Service "	60·00	60·00
(5)	" via Empiradio / Cable via Imperial "	60·00	60·00
(6)	" via Empiradio / Telephone Service "	60·00	60·00
(7)	" Saving is Simple / Home Safe " (*Setting 1*) ..	60·00	60·00
(8)	" Telephone Service / Air Mails (enquire) " ..	60·00	60·00
(9)	" Telephone Service / Air Mails, letters and parcels " (*Setting 1*)	60·00	60·00
(10)	" Telephone Service / Cable via Imperial "	60·00	60·00

Pane Nos. NB15 *or* NB15a	*Wmk Upright*	*Wmk Inverted*

J. J. Cash Ltd. Adverts:

(11) " Cash's names. The best method of marking personal and household linen / List of styles. J. & J. Cash "	60·00	60·00
(12) " Cash's washing ribbons. Ideal for shoulder straps / Book of ribbons. J. & J. Cash " (*unnumbered, or numbered* 144, 152, 160, 163, 167 *or* 175) ..	60·00	60·00
(13) " Cash's names. The best method of marking all linen / Cash's booklet, " Lose less linen ", J. & J. Cash " (*numbered* 150)	75·00	75·00
(14) " Cash's lingerie ribbons. Ideal for shoulder straps / Book of ribbons. J. & J. Cash " (*numbered* 181) ..	60·00	60·00
(15) Do. but with " Cash's " in larger type and numbered 185	60·00	60·00
(16) " Cash's " Lose less linen " book / Free booklet. J. & J. Cash " (*numbered* 3 *or* 196)	75·00	75·00
(17) " Cash's " Safety first. Cash's names " booklet / Free booklet J. & J. Cash " (*numbered* 237) (*Setting* 1) ..	75·00	75·00
(18) " Cash's satin lingerie ribbons / Cash's ribbon booklet. J. & J. Cash " (*numbered* 2, 190, 207, 225 *or* 229) ..	60·00	60·00
(19) " Cash's satin lingerie ribbons / Samples [central] of Cash's ribbons J. & J. Cash " (*numbered* 4, 5, 243 *or* 249) (*Setting* 1)	60·00	60·00

Castell Bros. Adverts:

(20) " Bodiam. Use it with pride / Bodiam. Castell Bros."	60·00	60·00
(21) " Castletone fashionable writing paper / Castell Bros."	75·00	75·00
(22) " Castletone Stationery / Castell Bros." ..	75·00	75·00
(23) " Bodiam. [Six named colours] / Bodiam Castell Bros."	75·00	75·00
(24) " Pepys Stationery. Bodiam Castletone / Royal York. Stonehenge "	60·00	60·00

Cruise Departments Adverts:

(25) " American Holiday £40 / ss. Minnekahda. Atlantic Transport Co.".	60·00	60·00
(26) " Holiday Trips £40. Tourist 3rd Cabin only [in four lines] / ss. Minnekahda and Minnesota Atlantic Transport Co. Ltd."	60·00	60·00
(27) " Holiday Trips £40. Tourist 3rd Cabin [in two lines] / ss. Minnekahda and Minnesota Atlantic Transport Line "	75·00	75·00
(28) " Holiday Trips £40. Tourist 3rd Cabin only [in three lines] / ss. Minnekahda and Minnesota Atlantic Transport Line "	75·00	75·00
(29) " Your holiday problem solved. £39 15s. od. [wording upright] / Atlantic Transport Line [wording sideways] "	75·00	75·00
(30) " South Africa for Sunshine / Union Castle Line " ..	75·00	75·00
(31) " Your 3 weeks holiday. A trip to New York £38 / White Star Line "	75·00	75·00
(32) " Your 3 weeks holiday. Why not a trip? £38 / White Star Line "	75·00	75·00
(33) " Your 3 weeks holiday. Take a trip. £38 / White Star Line "	60·00	60·00
(34) " Your Holiday. Cruise British by White Star / The Cruise Department "	75·00	75·00
(35) " 33 Spring and Summer Cruises / White Star Line "	75·00	75·00

John Knight Ltd. Adverts:

(36) " Have YOU tried Knight's Castile / John Knight Ltd "	75·00	75·00
(37) " For a limited period, Knight's Castile / Robinson and Cleaver Ltd."	75·00	75·00
(38) " [Soap picture] Knight's Castile / [Knight picture] Knight's Castile "	75·00	75·00
(39) " Try the three perfumes of Knight's Castile / Three visitors' tablets [small type] "	75·00	75·00
(40) " Try the three perfumes of Knight's Castile / Three visitors' tablets [large type] "	75·00	75·00
(41) " Knight's Castile, delicately perfumed / A British soap "	75·00	75·00

Pane Nos. NB15 *or* NB15a

		Wmk Upright	*Wmk Inverted*
(42)	" You ought to try ' zyxt ' / John Knight Ltd." ..	75·00	75·00
(43)	" What is your week-end job? ' ZYXT / John Knight Ltd."	75·00	75·00
(44)	" Whatever your week-end job, ' ZYXT / John Knight Ltd."	75·00	75·00
(45)	" [Picture of zyxt] / ' zyxt ' is 4d. a tablet "	75·00	75·00
(46)	" Knight's Castile, new artistic pack / John Knight Ltd."	75·00	75·00
(47)	" Free to users of Family Health Soap / John Knight Ltd."	75·00	75·00
(48)	" Royal Primrose Soap / John Knight Ltd."	75·00	75·00
(49)	" Have you had your copy of the new list of British Gifts. Family Health Soap / John Knight Ltd." ..	75·00	75·00
(50)	" Family Health and Hustler Too!/John Knight Ltd."	75·00	75·00
(51)	" John Knight Ltd. / Family Health and Hustler Too!"	75·00	75·00
(52)	" Have YOU tried Shavallo? / John Knight Ltd." ..	75·00	75·00
(53)	" To obtain real luxury in shaving, Shavallo / 21 days for 2d. SHAVALLO "	75·00	75·00
(54)	" Why not try Shavallo shaving cream? / John Knight Ltd."	75·00	75·00
(55)	" John Knight's Shavallo 1/- / It's British "	75·00	75·00

Sundry Adverts:

		Wmk Upright	*Wmk Inverted*
(56)	" If interested in Billiards / The Billiard Player " ..	75·00	75·00
(57)	" Bring the breath of the pine forest, etc. Cleaver's Terebene / F. S. Cleaver, Twickenham "	75·00	75·00
(58)	" Have YOU tried Cleaver's Terebene? / F. S. Cleaver, London "	75·00	75·00
(59)	" Desti cigarettes / Silmos Lollies "	75·00	75·00
(60)	" Desti cigarettes / Telephone Service " ..	75·00	75·00
(61)	" Dutton's shorthand / Reginald P.O. Dutton " ..	75·00	75·00
(62)	" Buy Gilette blades / The blade with a shave in it " ..	75·00	75·00
(63)	" Garden work for amateurs / Cable via Imperial " ..	75·00	75·00
(64)	" Gaze's all weather tennis courts [sideways] / Send to Harmer, Rooke, Auctions [upright] " ..	60·00	60·00
(65)	" Glastonbury's / Soft Sheepskin Shoes "	75·00	75·00
(66)	" Gospo / Cable via Imperial "	60·00	60·00
(67)	" Auctions, Harmer, Rooke, cash advanced, 69 Fleet Street [inverted] / Harmer Rooke, Auctions [upright] "	75·00	75·00
(68)	" Note new address, Harmer Rooke / Stamp collectors should visit 188/189 Strand W.C.2 " ..	75·00	75·00
(69)	" Auctions, Harmer, Rooke, cash advanced, 188 Strand [inverted] / Harmer, Rooke, Auctions [upright] " ..	75·00	75·00
(70)	" Best seats [sideways] / Keith Prowse [sideways] " ..	75·00	75·00
(71)	" La Corona, Havana Cigars / Acknowledged the world over "	75·00	75·00
(72)	" India Rubber Sponge [in green] / R. G. McKinlay [in green] "	£1100	£1100
(73)	" Millennium Oat-Flakes / Wright's Coal Tar Soap "	60·00	60·00
(74)	" Pitman's correspondence course / Pitman's W.C.1 "	75·00	75·00
(75)	" Pomeroy skin food. Helps the plain / Mrs. Pomeroy "	75·00	75·00
(76)	" Pomeroy skin food. Trial size jar / Superfluous hair. Mrs. Pomeroy "	75·00	75·00
(77)	" Poultry World. Free copy / Poultry World, 27 Stamford Street, S.E.1 "	75·00	75·00
(78)	" H.T. Battery / Ripaults Ltd. [known in two settings: top to bottom measuring 43 and 44 mm] "	60·00	60·00
(79)	" Robinson and Cleaver famous for linen handkerchiefs / Hemstitched Handkerchiefs "	60·00	60·00
(80)	" Robinson and Cleaver famous for Irish Linens / Ladies' Linen Hemstitched Handkerchiefs "	75·00	75·00
(81)	" Scarborough's Hotels / Cable via Imperial " ..	60·00	60·00
(82)	" Scarborough's Hotels / Harmer, Rooke weekly Stamp Auctions."	60·00	60·00
(83)	" Scarborough's Hotels / Wright's Coal Tar Soap " ..	60·00	60·00
(84)	" Wireless World. Free copy / Complete foreign programmes. Wireless World "	75·00	75·00
(85)	" Save the outside wrappers. Wright's Coal Tar Soap Wright to the Proprietors, 46 Southwark Street, S.E.1 "	75·00	75·00
(86)	" Wright's Coal Tar Soap / Telephone Service " ..	75·00	75·00
(87)	" Wright's Lysol / Air Mail, letters and parcels " ..	75·00	75·00

		Wmk Upright	*Wmk Inverted*
Pane Nos. NB15 *or* NB15a			
From Harrison Booklets BB14 and BB35:			
(88)	" Telephone Service / Air Mails, letters and parcels " (*Setting 2*: bolder type; line under " Installed free " has only three loops)..	70·00	70·00
(89)	" Saving is Simple / Home Safe " (*Setting 2*: larger type than *Setting 1*)	70·00	70·00
(90)	" Cash's satin lingerie ribbons / Samples [central] of Cash's ribbons, J. & J. Cash " (*Setting 2*: bolder type than Setting 1) (*numbered 4, 5, 257, 275 or 285*)	70·00	70·00
(91)	" Cash's " Safety first. Cash's names " booklet / Free booklet J. & J. Cash " (*Setting 2*) (*numbered 7 or 263*)..	85·00	85·00
(92)	" Pepys Stationery / Ruskin Linen "	85·00	85·00
(93)	" Pepys Stationery. Castletone/Castells, London "	85·00	85·00
(94)	" Pepys Stationery. Bodiam in white and six colours/Just added: Bodiam Grey. Castells " ..	70·00	70·00
(95)	" For every woman. Bodiam in 7 colours / Pepys Stationery "	85·00	85·00
(96)	" For every woman, Bodiam. For every man, Royal York / White and azure. Pepys Stationery Productions "	85·00	85·00
(97)	" Kargo. (Card Golf) / Castell Bros. (Pepys Stationery) "	85·00	85·00
(98)	" Cruises [picture of sailor] / White Star Line " ..	85·00	85·00
(99)	" Poultry World. Free copy / Poultry World, 31 Stamford Street, S.E.1 "	85·00	85·00
(100)	" Shavallo for a swift smooth shave / Shavallo, Barbers use it "	70·00	70·00
(101)	" corot models. 33, old bond street / corot. 33, old bond street "	85·00	85·00
(102)	" corot models. 33, old bond street, sb. 19 / corot 33, old bond street "	85·00	85·00
(103)	" corot models. 33, old bond street / corot (dept. s.b 20) 33, old bond street "..	85·00	85·00

The numbers printed on the panes (i.e. on NB15(12) onwards) correspond to the numbers of the booklets in which they were issued. See Appendix 2.

Coils

Vertical delivery printed in continuous reels

Code No.	Issued	Number in roll	Face value	
K	June 1924	960	£6.0.0	Bottom delivery
L	June 1924	480	£3.0.0	Top delivery

Sideways delivery made up from sheets with joins every 12th stamp

N	1924	480	£3.0.0	Left side delivery

Sideways delivery printed in continuous reels with watermark sideways

N	Aug. 1924	480	£3.0.0	Left side delivery

Imprimaturs from the National Postal Museum Archives

Imperforate, watermark Type W15

Watermark upright
Watermark sideways

Booklet pane of six. Imperforate, watermark Type W15

Two panes as No. NB14 arranged horizontally *tête-bêche* with marginal pillars at right

Booklet pane of four with blank advertisement label. Imperforate, watermark Type W15

Two panes as No. NB15 arranged horizontally *tête-bêche* with marginal pillars at right

Specimen and Cancelled overprints from the National Postal Museum Archives

Booklet pane of six. Perf. 15 × 14, watermark Type W15 (inverted)

" Specimen ", Type 32 and upper left stamp with punch hole

Booklet pane of four with advertising labels. Perf. 15 × 14, watermark Type W15 (inverted)

No. NB15a (18) numbered " 2 " with stamps overprinted " Specimen ", Type 32 and upper label with punch hole

Plate Markings

Plate	Marking
1	Dot (base) under PE of 1st
2	Small dot (base) under HA of 2nd
3	Small dot (base) under AL of 3rd
4	Small dot 20th left side, 14½ mm.
5	Small dot 19th left side, 16 mm.
6	½ dot (outer) and full dot 18th left side, 21, 10 mm.
7	19th outer left side scooped out 4–6 mm. Dot 18th right side, 13 mm.
8	Nick (outer) 19th left side, 8½ mm. Dot under F of 4th. Dot 20th right side
9	Dot and ½ dot (inner) 19th left side, 9½, 10½ mm.
10	½ dot (outer) 20th left side, 5 mm. 19th left side badly scored (outer) (Harrison Plate 41)
11	½ dot (base) under A of 4th (Harrison Plate 43)
12	Line under 1st bevelled at left. Nick (outer) base of 20th right side. Large dot 4th left side
13	Dot 20th left side, 11 mm.
14	Oval dot 19th left side, 8 mm.
15	19th left side bulges in middle. 20th left side thins at base
16	Large dot 1st left side, 12 mm. Dot at left over 1st top row. Base of 20th left side bent inwards
17	Dot 20th left side, 10 mm.
18	Fine dot (inner) 20th left side, 11 mm.
19	Nick (outer) 19th left side, 14 mm. Dot 1st left side, 11 mm.
20a	Large dot (top) under LF of 1st
20b	Added fine dot under EN of 3rd
21a	Dot (top) under AL of 2nd
21b	Added dot 20th left side, 10 mm.
21c	Added minute dot under A of 1st
22a	Notch (base) to right of (C)E of 2nd. Base of 19th left side bevelled 1–2 mm.
22b	Added minute dot under L of 1st
23	Minute dot under EH of 2nd
24	Tiny dot under F of 3rd
25	Tiny dot under L of 4th
26	Large and small dot 20th left side. Both 6½ mm.
27	Dot 19th left side, 8 mm. Small nick (base) under FP of 3rd
28	Two minute dots under HA of 1st (usually visible). Two minute dots under NC of 2nd
29	Double nick at left of 2nd
30	Scratch under NC of 3rd
31a	Double notch (base) under EN of 2nd
31b	Added notch (base) under FP of 2nd
32	Vertical score 20th left side
33	½ dot (base) under HA of 3rd
34	Small dot (top) under HA of 3rd. 19th left damaged (outer), 8–10 mm.
35	Oval dot under EE of 3rd
36	Dot (base) under HR of 3rd
37	2 dots, top and bottom, 20th left side, 19½, 3 mm.
38	2 dots, top and bottom, 19th left side, 21, 3 mm.
39	No marking. 20th left side thick and irregular
40	2 dots top and bottom, 20th left side, 21, 2 mm.
41	2 dots top and bottom, 19th left side, 20½, 1½ mm. Cut 18th left side, 11 mm.
42	Base of 20th left side bends inwards.
43	Small dot 20th right side, 6½ mm.
44	Internal cut 17th left side, 7½ mm.
45	2 internal cuts 15th right side at top
46	20th left side tapers from 8 mm. to base
47a	Internal score 19th left side, 17–19 mm.
47b	Added dot 19th left side, 16½ mm.
48	Tiny nick under base of N of 3rd
49	Small dot under C of 1st
50	Small dot 17th right side, 14½ mm.
51	Dot 16th left side, 10 mm.
52	19th left side damaged (outer), 7½–11 mm.
53	Dot over 1st in upper row. Dot 1st left side, 11 mm.
54	Tiny dots under E(E) of 12th and 20th right side (inner), 12 mm.
55	Dot 17th left side, 10½ mm. Minute dot under HA of 11th. Two dots 19th right side, 7, 9½ mm.
56	Tiny dot 15th left side, 16 mm. Scoop (outer) 16th left side, 16–20 mm.
57	Dot 2nd left side, 16 mm. Dot under HA of 9th.
58a	Dot 3rd left side, 13 mm.
58b	Added dot under F of 10th.

Index to Marginal Markings

Top Row, Stamp Numbers

Stamp No.	Plate
1 ..	16, 53

Bottom Row, Stamp Numbers

Stamp No.	Plate
1 ..	1, 12, 20a, 20b, 21c, 22b, 28, 49
2 ..	2, 21a, 21b, 21c, 22a, 22b, 23, 28, 29, 31a, 31b
3 ..	3, 20b, 24, 27, 30, 33, 34, 35, 36, 48
4 ..	8, 11, 25
9 ..	57
10 ..	58b
11 ..	55
12 ..	54

Left Margin, Row Numbers

Row No.	Plate
1 ..	16, 19, 53
2 ..	57
3 ..	58a
4 ..	12
15 ..	56
16 ..	51, 56
17 ..	44, 55
18 ..	6, 41
19 ..	5, 7, 8, 9, 10, 14, 15, 19, 22a, 22b, 27, 34, 38, 41, 47a, 47b, 52
20 ..	4, 10, 13, 15, 16, 17, 18, 21b, 21c, 26, 32, 37 39, 40, 42, 46

Right Margin, Row Numbers

Row No.	Plate
15 ..	45
17 ..	50
18 ..	7
19 ..	55
20 ..	8, 12, 43, 54

Control Schedule

Waterlow Printings, 1924–33

Control	Plates employed
A 24 ..	1, 2, 3, 4, 5, 6, 8, 44, 48
B 24 ..	1, 2, 3, 4, 7, 8, 28, 43, 44, 48, 50, 55
C 25 ..	1, 2, 3, 7, 8, 9, 10, 43, 54
D 25 ..	1, 2, 3, 7, 8, 9, 10, 11, 43, 54, 55
E 26 ..	1, 8, 11, 12, 13, 14, 15, 19, 56
F 26 ..	3, 10, 12, 13, 14, 16, 43, 45, 56, 58a
G 27 ..	12, 13, 14, 16, 58
H 27 ..	13, 15, 17, 18
I 28 ..	13, 15, 17, 18, 19, 57, 58b
J 28 ..	18, 19, 20a, 21a, 22a, 47a, 51
K 29 ..	20a, 21a, 22a, 47a

Control	Plates employed
L 29 ..	20a, 21a, 21b, 22b, 23, 24, 25, 47b
M 30 ..	19, 20b, 22b, 24, 26, 27, 28, 47b
N 30 ..	26, 27, 28, 29, 30
O 31 ..	21b, 21c, 27, 28, 29, 31a, 32
P 31 ..	29, 31a, 31b, 32, 46
Q 32 ..	28, 29, 31b, 32
R 32 ..	28, 29, 32, 52
S 33 ..	33, 34, 35, 36, 37, 49, 52
T 33 ..	34, 35, 36, 37, 38, 39, 40, 41
? ..	53

Somerset House Printing, 1926
E 26 .. 15

Waterlow Provisional Printings, 1934
U 34 .. 38, 39

Harrison Provisional Printings, 1934
U 34 .. 38, 39, 40, 41, 42   V 34 .. 38, 39, 40, 42

Cat. No.	S.G. No.					Shades	Unused	Used

1924 (SEPTEMBER).   **2d. ORANGE, TYPE N7, DIE II**

N36   421

					Shades	Unused	Used
					(1) Orange	80	60
					(2) Deep orange	2·00	45
a.	No watermark ..	..	..	£400	(3) Yellow-orange	1·00	45
b.	Watermark inverted	..	..	10·00 4·50	(4) Deep yellow-orange	8·00	85
c.	Watermark sideways (7.26)	..	70·00 55·00		(5) Pale yellow-orange	4·00	45
d.	Doubly printed ..	..	..	£10000			
e.	Coil join (vert. pair)	..	..				
f.	Coil join (horiz. pair)	..	..				
s.	"Specimen", Type 23 ..	..	16·00		*t.* "Specimen", Type 32 ..		
sa.	Imperf. optd. "Specimen",				*u.* "Specimen", Type 32 and		
	Type 23, wmk. sideways	..	£100		"Cancelled", Type 34 ..		

Variety *a*, One sheet of 240 was found from Control C 25

Controls

Waterlow Printings:

	I.	P.				I.	P.				I.	P.
A 24	.. ..	5·00	†	H 27	.. ..	1·00	†	O 31	.. ..	2·00	†
B 24	.. ..	1·00	16·00	I 28	.. ..	1·00	22·00	P 31	.. ..	1·00	†
C 25	.. ..	1·00	†	J 28	.. ..	1·00	†	Q 32	.. ..	1·00	†
D 25	.. ..	1·00	†	K 29	.. ..	1·00	†	R 32	.. ..	2·50	35·00
E 26	.. ..	1·00	†	L 29	.. ..	1·50	†	S 33	.. ..	6·00	†
F 26	.. ..	1·00	†	M 30	.. ..	1·50	†	T 33	.. ..	1·75	†
G 27	.. ..	1·00	†	N 30	.. ..	1·00	†	U 34	.. ..	—	†

Watermark varieties known:
Wmk inverted: A 24, B 24, C 25, D 25, E 26, F 26, G 27, H 27, I 28, J 28, K 29, M 30, P 31, R 32.
No wmk: C 25.

Harrison Printings:

	I.	P.
U 34	.. ..	3·00	†
U 34 [streaky gum]	4·00	†
V 34 [streaky gum]	3·00	—

Coils

Vertical delivery made up from sheets with joins every 20th stamp

Code No.	Issued	Number in roll	Face value	
Q	1924	960	£8.0.0	Bottom delivery
R	1924	480	£4.0.0	Top delivery

Sideways delivery made up from sheets with joins every 12th stamp

T	1924	480	£4.0.0	Left side delivery

Sideways delivery printed in continuous reels with watermark sideways

T	July 1926	480	£4.0.0	Left side delivery

Imprimaturs from the National Postal Museum Archives

Imperforate, watermark Type W15

Watermark upright
Watermark sideways

Plate Markings

Plate	Marking
1	Base of 20th left side rounded off
2	Left of rule under 1st pointed below; base of rule under 12th irregular and bevelled at left; large dot 18th right side, 11 mm.
3	Minute dot 20th left side, 11½ mm.; rule under 1st slightly scooped out under OP
4	Dot 20th left side, 13 mm. (Harrison Plate 4)
5a	Dot 19th left side, 13 mm. (Harrison Plate 5)
5b	Added minute dot under P of 2nd
6	Dot 19th left side breaking right, 9 mm. Base of rules under 1st, 2nd and 3rd very irregular
7	Lower portion of 19th left side shows internal damage; ¼ dot (inner) 20th left side, 11 mm., with minute dot to left of it
8	Flaw in base of 19th left side; dot with offshoot dot above and to right of it 20th left side, 13 mm.; nick to left of 1st at base
9	Dot 19th left side, 11¾ mm.; minute dot (base) under P of 2nd
10	Large dot (breaking top) under P of 1st
11	½ dot (top) under P of 2nd
12	Dot 19th left side, 11½ mm. Nicks (base) at left and right of 2nd
13	Dot 20th left side, 12 mm.
14a	Dot 19th left side, 11 mm.; indent base under and to right of E of 2nd
14b	Added dot 19th left side, 13 mm.
15	No marking
16	Indent (base) under C of 1st
17	Dot (top) under OP of 9th; dot (breaking inner) 17th right side, 12½ mm. (Harrison Plate 3)
18	Dot under P of 10th; dot (central) 18th right side, 13 mm.; rule under 2nd appears thinner than those under 1st and 3rd. (Harrison Plate 6)

Index to Marginal Markings

Bottom Row, Stamp Numbers

Stamp No.	Plate
1	2, 3, 6, 8, 10, 16
2	5b, 6, 9, 11, 12, 14a, 14b, 18
3	6
9	17
10	18
12	2

Left Margin, Row Numbers

Row No.	Plate
19	5a, 5b, 6, 7, 8, 9, 12, 14a, 14b
20	1, 3, 4, 7, 8, 13

Right Margin, Row Numbers

Row No.	Plate
17	17
18	2, 18

No Marking: Plate 15

Control Schedule

Waterlow Printings, 1924–33

Plate	Controls	Plate	Controls	Plate	Controls
1	A 24, B 24, C 25	6	F 26, G 27, H 27, I 28, J 28	12	N 30, Q 32, R 32, S 33, T 33, U 34
2	A 24, B 24, F 26, L 29, M 30, N 30, P 31, Q 32, R 32	7	F 26, G 27, H 27, K 29, L 29, M 30	13	N 30, O 31, R 32, T 33
3	B 24, D 25, F 26, H 27, I 28, K 29, L 29	8	J 28, K 29, L 29	14a	O 31
4	B 24, C 25, D 25, E 26	9	J 28, K 29, L 29	14b	O 31, Q 32, R 32, S 33, T 33
5a	B 24, D 25, E 26, I 28, J 28	10	M 30, N 30, O 31, P 31	17	E 26
5b	J 28, K 29, L 29	11	M 30, N 30, O 31, P 31, Q 32, R 32	18	D 25

Harrison Provisional Printings, 1934

Plate	Controls	Plate	Controls	Plate	Controls
12	U 34	15	U 34, V 34	16	V 34

Cat. No.	S.G. No.				Shades	Unused	Used

1924 (OCTOBER). 2½d. BLUE, TYPE N5

N37   422

				Shades	Unused	Used
a.	No watermark	£550		(1) Blue	4·50	90
b.	Watermark inverted ..	19·00	9·00	(2) Pale blue (1924)	4·25	70
c.	Error. Watermark sideways	†	—	(3) Bright blue	4·25	70
e.	Coil join (vert. pr.) (9.29) ..			(4) Ultramarine	6·00	95
f.	Coil join (horiz. pr.) (2.35)					
s.	"Specimen", Type 23 ..					
t.	"Specimen", Type 32 ..					
u.	"Specimen", Type 32 and					
	"Cancelled", Type 34 ..					

Variety a. Two sheets known to exist from Control B 24.

One used example of No. N37c has been reported.

Controls

Waterlow Printings:

			I.	P.				I.	P.				I.	P.
B 24	..	..	5·00	†	H 27	..	..	7·50	†	O 31	..	..	£750	†
C 25	..	..	5·00	†	I 28	..	..	5·00	†	Q 32	..	..	5·00	†
D 25	..	..	5·00	†	K 29	..	..	5·00	†	R 32	..	..	5·00	†
E 26	..	..	5·00	†	M 30	..	..	5·00	†	S 33	..	..	7·50	†
G 27	..	..	5·00	50·00	N 30	..	..	5·00	†	T 33	..	..	6·50	†

Watermark varieties known:
Wmk inverted: B 24, C 25, D 25, E 26, G 27, I 28, M 30.
No wmk.: B 24.

Harrison Printings:

			I.	P.
V 34	..	..	6·50	†
W 35	..	..	10·00	15·00

Watermark varieties known:
Wmk inverted: V 34.

Coils

Vertical delivery made up from sheets with joins every 20th stamp

Code No.	Issued	Number in roll	Face value	
F	Sep. 1929	960	£10.0.0	Bottom delivery

Sideways delivery made up from sheets with joins every 12th stamp

M	Feb. 1935	480	£5.0.0	Left side delivery

Imprimatur from the National Postal Museum Archives

Imperforate, watermark Type W15

Watermark upright

Plate Markings

Plate	Marking
1a	Tiny dot 19th right side; nick (base) to right of 8th
1b	Added dot 19th left side (inner), 12 mm.
2	20th left side very thick and irregular rule under 1st curves slightly upwards towards left end. Large dot 2nd left side
3	Dot (inner) 20th left side, 13½ mm.
4	Cut under F of 2nd. (Harrison Plate 11b)
5	Large dot (outer) 19th left side, 11½ mm.
6	Circular dot under P of 1st. (Harrison Plate 8b)

Plate	Marking
7	Dot 20th left side, 10½ mm.
8	Small dot 19th left side, 11 mm.
9	20th left side bends in at base; rule under 1st splays out at left end; minute dot under Y of 2nd
10	Dot 20th left side, 7 mm.; minute dot at right of 2nd
11	Scratch in rule under Y of 1st
12	Dot 19th left side, 10½ mm.
13	Base of 20th left side has an inward projection
14	No marking
15	Cut under (P)E of 1st. (Harrison Plate 10)

Control Schedule
Waterlow Printings, 1924–33

Plate		Controls employed	Plate		Controls employed
1a	..	B 24, C 25	8	..	I 28
1b	..	D 25	9	..	Q 32, R 32, S 33
2	..	M 30, N 30, O 31, Q 32, R 32, S 33	10	..	K 29
3	..	D 25, E 26, G 27	11	..	T 33
4	..	E 26, G 27, I 28	12	..	K 29
5	..	E 26, G 27, I 28	13	..	Q 32, T 33
6	..	G 27, H 27	14	..	I 28, M 30, N 30
7	..	I 28			

Harrison Provisional Printings, 1934–35

Plate		Controls employed	Plate		Controls employed
11	..	V 34	15	..	V 34, W 35
13	..	V 34, W 35			

Cat. No.	S.G. No.				Shades	Unused	Used

1924 (OCTOBER). 3d. VIOLET, TYPE N7

N38   423
a. Watermark inverted .. 16·00 8·00
b. Coil join (vert. pr.) (9.32) ..
c. Coil join (horiz. pr.) (2.35) ..
d. Right 3 broken (Pl. 5, R. 20/2) .. .. .. 30·00
s. " Specimen ", Type 23 ..
t. " Specimen ", Type 32 ..
u. " Specimen ", Type 32 and " Cancelled ", Type 34 ..
v. " Cancelled ", Type 33 ..

(1) Violet   5·50   60
(2) Pale violet (1924-25)   6·00   60
(3) Pale dull reddish violet
    (1924-25)   8·00   65
(4) Deep violet   6·50   75
(5) Bright violet   6·00   65
(6) Deep brownish violet   15·00   85

N38d

This variety also exists with watermark inverted.

Controls

Waterlow Printings:

		I.	P.				I.	P.				I.	P.
B 24	..	.. 6·50	†	I 28	..	..	6·50	†	R 32	..	..	6·50	†
C 25	..	.. 6·50	†	K 29	..	..	15·00	†	S 33	..	..	12·50	†
D 25	..	.. 6·50	†	M 30	..	..	6·50	†	T 33	..	..	12·50	†
E 26	..	.. 6·50	†	N 30	..	..	6·50	†					
G 27	..	.. 6·50	85·00	P 31	..	..	7·50	†					

Watermark varieties known:
Wmk inverted: B 24, C 25, D 25, E 26, G 27, I 28.

Harrison Printings:

		I.	P.
V 34	..	.. 12·50	†

Coils

Vertical delivery made up from sheets with joins every 20th stamp

Code No.	Issued	Number in roll	Face value	
C	Sep. 1932	960	£12.0.0	Bottom delivery

Sideways delivery made up from sheets with joins every 12th stamp

| S | Feb. 1935 | 480 | £6.0.0 | Left side delivery |

Imprimatur from the National Postal Museum Archives

Imperforate, watermark Type W15
Watermark upright

Plate Markings

Plate	Marking
1a	Tiny nick (base) to right of 2nd bottom row
1b	Added cut 20th left side, 10 mm.
2	20th left side heavy and irregular
3	Dot 19th left side, 13 mm. (Harrison Plate 10
4	½ dot (inner) 20th left side, 12¾ mm. (Harrison Plate 9)

Plate	Marking
5	Tiny dot 20th left side, 11 mm.
6	Tiny dot (inner) 19th left side, 9 mm.
7	No marking. 20th left side irregular
8	No marking. 20th left side sharply defined

229

Control Schedule

Waterlow Printings, 1924–33

Plate		Controls employed	Plate		Controls employed
1a	..	B 24	5	..	E 26, G 27, I 28, K 29, M 30, N 30,
1b	..	B 24, C 25, D 25			P 31, R 32, S 33, T 33
2	..	B 24, C 25	6	..	I 28, K 29, M 30, N 30, P 31
3	..	D 25, E 26, G 27, R 32	7	..	M 30, N 30, P 31, R 32, S 33, T 33
4	..	E 26, G 27, I 28, K 29, M 30, P 31, R 32	8	..	S 33, T 33

Harrison Provisional Printings, 1934

3	..	V 34	4	..	V 34

Cat. No.	S.G. No.			Shades	Unused	Used

1924 (NOVEMBER).   4d. GREY-GREEN, TYPE N7

					Unused	Used
N39	424			(1) Deep grey-green	8·00	80
a.	Watermark inverted	.. 18·00	8·00	(2) Grey-green	7·50	90
b.	Printed on the gummed side	£1100	†	(3) Very deep grey-green		
s.	" Specimen ", Type 23	..		(1934-35)	20·00	1·60
t.	" Specimen ", Type 32	..				
u.	" Cancelled ", Type 28	..				
v.	" Specimen ", Type 32 and					
	" Cancelled ", Type 34	..				
w.	" Cancelled ", Type 33	..				

Controls

Waterlow Printings:

		I.	*P.*				*I.*	*P.*				*I.*	*P.*
B 24	..	.. 11·00	†	I 28	..	.. 11·00	†	Q 32	..	.. 11·00	†
C 25	.. ✓	.. 11·00	†	K 29	..	.. 11·00	†	R 32	..	.. 11·00	†
E 26	..	.. 13·00	†	M 30	..	.. 11·00	†	T 33	..	.. 11·00	†
G 27	..	.. 11·00	†	O 31	..	.. 11·00	†				

Watermark varieties known:
Wmk inverted: B 24, C 25, E 26, G 27, I 28, M 30, O 31.

Harrison Printings:

		I.	*P.*
V 34	..	.. 15·00	†
W 35	..	.. 25·00	†
X 35	..	.. 15·00	—

Imprimatur from the National Postal Museum Archives

Imperforate, watermark Type W15

Watermark upright

Plate Markings

Plate	Marking		Plate	Marking
1a	2 diagonal cuts 20th right side, 4, 7 mm. Base of 2nd bottom row bevelled at right		5	Dot at top of 19th left side
			6	No marking
1b	Base of 2nd repaired		7	No marking. 20th left side irregular. Rule under 1st, 2nd and 3rd bottom row thinner than Plate 6
2a	Base of 20th left side splays out to left. ½ dot (outer) 4th left side, 12½ mm			
2b	Added tiny dot under P of 11th bottom row 2 cuts 20th left side 17, 18½ mm.		8	Dot under RP of 2nd bottom row (Harrison Plate 2d)
4	Dot under RP of 1st bottom row (Harrison Plate 4)			

Control Schedule

Waterlow Printings, 1924–33

Plate	Controls employed		Plate	Controls employed
1a	..	B 24, C 25, E 26	3	..	E 26, G 27, I 28, K 29, M 30, O 31
1b	..	G 27, I 28, K 29, Q 32, R 32, T 33	4	..	Q 32
2a	..	B 24, C 25, E 26, G 27	5	..	O 31, Q 32, R 32, T 33
2b	..	K 29, M 30, O 31	6	..	R 32

Harrison Provisional Printings, 1934–35

Plate			Plate	
5	..	V 34, W 35	7	.. V 34, X 35
6	..	V 34	8	.. X 35

1924 (NOVEMBER). 5d. BROWN, TYPE N8

N40　　425
a.	Watermark inverted	.. 19·00	7·00
s.	"Specimen", Type 23	.. 35·00	
t.	"Specimen", Type 26	..	
u.	"Specimen", Type 32	..	
v.	"Specimen", Type 32 and		
	"Cancelled", Type 34	..	
w.	"Cancelled", Type 33	..	

(1) Brown	17·00	1·40
(2) Deep brown	20·00	1·40
(3) Reddish brown (1927-28)	20·00	1·75
(4) Bright ochre-brown	14·00	1·40
(5) Deep bright ochre-brown (1934)	25·00	2·75

Controls

Waterlow Printings:

	I.	P.			I.	P.				I.	P.
A 24	..	.. 16·00	16·00	K 29	..	.. 19·00	†	S 33	..	.. 19·00	†
C 25	..	.. 16·00	†	L 29	..	.. 19·00	†	T 33	..	.. £125	†
F 26	..	.. 16·00	†	M 30	..	.. 25·00	†	U 34	..	.. —	†
H 27	..	.. 20·00	†	O 31	..	.. 16·00	†				
I 28	..	.. 16·00	†	Q 32	..	.. 25·00	†				

Watermark varieties known:
Wmk inverted: A 24, C 25, F 26, I 28.

Harrison Printings:

	I.	P.
U 34	.. .. 30·00	†
V 34	.. .. 20·00	†
X 35	.. .. 20·00	†

Imprimatur from the National Postal Museum Archives

Imperforate, watermark Type W15

Watermark upright

Plate Markings

Plate	Marking	Plate	Marking
1a	No marking. Tiny diagonal internal cut, 14 mm. 19th right side. (Harrison Plate 3)	2a	Base of 20th left side slightly bent inwards
1b	Added dot 19th left side, 10 mm.	2b	Added dot 20th left side, 14 mm.

Control Schedule

Waterlow Printings, 1924–33

Plate		Controls employed	Plate		Controls employed
1a		A 24, C 35	2a	..	C 25
1b	..	C 25, F 26, H 27, I 28, K 29, L 29, M 30, O 31, Q 32, S 33, T 33	2b	..	C 25, F 26, H 27, I 28, K 29, L 29, M 30, O 31, Q 32, S 33, T 33

Waterlow Provisional Printing, 1934
2b　..　U 34

Harrison Provisional Printings, 1934–35

1b	..	U 34, V 34, X 35	2b	..	U 34, V 34, X 35

Cat. No.	S.G. No.		Shades	Unused	Used

1924 (SEPTEMBER) and 1936.   6d. PURPLE, TYPE N8.   CHALK-SURFACED PAPER

N41   426   Somerset House Printings (1924/5)

a. Watermark inverted   ..   16·00   9·00
b. Watermark inverted and reversed   ..   ..   ..   50·00

		Unused	Used
(1) Plum		15·00	3·00
(2) Rosy mauve		12·00	1·75

Harrison Printings (1936)

| (3) Reddish purple | 5·00 | 1·50 |
| (4) Deep reddish purple | 10·00 | 1·50 |

Controls

Somerset House Printings:

			I.	P.
B. 24	..	..	15·00	†
C. 25	..	..	15·00	†
D. 25	..	..	20·00	†

Watermark varieties known:
Wmk inverted: B. 24, C. 25, D. 25.
Wmk inverted and reversed: B. 24, C. 25.

Harrison Printings:

			I.	P.
Y 36	..	..	35·00	†
Z 36	..	..	15·00	†

Watermark varieties known:
Wmk inverted: Z 36.

Imprimatur from the National Postal Museum Archives

Imperforate, watermark Type W15

Watermark upright

Plate Markings

Somerset House Printings, 1924–25

Plates with interpane margin.

Plate markings such as those used by Harrison and Waterlow were not used at Somerset House, and plating can only be accomplished by the study of fortuitous marks. It seems that the 6d. stamps were printed in pairs of plates and these were marked above the top rows of the panes with a dot above the 1st or 2nd stamps to signify the position in the press.

Plate	Marking	Plate	Marking
6	Dot above 2nd in upper pane (to left of rule)	13	Protrusion top of 1st under C
	Small projection under X of 1st	14	Two small diagonal nicks under PE, C of 2nd
8	Scoop above 1st top row	15	Minute dot under P of 2nd
	Minute dot under EN of 2nd	16	Tiny nick under to left of S of 2nd; rule under
9	Rule under 1st thin at left and thick at right		1st thinner at left
	Rules under 2nd and 3rd irregular	17	Nick (top) under I of 1st
10	No marking. Thin rules	18	No marking
11	Nick under N of 2nd		Thick rules
12	Scoop (base) to left of 2nd		

Plate 6 was also used with the Simple Cypher watermark.

Harrison Printings, 1936

Plate	Marking	Plate	Marking
19a	No marking	21	2 cuts 1st left side
19b	Rule under 3rd shows progressive wear to right	22	Rules 19th and 20th left side thin
	(base). Finally showing nick under N	23	Cut 1st left side; shallow nick (base) under CE
20	19th and 20th left sides bevelled at their		of 1st; horizontal mark in 2nd, under E(N)
	adjacent ends		

Index to Plate Markings

Top Margin, Stamp Numbers

Stamp No.	Plate	Stamp No.	Plate
1	.. 8	2	.. 6

Bottom Margin, Stamp Numbers

1	.. 6, 9, 13, 16, 17, 23	3	.. 9, 19b
2	.. 8, 9, 11, 12, 14, 15, 16, 23		

Left Margin, Row Numbers

Row No.	Plate	Row No.	Plate
1	.. 21, 23	20	.. 20, 22
19	.. 20, 23		

No Markings: Plates 10 (thin rules), 18 (thick rules), 19a

Control Schedule
Somerset House Printings, 1924–25

Plate	Controls employed		Plate	Controls employed
6	..	B. 24	8	..	C. 25, D. 25

Harrison Printings, 1936

Plate	Controls employed		Plate	Controls employed
16	..	Y 36	19b	..	Z 36
19a	..	Y 36		

Cat. No.	S.G. No.			Shades	Unused	Used

1926 (JUNE) and 1934–38.   As last, but ORDINARY PAPER

N42   426a

a.	Watermark inverted	..	16·00	9·00
s.	" Specimen ", Type 23	..		
t.	" Specimen ", Type 26	..		
u.	" Specimen ", Type 32	..		
w.	" Specimen ", Type 26 and			
	" Cancelled ", Type 34	..		
x.	" Cancelled ", Type 33			
	(Somerset House)	..		

Somerset House Printing (1926–33)

		Unused	Used
(1)	Rosy mauve	3·00	35
(2)	Pale rosy mauve (1927-28)	3·00	25
(3)	Reddish purple (1932-33)	2·25	25

Harrison Printings (1934–38)

		Unused	Used
(4)	Deep reddish purple (1934-36)	2·25	25
(5)	Purple (1935-38)	2·00	35
(6)	Deep purple (1935-38)	5·00	60

Controls
Somerset House Printings:

			I.	P.				I.	P.				I.	P.
D. 25	..	..	85·00	†	J. 28	..	..	4·00	10·00	P. 31	..	..	4·00	†
E. 26	..	..	4·00	65·00	K. 29	..	..	4·00	†	Q. 32	..	..	4·00	†
F. 26	..	..	4·00	†	L. 29	..	..	4·00	†	R. 32	..	..	4·00	†
G. 27	..	..	4·00	†	M. 30	..	..	4·00	£150	S. 33	..	..	6·00	†
H. 27	..	..	4·00	†	N. 30	..	..	4·00	†	T. 33	..	..	4·00	†
I. 28	..	..	4·00	10·00	O. 31	..	..	4·00	†					

Watermark varieties known:
Wmk inverted: E. 26, F. 26, G. 27, H. 27, I. 28, J. 28, K. 29, L. 29, M. 30, N. 30.

Harrison Printings:

			I.	P.				I.	P.				I.	P.
V 34	..	..	4·00	†	Y 36	..	..	4·00	†	B 37	..	..	50·00	£250
W 35	..	..	7·50	4·00	Z 36	..	..	4·00	†	C 38	..	..	10·00	†
X 35	..	..	6·00	4·00	A 37	..	..	4·00	†	D 38	..	..	8·00	35·00

Watermark varieties known:
Wmk inverted: V 34, W 35, X 35, Y 36, Z 36, A 37, B 37, C 38, D 38.

Imprimatur from the National Postal Museum Archives
Imperforate, watermark Type W15

Watermark upright

Control Schedule
Somerset House Printings, 1926–33

Plate	Controls employed		Plate	Controls employed
8	..	D. 25, E. 26, F. 26, G. 27, H. 27	13	..	K. 29, L. 29, M. 30, N. 30, R. 32
9	..	G. 27, H. 27, I. 28, J. 28, K. 29, M. 30, P. 31	14	..	N. 30, O. 31, P. 31
10	..	E. 26, F. 26, G. 27, I. 28, L. 29	15	..	O. 31, T. 33
11	..	E. 26, J. 28, K. 29	16	..	R. 32, S. 33, T. 33
12	..	K. 29, L. 29, M. 30, N. 30	17	..	S. 33, T. 33
			18	..	Q. 32, S. 33, T. 33

Harrison Printings, 1934–38

Plate	Controls employed		Plate	Controls employed
16	..	V 34, W 35, X 35, Z 36	21	..	X 35, Z 36, A 37, B 37, C 38, D 38
19a	..	V 34, W 35	22	..	Z 36, A 37, C 38
19b	..	X 35, Y 36, Z 36	23	..	Z 36, A 37, B 37, C 38, D 38
20	..	X 35, Y 36, Z 36, A 37		

Cat. No.	S.G. No.			Shades	Unused	Used

1924 (DECEMBER). 9d. OLIVE-GREEN, TYPE N9

					Unused	Used
N43	427			(1) Olive-green	9·00	2·25
a.	Watermark inverted	..	25·00	7·00	(2) Pale olive-green	12·00	1·75
s.	" Specimen ", Type 23	..	35·00		(3) Deep olive-green	11·00	1·75
t.	" Specimen ", Type 26	..			(4) Olive-yellow-green (1933)	25·00	7·00
u.	" Specimen ", Type 32	..					
v.	" Specimen ", Type 32 and						
	" Cancelled ", Type 34	..					

Controls

Waterlow Printings:

			I.	P.				I.	P.				I.	P.
A 24	..	..	11·00	11·00	J 28	..	..	11·00	†	R 32	..	..	11·00	†
C 25	..	..	11·00	†	L 29	..	..	11·00	†	T 33	..	..	35·00	†
F 26	..	..	11·00	†	N 30	..	..	11·00	†					
I 28	..	..	15·00	†	P 31	..	..	11·00	†					

    Watermark varieties known:
    Wmk inverted: A 24, C 25, F 26, I 28, J 28, P 31.

Harrison Printings:

V 34	..	..	17·00	†
W 35	..	..	18·00	†
X 35	..	..	17·00	25·00

Imprimatur from the National Postal Museum Archives

    Imperforate, watermark Type W15

    Watermark upright

Plate Markings

Plate	Marking
1	Irregular cuts 19th left side, 11 mm.
2	Sloping internal cut 20th left side, 13mm. After re-chroming in 1926, this cut got progressively smaller, finally showing as a tiny dot

Plate	Marking
3	Minute dot 19th left side, 11 mm.
4	No marking. Thick rules at left
5	No marking. Thin rules at left

Control Schedule

Waterlow Printings, 1924–33

Plate		Controls employed
1	..	A 24, C 25, F 26, I 28, J 28, L 29, N 30, P 31, R 32, T 33
2	..	A 24, C 25, F 26, I 28, J 28, L 29 N 30, P 31, R 32, T 33

Harrison Provisional Printings, 1934–35

Plate		Controls employed
1	..	V 34, W 35
2	..	V 34, W 35, X 35
3	..	V 34, W 35
4	..	W 35, X 35
5	..	X 35

Cat. No.	S.G. No.		Shades	Unused	Used

1924 (NOVEMBER). 10d. TURQUOISE, TYPE N9

N44   428

a.	Watermark inverted ..	£600	(1) Turquoise-blue	24·00	16·00
b.	Frame breaks, at top right		(2) Deep greenish blue	35·00	15·00
	and at right	£250	(3) Dull greenish blue	24·00	14·00
ba.	Frame break at bottom left	£150	(4) Deep dull greenish blue		
s.	"Specimen", Type 23 ..		(1935)	28·00	18·00
t.	Do. Imperf.	35·00			
u.	"Specimen", Type 32 ..				
v.	"Specimen", Type 32 and				
	"Cancelled", Type 34 ..				

N44b/ba

Controls

Waterlow Printings:

		I.	P.			I.	P.			I.	P.
A 24	..	35·00	25·00	J 28	..	25·00	†	S 33	..	50·00	†
D 25	..	25·00	†	L 29	..	28·00	†	U 34	..	—	†
F 26	..	25·00	†	O 31	..	60·00	†				
G 27	..	25·00	†	Q 32	..	60·00	†				

Watermark varieties known:
  Wmk inverted: D 25, F 26.

Harrison Printings:

U 34	..	£100	†
V 34	..	90·00	†
W 35	..	30·00	†

Imprimatur from the National Postal Museum Archives

Imperforate, watermark Type W15

Watermark upright

Plate Markings

Plate	Marking	Plate	Marking
1c	Base of 20th left side bends inwards. Two minute dots under PE of 1st. Large dot under P of 2nd	2b	Base of 16th right side bevelled. Large dot under PE of 1st
		3	Dot and minute dot left side, 18, $22\frac{1}{2}$ mm

Plates 1c and 2b were also used with the Simple Cypher watermark.

Control Schedule

Waterlow Printings, 1924–33

Plate	Controls employed	Plate	Controls employed
1c ..	A 24, D 25, F 26, G 27, J 28, L 29, O 31, Q 32, S 33	2b ..	A 24, D 25, F 26, G 27, J 28, L 29 Q 31, Q 32, S 33
		3 ..	G 27

Waterlow Provisional Printing, 1934

1c .. U 34

Harrison Provisional Printings, 1934–35

1c ..	V 34	3 ..	W 35
2b ..	U 34, V 34, W 35		

Cat. No.   S.G. No.   Shades   Unused   Used

1924 (OCTOBER). 1s. BISTRE-BROWN, TYPE N9

N45   429   (1) Bistre-brown   10·00   75
  a. Watermark inverted   ..   £200 (2) Buff-brown   18·00   60
  s. "Specimen", Type 23   ..   (3) Pale buff-brown (1924-25) 24·00   1·00
  t. Do. Imperf...   ..   .   35·00 (4) Fawn-brown   25·00   60
  u. "Specimen", Type 32   ..   (5) Deep fawn-brown (1935)   55·00   2·00
  v. "Specimen", Type 32 and
      "Cancelled", Type 34   ..
  w. "Specimen", Type 31 in
      violet or black   ..   ..

Controls

Waterlow Printings:

		I.	*P.*				*I.*	*P.*				*I.*	*P.*
A 24	..	20·00	30·00	I 28	..	..	20·00	†	P 31	..	..	20·00	†
B 24	..	30·00	†	J 28	..	..	20·00	†	R 32	..	..	25·00	†
D 25	..	20·00	†	K 29	..	..	30·00	†	S 33	..	..	25·00	†
F 26	..	20·00	†	L 29	..	..	20·00	†	U 34	..	..	—	†
H 27	..	25·00	†	N 30	..	..	20·00	†					

Watermark varieties known:
  Wmk inverted: A 24, D 25, F 26, I 28, J 28, L 29.

Harrison Printings:

U 34	..	..	30·00	†
V 34	..	..	30·00	50·00
W 35	..	..	30·00	†
X 35	..	..	30·00	†

Imprimatur from the National Postal Museum Archives

Imperforate, watermark Type W15
  Watermark upright

Plate Markings

Plate   Marking   Plate   Marking
1 No marking   4a ½ dot (inner) 19th left side, 13 mm.; small
2 Cut 19th left side, 18½ mm. (Harrison Plate 4)   nicks at each end of rule under 2nd
3a Dot 20th left side, 12½ mm.   4b Added dot (outer) 19th left side, 6 mm.
3b Added large dot 20th left side   5   Cut under S of 1st. (Harrison Plate 5c)

Control Schedule

Waterlow Printings, 1924–33
Plate   Controls employed   Plate   Controls employed
1   .. A 24, B 24, D 25   3b   .. R 32, S 33
2   .. A 24, B 24, D 28   4a   .. F 26, H 27, I 28, J 28, K 29, L 29,
3a .. F 26, H 27, I 28, J 28, K 29, L 29,   N 30, P 31, R 32, S 33
        N 30, P 31, R 32   4b   .. S 33

Waterlow Provisional Printing, 1934   Harrison Provisional Printings, 1934–35
3b   .. U 34   3b   .. U 34, V 34, W 35, X 35
4b   .. U 34   4b   .. U 34, V 34
                                             5   .. W 35, X 35

General Notes on the Photogravure Issues (1934-36)

INTRODUCTION. In 1934 Harrison & Sons regained the contract for printing the low values as well as the commemorative issues through pioneering in this country the use of the photogravure process for printing stamps. The Mackennal Head continued to be used.

The main advantages of the photogravure process were high-speed production and lower cost. As the original designs are based on photographs a new issue can reach the printing cylinder stage much more quickly than printing plates can be prepared by the typographic process. Also double cylinders of 480 were used instead of printing plates of 240, whilst the rotary machines run very much faster. Thus it was possible to supply the greatly increased quantities of stamps required by the Post Office and at the same time effect considerable economies in production.

The following is a brief description of the terms used in connection with the photogravure process.

MULTIPOSITIVE. The prepared design is photographed in such a manner as to give a positive image on the plate. This positive is then used to make the multipositive plate. This plate contains 480 images, the equivalent of two post office sheets. The images on the plate will appear as negatives.

A photograph of the multipositive is now reproduced on to a carbon tissue. This has been prepared with a screen of fine lines which are insoluble, and result in the break-up of the design with numerous tiny rectangles of exactly the same area. The precise depth of these rectangles, or cells, will vary according to the amount of light which has been allowed to affect the carbon tissue.

THE CYLINDER. The carbon (with a positive impression) is now wrapped round the copper cylinder and treated with an acid resistant. The lighter portions of the design will leave shallower recesses on the cylinder. Several cylinders may be made from a single multipositive, and constant flaws existing on two or more cylinders are called multipositive flaws.

PRINTING. The cylinder is inked by means of an inking roller, and then scraped with the doctor knife. This leaves the cylinder clean but for the ink left in the recesses. The cylinder now meets the paper on the impression roller and the printing is thus accomplished.

Each revolution of the cylinder prints two panes of 240 stamps and these revolutions are continuous until the whole of the reel of paper has been printed. This is known as " web " printing.

In some cases one of the panes must have been faulty as cylinder blocks are known from only one side of the cylinder. Some cylinder numbers are unique, or perhaps only two or three copies are known. They are probably registration sheets that were put into circulation, and provide the collector of modern issues the same excitement of discovery as a Victorian " abnormal ". These numbers are shown in the cylinder listings with an asterisk. Single pane cylinders have been used, however, first in the reign of King George VI and note is made of these in our listing.

Occasionally the paper breaks and is simply joined by overlapping and sticking together the two ends. This gives rise to the joined paper varieties, where stamps are printed on paper of double thickness.

CYLINDER MARKS. Various marginal markings were etched on the cylinders, such as perforation register squares, and small lines and crosses used as guide marks. The punched holes are to facilitate accurate perforation. They fit on to lugs at the sides of the perforating machine.

CYLINDER NUMBERS. There are records of every cylinder made, whether or not they were put to press. They were etched twice on each cylinder. The left-hand pane had the number without a full stop, and the right-hand pane had a full stop after the number. When the cylinder number was followed by the letter " R ", it signified that the cylinder had to be worked in the reverse direction. This only applied in the early days, when Harrison & Sons were using German machines that only printed one sheet at a time. From these early printings came the varieties " printed on the gum " and inverted watermarks on the stamps with large format.

CONTROLS. The control was now no longer screwed into the plate, but etched on the cylinder in the margin. When it became necessary to change the control, the old control had to be filled in, and a new one etched in its place. Traces of the old control are sometimes visible.

PERFORATORS. These are described and illustrated in Appendix 1.

ARRANGEMENT. The stamps are listed in order of value with the sheet stamps first followed by the sheet controls and cylinder numbers listed according to the perforators used. Then follows the booklet panes and the booklet cylinder numbers and perforation types.

VARIETIES. To produce a perfect cylinder by the methods described must be difficult, and probably many cylinders were spoiled and not used. The gaps in the numbering of the cylinders known to philatelists point to that conclusion. Even with the cylinders that are used, most show a small number of minor flaws inherent in the process. Larger and more obvious flaws are collectable items, more especially when attempts at retouching have been made after the cylinder has been put to press. Retouches can be made to the multipositive, or to the cylinder, and most of the retouches known are in the latter category. Some of these repairs are well executed, and others can be detected with the naked eye.

STAMP SIZES. After the initial printings of the 1d. and 1½d. values, the sizes of the designs were reduced slightly to allow for more accurate perforation and the ½d., 1d., 1½d. and 2d. appeared thus. Later the size was reduced again and this was adopted for all values. They are known as the Large, Intermediate and Small Format stamps respectively. Within these three groups there are further slight variations in size of the stamps from booklets and coils. In all cases the actual sizes are given. The 2½d. to 1s. were all in the small size, 17.9 × 21.7 mm.

WATERMARK AND PERFORATION. All stamps in this Section are watermarked Multiple Block Cypher, Type **W15** and perforated 15 × 14.

POSITIONS OF CONTROLS AND CYLINDER NUMBERS. For the 1½d. Large Format the controls U 34 and V 34 appeared in the bottom margin under the second stamp (as had been the practice in the typographed stamps) and the cylinder numbers appeared in the left margin of the 20th row. (*Position A.*)

In later printings of the 1½d. Large Format, the 1d. Large Format and the ½d., 1d. and 1½d. Intermediate Format the control V 34 appeared as a fraction in the left margin of the 19th row, the cylinder number remaining in the 20th row. (*Position B.*)

A further change was made in the Intermediate Format where the ½d. and 1d. control W 35 appeared in the left margin of the 18th row, the position of the cylinder number remaining unchanged. (*Position C.*)

Finally the Intermediate Format 1½d. control V 34 and 2d. controls V 34 and W 35 had the control and cylinder number in the left margin of the 18th row. This became the norm and applied to all values in the Small Format. (*Position D.*)

On the lesser used values from 3d. upwards where new cylinders were less often needed, the practice was to add a line under the control to show a new accounting period. Subsequently another line was added at the left and so on until the whole control was " boxed in ". These are listed in small type.

The control positions are illustrated below.

A

B

Boxed
Control

         C   D

ASTERISKS. Asterisks against cylinder numbers indicate that they are " abnormals ". See under " Printing " on the first page of these notes.

Asterisks against prices for cylinder blocks indicate that they contain a listed **variety.**

BOOKLET CYLINDER NUMBERS. Booklets are printed from specially made up double pane cylinders (no stop and stop) and the layout corresponds to that used for the typographed booklets, with half the stamps having the watermark inverted.

They are in panes of six (the 1½d. values also existing incorporating two advertising labels). The cylinder number in the bottom row of the cylinder appears in the binding margin. It comprises a letter and number. E was used for the ½d., F for the 1d. and G for the 1½d. Sometimes the letter is trimmed off.

The prices for booklet cylinder panes are for stamps with the watermark upright, except where otherwise stated.

Booklet Cylinder Number

BOOKLET PERFORATORS. Booklet cylinder number panes are listed according to the perforator type. Further information on these is given in Appendix E. The letters in brackets above the price columns indicate the appearance of the binding margin of the pane as follows:

   (E)   Extension hole in the margin in each row
   (I)   Imperf. margin
   (P)   Perf. margin

COILS. These are listed in the same way as in the typographed issues and the notes about coil stamps which appear under Section N also apply here. Only the 2d., 2½d. and 3d. values exist made up from sheets with coil joins.

241

TRIALS FOR PHOTOGRAVURE STAMPS

Trials were prepared using frames of the typographed issues of 1912–22 in combination with the head actually used for the eventual photogravure issue but in the sizes employed in the typographed stamps.

Trials of the 1d., 1½d. and 4d. designs were printed in various colours using a solid back-ground to simulate the effect of photogravure.

On glazed, unwatermarked paper without gum.   Imperf.

1d., 1½d. and 4d. each in red, emerald-green, royal blue, bright magenta and
purple   ..   ..   *Each from* £250

On ordinary, unwatermarked paper with gum.   Imperf.

1d., 1½d. and 4d. each in red, pearl-green, emerald-green, royal blue, dull
lilac and brown ..   ..   *Each from* £200

Trial for a lighter background to the King's head. This was not approved, but the following exists on card marked "Normal" and "Suggested". The trial is affixed next to the issued stamp.

½d. green small format *with* lighter background, perforated 15 × 14   ..   ..

ESSAY

Imperf. on paper watermarked Block Cypher. Similar to issue design, but with large head

1d. scarlet   ..   ..   50·00

ESSAY FOR UNISSUED 6d. VALUE

1935. Wmk. Block Cypher. Perf. 15 × 14
    6d. purple with "Cancelled", Type 28   ..   ..

Proof
1936 February. As illustrated but with toned background to the head. On coated paper, perforated 15 × 14.

    6d. purple (doubly fugitive ink)   ..   ..

Production of this stamp commenced in February 1935 but Harrisons were unable to obtain satisfactory impressions from the cylinders in the doubly fugitive ink required for this denomination and no registration sheet was approved.   Production was abandoned in May 1936 after 21,484 sheets of 240 had been printed and all were destroyed except for reference examples now in the Post Office. The examples with dark background in private hands have the "Cancelled" overprint.

The 5d. value, which was issued on 17 February 1936, is also known printed in magenta. An example exists which is imperforate and overprinted "Cancelled" as Type 33.   In the N.P.M. there is an imperforate block of the 5d. which is printed from a single plate of six impressions. These stamps, which are not overprinted, are in doubly fugitive purple ink intended for the 6d. value.   These were submitted to the Post Office in December 1933 by Harrison & Sons.

Further information on the background to this value was published in *The GB Journal* for October 1979, Volume 17, no. 5 and in the Post Office *Philatelic Bulletin*, Volume 16, nos. 7 and 8.

N11   N12   N13

N14   N15

½d.   Green, Type N11

Cat. No.	S.G. No.	Shades	Unused	Used

1934 (NOVEMBER 19).   INTERMEDIATE FORMAT (18.4 × 22.2 mm.)

N46   —

a. Watermark inverted   ..   15·00   12·00   (1) Green   30   15
b. Imperf. three sides†   £750   (2) Bluish green   50   15
s. "Specimen", Type 32   ..   *u.* "Cancelled", Type 33   ..
t. "Cancelled", Type 28P   ..   *v.* "Specimen", Type 23   ..   £200

†This is known in a block of four in which the bottom pair is imperf. at top and sides; it comes from a sheet.

Controls and Cylinder Numbers
Blocks of four (Position B)

| | | | | | | Perf. Type | | | |
Cyl. No.	Control					2 No dot	2A Dot	4 No dot	6 No dot	6B Dot
3	V 34 ..	..	..	..	..	5·50	2·25	2·25	1·75	1·75
4	V 34 ..	..	..	..	..	3·25	2·25	2·25	1·75	1·75

Blocks of six (Position C)

| | | | | Perf. Type | | | | | |
				2 No dot	2A Dot	5 No dot	5 Dot	6 No dot	6B Dot
4	W 35	..	..	12·00	12·00	2·75	2·75	2·50	2·50

Cylinder 4 dot is known with Perforation Type 3 but with no extension hole in bottom margin. This occurs with Controls V 34 (*very rare*) and W 35 (*price £14*).

Booklet Panes of Six (Stamps 18.4 × 21.9 mm.)
From Booklets BB15, BB27 and BB36

NB20 Watermark upright   35·00   NB20a Watermark inverted   90·00
   t. "Cancelled", Type 28P ..   ..   *at.* "Cancelled", Type 28P ..
   u. "Cancelled", Type 33 ..   ..
   v. "Cancelled", Type 33P ..   ..

Booklet Cylinder Numbers
Panes of six

| | | Perf. Type | | |
Cyl. No.		B3(I) No dot	B3A(P) Dot	B4(E) No dot	B4A(I) Dot
E1	.. ..	—	—	50·00	50·00

Imprimaturs from the National Postal Museum Archives
Imperforate, watermark Type W15. Intermediate Format
Watermark upright

Booklet pane of six. Imperforate, watermark Type W15
Two panes as No. NB20 arranged horizontally *tête-bêche*

Cat. No.	S.G. No.			Shades		Unused	Used
1935.	**SMALL FORMAT (17.9 × 21.7 mm.)**						
N47	439			(1) Green		15	15
a.	Watermark inverted	6·00	1·00	(2) Bluish green		15	15
b.	Watermark sideways Crown						
	pointing to left	10·00	2·75				
c.	Ditto Crown pointing to right	£175	75·00	s. "Cancelled", Type 28P		15·00	
d.	Horn variety (Cyl. 36 No dot,			t. "Cancelled", Type 33P		13·00	
	R.1/12)	£125		u. "Cancelled", Type 33		20·00	

N47d

Controls and Cylinder Numbers
Blocks of six (Position D)

		Perf. Type					
		2	2A	5	5	6	6B
Cyl. No.	Control	No dot	Dot	No dot	Dot	No dot	Dot
11	W 35	4·00	4·00	2·00	2·00	1·10	1·10
12	W 35	†	—	†	†	†	†
13	W 35	5·00	5·00	4·00	4·00	1·00	1·00
18	W 35	†	†	1·25	1·25	1·50	1·50
22	W 35	4·00	4·00	1·00	1·00	1·00	1·00
24*	W 35	†	25·00	†	†	†	†
25	W 35	†	15·00	1·00	1·00	1·10	1·10
27	W 35	†	†	4·00	4·00	4·00	4·00
30	X 35	†	†	1·00	1·00	1·00	1·00
31	X 35	†	†	1·00	1·00	1·00	1·00
32	X 35	†	†	1·00	1·00	1·00	1·00
36	X 35	6·00	6·00	1·00	1·00	1·00	1·00
39	X 35	6·00	6·00	1·00	1·00	1·00	1·00
39	Y 36	†	†	1·00	1·00	1·00	1·00
40	X 35	†	†	1·00	1·00	†	†
41	X 35	8·00	†	1·00	1·00	1·00	1·00
41	Y 36	†	†	2·00	1·50	†	†
42	X 35	—	†	1·00	1·00	1·00	1·00
42	Y 36	8·00	15·00	1·00	1·00	1·00	1·00
44	Y 36	†	†	1·00	1·00	†	†
45	Y 36	†	20·00	1·00	1·00	†	†
46*	Y 36	†	†	†	—	†	†
48	Y 36	†	†	1·00	1·00	†	—
48	Z 36	†	†	1·10	1·10	†	†
49	Y 36	†	†	1·00	1·00	1·50	1·50

The only known example of cylinder 12 dot is a single specimen with attached control.
Cylinder 49 no dot has been recorded with perforator Type 2A.
*See under "Printing" in the General Notes.

Booklet Panes of Six (Stamps 17.8 × 21.65 mm.)

From Booklets BB17, BB29 and BB37

NB21   Watermark upright   5·00

t. " Cancelled ", Type 33P .. 80·00
u. ".Cancelled ", Type 33 .. £120
v. " Cancelled ", Type 28P .. 90·00

NB21a   Watermark inverted 38·00

at. " Cancelled ", Type 33P .. 80·00
au. " Cancelled ", Type 33 .. £120
av. " Cancelled ", Type 28P .. 90·00

Booklet Cylinder Numbers

Panes of six

	Perf. Type				
Cyl. No.	B3(I) No dot	B3A(P) Dot	B4(E) No dot	B4A(I) Dot	B4B(E) Dot
E 4	—	15·00	10·00	10·00	†
Wmk. inverted	—	†	—	—	†
E 5	†	†	10·00	10·00	—
E 6	†	†	10·00	10·00	10·00

Coils (Stamps 17.9 × 21.7 mm.)

Vertical delivery printed in continuous reels

Code No.	Issued	Number in roll	Face value	
D	1935	960	£2.0.0	Bottom delivery
G	1935	480	£1.0.0	Bottom delivery
W	1935	960	£2.0.0	Bottom delivery
Y	1935	1920	£4.0.0	Bottom delivery

Sideways delivery printed in continuous reels with watermark sideways (Crown to left)

P	1935	480	£1.0.0	Left side delivery

As last but watermark with Crown to right, printed on Timson Press

P	1935	480	£1.0.0	Left side delivery

Imprimaturs from the National Postal Museum Archives

Imperforate, watermark Type W15. Small Format

Watermark upright
Watermark sideways

Booklet pane of six. Imperforate, watermark Type W15

Two panes as No. NB21 arranged horizontally *tête-bêche*

1d.   Scarlet, Type N12

Cat. No.   S.G. No.   Shades   Unused   Used

1934 (SEPTEMBER 24).   LARGE FORMAT (18.7 × 22.5 mm.)

N48   —   (1) Scarlet   1·25   30
  a.   Watermark inverted . .   . .   45·00   (2) Bright scarlet   1·25   30
  b.   Printed on the gummed side   £500   †
  c.   Imperf. between (pair)   . .   £1500

Controls and Cylinder Numbers
Blocks of four (Position B)

| | | | | | | | | Perf. Type | | | |
| | | | | | | | | 2 No dot | 2A Dot | 2 Dot | 4 No dot |
Cyl. No.	Control										
1	V 34	..	..	..	..	..	..	4·25	4·25	†	5·25
2	V 34	..	..	..	..	..	..	4·25	4·25	32·00	5·25
5R	V 34	..	..	..	..	..	..	4·25	4·25	†	5·25
6R	V 34	..	..	..	..	..	..	4·25	4·25	†	5·25
9R*	V 34	..	..	..	..	..	..	†	†	—	†
10R	V 34	..	..	..	..	..	..	38·00	38·00	†	†
11R	V 34	..	..	..	..	..	..	4·25	4·25	†	4·25
14	V 34	..	..	..	..	..	..	13·00	13·00	†	†
15	V 34	..	..	..	..	..	..	13·00	13·00	†	13·00

Cylinder Nos. 1, 2, 5R, 11 R and 15 are known with watermark inverted.
Cylinder 6R (no dot) has a small split dot which was added in error.
*See under " Printing " in the General Notes.

Cat. No.   S.G. No.   Shades   Unused   Used

1934.   INTERMEDIATE FORMAT (18.4 × 22.2 mm.)

N49   —   (1) Scarlet   3·00   50
  a.   Watermark inverted   . .   15·00   12·00   (2) Bright scarlet   3·00   50
  s.   " Specimen ", Type 32   . .   (3) Pale scarlet   6·50   2·50
  t.   " Cancelled ", Type 28P   . .
  u.   " Cancelled ", Type 33   . .
  v.   " Specimen ", Type 23   . .   £200

Controls and Cylinder Numbers
Blocks of four (Position B)

| | | | | | | | Perf. Type | | | | |
| | | | | | | | 2 No dot | 2A Dot | 4 No dot | 6 No dot | 6B Dot |
Cyl. No.	Control										
20	V 34	..	..	..	..	..	20·00	18·00	†	18·00	—
24	V 34	..	..	..	..	..	18·00	18·00	18·00	12·00	12·00
25	V 34	..	..	..	..	..	12·00	12·00	12·00	12·00	12·00
28	V 34	..	..	..	..	..	†	60·00	60·00	55·00	55·00

Variety (Reverse feed). Cylinder 25 no dot exists with Perforation Type 2A.
Cylinder 28 no dot is known with experimental use of Perforation Type 5.

Blocks of six (Position C)

| | | | | | Perf. Type | | | |
| | | | | | 5 No dot | 5 Dot | 6 No dot | 6B Dot |
Cyl. No.	Control							
24	W 35	..	..	..	32·00	32·00	32·00	32·00

Booklet Panes of Six (Stamps 18.4 × 21.9 mm.)
From Booklets BB15, BB27 and BB36

NB22 Watermark upright   35·00   NB22a Watermark inverted 90·00
  t. " Cancelled ", Type 28P ..   at. " Cancelled ", Type 28P ..
  v. " Cancelled ", Type 33P ..   au. " Cancelled ", Type 33 ..

Booklet Cylinder Numbers
Panes of six

| | Perf. Type | | |
| | B3(I) No dot | B4(E) No dot | B4A(I) Dot |
Cyl. No.			
F1	—	50·00	50·00

Coils (Stamps 18.75 × 22.25 mm.)
Vertical delivery printed in continuous reels

Code No.	Issued	Number in roll	Face value	
E	1934	480	£2.0.0	Bottom delivery

Imprimaturs from the National Postal Museum Archives

Imperforate, watermark Type W15. Intermediate Format

Watermark upright

Booklet pane of six. Imperforate, watermark Type W15

Two panes as No. NB22 arranged horizontally *tête-bêche*

Cat. No.	S.G. No.			Shades	Unused	Used
1935.	**SMALL FORMAT (17.9 × 21.7 mm.)**					
N50	440			(1) Scarlet	15	15
a.	Watermark inverted	6·00	2·50	(2) Bright scarlet	15	15
b.	Watermark sideways Crown					
	pointing to left	10·00	3·25	f. Double impression .. .. †		£9500
c.	Ditto Crown pointing to right	30·00		s. "Cancelled", Type 28P .. 15·00		
d.	Imperf. (pair)	£975		t. "Cancelled", Type 33P .. 13·00		
e.	Imperf. 3 sides (pair) ..	£975		u. "Cancelled", Type 33 .. 20·00		

N50 *f*

The stamp shown above has a light wavy line postmark and it is believed to be unique.

Controls and Cylinder Numbers

Blocks of six (Position D)

					Perf. Types			
Cyl. No.	Control				2 No dot	2A Dot	5 No dot	5 Dot	6 No dot	6B Dot

Cyl. No.	Control					2 No dot	2A Dot	5 No dot	5 Dot	6 No dot	6B Dot
32	W 35	..	..	..	..	15·00	†	†	16·00	15·00	15·00
34	X 35	..	..	..	..	†	†	1·50	1·50	1·75	1·75
35	X 35	..	..	..	..	†	†	1·50	1·50	†	†
39	X 35	..	..	..	..	†	†	1·50	1·50	1·75	1·75
40*	X 35	..	..	..	..	†	†	—	—	†	†
41	X 35	..	..	..	..	†	†	†	†	2·00	2·00
42	X 35	..	..	..	..	—	†	1·50	1·50	1·75	1·75
44	X 35	..	..	..	..	†	†	6·00	6·00	7·00	7·00
45	X 35	..	..	..	..	†	†	9·00	9·00	†	†
46	X 35	..	..	..	..	4·50	4·50	1·50	1·50	1·50	1·50
50	X 35	..	..	..	..	4·50	4·50	1·50	1·50	1·50	1·50
50	Y 36	..	..	..	..	4·00	4·00	1·50	1·50	†	—
53	Y 36	..	..	..	..	4·00	4·00	1·50	1·50	2·00	2·00
54	Y 36	..	..	..	..	6·00	6·00	1·50	1·50	†	†

Cylinder 53 no dot has been recorded with perforator Type 2A.

*See under " Printing " in the General Notes.

Booklet Panes of Six (Stamps 17.9 × 21.65 mm.)

From Booklets BB17, BB29 and BB37

NB23 Watermark upright 5·00
t. "Cancelled", Type 33P .. 80·00
u. "Cancelled", Type 33 .. £120
v. "Cancelled", Type 28P .. 90·00

NB23a Watermark inverted 38·00
at. "Cancelled", Type 33P .: 80·00
au. "Cancelled", Type 33 .. £120
av. "Cancelled", Type 28P .. 90·00

Booklet Cylinder Numbers

Panes of six

							Perf. Type				
Cyl. No.							B3(I) No dot	B3A(P) Dot	B4(E) No dot	B4A(I) Dot	B4B(E) Dot
F 6 ..	..	..	..	..	..	..	8·50	8·50	6·50	6·50	†
F 7 ..	..	..	..	..	..	..	—	—	6·50	6·50	6·50

Coils

Vertical delivery printed in continuous reels (Stamps 18·15 × 21·7 mm.)

Code No.	Issued	Number in roll	Face value	
B	1935	960	£4.0.0	Bottom delivery
E	1935	480	£2.0.0	Bottom delivery
X	1935	960	£4.0.0	Bottom delivery
Z	1935	1920	£8.0.0	Bottom delivery

Sideways delivery printed in continuous reels with watermark sideways (Crown to left) (Stamps 17·9 × 21·7 mm.)

O	1935	480	£2.0.0	Left side delivery

As last but watermark with Crown to right, printed on Timson Press

O	1935	480	£2.0.0	Left side delivery

Imprimaturs from the National Postal Museum Archives

Imperforate, watermark Type W15. Small Format

Watermark upright
Watermark sideways

Booklet pane of six. Imperforate, watermark Type 15

Two panes as No. NB23 arranged horizontally *tête-bêche*

1½d. Red-Brown, Type N11

Cat. No. S.G. No.		Shades	Unused	Used

1934 (AUGUST 20). LARGE FORMAT (18.7 × 22.5 mm.)

Cat. No.	S.G. No.	Shades	Unused	Used
N51	—	(1) Red-brown	70	30
a. Watermark inverted ..	70·00	(2) Bright red-brown	70	30
b. Imperf. (pair)				
c. Frame break under E of				
PENCE (Cyls. 38, 42, 43, 45,				
54, 55, all Dot (R. 20/3) ..	25·00			

No. N51*b* came from the bottom row of a sheet (Cyl. 97 no dot).

N51*c*

Controls and Cylinder Numbers

Pairs (Position A)

		Perf. Type					Perf. Type	
		2	2A				2	2A
Cyl. No.	Control	No dot	Dot	Cyl. No.	Control		No dot	Dot
8	U 34	6·50	6·50	38	V 34	.. ..	4·25	1·25
13	V 34	3·25	3·25	42	V 34	.. ..	3·25	3·25
34	U 34	6·50	6·50	43	V 34	.. ..	4·25	4·25
34	V 34	3·25	3·25	45	V 34	.. ..	3·25	3·25

Cylinder 34 no dot is known with " 3 " omitted in later printings with control U 34.
Cylinder 45 no dot is also known with Perforation Type 2A.

Blocks of four (Position B)

			Perf. Type				
			2	2A (or 6A)	4	6	6B
Cyl. No.	Control		No dot	Dot	No dot	No dot	Dot
17	V 34		19·00	14·00	†	†	†
46	V 34		4·50	4·50	32·00	5·50	†
47	V 34		3·50	3·50	32·00	5·50	†
49*	V 34		60·00	60·00	†	—	†
54	V 34		3·50	3·50	†	†	†
55	V 34		3·50	3·50	†	†	†
63*	V 34		75·00	†	†	†	†
68R	V 34		3·50	3·50	4·00	†	†
69	V 34		3·50	3·50	8·00	†	†
70*	V 34		†	60·00	60·00	†	†
94	V 34		6·00	6·00	6·00	3·50	†
97	V 34		4·50	3·50	4·25	3·50	†
98	V 34		3·50	3·50	3·50	3·50	3·50
100	V 34		3·50	3·50	3·50	3·50	3·50
101	V 34		3·50	3·50	3·50	3·50	3·50
102	V 34		4·00	4·00	4·00	10·00	5·50

Variety (Reverse feed). Cylinder 68R and cylinder 101 from the no dot panes, are known with Perforation Type 2A.

Cylinder 68R dot is known with watermark inverted.

Cylinder 98 no dot is known with experimental use of Perforation Type 5.

*See under " Printing " in the General Notes.

Colour Trials

Imperf. on paper watermarked Block Cypher

1½d. in the large format

Ultramarine, deep grey-green or scarlet	..	..	..	..	..	..	*From*	50·00
Red-brown ..	..	..	..	..	..	..	..	60·00
Red-brown with "Cancelled", Type 33*	..	..	..	..	..		

Care should be taken not to confuse the red-brown colour trial with the issued Imperf. The colour trial exhibits all the traits of a finished proof. The highlights are noticeable when compared with the rather flat impression of the issued stamps and the paper is of better quality.

All four trials including red-brown, overprinted "Cancelled", are known with Cyl. No. 16 below R. 20/1 but no issued stamps were printed from this cylinder.

Imprimaturs from the National Postal Museum Archives

Imperforate, watermark Type W15. Large Format

Watermark upright

Cat. No.	S.G. No.		Shades	Unused	Used

1934.   INTERMEDIATE FORMAT (18.4 × 22.2 mm.)

N52	—		Red-brown	2·00	50

a.	Watermark inverted ..	..	7·50	5·00		
b.	Imperf. (pair)	..	£300†		*u.* "Cancelled", Type 33	..
c.	Imperf. three sides (vert. pair)	.. ..	£550		*v.* "Specimen", Type 23	.. £200
d.	Imperf. between (horiz. pair)					
t.	"Cancelled", Type 28P	..				

†No. N52*b* exists from NPM archive sales.

Coils (Stamps 18·75 × 22·5 mm.)

Vertical delivery printed in continuous reels

Code No.	Issued	Number in roll	Face value	
L	1934	480	£3.0.0	Top delivery

Controls and Cylinder Numbers

Blocks of four (Position B)

						Perf. Type			
Cyl. No.	Control					2 No dot	2A Dot	4 No dot	6 No dot	6B Dot
104	V 34	..	..	..	..	11·00	11·00	11·00	11·00	11·00
105	V 34	..	..	..	..	11·00	8·50	21·00	12·00	12·00
106	V 34	..	..	..	..	12·00	12·00	16·00	11·00	11·00
107	V 34	..	..	..	..	†	—	—	16·00	16·00

Cylinder 104 no dot is known with experimental use of Perforation Type 5.

Blocks of six (Position D)

					Perf. Type		
Cyl. No.	Control				2A (or 6A) Dot	6 No dot	6B Dot
113	V 34 ..	..	..		—	25·00	20·00

Booklet Panes of Six (Stamps 18.4 × 21.9 mm.)

From Booklets BB15, BB27 and BB36

NB24 Watermark upright   18·00   NB24a Watermark inverted 55·00
  t.   " Cancelled ", Type 28P ..   *at.* " Cancelled ", Type 28P .. ..
  u.   " Cancelled ", Type 33   ..   *av.* " Cancelled ", Type 33P ..

NB25/a, NB27/a (various advertisements)

Booklet Panes with Advertising Labels (Stamps 18.0 × 21.9 mm.)

Panes of six, comprising two printed labels and four stamps. The advertisements were etched on the printing cylinders, and therefore appear in the colour of the stamps

From Booklets BB15 and BB36

NB25 Watermark upright   60·00
   t. "Cancelled", Type 28P ..

NB25a Watermark inverted   60·00
   at. "Cancelled", Type 28P ..
   au. "Specimen", Type 23 ..
   av. "Cancelled", Type 33P ..

		Wmk Upright	Wmk Inverted
(1)	"Cash's satin lingerie ribbons / Samples of Cash's ribbons. J. & J. Cash Ltd."	75·00	75·00
(2)	"For Safety of Capital / Amalgamated Fixed Trust "..	60·00	60·00
(3)	"For Safety of Capital / Commercial Fixed Trust " ..	60·00	60·00
(4)	"For Safety of Capital / National Fixed Trust " ..	60·00	60·00
(5)	"Saving is Simple / Home Safe "	75·00	75·00
(6)	"Telephone Service / Air Mails, Letters & Parcels " ..	75·00	75·00

Booklet Cylinder Numbers
Panes of six

		Perf. Type		
	B3(I)	B3A(P)	B4(E)	B4A(I)
Cyl. No.	No dot	Dot	No dot	Dot
G4	—	—	30·00	30·00

Panes of six including two labels

No dot cylinders

Cyl. No.	Advert.	Perf. Type	
		B3(I)	B4(E)
G 7.	NB25(5)	†	£120
G 9.	NB25(4)	†	£100
G 10.	NB25(2)	†	£100
G 15.	NB25(4)	†	£100
G 16.	NB25(4)	£120	£100
G 17.	NB25(3)	†	£120

Dot cylinders

Cyl. No.	Advert.	Perf. Type	
		B3A(P)	B4A(I)
G 7.	NB25(6)	—	£120
G 9.	NB25(1)	†	£120
G 10.	NB25(3)	†	£100
G 15.	NB25(3)	—	£100
G 16.	NB25(2)	£120	£100
G 17.	NB25(3)	—	£100

Imprimaturs from the National Postal Museum Archives
Imperforate, watermark type W15. Intermediate Format
Watermark upright

Booklet pane of four with advertisements. Imperforate, watermark Type W15
Two panes as No. NB25(4) arranged horizontally *tête-bêche*

Cat. No. S.G. No.

1935.   SMALL FORMAT (17.9 × 21.7 mm.)

						Shades	Unused	Used

N53   441

				Unused	Used
			(1) Red-brown	10	15
			(2) Bright red-brown	10	15

a.	Watermark inverted ..	1·50 30
b.	Watermark sideways ..	6·00 2·00
ba.	Wmk. sideways-inverted ..	
c.	Flaw in N.E. corner (Cyls.	
	116, 119, No dot, R.19/1) ..	20·00
d.	Ditto retouched (Cyl. 116,	
	No dot, R.19/1)	20·00

s.	"Cancelled", Type 28P	..	13·00
t.	"Cancelled" Type 33P	..	12·00
u.	"Cancelled" Type 33	..	18·00
v.	"Specimen", Type 32	..	

N53*c*   N53*d*

Coils (Stamps 17.9 × 21.7 mm.)

Vertical delivery printed in continuous reels

Code No.	Issued	Number in roll	Face value	
K	1935	960	£6.0.0	Bottom delivery
L	1935	480	£3.0.0	Top delivery
L	1935	480	£3.0.0	Bottom delivery

Sideways delivery printed in continuous reels with watermark sideways

N	1935	480	£3.0.0	Left side delivery

Controls and Cylinder Numbers

Blocks of six (Position D)

				Perf. Types				
			2	2A	5	5	6	6B
Cyl. No.	Control		No dot	Dot	No dot	Dot	No dot	Dot
116	W 35	.. ..	25·00*	1·50	25·00*	2·50	25·00*	1·00
119	W 35	.. ..	25·00*	1·50	†	—	25·00*	1·00
124	W 35	.. ..	†	†	1·00	1·00	1·25	1·25
127	X 35	.. ..	†	†	1·25	1·25	1·00	1·00
128	X 35	.. ..	†	†	†	†	1·00	1·00
130	X 35	.. ..	†	†	1·00	1·00	1·00	1·00
132	X 35	.. ..	7·00	7·00	1·00	1·00	1·00	1·00
133	X 35	.. ..	†	†	1·00	1·00	†	†
135	X 35	.. ..	7·00	7·00	1·00	1·00	†	†
135	Y 36	.. ..	†	†	1·00	1·00	†	†
137	X 35	.. ..	†	7·00	1·00	1·00	†	†
137	Y 36	.. ..	†	4·00	1·00	1·00	†	†
139	Y 36	.. ..	†	†	2·00	2·00	†	†
140	Y 36	.. ..	†	†	1·00	1·00	†	†
141	X 35	.. ..	†	†	1·00	1·00	†	†
141	Y 36	.. ..	†	†	1·00	1·00	†	†
143 (i)	Y 36	.. ..	†	15·00	1·25	1·25	†	†
143 (ii)	Y 36	.. ..	†	†	3·00	†	†	†
144	Y 36	.. ..	6·00	6·00	1·00	1·00	6·00	6·00
144	Z 36	.. ..	7·50	7·50	1·00	1·00	†	†
146	Y 36	.. ..	10·00	10·00	1·00	1·00	†	†
148	Y 36	.. ..	5·00	5·00	1·00	1·00	†	†
149	Y 36	.. ..	8·00	8·00	1·00	1·00	†	†
149	Z 36	.. ..	11·00	11·00	1·00	1·00	†	†
153	Y 36	.. ..	†	†	†	—	†	†
153	Z 36	.. ..	8·00	8·00	1·00	1·00	†	†

Varieties:

Cylinder 116 known Perforation Type 5 with extension hole missing (£16).
Cylinder 139 dot. (Reverse feed) Perforation Type 2 (£16).
Cylinder 149 dot. (Reverse feed) Perforation Type 2 (£11).
Cylinder 143 no dot exists in two states. The second state (ii) shows a large flaw in the margin opposite the 19th row and retouching to the base of figures 36 of the control.
*These cylinder blocks include a listed variety.

253

Booklet Panes of Six (Stamps 17.8 × 21.65 mm.)

From Booklets BB17, BB29 and BB37

NB26 Watermark upright   5·00

t.	" Cancelled ", Type 33P ..	50·00
u.	" Cancelled ", Type 33 ..	80·00
v.	" Cancelled ", Type 28P ..	55·00

NB26a Watermark inverted   16·00

at.	" Cancelled ", Type 33P ..	50·00
au.	" Cancelled ", Type 33 ..	80·00
av.	" Cancelled ", Type 28P ..	55·00

Booklet Panes with Advertising Labels (Stamps 17.8 × 21.65 mm.)

Panes of six, comprising two labels typographed in *black* and four stamps

From Booklets BB17 and BB37

NB27 Watermark upright   30·00

u.	" Cancelled ", Type 33 ..	80·00
v.	" Cancelled ", Type 33P ..	65·00

NB27a Watermark inverted   30·00

at.	" Cancelled ", Type 28P ..	
au.	" Cancelled ", Type 33 ..	80·00
av.	" Cancelled ", Type 33P ..	65·00

		Wmk Upright	Wmk Inverted
(1)	" Cash's " Lose less Linen " book / Free booket J. & J. Cash " (*numbered* 318) ..	45·00	45·00
(2)	" Cash's satin lingerie ribbons / Samples [central] of Cash's ribbons. J. & J. Cash " (*numbered* 306) ..	35·00	35·00
(3)	" Cash's satin lingerie ribbons / Samples [in text] of Cash's ribbons. " Attach this to a " J. & J. Cash " (*numbered* 323, 331, 335, 342 *or* 348)	30·00	30·00
(4)	" Cash's satin lingerie ribbons / Samples [in text] of Cash's ribbons. " Attach this to a post- ", J. & J. Cash " (*numbered* 312)	35·00	35·00
(5)	" Number One Bond / Pepys Stationery "	35·00	35·00
(6)	" Kargo 2/6 per pack / Castell Bros. (Pepys Stationery)"	35·00	35·00
(7)	" Drages fine furniture / 50 months to pay "	35·00	35·00
(8)	" For Safety of Capital / Amalgamated Fixed Trust "..	30·00	30·00
(9)	" For Safety of Capital / Century Fixed Trust (pointer) [in large type] "	35·00	35·00
(10)	" For Safety of Capital / Century Fixed Trust (pointer) [in small type] "	35·00	35·00
(11)	" For Safety of Capital / Century Fixed Trust (see last page) "	30·00	30·00
(12)	" For Safety of Capital / Commercial Fixed Trust " ..	30·00	30·00
(13)	" For Safety of Capital / National Fixed Trust " ..	30·00	30·00
(14)	" For Safety of Capital / Universal Fixed Trust (Pointer) [in large type] "	35·00	35·00
(15)	" For Safety of Capital / Universal Fixed Trust (see last page) "	35·00	35·00
(15a)	Advertisement transposed	85·00	85·00
(16)	" Saving is Simple / Home Safe "	45·00	45·00
(17)	" Telephone Service / Air Mails, letters and parcels [" Installed free " deleted by handstamp] " ..	45·00	45·00

The numbers on panes NB27(1)–27(4) correspond to the numbers of the booklets in which they were issued. See Appendix 2.

Booklet Cylinder Numbers

Panes of six

Cyl. No							B3(I) No dot	B3A(P) Dot	Perf. Type B4(E) No dot	B4A(I) Dot	B4B(E) Dot
G 20	..	..	..	..	..	..	—	16·00	14·00	14·00	†
G 24	..	..	..	..	..	..	—	†	14·00	†	†
G 27	..	..	..	..	..	..	—	—	†	—	†
G 30	..	..	..	..	..	..	†	†	14·00	14·00	14·00
G 31	..	..	..	..	..	..	†	†	19·00	19·00	†

Cylinder G 24 dot was used with advertisement labels and is listed below.

Panes of six including two labels

Cyl. No.	Advert.	B3(I) No dot	B3A(P) Dot	B4(E) No dot	B4A(I) Dot	B4B(E) Dot
G 24	NB27(2) ..	†	†	†	45·00	†
G 24	NB27(12)	†	†	†	40·00	†
G 24	NB27(13)	†	†	†	40·00	†
G 24	NB27(16)	†	†	†	55·00	†
G 24	NB27(17)	†	†	†	60·00	†
G 26	NB27(3) (No. 323)	—	†	40·00	40·00	†
G 26	NB27(4) ..	†	50·00	†	45·00	†
G 26	NB27(5) ..	†	†	45·00	45·00	†
	Wmk. inverted	†	†			†
G 26	NB27(6) ..	†	†	45·00	45·00	†
G 26	NB27(8) ..	45·00	†	40·00	40·00	†
G 26	NB27(12)	45·00	45·00	40·00	40·00	†
	Wmk. inverted	†	†	—	—	†
G 26	NB27(13)	—	45·00	40·00	40·00	†
	Wmk. inverted	†	†	†	—	†
G 28	NB27(3) No. 331)	†	†	40·00	40·00	†
G 28	NB27(3) No. 335)	†	†	40·00	40·00	†
G 28	NB27(3) (No. 342)	†	†	45·00	45·00	45·00
G 28	NB27(3) (No. 348)	†	†	50·00	50·00	†
G 28	NB27(7) ..	†	†	45·00	50·00	
G 28	NB27(8) ..	†	†	40·00	40·00	45·00
G 28	NB27(9) ..	†	†	45·00	50·00	50·00
G 28	NB27(10)	†	†	45·00	50·00	†
G 28	NB27(11)	†	†	40·00	40·00	45·00
G 28	NB27(12)	†	†	40·00	40·00	†
G 28	NB27(13)	†	†	40·00	40·00	45·00
G 28	NB27(14)	†	†	50·00	50·00	†
G 28	NB27(15)	†	†	50·00	50·00	50·00

No examples of cylinder G 26 with advertisement NB27(1) have been found.

Imprimaturs from the National Postal Museum Archives

Imperforate, watermark Type W15. Small Format

Watermark upright
Watermark sideways

Booklet Pane of four with blank advertisement labels. Imperforate, watermark Type W15

Two panes as No. NB27 arranged horizontally *tête-bêche* without marginal markings

Specimen overprints from the National Postal Museum Archives

Booklet pane of six. Perf. 15 × 14, watermark Type W15 (inverted)

"Specimen", Type 32 and upper left stamp with punch hole

Booklet pane of four with advertising labels. Perf. 15 × 14, watermark Type W15 (inverted)

No. NB27a(14) with stamps overprinted "Specimen", Type 32 and upper label with punch hole

2d.   Orange, Type N13

Cat. No.	S.G. No.		Shades	Unused	Used

1935 (JANUARY 21).   INTERMEDIATE FORMAT (18.4×22.2 mm.)

N54   —

			(1) Orange	2·25	70
			(2) Bright orange	2·25	70
a.	Imperf. (pair)	£1250			
b.	Broken tablet (Cyl. 5 No dot, R.20/9)	35·00			
c.	Ditto retouched	15·00			

No. N54 is known postmarked on 19 January, two days prior to the official first day of issue.

N54b

Controls and Cylinder Numbers

Blocks of six (Position D)

							Perf. Type			
						2 No dot	2A (or 6A) Dot	5 No dot	5 Dot	6 No dot	6B Dot
Cyl. No.	Control										
5 (i)	V 34 ..	..	..	..		†	20·00	†	†	19·00	19·00
5 (i)	W 35 ..	..	..	..		†	†	17·00	17·00	19·00	19·00
5 (ii)	W 35 ..	..	..	..		20·00	22·00	†	†	17·00	17·00

Cylinder 5 exists in two states: (i) 5 very faint; (ii) the 5 has been re-etched to appear bolder and **larger**.

Imprimatur from the National Postal Museum Archives

Imperforate, watermark Type W15. Intermediate Format

Watermark upright

1935.   SMALL FORMAT (18.15×21.7 mm.)

N55   442

				(1) Orange		30	30
				(2) Bright orange		30	30
a.	Watermark sideways (17·9× 21·7mm.)	60·00	35·00				
c.	Retouched leaves (Cyl. 13 Dot. Control A 37. R. 18/1)	15·00		s.	"Specimen", Type 30 ..		
d.	Broken value tablet (Cyl. 8 No dot, R.20/1)	35·00		t.	"Specimen", Type 32 ..		
e.	Coil join (vert. pair) ..			u.	Wmk. sideways, "Cancelled" Type 28		

N55c

N55d

No. N55c only exists from late printings so not all positional examples show the retouches.

Coils

Vertical delivery made up from sheets with coils joins every 20th stamp (Stamps 18.15 × 21.7 mm.)

Code No.	Issued	Number in roll	Face value	
Q	1935	960	£8.0.0	Bottom delivery
R	1935	480	£4.0.0	Top delivery

Sideways delivery printed in continuous reels with watermark sideways (Stamps 17.9 × 21.7 mm.)

T	1935	480	£4.0.0	**Left side delivery**

Controls and Cylinder Numbers

Blocks of six (Position D)

						2	2A	Perf. Type 5	5	6	6B
Cyl. No.	Control					No dot	Dot	No dot	Dot	No dot	Dot
8	X 35	..	..	••	..	†	†	13·00*	3·25	13·00*	3·25
10	X 35	..	..	••	..	†	†	3·00	3·00	3·00	3·00
10	Y 36	..	..	••	..	†	†	3·00	3·00	†	†
10	Z 36	..	..	••	..	5·50	†	3·25	3·25	3·00	3·00
12	X 35	..	..	••	..	†	†	3·00	3·00	3·25	3·25
12	Y 36	..	..	••	..	†	†	3·00	3·00	†	—
12	Z 36	..	..	••	..	7·50	†	3·00	3·00	†	†
12	A 37	..	..	••	..	†	†	3·00	3·00	†	†
13	Z 36	..	..	••	..	11·00	11·00	3·00	3·00	3·25	3·25
13	A 37	..	..	••	..	†	†	3·00	16·00*	†	†

Variety: Cylinder 10 dot known Perforation Type 3 with control Y 36.

*These cylinder blocks include a listed variety.

Imprimaturs from the National Postal Museum Archives

Imperforate, watermark Type W15. Small Format

Watermark upright
Watermark sideways

2½d. Blue, Type N12

Cat. No.	S.G. No.
1935 (MARCH 18)	

N56   443
- *a.* Retouched panel (Cyl. 8 Dot, R.18/1) .. .. ..   10·00
- *b.* Retouched panel (Cyl. 8 No dot, R.18/1) .. .. ..   10·00
- *c.* Coil join (vert. pair)   ..
- *s.* " Specimen ", Type 23   ..

Shades	Unused	Used
(1) Bright blue	1·10	60
(2) Ultramarine	1·10	60

N56*a*   N56*b*

Controls and Cylinder Numbers

Blocks of six (Position D)

Cyl. No.	Control						Perf. Type			
							2 No dot	2A Dot	5 No dot	5 Dot
6	W 35	..	..	..	..	..	11·00	11·00	9·00	9·00
7	W 35	..	..	..	..	..	11·00	11·00	9·00	9·00
8	Y 36	..	..	..	..	..	20·00*	20·00*	18·00*	18·00*
9	Y 36	..	..	..	..	..	32·00	†	23·00	23·00

*These cylinder blocks include a listed variety.

Coils

Vertical delivery made up from sheets with joins every 20th stamp

Code No.	Issued	Number in roll	Face value	
F	1935	960	£10.00.	Bottom delivery

Imprimatur from the National Postal Museum Archives

Imperforate, watermark Type W15

Watermark upright

3d. Violet, Type N13

Cat. No. S.G. No.						Shades	Unused	Used

1935 (MARCH 18)

N57	444			(1) Reddish violet	1·00	50

- *a.* Coil join (vert. pair) .. ..
- *b.* Coil join (horiz. pair) .. ..
- *c.* Watermark inverted .. .. — £300
- *s.* "Specimen", Type 30 .. ..
- *t.* "Specimen", Type 23 .. ..
- *u.* "Cancelled", Type 33 .. ..
- *v.* "Cancelled", Type 28 .. .. £225

(1) Reddish violet   1·00   50
(2) Violet   1·00   50

Controls and Cylinder Numbers

Blocks of six (Position D)

						2 No dot	2A Dot	Perf. Type 5 No dot	5 Dot	6 No dot	6B Dot
Cyl No.	Control										
1	W 35	..	..	..	..	11·00	11·00	†	†	†	†
2	W 35	..	..	..	..	12·00	12·00	†	†	†	†
3*	W 35	..	..	..	..	†	£200	†	†	†	†
6	X 35	..	..	..	..	†	†	11·00	11·00	11·00	11·00
12	Y 36	..	..	..	..	†	†	12·00	12·00	†	†
13	Y 36	..	..	..	..	†	†	11·00	11·00	†	†
14	Y 36	..	..	..	..	18·00	18·00	11·00	11·00	†	†
14	Z 36	..	..	..	..	18·00	18·00	11·00	11·00	†	†
14	Z 36 bar—	..	..	..	..	†	†	11·00	11·00	12·00	12·00
14	Z 36 bars⌐	..	..	..	..	†	†	11·00	11·00	†	†

Variety: Cylinder 1 dot known Perforation Type 3.

*See under " Printing " in the General Notes.

Coils

Vertical delivery made up from sheets with joins every 20th stamp

Code No.	Issued	Number in roll	Face value	
C	1935	960	£12.0.0	Bottom delivery

Sideways delivery made up from sheets with joins every 12th stamp

S	1935	480	£6.0.0	Left side delivery

Imprimatur from the National Postal Museum Archives

Imperforate, watermark Type W15

Watermark upright

4d.   Grey-Green, Type N13

Cat. No. S.G. No.		Shades	Unused	Used

1935 (DECEMBER 2)

N58   445   (1) Deep grey-green   1·50   55
  a.   Watermark inverted   ..   †   —   (2) Blackish green   6·00   2·25
  s.   " Specimen ", Type 23   ..
  t.   " Cancelled ", Type 28   ..

Controls and Cylinder Numbers

Blocks of six (Position D)

					2	2A	5	5	6	6B
Cyl. No. Control					No dot	Dot	No dot	Dot	No dot	Dot
3	W 35	..	..	..	—	13·00*	†	†	†	†
8	X 35	..	..	..	†	†	14·00	14·00	†	†
9	X 35	..	..	..	†	†	21·00	21·00	†	†
11	X 35	..	..	..	18·00	18·00	13·00	13·00	13·00	14·00
11	Y 36	..	..	..	†	†	13·00	13·00	†	†
11	Y 36 bar —	..	..	..	†	†	13·00	13·00	13·00	14·00
11	Y 36 bars ⌊	..	..	..	†	†	13·00	13·00	16·00	14·00
11	Y 36 bars ⌶	..	..	..	†	†	13·00	13·00	†	†
11	Y 36 bars □	..	..	..	†	†	13·00	13·00	†	†

Perf. Type spans columns 2 through 6B.

*Cylinder 3 in Perforation Type 2A has no dot, presumably omitted in error.

Imprimatur from the National Postal Museum Archives

Imperforate, watermark Type W15

Watermark upright

5d.   Yellow-Brown, Type N14

Cat. No.   S.G. No.   Shades   Unused   Used

1936 (FEBRUARY 17)

N59   446   (1) Yellow-brown   5·00   1·50
  s.   " Specimen ", Type 23 ..   (2) Deep yellow-brown   5·00   1·50
  t.   " Cancelled ", Type 33 ..

For this value printed in magenta, see the note describing the unissued 6d. under
Photogravure, Trials and Essays at the front of this Section.

Controls and Cylinder Numbers

Blocks of six (Position D)

						Perf. Type					
						2 No dot	2A Dot	5 No dot	5 Dot	6 No dot	6B Dot
Cyl. No.	Control										
5	X 36	..	..	..	..	†	†	65·00	65·00	†	†
5	Y 36	..	..	..	..	35·00	35·00	32·00	32·00	†	†
5	Z 36	..	..	..	..	†	†	†	†	32·00	32·00
5	Z 36 bar — ..	..	..	..	†	35·00	32·00	32·00	32·00	32·00	
5	Z 36 bars ⌊ ..	..	..	..	†	†	†	†	32·00	32·00	
5	Z 36 bars ⊔ ..	..	..	..	†	†	32·00	32·00	†	†	
5	Z 36 bars ☐ ..	..	..	..	†	†	32·00	32·00	†	†	

Imprimatur from the National Postal Museum Archives

Imperforate, watermark Type W15

Watermark upright

9d.   Olive-Green, Type N15

Cat. No.   S.G. No.   Shades   Unused   Used

1935 (DECEMBER 2)

N60   447   Deep olive-green   9·00   1·60
  s.   " Specimen ", Type 23 ..
  t.   " Cancelled ", Type 28 ..

Controls and Cylinder Numbers

Blocks of six (Position D)

							Perf. Type			
							5 No dot	5 Dot	6 No dot	6B Dot
Cyl. No.	Control									
15	X 35	..	..	..	..	..	90·00	90·00	90·00	90·00
15	X 35 bar —	..	..	..	..	..	†	†	90·00	90·00
15	X 35 bars ⌊	..	..	..	..	..	95·00	95·00	†	†
15	X 35 bars ⊔	..	..	..	..	..	95·00	95·00	†	†
15	X 35 bars ☐	..	..	..	..	..	†	†	95·00	95·00

Imprimatur from the National Postal Museum Archives

Imperforate, watermark Type W15

Watermark upright

10d. Turquoise-Blue, Type N15

Cat. No.	S.G. No.		Shades		Unused	Used
1936 (FEBRUARY 24)						
N61	448		Turquoise-blue		12·00	8·00
s.	"Specimen", Type 32	..				
t.	"Cancelled", Type 33	..				
u.	"Specimen", Type 23	..				

Controls and Cylinder Numbers
Blocks of six (Position D)

					Perf. Type				
Cyl. No.	Control				2 No dot	2 Dot	5 No dot	5 Dot	6 No dot	6B Dot
3	Y 36	..	..		†	—	95·00	95·00	†	†
3	Y 36 bar —	..	..	..	£120	—	95·00	95·00	†	†
3	Y 36 bars ⌐	..	..	..	†	†	95·00	95·00	†	†
3	Y 36 bars ⊔	..	..	..	†	†	95·00	95·00	†	†
3	Y 36 bars ☐	..	..	..	†	†	†	†	£100	£100

Imprimatur from the National Postal Museum Archives

Imperforate, watermark Type W15

Watermark upright

1s. Bistre-Brown, Type N15

Cat. No.	S.G. No.		Shades		Unused	Used
1936 (FEBRUARY 24)						
N62	449		Bistre-brown		12·00	40
a.	Double impression ..	..	t.	"Specimen", Type 23 ..		
s.	"Specimen", Type 32	.. 40·00	u.	"Cancelled", Type 33 ..		

N62a

Controls and Cylinder Numbers
Blocks of six (Position D)

						Perf. Type			
Cyl. No.	Control					5 No dot	5 Dot	6 No dot	6B Dot
3	Y 36	..	..	..	..	..	80·00	80·00	†	†
4	Y 36	..	..	..	..	..	80·00	80·00	†	†
5	Z 36	..	..	..	..	..	85·00	85·00	—	—
5	Z 36 bar —	..	..	..	..	..	85·00	85·00	†	†
5	Z 36 bars ⌐	..	..	..	..	..	£100	£100	†	†
5	Z 36 bars ⊔	..	..	..	..	..	£100	£100	†	†
5	Z 36 bars ☐	..	..	..	..	..	†	†	£100	£100

On cylinder 5 both panes show an erased " 1 " before the " 5 ".

Imprimatur from the National Postal Museum Archives

Imperforate, watermark Type W15

Watermark upright

General Notes on the Recess-Printed High Values (1913-34)

INTRODUCTION. The high values, 2s. 6d., 5s., 1os. and £1 were designed by Bertram Mackennal, and were originally to be produced from a single master die engraved by J. A. C. Harrison and then have the original values engraved in. However, the first master die produced had the Union Jack in Britannia's shield heraldically incorrect and consequently each value ended up not only having the value engraved but also its own flag which naturally differs slightly from value to value.

The original printers, Waterlow Bros. & Layton, relinquished the contract to De La Rue & Co. in 1915, who were in turn replaced by Bradbury, Wilkinson & Co. in 1918. The £1 value, which passed from currency in 1915, was only printed by Waterlow.

When, in 1934, the contract passed back to Waterlow & Sons, the re-engraved dies were used. The re-engraved dies were produced from the 5s. value which was modified to form a master die. These were also engraved by J. A. C. Harrison. It is believed that the re-engraving was introduced to coincide with the photogravure series of the same year.

RECESS-PRINTING. This term means the same as "Line-Engraved" and "Intaglio" printing. It is the opposite to typography (described in the General Notes to Section M) as the engraver cuts out of the die the part of the design that *is* to be inked. The master die is hardened and a circular steel die is softened and applied under pressure to the master die. This "Transfer Roller", as it is called, is then hardened and used to roll or rock in the individual impressions on the printing plate. This process is more fully described in the General Notes to the Line-Engraved issues in Vol. 1. In printing, the cut-out hollows of the plate are filled with ink, any surplus being wiped away. The resulting impression has a depth of ink equal to the depth of the cuts in the original die and the raised image can usually be felt with the finger.

It is interesting that the freelance engraver, J. A. C. Harrison, who had specialised in line-engraving, was commissioned by the Royal Mint to engrave the heads and frames for the typographed issues produced by Harrison & Sons and showed that he was equally at home in this reverse process. Later he was employed by Waterlow and engraved the renowned "Sea Horses", the 1924-25 British Empire Exhibition and £1 P.U.C. designs.

HOW TO DISTINGUISH BETWEEN THE PRINTINGS. The vertical measurement of the Waterlow and De la Rue stamps was exactly 22 mm. A good deal of the De La Rue work was from the previously used Waterlow plates, and printings from worn plates are attributable to them. In the De La Rue printings, the gum is usually patchy and yellowish, and the colour of the stamp, particularly the 5s., tends to show through the back. The holes of the perforation are smaller than those of the other two printers.

Bradbury Wilkinson used rotary plates, and the height of the stamps is now 22¾ or 23 mm. On most of the 22¾ mm. high stamps, a minute coloured dot appears in the margin just above the middle of the upper frame line. This dot was on the transfer roller and assisted the craftsman in the laying down of the plate. If the roller was not rocked to its full extent then the dot would not appear. The Bradbury, Wilkinson plates were made from roller transfers from the original dies and the differences in the vertical measurements came about through bending the plates for use in the rotary presses.

In 1927, Bradbury Wilkinson made a new set of plates, none of which showed the guide dots. The printed stamps are now 23 mm. high but it is not known whether this slight variation in height is due to expansion caused by bending the plates or because the earlier plates were used with dampened paper which shrunk on drying, consequently resulting in the printed stamps being smaller in size. For this reason, we are not listing the sizes in the catalogue.

The Waterlow printings in 1934 were from re-engraved dies, the most noticeable difference being the crosshatch shading in the medallion.

PLATES. All the plates for the Waterlow and De La Rue printings were made by the Royal Mint in sets of 40. The Mint supplied Bradbury, Wilkinson with a die for each value and from these they made sets of roller punches which they used to roll out their plates. These were in sets of 80 and the sheets were divided into Post Office sheets of 40 after printing.

MARGINAL MARKINGS ON THE PLATES. Each sheet contained 40 stamps arranged in 10 rows of 4, and showed hand engraved marginal markings. On each Waterlow and De La Rue plate, marginal crosses appear centrally on the four sides of each sheet. Plate numbers were also engraved in the top margin, although they were so far above the stamps that they rarely appear on the issued sheets.

On the Bradbury Wilkinson plates, lines were engraved on either side of the crosses—horizontally in the top and bottom margins, and vertically in the side margins. As these lines and crosses were engraved by hand, slight differences in the lengths are apparent, and are an aid in plating.

The official plate numbers were almost invariably removed when the sheets were trimmed. However, many of the plates can be distinguished by specialists by reference to the precise positions of the sheet markings. It would be beyond the scope of this catalogue to describe all these but most of the information is contained in various articles in *The GB Journal* (see Cumulative Index) and also in Part 4 of *The Postage Stamps of Great Britain* (Beaumont and Stanton). We record the number of plates used by the different printers. The philatelic plate numbers are recorded for the re-entries we list.

VARIETIES. In addition to the major re-entries that we list there are numerous stamps showing double frame lines, many of which were repaired and strengthened. To list these would be beyond the scope of this catalogue.

PAPER. The paper was stout wove until 1926, when printings were made on undampened paper. From this date until 1934, the paper was softer and more porous. In 1921 some stamps were issued on paper with a ribbed appearance, somewhat similar to laid paper. When held up to the light faint horizontal lines are noticeable in the paper texture. This was due to the incorrect pressure of the gumming rollers. Such items are described in the lists as on ribbed paper.

Stages of Original Master Die

Stage 1 has the Union Jack in the shield more or less heraldically correct (no horizontal lines in the St. Andrew's Cross). Stages 2 to 5a have incorrect shield in that there are horizontal lines in the St. Andrew's Cross. Stage 6 is without shield and Stage 6a has a "Z" in the space for the shield. Other features of the various stages are noted below.

Stage 1

Proofed 24 August 1912. Upper garlands incomplete; no circles above top frame line; centre horses's head and Britannia's arms, dress and foot quite pale and unshaded. The only recorded example is in the H. C. V. Adams collection at the Royal Philatelic Society. However it is possible that others may exist in private hands.

Stage 2

Proofed 30 August 1912. Upper garlands completed; incomplete circles on top frame line; centre horse's head and Britannia's arms, dress and foot unshaded as before; dark horse has ring of white around the mouth and only light shading to hoof.

Stage 3

Proofed 6 September 1912.   The 2nd and 3rd circles on top frame line are completed; centre horse's head shaded and some shading added to Britannia's arm and dress but foot remains unshaded; the ring of white around dark horse's mouth has been removed but hoof is unchanged.

Stage 4

Proofed 11 September 1912.   All circles except the first now completed; Britannia's foot shaded and finer shading added to her dress; dark horse's head further shaded but hoof as before.

Stage 5

Proofed 18 September 1912.   The 1st circle is still uncompleted; the dark horse's hoof is now shaded; the bottom frame line at left is missing.   The die was hardened on 20 December 1912 (stage 5a).

Stages 6 and 6a were then produced from a transfer roller that was taken up from the stage 5a die but with the shield removed.

Stage 6

Proofed 23 September 1912.   Blank shield.   Outer frame line and all circles at top removed.

Stage 6a

Proofed late September 1912. Blank shield has a zig-zag line in it. Outer frame line restored with all circles except the first, which is still incomplete.

Stages of Completed Dies with Values and Shields Inserted

Corrected Flag

Each value had its own figures, lettering and shields engraved in from dies laid out from the roller with the blank shield. They are listed under each individual value but exist in two states for each value. Those illustrated here are from the 2s. 6d. value but they are the same for the other values.

(a)   (b)

State (a) Completed but first circle still unfinished.   Guide lines around design still visible (not illustrated).

State (b) Fully completed with first circle finished and guide lines removed.

Die Proofs

Stage 1
  In light brown on thick card   ..   ..

Stage 2
  In indigo-black or grey-blue on thick card   ..   .. *From* £5000
  In grey-blue on laid paper £5000
  In brown on card £5000

Stage 3
  In grey-brown on thick card £4250

Stage 4
  In carmine, green, grey-green, indigo or brown on thick card   ..   ..   .. *From* £3500

Stage 5.   Before hardening
  In dull green, indigo, brown or red-brown on thick card   ..   .. *From* £3500

Stage 5a.   After hardening, taken on 3 September 1912 and later
  In green, chestnut, sepia or indigo-black on card   ..   .. *From* £3500

Stage 6
  In indigo-black on wove paper ..   ..

Stage 6a
  In indigo-black on esparto paper with or without pale colouring around frame £5750

Colour Trial

Taken on 28 January 1913 from Stage 5a die and endorsed " From Master
  Plate—Waterlow's Ink " in manuscript
  In ultramarine on wove paper £4500

All stamps in this Section are Type **N10**, watermarked Single Cypher, Type **W17** and the word " POSTAGE " in each of the four margins and perforated 11 × 12. Printed in sheets of 40 (10 horizontal rows of 4).

PRICES FOR STAMPS IN USED CONDITION
Many of the stamps in this Section were used on parcels and as a result were subject to heavy cancelling. The "used" prices in this catalogue are for fine used examples; inferior examples with very heavy or smudged postmarks are of less value. On the other hand there is a premium of **25%** for well centred lightly used stamps Nos. N63 to N72 (background Type A).

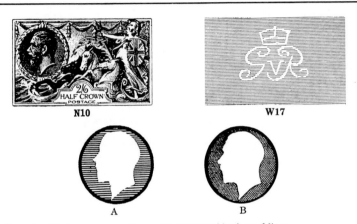

N10   W17

A   B

Type A. Background around portrait consists of horizontal lines
Type B. Background around portrait consists of horizontal and diagonal lines

---

Background Type A

Cat. No. S.G. No.	Date	Shades	Unused	Used

1913-18. 2s. 6d. BROWN
  (a) Waterlow printings

					Unused	Used
N63	399/400	30.6.13		(1) Deep sepia-brown	£175	65·00 ✓
				(2) Sepia-brown	£175	60·00
a.	Re-entry (R.2/1)	.. ..	£900	£400		
b.	Ribbed paper ..	..	£250			
s.	"Specimen", Type 26	..	£200			
t.	"Specimen", Type 29	..	£425			
u.	"Cancelled", Type 24	..	£300			
v.	"Cancelled", Type 27	..	£450			
w.	"Cancelled", Type 27					
	Imperf.					

Plates. Waterlow used two plates.

Die Proofs

State (a)

In blue-green on card marked " 3 " above design	.. ..	£4000
In blue-green on card	.. ..	£3750

State (b)

In deep green on card marked " 3 " above design	.. ..	£3750
In deep green or dull grey-blue on card	.. .. *From*	£2750
In deep red-brown on thin wove paper	.. ..	£2750
In vermilion or brown on India paper ..	.. .. *From*	£2750

Plate Proofs

Three impressions together from supposed trial plate arranged 17 mm. apart horizontally. Size 39 × 22·25 mm.

In black on soft card .. .. *Strip of three* £3000

Proofed on 19 December 1912. Impressions 5 mm. apart horizontally and vertically. Size 39 × 22·5 mm. Very clear impressions

In dull blue-green on glazed card £650

Size approx. 38·8 × 22 mm. (depending on shrinkage)
Thin plate-glazed paper without gum or watermark

In red, blue, green, brown or black .. .. *From* £450

Thicker wove paper without gum or watermark

In deep carmine, carmine, vermilion, orange-chrome, olive-green, bottle-green, blue-green, ultramarine, purple-brown or sepia-brown .. .. *From* £450

Thin gummed wove paper watermarked " James Weighley—219 "

In black.. .. .. £750

Thin card

In green, after plate had been cleaned £750

Colour Trials

Imperf. on thin paper pasted on card

In green endorsed "30–4–13" in M/S and stamped "WATERLOW BROS. & LAYTON, LTD." £2500

Imperf. on ungummed paper watermarked " James Weighley—219 "

In 19 different colours .. .. *From* £450

(b) De La Rue printings

N64   405/408   12.15

a.	Re-entry (R.2/1)	.. £700	£400
b.	Re-entry (R.10/4)	.. £1200	
c.	No watermark ..	.. £1500	
d.	Wmk. " POSTAGE " inverted. Strip of 3 ..	.. £2500	
e.	Wmk. " POSTAGE " reversed. Strip of 3 ..	.. £2500	
ea.	Wmk. "POSTAGE" reversed. Vert. strip of 4	.. £2500	
f.	Wmk. inverted:		
	Shade (1) ..	.. £350	
	,, (2) ..	.. £300	
	,, (8) ..	.. £300	
	,, (9) ..	.. £700	
	,, (10) ..	.. £300	
	,, (11) ..	..	
g.	Wmk. reversed:		
	Shade (2) ..	.. £300	
	,, (8) ..	.. £350	
	,, (10) ..	.. £300	
	,, (11) ..	..	
h.	Wmk. inverted and reversed, Shade (2)	.. £900	

(1)	Deep yellow-brown	£200	70·00
(2)	Yellow-brown	£200	65·00
(3)	Pale yellow-brown	£225	45·00
(4)	Bright yellow-brown	£225	50·00
(5)	Cinnamon-brown	£900	£500
(6)	Grey-brown	£175	45·00
(7)	Pale brown	£175	45·00
(8)	Pale brown (worn plate)	£175	65·00
(9)	Very deep brown	£900	£450
(10)	Seal-brown (sepia)	£200	70·00
(11)	Blackish brown	£650	£375

Shades (10) and (11) are often found with dark brown gum. Shade (9) is usually found with watermark low and inverted.

s. " Specimen ", Type 23 .. £450
t. " Cancelled ", Type 24 .. £300

No. N64*a* is from the Waterlow plate, and the re-entry marks are identical. **Known** with watermark upright and inverted.

No. N64*b* is from a worn plate, and the re-entered lines are very clear. This re-entry **was** probably made after the plate had been put to press.

Plates. De La Rue used the two Waterlow plates and three additional plates.

Colour Trials

Size 38·7 × 22·1 mm. Imperf on gummed paper wmk. Type **W17**

In issued shades (1), (2) and (3)   ..   ..   *From* £300

Perf. 11 × 12 on gummed paper. Wmk. Type **17**

Ultramarine, indigo, green, purple, grey or brown ..   ..   *From* £2000

Perf. **11 × 12** on ungummed paper. No wmk.

Bright brown, bright blue, magenta, sepia, carmine, indigo or green   ..   *From* £2000

Imprimatur from the National Postal Museum Archives

Imperforate, watermark Type W17

Watermark upright

An example exists showing a reversed plate number " 12 " in sheet margin at top.

2s. 6d. Re-entries

N63/4*a*

N64*b*

N65*a*

N65*b*	Normal	N65*b*, N65*d*

Nos. N65*b* and N65*d* show the shield with doubling of the vertical, and several of the diagonal, lines of shading.

N65*c*	N65*ca*

Nos. N65*c*/*ca* also show doubling under the front leg of the black horse. A similar variety occurs on R. 2/4 of Plate 6 which also contains a doubling of the wreath just above the back of the King's head.

Cat. No.	S.G. No.	Date	Shades	Unused	Used

(c) Bradbury, Wilkinson printings

N65   413*a*/415*a*   12.18

			Shades	Unused	Used
a.	Re-entry (Pl. 3, R.1/2)	£600 £250	(1) Olive-brown	70·00	25·00 ✓
b.	Re-entry (Pl. 2, R.1/3)	£200 £100	(2) Chocolate-brown	90·00	30·00 ✓
c.	Re-entry (Pl. 11, R.1/4)	£175 85·00	(3) Reddish brown	95·00	30·00 ✓
ca.	Re-entry (Pl. 11, R.2/4)	£175 85·00	(4) Pale brown	80·00	25·00 ✓
d.	Re-entry (Pl. 2, R.7/1)				
e.	Ribbed paper	£150 40·00			
s.	"Specimen", Type 15				
t.	"Specimen", Type 23	£250	*w.* "Cancelled", Type 24	£160	
u.	"Specimen", Type 26		*x.* "Cancelled", Type 28		
v.	"Specimen", Type 31 in		*y.* "Cancelled", Type 33	£400	
	violet or black	£350	*z.* "Specimen", Type 23 and		
va.	"Specimen", Type 32		"Cancelled", Type 24		

Nos. N65*b* and *d* also occur on ribbed paper.

N65*e* and N68*a* were formerly described as being on laid paper but it has now been confirmed that such paper was never supplied to the printer. The "laid" effect resulted from incorrect pressure of the gumming rollers; "ribbed paper" is considered a more accurate description.

272

Plates.   Bradbury, Wilkinson used thirteen 22¾ mm. plates and five 23 mm. plates.

Rough Plate Proofs

On buff paper in brown, carmine or indigo..   ..   ..   .. *From*   25·00

Experimental printing on paper watermarked Type **W14** (sideways and
reversed), perf. 11 × 12, 22¾ mm. high and overprinted "Cancelled",
    Type 24   ..   ..   £250
Do., watermark "POSTAGE"   ..   ..   *Strip of* 3   £1500
Do., but without watermark ..   ..

Imprimatur from the National Postal Museum Archives

Imperforate, watermark Type W17

Watermark upright

1913-18 5s. CARMINE

Cat. No. S.G. No.	Date			Shades	Unused	Used

(a) Waterlow printings

N66	401	4.7.13				

				(1) Rose-carmine	£300	£130
s.	"Specimen", Type 26	..	£175	(2) Pale rose-carmine	£300	90·00
t.	"Cancelled", Type 24	..	£400	(3) Carmine-red	£300	90·00
u.	"Cancelled", Type 27	..	£750			
v.	"Cancelled", Type 27					
	Imperf.	.. ..	..			

Plates. Waterlow used two plates.

Die Proofs

State (a) but with first circle completed

In sepia-brown on card showing guide lines outside design £2500

State (b)

In deep grey-brown on card still showing guide lines	..	..	..	..	£2500
In sepia, deep grey-blue, indigo or blue-green on card	..	..	..	*From*	£2250
In grey-brown on card endorsed " 10 October 1912 " ..	..	..	..	..	£2250
In blue, brown, carmine or green on India paper	..	..	..	*From*	£2250

In red-brown, dark brown, chestnut-brown, deep blue, carmine, green or blue-green on
thin paper   ..   .. *From* £2250
In red-brown on thin paper endorsed " 14 October 1912 " £2500
In indigo-blue on esparto paper £2250

(b) De La Rue printings

N67	409/410	12.15			(1) Bright carmine	£325	£140
a.	No watermark	..	..	£2250	(2) Carmine	£350	£130
b.	Watermark inverted		£950		(3) Pale carmine (worn plate)	£325	£140 ✓
c.	Watermark reversed	..	£850				
d.	Watermark inverted and reversed	..	..	..			
e.	Wmk. "POSTAGE" inverted. Strip of 3 (Shade 1)		£3000				

s. | "Specimen", Type 23 | .. | £300
t. | "Cancelled", Type 24 | .. | £400

On shade (2) the colour shows through to
the back of the stamp.

Plates. De La Rue used only the two Waterlow plates.

Certain stamps from the first and second vertical rows of the second plate had the left frame
lines strengthened.

Imprimatur from the National Postal Museum Archives

Imperforate, watermark Type W17

Watermark upright

(c) Bradbury, Wilkinson printings

N68	416	1.19			(1) Rose-carmine	£175	35·00 ✓
a.	Ribbed paper	..	..	£400	(2) Rose-red	£175	35·00 ✓
s.	"Specimen", Type 15	..					
sa.	"Specimen", Type 23	..					
t.	"Specimen", Type 26	..	£400				
u.	"Specimen", Type 31 in						
	violet or black	..	..	£350			
v.	"Specimen", Type 32	..					

w. | "Cancelled", Type 24 | .. | £250
x. | "Cancelled", Type 28 | ..
y. | "Cancelled", Type 33 | ..
z. | "Specimen", Type 23 and
   | "Cancelled", Type 34 | ..

Plates. Bradbury, Wilkinson used eight 22¾ mm. plates and at least one 23 mm. plate.

Rough plate proof on buff in carmine ..   .. 30·00

Experimental printing on paper watermarked Type **W14** (sideways)

perf. 11 × 12, 22¾ mm. high and overprinted " Cancelled " Type 24 .. £350
Do. but watermark upright and 23 mm. high* £500
  *This contains the positional dot in the upper margin normally absent from issued 23 mm.
stamps.

Imprimatur from the National Postal Museum Archives

Imperforate, watermark Type W17

Watermark upright

1913-18 10s. BLUE

Cat. No.   S.G. No.   Date

(a) Waterlow printings

					Shades	Unused	Used

N69   402   1.8.13

(1) Indigo-blue   £500   £225
(2) Indigo   £450   £225

s. " Specimen ", Type 23   ..
t. " Specimen ", Type 26   ..   £400
u. " Specimen ", Type 29   ..   £700
v. " Cancelled ", Type 24   ..   £600

w. " Cancelled ", Type 27   ..
x. " Cancelled ", Type 28   ..

Plates. Waterlow used two plates.

Die Proofs

State (a)

In blue-green on card marked " 2 " above design £5000
In blue-green on card £4750

State (b)

In blue-green on card £4750
In deep green on card marked " 2 " above design £5000
As last but endorsed " 12 November 1912 " £5000

Colour Trial

On paper watermarked Type **W17**, gummed, in near to issued colour   ..   ..   ..

(b) De La Rue printings

N70   411/413   12.15

(1) Blue   £900   £250
(2) Deep blue   £1100   £300
(3) Deep blue (worn plate)   £1500   £275
(4) Deep (intense) bright blue   £2250
(5) Bright (" Cambridge ") blue   £2750
(6) Pale blue   £900   £250

c. Watermark inverted and reversed (shade (1))..   ..
s. " Specimen ", Type 26   ..   £800
t. " Cancelled ", Type 24   ..   £1000

Plates. De La Rue used only the two Waterlow plates.

Imprimatur from the National Postal Museum Archives

Imperforate, watermark Type W17

Watermark upright

(c) Bradbury, Wilkinson printings

N71   417   1.19

(1) Dull blue   £300   75·00 ✓
(2) Dull grey-blue   £300   80·00
(3) Steel-blue   £2500   £400

a. Re-entry (Pl. 5, R.1/1)   ..   £950   £300
ab. Re-entry (Pl. 5, R.2/1)   ..   £550   £350
b. Re-entry (Pl. 2, R.6/1)   ..   £1300   £350
s. " Specimen ", Type 15   ..
sa. " Specimen ", Type 23   ..   £500
t. " Specimen ", Type 26   ..
u. " Specimen ", Type 31 in violet or black £450
v. " Specimen ", Type 32   ..
w. " Cancelled ", Type 24   ..

x. " Cancelled ", Type 28   ..   £700
y. " Cancelled ", Type 33   ..
z. " Specimen ", Type 23 and " Cancelled ", Type 34   ..
za. " Specimen ", Type 23 and " Cancelled ", Type 24,   ..

On some plates, every stamp shows a broken " S " in " POSTAGE ". No. N71a is from one of these plates. The re-entry marks on No. N71b are similar but more pronounced, and the letter " S " in " POSTAGE " is perfect.

Imprimatur from the National Postal Museum Archives

Imperforate, watermark Type W17

Watermark upright

N71a   N71b

N71ab. This re-entry, which adjoins No. N71a, shows doubling of LL and GS of SHIL-LINGS and also GE of POSTAGE.

Plates. Bradbury, Wilkinson used seven 22¾ mm. plates and two 23 mm. plates.

Experimental Plate Proofs

10 October 1933. From special curved plate comprising nine complete rolled in impressions and one part impression with outer frame lines incomplete. Imperforate

In black on hard unwatermarked paper .. ..   *The sheet* £5000

Two sheets are known, one inscribed " EXPERIMENTAL PLATE " in reverse and the other unmarked. It is believed that they represent before and after hardening states.

Cat. No.	S.G. No.	Date		Shades	Unused	Used
1913	**£1 GREEN.**	**Printed by Waterlow**				
N72	403/404	1.8.13		(1) Green	£1250	£600
s.	"Specimen", Type 23	..	£1500	(2) Deep green	£1500	£700
t.	"Specimen", Type 26	..	£1000	(3) Dull blue-green	£1250	£650
u.	"Cancelled", Type 24 Shade					
	(3)	..	£2000			
ua.	"Cancelled", Type 24†	..	£550			
v.	"Cancelled", Type 27	..				
w.	"Cancelled", Type 28	..				

†No. N72ua exists from NPM archive sales only in a yellowish green shade rather than an issued colour. No. N72u is in dull blue-green and was not included in the NPM sales.

Plates. Waterlow used two plates.

Die Proofs
State (a)

In blue-green on card marked " 4 " above design £5000
In blue-green on card £4500

State (b)

In deep green on card marked " 4 " above design £5000
As last but endorsed " 12 November 1912 " £5000

Colour Trial
On paper, watermarked Type **W17**, in near to issued colour (yellowish) .. .. ..

Background Type B.   The re-engraved Die

The background to the portrait consists of horizontal and diagonal lines.   There are numerous other minor differences between this and the original die.
Printed in sheets of 40, in 10 rows of 4.   The sheet was marked with horizontal and vertical lines in all four corners.   There were also short vertical lines in the perforation gutter between the second and third stamps in the top and bottom rows.

Printed by Waterlow

Cat. No.	S.G. No.		Shades	Unused	Used
1934 (OCTOBER). 2s. 6d. BROWN					
N73	450		(1) Chocolate-brown	50·00	15·00
s.	" Specimen ", Type 30 ..		(2) Reddish brown	50·00	15·00

Imprimatur from the National Postal Museum Archives

Imperforate, watermark Type W17
Watermark upright

1934 (OCTOBER). 5s. RED					
N74	451		Bright rose-red	£100	30·00
s.	" Specimen ", Type 30 ..		rose·red		

Imprimatur from the National Postal Museum Archives

Imperforate, watermark Type W17
Watermark upright

1934 (OCTOBER). 10s. INDIGO					
N75	452		Indigo	£200	40·00
s.	" Specimen ", Type 30 ..				

Imprimatur from the National Postal Museum Archives

Imperforate, watermark Type W17
Watermark upright

Commemorative Issues (1924-35)

All stamps in this section are watermarked Multiple Block G v R and Crown, Type **W15**, except No. NCom9.

N16 N17

(Des. Harold Nelson. Dies eng. J. A. C. Harrison)

1924 and 1925 BRITISH EMPIRE EXHIBITION

Recess-printed by Waterlow & Sons from dies and plates of their own manufacture and printed in sheets of 120 stamps in two panes of 60, the panes being separated before issue into post office sheets of 10 rows of 6. There were no Controls or plate numbers.

It is probable that there was a single plate for each of the 1924 values; the Post Office collection contains the original proofs which were submitted about 12 April 1924. It was decided to re-issue the stamps in 1925 and the original dies were changed to the new date. Waterlow returned the 1925 dies to the Royal Mint and they were later transferred to the National Postal Museum. The 1½d. bears the engraved number "10289" and the 1d. is numbered "10290". Die proofs exist which confirm that both issues were from the original dies and that the transfer rollers for 1924 and 1925 stamps were taken from them. There are many flaws which are merely transient and unrelated to plate defects.

The perforation was at first by a line machine which had very small holes. Later this was changed for a comb machine with larger holes.

The 1924 1½d. value is known printed on both sides, the one on the back being partly sideways; we do not list this as a variety, being more in the nature of a freak.

The coil stamps were made by the British Stamp and Ticket Automatic Delivery Co. Ltd. for use in the vending machines they supplied and which were installed in various places inside the Exhibition.

It had been the intention of the Exhibition Board that the stamps would only be available to personal callers. However, such was the interest and demand for the stamps that it was agreed to supply the stamps by post from 1 July 1924. It is not clear from records whether all postal sales were dealt with by the Exhibition Post Offices. It is known that the London Chief Office supplied bulk orders to stamp dealers to the value of £391 18s. 11d. during the first few weeks of the 1924 Exhibition. Stamps of both issues were available from the Chief Office for a short period after the close of the Exhibition in 1925.

1924 (APRIL 23). TYPE N16, DATED "1924"

Cat. No.	S.G. No.	Perforation		Description		Unused	Used
NCom1	430	Line 14		1d. Scarlet		2·25 ✓	6·00 ✓
a.		Bottom margin imperf. ..	£850				
aa.		Left side margin imperf. ..	£950				
b.		Tail to N of EXHIBITION					
		(Left pane, R.1/5)	35·00	s.	"Specimen", Type 15	..	
c.		Comb perf. 14	3·00	6·00	t.	"Specimen", Type 23	..	£200
d.		Do. with Var. b	30·00	u.	"Specimen", Type 30	..	
e.		Coil join (vert. pair) (7.24)..		v.	"Cancelled", Type 28	..	£175
NCom2	431	Line 14		1½d. Brown	..	4·00	11·00 ✓
a.		Comb perf. 14	5·00	9·00			
b.		Left side margin imperf. ..	£850	t.	"Specimen", Type 23	..	£200
c.		Coil join (vert. pair) (7.24)..		u.	"Cancelled", Type 24	..	
s.		"Specimen", Type 15 ..		v.	"Cancelled", Type 28	..	£175

First Day Cover (NCom1/2) .. £350

NCom*1b*

Essays

Various designs by Harold Nelson   ..   ..   *From* £350

Essays were also submitted by Eric Gill, N. Rooke, J. D. Batten and E. W. Tristan.

Die Proofs

1924.   Finished die proofs on wove proof paper

1d. in black .. .., ...	£2500
1½d. in black endorsed " 21 March 1924 "	£2500
1½d. in pale brown endorsed " 21 March 1924 "	£2500
1½d. in deeper brown endorsed " 24 March 1924 "	£2500

1924.   On sunken card and signed " Harold Nelson 1924 "

1d. and 1½d. together in issued colours with very large margins*	£2000

*Beware of signed cards showing issued stamps with the perforations trimmed off.

Progressive proofs of the 1½d. in black and also in the issued colour exist in the J. A. C. Harrison collection at the British Museum.

Coils

Vertical delivery made up from sheets with joins every 10th stamp

Code No.	Value	Issued	Number in roll	Face value	
—	1d.	July 1924	1200	£5. 0.0	Bottom delivery
—	1½d.	July 1924	1200	£7.10.0	Bottom delivery

The above are believed to exist with comb as well as line perforation.

1925 (MAY 9), TYPE N17, DATED " 1925 "

Cat. No.	S.G. No.	Perforation	Description	Unused	Used
NCom3	432	Comb 14 ✓	1d. Scarlet	7·50 ✓	15·00 ✓
a. Coil join (vert. pair) ..					
s. " Specimen ", Type 30 .. £175					
NCom4	433	Comb 14	1½d. Brown	23·00 ✓	50·00 ✓
a. Coil join (vert. pair) .. £125					
s. " Specimen ", Type 30 .. £175					

> First Day Cover (NCom3/4) ..   £1200

Coils

Vertical delivery made up from sheets with joins every 10th stamp

Code No.	Value	Issued	Number in roll	Face value	
—	1d.	1925	1200	£5. 0.0	Bottom delivery
—	1½d.	1925	1200	£7.10.0	Bottom delivery

Withdrawn

The 1924 Exhibition closed on 1 November, but the special Exhibition post office continued to operate between the period of the two openings. During this time both stamps and stationery items dated 1924 were available. During the 1925 Exhibition sales of the 1924 issue were 1780 1d. and 1860 1½d.

The post office remained open after the official closure of the Exhibition on 31 October 1925 and finally closed on 19 December, when the stamps were withdrawn except for the 1925 1½d. which had sold out on 30 October 1925.

Quantities Sold

Figures are approximate as records show discrepancies

Coils	1924		1925	
	1d.	195 rolls	1d.	160 rolls
	1½d	60 rolls	1½d.	85 rolls

Sheets

The total printing order was for 17 million stamps. The quantities of stamps (not sets) sold at Wembley were; 1924 issue 13,214,491; 1925 issue 3,545,128.

N18

(Des. John Farleigh.
Eng. C. G. Lewis
at the Royal Mint)

N19

(Des. Ernest Linzell.
Eng. J. A. C. Harrison
at Waterlows)

N20

(Des. John Farleigh.
Eng. T. E. Storey
at the Royal Mint)

1929 (MAY 10) POSTAL UNION CONGRESS

A. Typographed Issues

The intermediate-sized medal head as employed for the 5d. to 8d. definitive stamps, was used on 15 January 1929 by the Royal Mint to produce the heads employed for the low values.

Typographed by Waterlow & Sons from plates made at the Royal Mint. The layout and perforation is the same as for the concurrent typographed set.

Cat. No	S.G. No.	Type	Perforation			Description		Unused	Used
NCom5	434	**N18**	15 × 14			½d. Green		50	90
a.		Watermark inverted	..	9·00	7·00				
b.		Watermark sideways	..	45·00	32·00				
c.		Varnish ink ..	..	..					
s.		Imperf. optd. "Specimen",				*t.*	"Cancelled", Type 33 ..	£110	
		Type 30	..	..		*u.*	"Cancelled", Type 33P ..	50·00	
NCom6	435	**N19**	15 × 14			1d. Scarlet		70	1·00
a.		Watermark inverted	..	9·00	7·00				
b.		Watermark sideways	..	45·00	38·00				
c.		Varnish ink ..	..	£2000					
d.		Broken wreath at left				*s.*	Imperf. Optd. "Specimen",		
		(Pl. 4, R. 19/12)	..	65·00			Type 30	..	..
e.		CO joined (Pl. 2, R. 19/11) ..		75·00		*t.*	"Cancelled", Type 33	£110	
f.		1829 for 1929 and closed				*u.*	"Cancelled", Type 33P ..	50·00	
		loop on 2 (Pl. 1, R. 2/3)	..	£150					
NCom7	436	**N19**	15 × 14			1½d. Purple-brown		60	90
a.		Watermark inverted	..	7·50	4·50				
b.		Watermark sideways	..	22·00	21·00				
c.		1829 for 1929 (R. 2/5)	..	£300		*f.*	Blob on ES (sideways coil)	50·00	
d.		Q for O in UNION				*s.*	Imperf. optd. "Specimen",		
		(booklet pane R. 2/1)	..	£225			Type 30	..	..
e.		Blob on 1 of 1929 (Pl. 6,				*t.*	"Cancelled", Type 33 ..	£100	
		R. 16/1)	..	..	£150	*u.*	"Cancelled", Type 33P ..	40·00	
NCom8	437	**N20**	15 × 14			2½d. (1) Blue		5·00	9·00
a.		Watermark inverted					(2) Pale blue	15·00	5·50
		Shade (1) ..	..	£600	£350				
		Shade (2) ..	..	£600	£350				
s.		Imperf. optd. "Specimen",				*t.*	"Specimen", Type 32 ..		
		Type 30 ..	..	..					

First Day Cover (NCom5/8) ..	..	£500
Sheets of notepaper with London		
address of P.U.C. franked with		
NCom5/8 cancelled with official		
First Day postmark	..	£750

The inverted watermarks listed above come from booklets. Inverted watermarks from sheets command a substantial premium over the above prices but they need to have sheet margins attached or to be in a block or strip of larger size or different shape to prove that they were not from booklet panes of six (3 × 2).

The stamps with watermark sideways come from coils.

NCom6*d*

NCom6*e*

NCom6*f*(1d.)

No. NCom6*f* is best collected as a positional piece to avoid confusion with over-inked examples.

NCom7*c* (1½d.)

NCom7*d* (1½d.)

NCom7*e* (1½d.)

Variety NCom7*d* exists with inverted watermark.

NCom7*f*

Controls

	I.	P.				I.	P.				I.	P.
½d.				**1½d.**					**2½d.**			
K 29	5·00	†		K 29	4·00	†		K 29	25·00	†
L 29	8·00	†		L 29	7·00	†		L 29	28·00	†
1d.												
K 29	4·00	†										
L 29	7·00	†										

Watermark varieties known:
Wmk inverted: ½d. K 29, L 29; 1d. K 29; 1½d. K 29, L 29; 2½d. K 29, L 29.

Booklet Panes of Six

From Booklets BB13 and BB25

NComB1 ½d. Watermark
upright 25·00
t. "Cancelled", Type 33 ..
u. "Cancelled", Type 33P .. £350

NComB1a ½d. Watermark
inverted 60·00
at. "Cancelled", Type 33 ..
au. "Cancelled", Type 33P .. £350

NComB2 1d. Watermark
　　　　upright   25·00
　t. " Cancelled ", Type 33 ..
　u. " Cancelled ", Type 33P .. £350

NComB3 1½d. Watermark
　　　　upright   15·00
　t. " Cancelled ", Type 33 ..
　u. " Cancelled ", Type 33P .. £300

NComB2a 1d. Watermark
　　　　inverted   60·00
　at. " Cancelled ", Type 33 ..
　au. " Cancelled " Type 33P .. £350

NComB3a 1½d. Watermark
　　　　inverted   50·00
　at. " Cancelled ", Type 33 ..
　au. " Cancelled ", Type 33P .. £300

NComB4/a (various advertisements)

Booklet Panes with Advertising Labels.

Panes of six, comprising two labels printed in *black* and four stamps

From Booklet BB13

NComB4 Watermark upright £130
　t. " Cancelled ", Type 33 ..
　u. " Cancelled ", Type 33P .. £600

NComB4a Watermark inverted £150
　at. " Cancelled ", Type 33 ..
　au. " Cancelled ", Type 33P .. £600

		Wmk Upright	Wmk Inverted
(1)	" Cash's washing Ribbons / J. & J. Cash Ltd. " ..	£130	£150
(2)	" Cleaver's Terebene / F. S. Cleaver & Sons Ltd. " ..	£130	£150
(3)	" Stamp Collectors / Desti Ltd. "	£130	£150
(4)	" Holiday trips £40 Tourist 3rd Cabin only [in three lines] / Atlantic Transport Line "	£130	£150
(5)	" Telephone Service / Air Mails, Letters & Parcels "	£130	£150

Coils

Vertical delivery printed in continuous reels

Code No.	Denomination	Number in roll	Face value	
G	½d.	480	£1.0.0	Top delivery
W	½d.	960	£2.0.0	Bottom delivery
Y	½d.	1920	£4.0.0	Bottom delivery
B	1d.	960	£4.0.0	Bottom delivery
E	1d.	480	£2.0.0	Top delivery
X	1d.	960	£4.0.0	Bottom delivery
Z	1d.	1920	£8.0.0	Bottom delivery
K	1½d.	960	£6.0.0	Bottom delivery
L	1½d.	480	£3.0.0	Top delivery

Sideways delivery printed in continuous reels with watermark sideways

P	½d.	480	£1.0.0	Left side delivery
O	1d.	480	£2.0.0	Left side delivery
N	1½d.	480	£3.0.0	Left side delivery

All the coils were issued from 10 May 1929.

Die Proofs

Head only
In black, uncleared, on card dated "15.1.29" ••   ••   ••   ••   ••   ••   •• £1750

(a)   (b)

(c)
(*Illustrations twice normal size*)

Progressive stages of master die for Linzell's design for 1d. and 1½d. in black on proof paper

(a) Crown is black and unfinished. Frame surrounds incomplete	£1750
(b) Left of Crown still uncompleted	£1750
(c) Completed master die, dated " January 22 1929 "	£2250

Completed die proofs, cleared

1d. in black on proof paper	£2750
1d. in red on wove paper, dated " 4.2.29 "	£3000
1½d. in black on proof paper	£2750
1½d. in pale brown on wove paper, dated " 4.2.29 "	£3000
1½d. in brown on proof paper, undated..	£2750

Plate Proofs

Specially prepared imperforate miniature sheet of four stamps on thin white glazed paper and mounted in sunken card frames for presentation purposes

½d. in green	.. ..	*Block of four* £3500
1d. in scarlet	.. ..	*Block of four* £3500
1½d. in purple-brown	.. ..	*Block of four* £3500
2½d. in blue	.. ..	*Block of four* £3500

Imprimaturs from the National Postal Museum Archives

Nos. NCom5/8 imperforate, watermark Type W15

Watermark upright (*set of* 4)

Nos. NCom5*b*/7*b* imperforate, watermark Type W15

Watermark sideways (*set of* 3)

Booklet panes of six. Imperforate, watermark Type W15

Two panes as No. NComB1 arranged horizontally *tête-bêche* with marginal pillars at right
As last but two panes as No. NComB2
As last but two panes as No. NComB3

Booklet pane of four with blank advertisement labels. Imperforate, watermark Type W15

Two panes as No. NComB4 arranged horizontally *tête-bêche* with marginal pillars at right

Plate Markings and Control Schedule

See the General Notes on the King Edward VII issues under " Plate Markings "

Plate No.	Description	Controls	
½d. Green			
1	½ dot (base) under 1st	K 29	L 29
2	½ dot (base) under 2nd	K 29	L 29
3	½ dot (top) under 3rd	K 29	L 29
4	Dot 20th left side 7 mm.	K 29	L 29
5	Dot 19th left side 7 mm.	K 29	L 29
6	Dot (inner) 19th left side 20 mm.	K 29	L 29
8	Large dot (breaking top) under 4th	K 29	L 29
1d. Scarlet			
1	Dot 1st left side; scoop 19th right side; dot 20th right side	K 29	L 29
2	Dot 2nd left side; minute dot 20th right side 10 mm.	K 29	L 29
3	Dot 3rd left side; vertical crack 19th left side	K 29	L 29
4	Dot 4th left side; tiny dot 2nd left side; dot 5th right side 21½ mm. (The rules 19th and 20th right side are thicker than those of plate 3)	K 29	L 29
1½d. Purple-brown			
1	Dot 1st left side	K 29	L 29
2	Dot 2nd left side; ½ cut top at right of 3rd	K 29	L 29
3	Dot 3rd left side; internal score 20th left side	K 29	L 29
4	Dot 4th left side; base of 3rd slightly ragged	K 29	L 29
5	Large dot above 1st top row; ½ cut (base) at right of 2nd	K 29	L 29
6	Large dot above 2nd top row	K 29	L 29
2½d. Blue			
1	½ dot (inner) 20th left side	K 29	L 29
2a	No marking	K 29	
2b	Added ½ dot (outer) 19th left side	K 29	L 29

It is not yet possible to correlate philatelic plate descriptions with the official plate numbers.

Quantities Sold ½p. 677,500,000; 1d. 341,000,000; 1½d. 751,250,000; 2½d. 26,750,000

N21   **W18**

(Des. Harold Nelson. Eng. J. A. C Harrison)

B. 1929 (MAY 10) Recess-printed Issue

Recess-printed by Bradbury, Wilkinson & Co. from a plate of their own manuacture in sheets of twenty (five rows of four). Watermark Type **W18**.

Cat. No.	S.G. No.	Type	Perforation	Description		Unused	Used
NCom9	438	**N21**	Line 12	£1 Black		£650	£450
s.	"Specimen ", Type 32 in						
	red		£750				

First Day Cover (NCom9)	£2000
First Day Cover (NCom5/9)	£2500
Sheets of notepaper with London address of P.U.C. franked with NCom5/9 cancelled with official First Day postmark	£3000

Most of the stamps in the sheet show traces of guide (hair) lines used when laying down the plate.

The contract for printing this stamp was only given to Bradbury, Wilkinson on condition that it was engraved by J. A. C. Harrison, at that time contracted to Waterlow & Sons who gave special permission for him to do the work.

Essays

Artist's drawings by Harold Nelson   ..   ..   *From* £500

Proof

From a specially prepared block of four stamps. Imperf. on thin white card ..   .. *Each stamp*   £2000

Quantity Sold 61,000

N22

N23

N24

N25

(Des. Barnett Freedman)

1935 (MAY 7) SILVER JUBILEE
Printed in photogravure by Harrison & Sons in sheets of 120 stamps (20 rows of 6).

Three different multipositives were used for the ½d., 1d. and 1½d. Type I was used for sheet stamps. Types II (inverted watermark) and III (upright watermark) were used for booklet printings.

Differences between the types:—

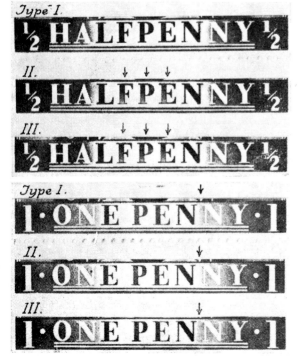

"FPE" with solid shading

"FPE" solid shading at top, lightly shaded at base

As Type II but frame lines below "HALFPENNY" thinner

Wide shading between "NN"

Narrow shading between "NN"

Wide shading between "NN", deeper shading in fleur-de-lis and surround than in Types I or II

Type I.

SILVER JUBILEE

Top frame lines thick

II.

SILVER JUBILEE

Top frame lines thin

III. ↓

SILVER JUBILEE

As Type II but upper
line thickened
above " JU "

Cat. No.	S.G. No.	Type	Perforation		Description	Unused	Used
NCom10	453	**N22**	15 × 14		½d. green (Type I)	50	20
a.	Type II (inv. wmk.)	..	4·00	1·25			
b.	Type III	..	5·00	1·25	*t.* " Cancelled ", Type 28P ..		
s.	" Specimen ", Type 23	..			*u.* " Cancelled ", Type 33P ..	50·00	
NCom11	454	**N23**	15 × 14		1d. Scarlet (Type I)	75	90
a.	Type II (inv. wmk.)..	..	4·00	1·25			
b.	Type III	..	5·00	1·25	*s.* " Specimen ", Type 23 ..		
c.	Repair below I of SILVER				*t.* " Cancelled ", Type 28P ..		
	(Cyl. 37, R. 2/2 cyl. pane) ..				*u.* " Cancelled ", Type 33P ..	50·00	
NCom12	455	**N24**	15 × 14		1½d. Red-brown (Type I)	50	20
a.	Type II (inv. wmk.)..	..	2·00	75			
b.	Type III	..	2·50	75			
c.	White dot after E (booklet				*u.* " Cancelled ", Type 28P ..		
	pane R. 1/1)	..	55·00		*v.* " Cancelled ", Type 33P ..	40·00	
s.	" Specimen ", Type 23	..					
t.	" Cancelled ", Type 28	..					
NCom13	456	**N25**	15 × 14		2½d. Blue	↓3·00	5·50
a.	Retouch to left panel and						
	top of 2½ (Cyl. 34., R.17/1)..	15·00					
s.	" Specimen ", Type 23	..					
NCom14	456*a*	**N25**	15 × 14		2½d. Prussian blue	£4000	£3750

> First Day Cover* (NCom10/13)   £350

*The price quoted is for the illustrated commemorative cover. Plain envelopes are worth less than the
figure quoted.

For a long time it was thought that the 2½d. Prussian blue came from colour trials but
it has now been proved that this could not be so as the issued stamps are in the normal
size of 38·4 × 22 mm. whereas the colour trials were printed from a different cylinder
producing stamps size 38·75 × 22·25 mm. The logical assumption is that the three sheets
came from the beginning of a printing for which the wrong ink was used and that after this
was discovered and rectified the faulty sheets got into the ordinary supply instead of being
destroyed. The sheets were issued at a post office in Edmonton.

Nos. NCom10/11 are known postmarked on 6 May at Pembury, Tunbridge Wells, one
day prior to the official first day of issue.

NCom11c (1d.)

NCom12c (1½d.)

NCom13a   Normal

The panel has been considerably
deepened and the retouch extends downwards
to the top of the figures "2½"

Controls and Cylinder Numbers (Blocks of Six)

All the following are found only with control W 35.

Descriptions of the Perforation Types will be found in Appendix 1. Type 5A is Type 5 but with the extension hole missing from the left margin.

							Perf. Type				
Value	Cyl. No.						5 No dot	5A No dot	5 Dot	6 No dot	6B Dot
½d.	18	..	..	..	..	..	2·50	2·50	2·50	2·25	2·25
	20*	..	..	..	..	..	—	†	†	†	†
	47	..	..	..	..	..	†	†	†	5·00	5·00
	55	..	..	..	..	..	2·25	2·75	2·25	2·50	2·50
	60	..	..	..	..	..	2·50	10·00	2·50	2·25	2·25
	61	..	..	..	..	..	2·75	9·00	2·75	2·50	2·50
	62	..	..	..	..	..	7·50	7·50	7·00	†	†
1d.	14	..	..	..	..	..	7·00	7·00	7·00	7·00	7·00
	22	..	..	..	..	..	8·00	12·00	8·00	8·00	8·00
1½d.	2*	..	..	..	..	..	†	—	†	†	†
	7	..	..	..	..	..	4·00	10·00	4·00	3·50	3·50
	21	..	..	..	..	..	4·00	3·50	3·50	3·50	3·50
	27	..	..	..	..	..	—	—	—	10·00	10·00
	48	..	..	..	..	..	3·50	3·50	3·50	3·50	3·50
2½d.	34	..	..	..	..	..	45·00	35·00	35·00	†	†

*Asterisks against cylinder numbers 2 and 20 indicate that they are "abnormals" (see under "printing" in the General Notes to Section ND).

The 1½d. cylinder 7 dot is known with Perforation Type 5 but with two extension holes in the left margin.

Four controls of the 2½d. Prussian blue exist. Two with no dot cylinder from the normal position and two examples with dot cylinder. Both dot examples come from the *right* of the no dot pane, the sheets having been divided by hand leaving the full interpane margin attached to the left pane. One of these exists as a single and the other in a strip of three.

Booklet Panes of Four
From Booklets BB16 and BB28

Type III

NComB5 ½d. Watermark
      upright   25·00
   s. " Cancelled ", Type 33P ..
   t. " Cancelled ", Type 33   ..

NComB6 1d. Watermark
      upright   25·00
   s. " Cancelled ", Type 33P ..
   t. " Cancelled ", Type 33   ..

NComB7 1½d. Watermark
      upright   12·00
   s. " Cancelled ", Type 33P ..

Type II

NComB5a ½d. Watermark
      inverted   30·00
   as. " Cancelled ", Type 33P ..

NComB6a 1d. Watermark
      inverted   30·00
   as. " Cancelled ", Type 33P ..

NComB7a 1½d. Watermark
      inverted   15·00
   as. " Cancelled ", Type 33P ..
   at. " Cancelled ", Type 33 ..

Booklet Cylinder Numbers
Panes of four
Perforation Type B1 (E)

Value	Cyl. No.				Value	Cyl. No.			
½d.	33	..	..	40·00	1½d.	30	..	..	28·00
	35	..	..	40·00		41	..	..	28·00
1d.	26	..	..	—		58	..	..	£250
	37	..	..	45·00*		59	..	..	28·00
						66	..	..	28·00

These were printed from double pane cylinders but after the panes were separated the interpane gutter containing the dot cylinder number was removed, so that only no dot cylinder panes survive.

*Contains the listed variety No. NCom 11c.

Essays

Artists' drawings in various designs   ..   .. *From* £600

A number of hand-painted essays by various artists were submitted.

Three designs by Barnett Freedman were selected and Harrisons were asked to produce essays in photogravure of three of them. They were all submitted for the 1½d. value, each set in the colours that were accepted plus the Prussian blue colour on unwatermarked paper, imperforate and mounted on card. They were numbered 1, 2, 3 and 4. The King accepted No. 4 but rejected the Prussian blue colour.

No. 1

No. 2

Design No. 1. As No. 1 but reduced to 25 × 30½ mm.
   Card containing 1½d. in yellow-green, scarlet, red-brown, Prussian blue and ultramarine ..

Design No. 2. As No. 1
   Card containing 1½d. in yellow-green, scarlet, red-brown, Prussian blue and ultramarine ..

Design No. 3. As No. 2
   Card containing 1½d. in yellow-green, scarlet, red-brown, Prussian blue and ultramarine ..

Design No. 4 (the accepted design)
   Card containing 1½d. in yellow-green, scarlet, red-brown, Prussian blue and ultramarine ..

Colour Trials

Special cylinders were used for the colour trials as they are larger than the issued stamps and show some slight differences in the shading.

Imperforate, watermarked, each gummed on soft card about 4 in. × 3 in. and dated 15th or 18th January 1935 on the back in pencil

½d. in green size 39 × 22·5 mm. instead of 38·4 × 22 mm. ..   ..
1d. in scarlet size as above   ..   ..
2½d. in Prussian blue size 38·75 × 22·25 mm. instead of 38·4 × 22 mm.   ..   ..   ..

Imprimaturs from the National Postal Museum Archives

Nos. NCom10/13 imperforate, watermark Type W15

Watermark upright (*set of* 4)

Booklet panes of four. Imperforate, watermark Type W15

Two panes as No. NComB5 arranged horizontally *tête-bêche*
One pane as No. NComB5a (wmk. inverted) with interpane margins at sides

Two panes as No. NComB6 arranged horizontally *tête-bêche*
One pane as No. NComB6 (wmk. upright) with interpane margins at sides

Two panes as No. NComB7 arranged horizontally *tête-bêche*
One pane as No. NComB7 (wmk. upright) with interpane margins at sides

Cancelled overprints from the National Postal Museum Archives

Booklet panes of four. Perf. 15 × 14, watermark Type W15

As No. NComB5a (wmk. inverted) with each stamp overprinted "Cancelled". Type 28 twice

As No. NComB6 (wmk. upright) with each stamp overprinted "Cancelled", Type 28 twice

As No. NComB7a (wmk. inverted) with each stamp overprinted "Cancelled", Type 28 twice

Quantities Sold (including those in booklets)

½d. 353,400,000; 1d. 150,400,000; 1½d. 490,000,000; 2½d. 14,200,000

German Propaganda Forgeries

Stamps designed in the style of the 1935 Silver Jubilee exist showing Stalin in the centre and dated 1939–1944.

KING GEORGE V MEMORIAL ESSAY

(*Illustration twice normal size*)

It was proposed to issue a stamp with a face value of 1½d. to be sold at 3d, the premium being devoted to King George's Jubilee Trust. After consideration the project was abandoned but a few of the essays exist. An example on a letter from King George's Jubilee Trust states that only eight of these stamps were proofed. We believe this to mean that only eight were stuck on letters.

From a plate of 6 (3 × 2) made by Harrison & Sons and proofed by Sir Donald Banks on gummed chalk-surfaced paper watermarked Type **W16**, in black.

Imperforate

Single on correct letter endorsed in M/S "Donald Banks" etc.	
Single off letter endorsed "2 CB"	£250
Block of six, one endorsed "2 CB"	£1350

Perf. 15 × 14

Single on correct letter endorsed "2 C" in pencil on back .. ..

The King Edward VIII Issue

SECTION P

INTRODUCTION. During the brief reign of King Edward VIII only the four most commonly used values were issued: ½d., 1d., 1½d. and 2½d. By contrast to previous definitive issues the design was kept extremely simple and was very suitable for reproduction by photogravure. It was suggested by H. J. Brown and the portrait was taken from a photograph by Hugh Cecil.

The stamps were watermarked Type **W19** and photogravure-printed by Harrison & Sons in sheets of 240 (20 horizontal rows of 12). They were perforated 15 × 14.

See also the information on photogravure printing in the General Notes on the King George V photogravure issues and the information on coil stamps in the General Notes on the King George V typographed issues.

Withdrawal dates are given for the sheet stamps but the booklets and the coils were not recalled because of delays in introducing the King George VI stamps in booklet and coil formats. The King Edward VIII booklets remained on sale until December 1937 and the coils were recalled on 5 January 1938.

CHECKLIST OF KING EDWARD VIII ISSUE

Description						Spec. Cat. Nos.	S.G. Nos.	Page
½d.	..	..	..	..	..	P1	457	294
1d.	..	..	..	..	..	P2	458	295
1½d.	..	..	..	..	..	P3	459	296
2½d.	..	..	..	..	..	P4	460	298

CHECKLIST OF KING EDWARD VIII BOOKLET PANES

Spec. Cat. Nos.	Description	From Booklets Nos.	Listed Below Cat. No.	Page
PB1, PB1a	6 × ½d.	BC2–4	P1	294
PB2, PB2a	6 × 1d.	BC2–4	P2	295
PB3, PB3a	6 × 1½d.	BC2–4	P3	296
PB4, PB4a	2 × 1½d.	BC1	P3	296
PB5, PB5a	4 × 1½d. and two printed labels	BC2, BC4	P3	297

UNUSED PRICE QUOTATIONS. Unused prices quoted in this Section are for mint unmounted examples.

W19

P1

Cat. No.	S.G. No.			Shades	Mint	Used

1936 (SEPTEMBER 1). ½d. GREEN, TYPE P1

P1	457			Green	20 ✓	12 ✓

a.	Watermark inverted ..	4·50 ✓	1·60 ✓		
b.	Pearl beside crown (Cyl. 7				
	Dot, 10 Dot or 12 Dot,				
	R.20/2)	8·00 ✓		s.	"Specimen", Type 30 ..
c.	White spot over T (Cyl. 25			t.	"Cancelled", Type 33P ..	7·00
	Dot, R. 1/6)			u.	"Cancelled", Type 33 ..	24·00
d.	Double impression			v.	"Specimen", Type 32 ..

Cyl. 7, 19 Dot P1b   Cyl. 12 Dot   P1c

Later states of No. P1b from re-chromed cylinders show the flaw very faintly

Controls and Cylinder Numbers (Blocks of Six)

Perforation Type 5 on both dot and no dot cylinders

Cyl. No.	Control	No dot	Dot	Cyl.	Control	No dot	Dot	Cyl. No.	Control	No dot	Dot
2*	A 36	†	—	12	A 36	2·00	12·00	21	A 37	2·00	2·00
4	A 36	4·00	4·00	13	A 36	2·00	2·00	22	A 37	2·00	2·00
5	A 36	2·50	2·50	15	A 36	2·00	2·00	24	A 37	2·00	2·00
7	A 36	2·00	12·00 ✓	16	A 36	2·00	2·00	25	A 37	2·00	2·00
10	A 36	2·00	12·00					26	A 37	2·00	2·00

Perforation Types 2 (no dot cylinder) and 2A (dot cylinder)

7	A 36	10·00	14·00*	10	A 36	10·00	14·00*	

*Asterisks against cylinder numbers indicate that they are "abnormals" (see under "Printing" in the General Notes to Section NC). Asterisks against prices for cylinder blocks indicate that they contain a listed variety.

Booklet Panes of Six

From Booklets BC2/4

PB1	Watermark upright	7·00		PB1a	Watermark inverted	30·00
s.	"Cancelled", Type 33P ..	45·00		as.	"Cancelled", Type 33P ..	45·00
u.	"Cancelled", Type 33 ..	£150		au.	"Cancelled", Type 33 ..	£150

Booklet Cylinder Numbers

Panes of six

							Perf. Type			
						B3(I)	B3A(P)	B4(E)	B4(I)	B4(B(E)
Cyl No.						No dot	Dot	No dot	Dot	Dot
E 2 ..	..	..	..	..	..	..	—	—	9·00	9·00	18·00
E 4 ..	..	..	..	..	..	..	†	†	12·00	12·00	†

Coils

Vertical delivery printed in continuous reels

Code No.	Issued	Number in roll	Face value	
D	1937	960	£2.0.0	Bottom delivery
G	1937	480	£1.0.0	Bottom delivery
W	1937	960	£2.0.0	Bottom delivery
Y	1937	1920	£4.0.0	Bottom delivery

Imprimaturs from the National Postal Museum Archives

Imperforate, watermark Type W19

Watermark upright
Watermark inverted
Tête-bêche pair
Tête-bêche pair with vertical gutter margin

Quantity Sold 1,739,250,000

Withdrawn 29.7.37

Cat. No.	S.G. No.			Shades		Mint	Used

1936 (SEPTEMBER 14). 1d. SCARLET, TYPE P1

P2	458			Scarlet			25 ✓	50 ✓
a.	Watermark inverted	..	4·50 ✓	1·00 ✓				
b.	Scar on cheek (Cyl. 3 No							
	dot, R. 13/7)	30·00						
s.	"Specimen", Type 30 ..				u.	"Cancelled", Type 33P ..	7·00	
t.	"Specimen", Type 32 ..				v.	"Cancelled", Type 33 ..	24·00	

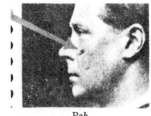

P2*b*

Controls and Cylinder Numbers (Blocks of Six)

Perforation Type 5 on both dot and no dot cylinders

Cyl. No.	Control	No dot	Dot	Cyl. No.	Control	No dot	Dot	Cyl. No.	Control	No dot	Dot
2	A 36	2·00	2·00	5	A 36	3·25	3·25	13	A 37	3·25	3·25
3	A 36	2·00	2·00	6	A 36	2·00	2·00	14	A 37	4·00	4·00
4	A 36	2·00	2·00								

Perforation Types 2 (no dot cylinder) and 2A (dot cylinder)

3	A 36	†	—	5	A 36	†	30·00	7*	A 36	—	†
4	A 36	—	†	6	A 36	—	—				

Booklet Panes of Six

From Booklets BC2/4

PB2	Watermark upright	7·00		PB2a	Watermark inverted	30·00
s.	"Cancelled", Type 33P ..	45·00		as.	"Cancelled", Type 33P ..	45·00
u.	"Cancelled", Type 33 ..	£150		au.	"Cancelled", Type 33 ..	£150

Booklet Cylinder Numbers

Panes of six

			Perf. Type			
		B3(I)	B3A(P)	B4(E)	B4A(I)	B4B(E)
Cyl. No.		No dot	Dot	No dot	Dot	Dot
F3	10·00	20·00	8·00	8·00	10·00
F6*	†	†	†	—	†

Coils

Vertical delivery printed in continuous reels

Code No.	Issued	Number in roll	Face value	
B	1937	960	£4.0.0	Bottom delivery
E	1937	480	£2.0.0	Bottom delivery
X	1937	960	£4.0.0	Bottom delivery
Z	1937	1920	£8.0.0	Bottom delivery

Imprimaturs from the National Postal Museum Archives

Imperforate, watermark Type W19

Watermark upright
Watermark inverted
Tête-bêche pair
Tête-bêche pair with vertical gutter margin

Quantity Sold 717,000,000

Withdrawn 29.7.37

Cat. No.	S.G. No.			Shades	Mint	Used

1936 (SEPTEMBER 1). 1½d. RED-BROWN, TYPE P1

P3   459   Red-brown   25 ✓   12 ✓

    a. Watermark inverted   ..   90 ✓ 90 ✓

    b. Hair flaw (Cyl. 2 No dot,   *s.* "Specimen", Type 30   ..

        R.18/1) .. ..   ..   15·00 ✓   *t.* "Cancelled", Type 33P   ..   6·00

    c. Ditto, retouched   ..   ..   20·00 ✓   *u.* "Cancelled", Type 33   ..   20·00

    d. Imperforate (pair) ..   ..   — †   *v.* "Specimen", Type 32   ..

†No. P3*d* exists from NPM archive sales.

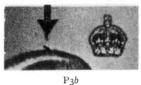   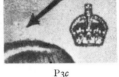

                P3*b*   P3*c*

The 1½d. in the issued colour imperforate on gummed paper with the word " PROOF " instead of " POSTAGE " is regarded as a bogus item.

Controls and Cylinder Numbers (Blocks of Six)

Perforation Type 5 on both dot and no dot cylinders

Cyl. No.	Control	No dot	Dot	Cyl. No.	Control	No dot	Dot	Cyl. No.	Control	No dot	Dot
2	A 36	15·00 ✓✓	2·00	12	A 36	2·00	2·00	16	A 36	2·00	2·00
4	A 36	2·00	2·00	12	A 37	9·00	9·00	16	A 37	2·25	2·25
6	A 36	2·00	2·00	13	A 36	2·00	2·00	17	A 37	2·25	2·25
8	A 36	2·00	2·00	13	A 37	2·00	2·00	18*	A 37	—	†
9	A 36	2·00	2·00	15	A 36	4·00	4·00	20	A 37	2·00	2·00
				15	A 37	2·00	2·00				

Perforation Types 2 (no dot cylinder) and 2A (dot cylinder)

2	A 36	—*	—	8	A 36	†	17·00	12	A 36	6·00	6·00
4	A 36	—	6·00	9	A 36	—	†				

Cylinder 12 dot (A 36) is known with Perforation Type 2 (Reverse feed)

Perforation Types 6 (no dot cylinder) and 6B (dot cylinder)

15	A 37	—	—	20	A 37	3·00	3·00

Booklet Panes of Six

From Booklets BC2/4

PB3   Watermark upright   7·00   PB3a   Watermark inverted   10·00

  s. "Cancelled", Type 33P ..   40·00   *as.* "Cancelled", Type 33P ..   40·00

  u. "Cancelled", Type 33 .. £130   *au.* "Cancelled", Type 33 .. £130

Booklet Panes of Two

From Booklet BC1

PB4 Watermark upright   3·00   PB4a Watermark inverted   3·00

The cylinder used to print Nos. PB4/4a was G7 and the cylinder number did not appear in the finished booklets. The selvedge was perforated through.

PB5/a (various advertisements) (imperf. margin)

Booklet Panes with Advertising Labels

Panes of six comprising two labels printed in *black* and four stamps

From Booklets BC2 and BC4

PB5 Watermark upright 35·00	PB5a Watermark inverted 35·00
s. " Cancelled ", Type 33P .. 50·00	*as.* " Cancelled ", Type 33P .. 50·00
t. "Cancelled", Type 33 ..	

	Wmk Upright	Wmk Inverted
(1) " Cash's " Lose Less Linen " book / Free booklet. J. & J. Cash " (*numbered* 364)	35·00	35·00
(2) " Cash's names for marking all linen / Free booklet. J. & J. Cash " (*numbered* 372) ..	35·00	35·00
(3) " Cash's satin lingerie ribbons / Samples [in text] of Cash's ribbons. " Attach this to a ". J. & J. Cash " (*numbered* 357 *or* 379)	28·00	28·00
(4) " Number One Bond / Castell Bros. " (*numbered* 368) ..	35·00	35·00
(5) " Ruskin Linen / Castell Bros." (*numbered* 374) ..	35·00	35·00
(6) " Kargo. 2/6 per pack. / Castell Bros." (*numbered* 355)..	35·00	35·00
(7) " Drages 50 per-way / Free book. Drages " (*numbered* 17, 367, 373, 378, 380, 381, 382 *or* 384)	28·00	28·00
(8) " Everitt's / Everitt's " (*numbered* 371) ..	35·00	35·00
(9) " For Safety of Capital / Century Fixed Trust (see last page) " (*numbered* 359)	28·00	28·00
(10) " For Safety of Capital / Universal Fixed Trust (see last page) " (*numbered* 356, 358 *or* 360)	28·00	28·00
(11) " Spread your Capital / Century Fixed Trust " [text on both panes diagonal] (*numbered* 361 *or* 363)	28·00	28·00
(12) " Spread your Capital / Universal Fixed Trust " [text on both labels diagonal] (*numbered* 362)	28·00	28·00
(13) " Stamp Collectors / Chas. Nissen " (*numbered* 362) ..	35·00	35·00
(14) " Saving is Simple / Home Safe " (*numbered* 365, 369, 375 *or* 383)	22·00	22·00
(15) " Come on the telephone / Air Mails, letters and parcels " (*numbered* 16, 366, 376, *or* 385)	22·00	22·00
(16) " Your friends are on the telephone / Air Mails, letters and parcels " (*numbered* 370 *or* 377)	22·00	22·00

The numbers printed in brackets refer to the edition numbers of the booklets in which the panes were issued.   Pane Nos. PB5(1), (2) and (3) were printed with numbers on the advert label. See Appendix 2.

All these panes can be found with a perforated margin showing both upright and inverted watermarks, from the central gutters of the two panes.

Booklet Cylinder Numbers

Panes of six

							Perf. Type				
							B3(I) No dot	B3A(P) Dot	B4(E) No dot	B4A(I) Dot	B4B(E) Dot
Cyl. No.											
G 4	..	..	..	..	..		†	—	13·00	12·00	—
G 5 (i)	..	..	..	..	..		—	10·00	5·00	5·00	9·00
G 5 (ii)	..	..	..	..	..		10·00	†	6·00	†	†

State (ii) of G 5 shows two faint horizontal lines in the margin at left of stamp No. 1.

Panes of six including two labels

Cyl. No.	Advert. No.	Perf. Types B4(E) No dot	B4A(I) Dot	B4B(E) Dot
G 7	PB5(1)	45·00	45·00	†
G 7	PB5(2)	45·00	45·00	†
G 7	PB5(3) (No. 357) ..	40·00	40·00	†
G 7	PB5(3) (No. 379) ..	40·00	40·00	†
G 7	PB5(4)	45·00	45·00	†
G 7	PB5(5)	45·00	45·00	55·00
G 7	PB5(6)	45·00	45·00	†
G 7	PB5(7)	40·00	40·00	45·00
G 7	PB5(8)	45·00	45·00	†
G 7	PB5(9)	40·00	40·00	†
G 7	PB5(10)	40·00	40·00	†
G 7	PB5(11)	40·00	40·00	†
G 7	PB5(12)	40·00	40·00	†
G 7	PB5(13)	45·00	45·00	†
G 7	PB5(14)	28·00	28·00	28·00
G 7	PB5(15)	28·00	28·00	28·00
G 7	PB5(16)	28·00	28·00	28·00

Imprimaturs from the National Postal Museum Archives

Imperforate, watermark Type W19

Watermark upright
Watermark inverted
Tête-bêche pair
Tête-bêche pair with vertical gutter margin
Tête-bêche pair with wide vertical gutter margin

Specimen overprints from the National Postal Museum Archives

Booklet pane of six. Perf. 15 × 14, watermark Type W19 (inverted)

"Specimen", Type 32 and upper left stamp with punch hole

Quantity Sold 1,814,250,000

Withdrawn 29.7.37

Cat. No.	S.G. No.	Shades	Mint	Used
1936 (SEPTEMBER 1). 2½d. BRIGHT BLUE, TYPE P1				
P4	460	Bright blue	25 ✓	50 ✓

a. Flaw in ear (Cyl. 2 Dot, R. 13/12) .. .. .. 15·00
b. Coil join (vert. pr.) (1937)
c. Coil join (horiz. pr.) (1937)
s. "Specimen", Type 30 ..
t. "Cancelled", Type 33 ..

P4*a*

Controls and Cylinder Numbers (Blocks of Six)

Perforation Type 5 on both dot and no dot cylinders

Cyl. No.	Control	No dot	Dot	Cyl. No.	Control	No dot	Dot
2	A 36	3·25	3·25	2	A 36 bar —	2·00	2·00

Coils

Vertical delivery made up from sheets with joins every 20th stamp

Code No.	Issued	Number in roll	Face value	
F	1937	960	£10.0.0	Bottom delivery

Sideways delivery made up from sheets with joins every 12th stamp

M	1937	480	£5.0.0	Left side delivery

Imprimatur from the National Postal Museum Archives

Imperforate, watermark Type W19

Watermark upright

Quantity Sold 32,000,000

Withdrawn 29.7.37

The King George VI Issues

CHECKLIST OF KING GEORGE VI ISSUES

Description	Spec. Cat. Nos.	S.G. Nos.	Page
1937–47 Photogravure Definitives, Original Colours			
½d. green	Q1	462	303
1d. scarlet	Q4	463	309
1½d. red-brown	Q7	464	319
2d. orange	Q10	465	326
2½d. ultramarine	Q13	466	330
3d. violet	Q16	467	336
4d. grey-green	Q19	468	338
5d.	Q21	469	340
6d.	Q22	470	341
7d.	Q23	471	342
8d.	Q24	472	344
9d.	Q25	473	344
10d.	Q26	474	345
11d.	Q27	474a	345
1s.	Q28	475	346
1937 Coronation of King George VI			
1½d.	QCom1	476	354
1939–48 Recess-Printed "Arms" High Values			
2s. 6d. brown	Q29	476	347
2s. 6d. yellow-green	Q30	476a	348
5s.	Q31	477	349
10s. dark blue	Q32	478	350
10s. ultramarine	Q33	478a	351
£1	Q34	478b	351
1940 Centenary of First Adhesive Postage Stamps			
½d.	QCom2	479	356
1d.	QCom3	480	356
1½d.	QCom4	481	356
2d.	QCom5	482	356
2½d.	QCom6	483	356
3d.	QCom7	484	356
1941–42 Photogravure Definitives, Lighter Colours			
½d. pale green	Q2	485	305
1d. pale scarlet	Q5	486	311
1½d. pale red-brown	Q8	487	322
2d. pale orange	Q11	488	327
2½d. light ultramarine	Q14	489	332
3d. pale violet	Q17	490	336
1946 Victory			
2½d.	QCom8	491	357
3d.	QCom9	492	357
1948 Silver Wedding			
2½d.	QCom10	493	359
£1	QCom11	494	359
1948 Channel Islands Liberation			
1d.	QCom12	C1	360
2½d.	QCom13	C2	360

Description	Spec. Cat. Nos.	S.G. Nos	Page
	1948 Olympics		
2½d.	QCom14	495	361
3d.	QCom15	496	361
4d.	QCom16	497	361
1s.	QCom17	498	361
	1949 Universal Postal Union		
2½d.	QCom18	499	363
3d.	QCom19	500	363
6d.	QCom20	501	363
1s.	QCom21	502	363
	1950–51 Photogravure Definitives, New Colours		
½d. pale orange	Q3	503	307
1d. light ultramarine	Q6	504	314
1½d. pale green	Q9	505	323
2d. pale red-brown	Q12	506	328
2½d. pale scarlet	Q15	507	335
4d. light ultramarine	Q20	508	338
	1951 Recess-Printed "Festival" High Values		
2s. 6d.	Q35	509	352
5s.	Q36	510	352
10s.	Q37	511	352
£1	Q38	512	353
	1951 Festival of Britain		
2½d.	QCom22	513	364
4d.	QCom23	514	364

CHECKLIST OF KING GEORGE VI BOOKLET PANES

Spec. Cat. Nos.	Description	From Booklets Nos.	Listed Below Cat. No.	Page
QB1, QB1a	6 × ½d. green	BD11–15, BD21–25	Q1	304
QB2, QB2a	4 × ½d. green, wmk. sideways	BD3–3a	Q1	304
QB3, QB3a	2 × ½d. green	BD2–2a	Q1	304
QB4, QB4a	6 × ½d. pale green	BD16–18, BD26–29	Q2	306
QB5, QB5a	4 × ½d. pale green	BD6–6a	Q2	306
QB6	2 × ½d. pale green	BD4	Q2	306
QB7, QB7a	6 × ½d. pale orange	BD19–20, BD30–32, F1–13, H1–5	Q3	307
QB8–8b	4 × ½d. pale orange	BD7–BD10	Q3	308
QB9	2 × ½d. pale orange	BD5	Q3	308
QB10, QB10a	6 × 1d. scarlet	BD11–12, BD21–24	Q4	309
QB11, QB11a	4 × 1d. scarlet, wmk. sideways	BD3–3a	Q4	309
QB12, QB12a	2 × 1d. scarlet	BD2–2a	Q4	309
QB13, QB13a	4 × 1d. pale scarlet Type II	BD6–6a	Q5A	313
QB14, QB14a	2 × 1d. pale scarlet Type I or II	BD4	Q5A	313
QB15, QB15a	6 × 1d. light ultramarine, Type 1c	BD32, H1–6	Q6D	315
QB16, QB16a	4 × 1d. light ultramarine Type II	BD7–7a	Q6D	315
QB16b, QB16c	4 × 1d. light ultramarine Type Ia	BD8–10	Q6D	315
QB17	2 × 1d. light ultramarine Type II	BD5	Q6D	315
QB18–20a	3 × 1d. light ultramarine and three printed labels Type Ib	BD20, BD31, F1–14	Q6D	315
QB21, QB21a	6 × 1½d. red-brown	BD11–12, BD21–24	Q7	320
QB22, QB22a	2 × 1½d. red-brown	BD1–1a, BD2–2a	Q7	320
QB23, QB23a	4 × 1½d. red-brown and two printed labels	BD11–12, BD23–24	Q7	320
QB24, QB24a	4 × 1½d. pale red-brown	BD6–6a	Q8	323
QB25	2 × 1½d. pale red-brown	BD4	Q8	323
QB26, QB26a	6 × 1½d. pale green	BD20, BD31–32	Q9	324
QB27–27b	4 × 1½d. pale green	BD7–10	Q9	324
QB28	2 × 1½d. pale green	BD5	Q9	324
QB29, QB29a	6 × 2d. orange	BD13–15, BD25	Q10	326
QB30, QB30a	6 × 2d. pale orange	BD16–18, BD26–29	Q11	327
QB31, QB31a	6 × 2d. pale red-brown	BD19, BD30, BD32, H1–7	Q12	329
QB32, QB32a	6 × 2½d. ultramarine	BD13–15, BD25	Q13	330
QB33, QB33a	6 × 2½d. light ultramarine	BD16–18, BD26–29	Q14	333
QB34, QB34a	6 × 2½d. pale scarlet	BD19–20, BD30–32	Q15	335

General Notes on the Photogravure Low Values (1937–51)

INTRODUCTION. The abdication, on 10 December 1936, placed the Post Office in a difficult position as the date fixed for the Coronation of King George VI on 12 May 1937, was the date originally chosen for his predecessor. The Post Office had been told by the King that the new stamps "should follow generally the design of the recent Edwardian issue, but that he desires that they should be somewhat more ornamental". Several artists were invited to submit designs in January 1937, but on 13 February the drawing of the King's head by Edmund Dulac was shown to the Director General of the Post Office. Essays were submitted to the King on 26 February and the final choice was Eric Gill's "four emblems" design used in conjunction with Dulac's portrait. The original plan was to issue the ½d., 1d., 1½d., and 2½d. values by Coronation Day. These values were issued on 10 May, but the 1½d. value was held back until it replaced the Coronation stamp of the same value on 30 July.

The 2d. and 3d. values followed on 31 January 1938. A new problem arose when Harrison & Son found that the deep etching and additional ink required was wearing the cylinders too quickly. Solid colour rules in the bottom sheet margins were introduced to offset this. Although not confirmed it is likely that in light colours the 4d. to 6d. values were selected because of this. The unified series was completed by the third group of 7d. to 1s. values. The Dulac head on a hexagonal background was chosen for this group and final colour essays were approved on 12 September 1938 for 9d., 10d., and 1s., followed on 9 January 1939 by 7d. and 8d.

The ½d. to 3d. were issued in pale colours between 1941 and 1942 as a wartime economy measure designed to save both wear on the cylinders and printing ink. By 1951 the ½d. to 2½d. values were those most in demand, and printing ink. By 1951 the ½d. to 2½d. and 4d. were issued in changed colours in accordance with the colour regulations of the Universal Postal Union for stamps with international use. The ½d. to 2½d. were issued to coincide with the opening of the Festival of Britain on 3 May 1951. An increase in the postage rate was made the following year on 1 May 1952 (see Appendix 6).

German Propaganda Forgeries

Propaganda forgeries of the low value stamps in deep colours were produced by the German authorities during the Second World War. They are of considerable interest to specialists. Printed in lithography on wavy-line watermarked paper they are easily recognised by the large gauge 11 perforation. Various design changes were made to include the Russian hammer and sickle and the Star of David.

PRINTER AND SHEET LAYOUT. All the low values were printed in photogravure by Harrison & Sons in sheets of 240 (20 horizontal rows of 12). They were printed in double pane width (no dot and dot) but were guillotined apart before being supplied to the Post Office. Further information is given in the General Notes, Section ND.

WATERMARK AND PERFORATION. All stamps in this Section are watermarked Block "GviR" (Type **W20**) and perforated 15 × 14.

BOOKLET ERRORS. Those listed as "Imperf. pane" show one row of perforations either at the top or bottom of the pane of six.

CYLINDER BLOCKS CONTAINING VARIETIES. These are indicated by asterisks against the prices.

COIL STAMPS. See the notes on these in the General Notes on the King George V typographed issues, which also apply here.

BOOKLET PERFORATORS. Booklet cylinder number panes are listed according to the perforator type. For descriptions and illustrations see Appendix 1. The letters in brackets above the price columns indicate the appearance of the binding margin of the pane as follows:

    (BP)   Perforations only extend across binding margin at foot
    (E)   Extension hole in the margin in each row
    (I)   Imperf. margin
    (Ie)   As (BP) except that the two perforation pins in the margin next to the stamp have been removed (leaving a single ½ hole in the margin)
    (P)   Perf. margin

UNUSED PRICE QUOTATIONS. Unused prices quoted in this Section are for mint unmounted examples.

W20

Q1
(Des. E. Dulac (head) and
Eric Gill (frames))

Q2

Q3
(Des. E. Dulac)

½d. Type Q1

1937 (MAY 10). GREEN

Cat. No.	S.G. No.	Shades	Mint	Used
Q1	462	Green	10 ✓	12 ✓

a.	Watermark inverted (8.37)		5·00	35
b.	Watermark sideways (1.38)		25 ✓	25 ✓
c.	Broken circle to value (Cyl. 18 No dot, R.19/2)		12·00	
s.	"Cancelled", Type 33 ..		8·00	
t.	"Cancelled", Type 33P ..		6·00	

Q1c

Controls and Cylinder Numbers (Blocks of Six)

Without pick up bar.   Perforation Type 5

Cyl. No.	Control	No dot	Dot	Cyl. No.	Control	No dot	Dot	Cyl. No.	Control	No dot	Dot
2	A 37	60	60	6	A 37	60	60	11	A 37	80	80
2	B 37	1·10	1·10	8	A 37	60	60	12	A 37	80	80
3	A 37	60	60	8	B 37	60	60	12	B 37	80	80
4	A 37	60	60	10	A 37	60	60				

Perforation Type 2A				Perforation Type 6 (no dot) and 6B (dot)			
6	A 37	†	14·00	2	A 37	80	80

With pick up bar.   Perforation Type 5

		No dot	Dot			No dot	Dot			No dot	Dot
2	B 37	90	90	58	C 38	1·20	1·20	90	F 39	1·10	1·10
12	B 37	80	80	58	D 38	90	90	93	E 39	90	90
16	B 37	60	60	59	C 38	90	90	95	E 39	80	80
17	B 37	60	60	61	C 38	60	60	98	E 39	80	80
18	B 37	9·00*		64	D 38	60	60	99	E 39	60	60
19	B 37	60	60	67	D 38	60	60	100	E 39		80
20	B 37	15·00	20·00	68	D 38	60	60	100	F 39	2·25	2·25
22	B 37	80	80	68	E 39	1·10	1·10	101	E 39	1·10	1·10
24	B 37	90	90	69	D 38	90	90	101	F 39	90	90
25	B 37	60	60	70	D 38	90	90	104	F 39	60	60
31	B 37	60	60	72 (i)	D 38	2·00	2·00	105 (i)	F 39	3·25	2·25
32	B 37	60	60	72 (ii)	D 38	90	90	105 (ii)	F 39	†	3·00
35	C 38	60	60	73	D 38	60	60	105 (iii)	F 39	4·00	5·00
37	C 38	60	60	74	D 38	80	80	106 (i)	F 39	90	90
40	C 38	60	60	76	D 38	90	90	106 (ii)	F 39	1·20	1·20
42	C 38	60	60	76	E 39	90	90	108	F 39	1·40	1·40
43 (i)	C 38	90	90	77	E 39	90	90	110	F 39	1·20	1·20
43 (ii)	C 38	90	90	78	E 39	60	60	113	F 39	60	60
52	C 38	90	90	81	D 38	90	90	119	G 40	1·40	1·20
53	C 38	60	60	81	E 39	90	90	120	G 40	60	60
55	C 38	60	60	82	D 38	80	80	120	I 41	1·40	60
56	C 38	60	60	90	E 39	90	90				

Perforation Type 6 (no dot) and 6B (dot)

58	D 38	1·20	1·20	72 (i)	D 38	2·25	2·25	76	E 39	90	90
67	D 38	1·10	1·10	72 (ii)	D 38	1·10	1·10	81	E 39	80	80
68	D 38	1·10	1·10	73	D 38	1·20	1·20	82	D 38	80	80
69	D 38	1·10	1·10	74	D 38	1·20	1·20	101	F 39	2·25	2·25
70	D 38	1·10	1·10	76	D 38	1·10	1·10				

Varieties:

Cylinder 3 dot exists in five states:

State (i) With no cutting line
State (ii) With cutting line engraved too close to the stamp
State (iii) With additional cutting line in correct place below
State (iv) With upper cutting line breaking up (various stages)
State (v) With upper cutting line removed

Cylinder 43 exists in two states:

State (i) both dot and no dot panes show " 43 " engraved over " 23 ", the " 2 " showing clearly.
State (ii) retouch on both panes, the " 2 " no longer visible. The base of figure " 38 " of control has been retouched.

Cylinder 72 exists in two states:

State (i) both dot and no dot panes show a very weak control
State (ii) both controls retouched.

Cylinder 98 no dot and dot exist in two states:

State (i) Numbers badly cut
State (ii) Numbers recut wider and wider apart

Cylinder 105 dot exists in three states:

State (i) Without retouch.
State (ii) " 3 " of control lightly retouched at base.
State (iii) Control completely retouched.

Cylinder 105 no dot exists in two states:

State (i) Pale control.
State (iii) Control strongly retouched.

Cylinder 106 exists in two states:

State (i) both dot and no dot panes show trace of a previous control. The F 39 control has been lightly retouched.
State (ii) The control has been further retouched, and the "shadow control" almost completely removed.

Retouched controls

The following F 39 controls were retouched before the cylinders were put to press: 90, 100, 100., 101, 101., 104

" Shadow " controls

Distinct traces of a previous control are seen on the following:

E 39 Cyl. 68, 68., 76, 76., 77, 77., 81, 81. (D 38)   G 40 Cyl. 119, 119., 120, 120. (F 39)
F 39 Cyl. 90, 90., 101, 104., 108, 110. (E 39)   I 41 Cyl. 120, 120. (F 39)

Booklet Panes of Six

From Booklets BD11/15 and BD21/25

QB1	Watermark upright	10·00
s.	" Cancelled ", Type 33P ..	40·00

QB1a	Watermark inverted	32·00
as.	" Cancelled ", Type 33P ..	45·00
at.	" Cancelled ", Type 33 ..	45·00

Booklet Panes of Four

From Booklets BD3/a made up from coil printings intended for sideways delivery

Selvedge at top
QB2 Watermark sideways   15·00

Selvedge at bottom
QB2a Watermark sideways   15·00

Booklet Panes of Two

From Booklets BD2/a

QB3 Watermark upright   5·00   QB3a Watermark inverted   12·00

Booklet Cylinder Numbers
Panes of six

Cyl. No.					Perf. Type B3(I) No dot	Perf. Type B3A(P) Dot	Cyl. No.			Perf. Type B4(E) No dot	Perf. Type B4A(I) Dot	B4B(E) Dot
E10	..	..	..	..	30·00	30·00	E 2	..	..	20·00	20·00	20·00
E 19	..	..	..	..	20·00	†	Wmk. inverted	..		60·00	60·00	60·00
E 22	..	..	..	..	20·00	†	E 5	..	..	20·00	20·00	20·00
E 28	..	..	..	..	20·00	†	E 10	..	..	20·00	20·00	20·00
E 29	..	..	..	..	20·00	†	E 18	..	..	20·00	20·00	20·00
E 38	..	..	..	..	20·00	†	E 35	..	..	20·00	25·00	20·00
E 39	..	..	..	..	20·00	†	E 36	..	..	20·00	20·00	†
E 41	..	..	..	..	20·00	†						
E 42	..	..	..	..	20·00	†						
E 43	..	..	..	..	—	†						
E 45	..	..	..	..	20·00	†						
E 46	..	..	..	..	20·00	†						
E 48	..	..	..	..	20·00	†						
E 49	..	..	..	..	20·00	†						
E 50	..	..	..	..	20·00	†						

In cylinder E 42 only the " 2 " shows and a small part of " 4 ", so that it can easily be taken for E 2.

Panes of four.　Watermark sideways

Cyl. No.				Perf. Type B4(E) No dot
A 40	..	..	..	40·00

Panes of two

E2						Perf. Type B3(I) No dot		E2				Perf. Type B4(E) No dot	Perf. Type B4A(I) Dot	B4B(E) Dot
E2	..	..	..	..	..	15·00		E2	..	..	..	†	15·00	18·00
E10	..	..	..	..	..	15·00		E10	..	..	..	†	15·00	†
E18	..	..	..	..	..	15·00		E18	..	..	..	18·00	†	†
E28	..	..	..	..	..	18·00								

Coils
Vertical delivery printed in continuous reels

Code No.	Issued	Number in roll	Face value	
D	1937	960	£2.0.0	Bottom delivery
G	1937	480	£1.0.0	Bottom delivery
W	Late 1937	960	£2.0.0	Bottom delivery
Y	1937	1920	£4.0.0	Bottom delivery

Sideways delivery printed in continuous reels with watermark sideways

P	Jan. 1938	480	£1.0.0	Left side delivery

Imprimaturs from the National Postal Museum Archives
Imperforate, watermark Type W20

Watermark upright
Watermark inverted
Watermark sideways
Tête-bêche pair
Tête-bêche pair with vertical gutter margin

1941 (SEPTEMBER 1).　PALE GREEN

Cat. No.	S.G. No.		Shades	Mint	Used
Q2	485		Pale green	12	10 ✓

a.	Tête-bêche (horizontal pair)	£2500			
b.	Watermark inverted	..	3·00	20 ✓	
c.	Imperf. (pair)	£1200†			
e.	Spur to R of REVENUE				
	(Cyl. 153 Dot, R.1/5) ..	20·00	s.	"Specimen", Type 9	..
f.	Closed final E of REVENUE		t.	"Cancelled", Type 33	..
	(Cyl. 153 No dot, R.3/1) ..	28·00	u.	"Cancelled", Type 34	..

†No. Q2c exists from NPM archive sales.

Q2/3*e*

Q2/3*f*

Controls and Cylinder Numbers (Blocks of Six)

Perforation Type 5

Cyl. No.	Control	No dot	Dot	Cyl. No.	Control	No dot	Dot	Cyl. No.	Control	No dot	Dot
124	J 41	6·00	6·00	129	P 44	3·00	2·00	141	U 47	1·50	1·50
124	K 42	85	85	130	N 43	85	85	142	S 46	85	85
124	L 42	85	85	130	P 44	85	85	142	T 46	85	85
125	J 41	85	85	132	P 44	85	85	143	U 47	85	85
125	K 42	85	85	134	Q 45	85	85	146	None	85	85
128	M 43	85	85	134	S 46	85	85	150	None	85	85
128	N 43	85	85	135	R 45	85	85	151	None	1·50	1·50
128	O 44	2·00	2·00	135	S 46	85	85	152	None	85	85
129	M 43	2·00	2·00	137	None	85	85	153	None	1·50	1·50
129	O 44	85	85	141	T 46	85	85				

Perforation Type 6

		No dot		Dot			No dot		Dot			No dot		Dot
		6	6B	6			6	6B	6			6	6B	6
124	J 41	2·50	4·00	4·00	125	J 41	85	85	85	132	P 44	1·50	1·50	†
124	L 42	2·25	85	85	130	P 44	85	85	†					

Perforation Type 5AE.   No dot cylinder only

129	P 44	1·50	132	P 44	1·50	134	Q 45	1·50	
130	P 44	85							

Booklet Panes of Six

From Booklets BD16/18 and BD26/29

QB4   Watermark upright   5·00   QB4a   Watermark inverted   20·00

Booklet Panes of Four

From Booklets BD/6a made up from sheets

Selvedge at top   Selvedge at bottom
QB5   Watermark upright   —   QB5a   Watermark upright   —

Booklet Panes of Two

From Booklet BD4 made up from sheets

QB6   Watermark upright   3·00

Booklet Cylinder Numbers

Panes of six

Cyl. No.					B3(I) No dot	B6(Ie) Dot	Cyl. No.					B3(I) No dot	B6(Ie) Dot
E 53	..	..	..	..	12·00	†	E 72	..	..	..	..	12·00	12·00
E 56	..	..	..	..	12·00	†	E 73	..	..	..	..	12·00	12·00
E 58	..	..	..	..	12·00	†	E 75	..	..	..	..	12·00	12·00
E 59	..	..	..	..	12·00	†	E 76	..	..	..	..	12·00	12·00
E 62	..	..	..	..	12·00	†	E 77	..	..	..	..	12·00	12·00
E 65	..	..	..	..	12·00	—	E 78	..	..	..	..	12·00	12·00
E 66	..	..	..	..	12·00	12·00	E 79	..	..	..	..	12·00	12·00
E 67	..	..	..	..	12·00	12·00	E 80	..	..	..	..	12·00	12·00
E 68	..	..	..	..	12·00	12·00	E 81	..	..	..	..	12·00	12·00
E 70	..	..	..	..	12·00	12·00	E 82	..	..	..	..	12·00	12·00
E 71	..	..	..	..	12·00	12·00	E 83	..	..	..	..	12·00	12·00

Cyl. No.					B4A(I) Dot	B5(BP) Dot
E 65	..	..	..	..	12·00	12·00
E 66	..	..	..	..	†	

Panes of two

Cyl. No.					Perf. Type E	
					No dot	Dot
137	..	..	..	..	12·00	12·00
143	..	..	..	..	—	†
147	..	..	..	..	22·00	†
150	..	..	..	..	12·00	12·00

Coils

Vertical delivery printed in continuous reels

Code No.	Issued	Number in roll	Face value	
D	1942	960	£2.0.0	Bottom delivery
G	1942	480	£1.0.0	Bottom delivery
W	1942	960	£2.0.0	Bottom delivery
Y	1942	1920	£4.0.0	Bottom delivery

Imprimaturs from the National Postal Museum Archives

Imperforate, watermark Type W20

Watermark upright
Watermark inverted
Watermark sideways
Tête-bêche pair
Tête-bêche pair with vertical gutter margin

1951 (MAY 3). PALE ORANGE

Cat. No.	S.G. No.		Shades	Mint	Used
Q3	503		Pale orange	10 ✓	12 ✓

a. Tête-bêche (horizontal pair) £2000
b. Watermark inverted .. 10   30✓
c. Imperf. (pair) .. .. ..
d. Imperf. pane of 6* .. ..
e. Spur to R of REVENUE
  (Cyl. 153 Dot, R.1/5) .. 18·00

f. Closed final E of REVENUE
  (Cyl. 153 No dot, R.3/1) .. 17·00
g. Broken middle E of REV-
  ENUE (Cyl. 154 No dot,
  R.20/1) .. .. 7·00
h. Coil join (horiz. pair) ..

*Booklet error. See General Notes.
No. Q3c exists from NPM archive sales.

Q3g

Cylinder Numbers (Blocks of Six)

Perforation Type 5

Cyl. No.					No dot	Dot	Cyl. No.					No dot	Dot
151	..	..	..	..	70	70	154	..	..	..	..	9·00*	70
152	..	..	..	..	70	70	155	..	..	..	..	70	70
153	..	..	..	..	70	70							

Booklet Panes of Six

From Booklets BD19/20, BD30/32, F1/13 and H1/5

QB7   Watermark upright   3·00   QB7a   Watermark inverted   2·00

Booklet Panes of Four

From Booklets BD7/10
Selvedge at top
QB8 Watermark upright 3·00

From Booklet BD7
Selvedge at bottom
QB8a Watermark upright 5·00

From Booklets BD8/10
Selvedge at top
QB8b Watermark inverted 3·00

Booklet Panes of Two

From Booklet BD5 made up from sheets
QB9 Watermark upright 3·00

Booklet Cylinder Numbers

Panes of six

Cyl. No.					Perf. Type B3(I) No dot	B6(Ie) Dot	Cyl. No.					Perf. Type B3(I) No dot	B6(Ie) Dot
E 82	..	..	..	..	8·50	8·50	E 84	..	..	..	..	8·00	8·00
E 83	..	..	..	..	9·00	9·00	E 85	..	..	..	..	8·00	8·00

Panes of two

Cyl. No.					Perf. Type No dot	E Dot	Cyl. No.					Perf. Type No dot	E Dot
151	..	..	..	..	†	8·00	154	..	..	..	..	8·00	†
153	..	..	..	..	8·00	8·00	155	..	..	..	..	8·00	†

Coils

Vertical delivery printed in continuous reels

Code No.	Issued	Number in roll	Face value	
D	May 1951	960	£2.0.0	Bottom delivery
G	May 1951	480	£1.0.0	Bottom delivery
W	May 1951	960	£2.0.0	Bottom delivery
Y	May 1951	1920	£4.0.0	Bottom delivery
EXP*	Feb. 1952	240	10.0	Bottom delivery
AA*	July 1954	240	10.0	Bottom delivery

Sideways delivery made up from sheets with joins every 12th stamp

P	May 1951	480	£1.0.0	Left side delivery

*The EXP (exposed) and AA coils were used in vending machines in exposed positions.

Imprimaturs from The National Postal Museum Archives

Imperforate, watermark Type W20

Watermark upright
Watermark inverted
Tête-bêche pair
Tête-bêche pair with vertical gutter margin

1d. Type Q1

1937 (MAY 10). SCARLET

Cat. No.	S.G. No.		Shades	Mint	Used
Q4	463		Scarlet	10 ✓	12 ✓

a.	Watermark inverted (8.37)	30·00	1·75	t.	"Cancelled", Type 33 .. 13·00
b.	Watermark sideways (2.38)	10·00 ✓	4·00 ✓	u.	"Cancelled", Type 33P .. 9·00

Controls and Cylinder Numbers (Blocks of Six)

Without pick up bar. Perforation Type 5

Cyl. No.	Control	No dot	Dot	Cyl. No.	Control	No dot	Dot	Cyl. No.	Control	No dot	Dot
1	A 37	30·00	†	7	A 37	60	60	9	A 37	30·00	†
3	A 37	60	60	8	A 37	60	60	10	A 37	85	85
4	A 37	60	60	8	B 37	85	85	11	B 37	75	75

Perforation Type 6 (no dot) | Perforation Type 2A
and 6B (dot)

7	A 37	75	75	11	B 37	†	16·00

With pick up bar. Perforation Type 5

Cyl. No.	Control	No dot	Dot	Cyl. No.	Control	No dot	Dot	Cyl. No.	Control	No dot	Dot
8	B 37	85	85	27	E 39	60	60	45	H 40	60	60
11	B 37	1·10	1·10	30	F 39	5·00	5·00	46	H 40	75	75
12	B 37	60	60	33	F 39	60	60	47	H 40	85	85
12	C 38	85	85	39	F 39	1·25	1·25	48	H 40	85	85
15	C 38	60	60	39	G 40	85	85	48	I 41	85	70
16	C 38	60	60	40	G 40	85	85	49	H 40	85	85
18	C 38	60	60	40	H 40	75	75	49	I 41	85	70
19	D 38	1·10	1·10	41	G 40	60	60	51	H 40	1·10	1·10
22	D 38	75	75	41	H 40	85	85	51	I 41	60	60
23	D 38	1·10	1·10	42	F 39	85	85	53	I 41	60	60
24	D 38	60	60	43	H 40	85	85	54	I 41	60	60
26	D 38	60	60	44	H 40	85	85	61	I 41	60	60
26	E 39	1·10	85	45	G 40	85	85				

Perforation Type 6 (no dot) and 6B (dot)

Cyl. No.	Control	No dot	Dot	Cyl. No.	Control	No dot	Dot	Cyl. No.	Control	No dot	Dot
26	E 39	1·10	70	30	F 39	85	85	39	F 39	85	85
27	E 39	60	60	31	F 39	85	85	42	F 39	85	85
27	F 39	1·25	1·25	33	F 39	85	85				

On cylinder 19 (both panes), the tail of the "9" was originally engraved short and close to the loop. Before being put to press, the tail was re-engraved long and wide of the loop.

" Shadow " controls

Distinct traces of the previous control are seen on the following:

C 38 Cyl. 12., 15, 15. (B 37)
E 39 Cyl. 26, 26., 27. (D 38)
G 40 Cyl. 40, 40. (F 39)
H 40 Cyl. 43. (G 40)
I 41 Cyl. 48, 48., 49, 49. (H 40)

Booklet Panes of Six

From Booklets BD11/12 and BD21/24

QB10	Watermark upright	10·00	QB10a	Watermark inverted	£200
s.	"Cancelled", Type 33P ..	60·00	as.	"Cancelled", Type 33P ..	60·00
			at.	"Cancelled", Type 33	

Booklet Panes of Four

From Booklets BD3/a made up from coil printings intended for sideways delivery

Selvedge at top			Selvedge at bottom		
QB11	Watermark sideways	40·00	QB11a	Watermark sideways	40·00

Booklet Panes of Two

From Booklets BD2/a

QB12	Watermark upright	5·00	QB12a	Watermark inverted	75·00

Booklet Cylinder Numbers

Panes of six

						Perf. Type					Perf. Type		
						B3(I)	B3A(P)				B4(E)	B4A(I)	B4B(E)
Cyl. No.						No dot	Dot	Cyl. No.			No dot	Dot	Dot
F 3	..	..	..	..	..	†	—	F 1	..	..	20·00	20·00	20·00
F 7	..	..	..	..		20·00	†	F 3	..	..	20·00	20·00	20·00
F 9	..	..	..	..		20·00	†	F 4	..	..	20·00	20·00	20·00
F 14	..	..	..	..		20·00	†	F 5	..	..	20·00	20·00	20·00
F 15	..	..	..	..		20·00	†	F 10	..	..	20·00	20·00	†
F 16	..	..	..	..		25·00	†						

Panes of four

Cyl. No.						Perf. Type B4(E) No dot
B 17	..	..	..	..	..	75·00

Panes of two

					Perf. Type		
Cyl. No.					B3(I) No dot	B4A(I) Dot	B4B(E) Dot
F 1	..	..	..	..	15·00	15·00	20·00
F 5	..	..	..	..	15·00	15·00	†
F 15	..	..	..	..	20·00	†	†

Coils

Vertical delivery printed in continuous reels

Code No.	Issued	Number in roll	Face value	
B	1937	960	£4.0.0	Bottom delivery
E	1937	480	£2.0.0	Bottom delivery
X	1937	960	£4.0.0	Bottom delivery
Z	25.9.37	1920	£8.0.0	Bottom delivery

Sideways delivery printed in continuous reels with watermark sideways

O	Feb. 1938	480	£2.0.0	Left side delivery

Imprimaturs from the National Postal Museum Archives

Imperforate, watermark Type W20

Watermark upright
Watermark inverted
Watermark sideways
Tête-bêche pair
Tête-bêche pair with vertical gutter margin

Variations in the Multipositives

For the 1d. in pale scarlet and the later issue in light ultramarine several master nega-tives were employed, these being retouched prior to the preparation of the multipositives.

Type I   Type II

Type I, used for sheet stamps from cylinders 75 to 172, has a white spot in front of the ear and a white strand of hair behind the ear and the upper lip is straight.

Type II (cylinders 174 to 190), has the white spot and strand of hair touched out and other minor differences but upper lip is concave.

Pre Type I   Type I

On sheet stamps only for cylinders 66 to 74 there is a further type which we call Pre Type I. The white spot and strand of hair are less prominent than Type I, resembling Type II, but the upper lip is straight. However, there is a further difference between this and Type I to be found in the thistle.

Pre Type I. The thistle is made up of five inner lines with a space between the third and fourth lines.

Type I. An additional short line has been added in this space in the thistle, the third line being ill-defined.

Further information about these can be found in an article by P. C. Worsfold in *Stamp Collecting* for 17 September 1970.

Cat. No. S.G. No.			Shades	Mint	Used
1941 (AUGUST 11). PALE SCARLET					
A. Type I					
Q5 486			Pale scarlet	12	10 ✓
a. Watermark sideways (10.42)	4·50	6·00 ✓			
b. Ditto, thick paper	10·00	8·00			
e. Imperf. between (vert pair)					
f. Flaw on cheek (Cyl. 149 No					
dot, R.3/4)	50·00				
g. Pre Type I	10	15			
h. Incomplete bottom frames			*s.* " Specimen ", Type 9 ..		
(Cyl. 74 No dot, R.20/1 and			*t.* " Cancelled ", Type 33 ..		
2) .. .. *Pair*	15·00		*u.* " Cancelled ", Type 34 ..		
B. Type II. (—.48)			Pale scarlet	30	25
Q5A —					
b. Thick paper	1·50				
c. Imperf. (pair)	£1250				
d. Imperf. three sides (pair) ..	£1000				

Q5f   Q5h

Controls and Cylinder Numbers (Blocks of Six)

Pre Type I. Perforation Type 5

Cyl. No.	Control	No dot	Dot	Cyl. No.	Control	No dot	Dot	Cyl. No.	Control	No dot	Dot
66	J 41	85	85	72	J 41	85	85	73	K 42	85	1·50
69	J 41	85	85	72	K 42	85	85	74	J 41	16·00*	1·50
70	J 41	85	85	72	L 42	1·50	1·50	74	K 42	16·00*	2·25
71	J 41	85	85	73	J 41	85	85				

Type I. Perforation Type 5

Cyl.	Control	No dot	Dot	Cyl.	Control	No dot	Dot	Cyl.	Control	No dot	Dot
75	K 42	85	85	100	O 44	85	85	130	S 46	85	85
76	K 42	85	85	101	P 44	85	85	132	T 46	85	85
76	L 42	1·50	1·50	102	O 44	1·50	1·50	133	T 46	85	85
76	M 43	85	85	102	P 44	85	85	134	T 46	85	85
78	L 42	85	85	105	O 44	1·50	1·50	136	T 46	85	85
80	M 43	85	85	105	P 44	85	85	139	T 46	85	85
81	L 42	85	85	106	P 44	4·00	85	140	T 46	85	85
82	L 42	85	85	106	Q 45	85	85	140	U 47	85	85
82	M 43	1·50	1·50	107	P 44	85	85	141	T 46	85	85
86	M 43	85	85	107	Q 45	85	85	142	T 46	85	85
90	N 43	1·50	85	112	P 44	85	85	143	T 46	85	85
90	O 44	1·50	85	113	P 44	85	85	145	None	85	85
91	N 43	1·50	85	113	Q 45	1·50	1·50	146	U 47	85	85
91	O 44	4·00	4·00	118	Q 45	85	85	148	U 47	85	85
91	P 44	1·50	1·50	118	R 45	85	85	149	U 47	85	85
92	M 43	85	85	120	Q 45	85	85	150	None	85	85
92	N 43	85	85	120	R 45	85	85	153	U 47	85	85
93	M 43	85	85	121	Q 45	85	85	155	U 47	85	85
94	N 43	1·50	1·50	122	Q 45	85	85	156	None	85	85
94	O 44	1·50	1·50	122	R 45	85	85	157	None	85	85
95	N 43	4·00	4·00	123	R 45	85	85	160	None	85	85
95	O 44	1·50	1·50	124	S 46	85	85	166	None	85	85
96	M 43	85	85	125	R 45	85	85	167	None	85	85
96	N 43	85	85	125	S 46	85	85	169	None	85	85
97	N 43	85	85	127	S 46	85	85	171	None	85	85
98	O 44	85	85	127	T 46	85	85	172	None	85	85
99	N 43	1·50	1·50	129	S 46	85	85				
100	N 43	4·00	4·00	129	T 46	85	85				

Pre Type I. Perforation Type 6 (no dot) and 6B (dot)

72	L 42	70	70

Type I. Perforation Type 6 (no dot) and 6B (dot)

Cyl. No.	Control	No dot	Dot	Cyl. No.	Control	No dot	Dot	Cyl. No.	Control	No dot	Dot
76	L 42	1·50	1·50	125	R 45	85	85	150	U 47	1·50	1·50
121	Q 45	85	85	125	S 46	85	85	153	U 47	85	85
123	S 46	1·50	1·50	127	S 46	85	85	171	None	6·00	6·00
124	S 46	85	85	129	S 46	85	85	172	None	85	85

Perforation Type 5AE (no dot cylinder only)

Cyl.	Control	No dot		Cyl.	Control	No dot		Cyl.	Control	No dot
90	O 44	1·50		98	O 44	85		106	P 44	1·50
91	N 43	1·50		100	O 44	85		106	Q 45	1·50
91	O 44	2·25		101	O 44	1·50		107	P 44	1·50
91	P 44	3·00		102	O 44	1·50		107	Q 45	4·00
94	N 43	1·50		102	P 44	1·50		112	P 44	1·50
94	O 44	1·50		105	O 44	1·50		113	P 44	1·50

Type II. Perforation Type 5

174	None	2·00	2·00	180	None	2·00	2·00	186	None	2·00	2·00
175	None	2·00	2·00	181	None	2·00	2·00	189	None	2·00	2·00
178	None	2·00	2·00	182	None	2·00	2·00	190	None	2·50	2·50
179	None	2·00	2·00	183	None	2·00	2·00	192	None	—	†

Perforation Type 6 (no dot) and 6B (dot)

174	None	2·00	2·00	180	None	2·00	2·00	185	None	2·00	2·00
179	None	2·00	2·00	181	None	2·00	2·00	190	None	2·50	2·50

Cylinder 124 sometimes shows a dot after the number. Printings from the no dot pane may always be recognised by the presence of a cut in the rule under the first stamp, bottom row.

Two sheets are known of Cyl. 192 no dot and an additional cylinder block has been reported. The arrows in the top and bottom margins are omitted.

"Shadow" control

Cylinder 156 dot shows traces of U 47 control and was only issued without control

Booklet Panes of Four
From Booklet BD6/a made up from sheets
Type II

Selvedge at top		Selvedge at bottom	
QB13 Watermark upright	—	QB13a Watermark upright	—

Booklet Panes of Two
From Booklet BD4 made up from sheets

Type I		**Type II**	
QB14 Watermark upright	2·00	QB14a Watermark upright	20·00

Booklet Cylinder Numbers
Panes of two

Type I Cyl. No.					Perf. Type E No dot	Dot
157	..	..	..	..	8·00	8·00
159	..	..	..	..	†	10·00
160	..	..	..	..	8·00	8·00
172	..	..	..	..	9·00	9·00

Type II Cyl. No.			Perf. Type E No dot	I No dot	E Dot
175	..	..	12·00	†	13·00
179	..	..	13·00	—	13·00

Coils
Types I and II
Vertical delivery printed in continuous reels

Code No.	Issued	Number in roll	Face value	
B	1942	960	£4.0.0	Bottom delivery
E	1942	480	£2.0.0	Bottom delivery
X	1942	960	£4.0.0	Bottom delivery
Z	1942	1920	£8.0.0	Bottom delivery

Type I
Sideways delivery printed in continuous reels with watermark sideways

O	Oct. 1942	480	£2.0.0	Left side delivery

Imprimaturs from the National Postal Museum Archives
Imperforate, watermark Type W20
Watermark upright
Watermark sideways

Variations in the Multipositives
Type Ia derives from panes of four from Booklets BD8/10. The upper lip is straight as Type I but the Crown and large pearls are as Type II. The hair at the back of the head has been retouched but the band of dark shading at the back of the neck is narrower and more clear-cut than Type II.

Type Ib is from pane Nos. QB18/a, QB19/a and QB20/a. The upper lip is straight as Type I. The white spot in the ear and pale strand of hair are partially touched out. The Crown and rose are similar to type II.

Type Ic derives from the ordinary panes of six Nos. QB15/a. The upper lip is straight as Type I. The white spot in the ear and the pale strand of hair have been touched out and the head blends into the background. The Crown shows as a clear impression and the lines in the rose and leaves are heavy as Type I.

Although these types normally show the upper lip straight, examples of the "concave" lip of type II can be found in booklet panes. These are isolated instances and cannot be identified by position. They are best collected in the pane so that their variation from the normal is clearly evident.

Further information about these can be found in an article by R. F. Strange in the *GB Journal* for June 1960.

Cat. No. S.G. No.	Shades	Mint	Used
1951 (MAY 3). LIGHT ULTRAMARINE			
A. Type II			
Q6 504	Light ultramarine	10 ✓	12 ✓
b. Imperf. (pair) .. .. £1100†			
c. Imperf. three sides (pair) .. £1000			
d. "Keyhole" flaw (Cyl. 192			
No dot, R.6/12) .. .. 75·00			
†No. Q6*b* exists from NPM archive sales.			

B. Type I
Horizontal coil with sideways watermark (5.51)

Q6A 504a	Light ultramarine	25 ✓	45 ✓
b. Retouched nose and forehead .. .. 12·00			

C. Type Ia. From pane nos. QB16b or QB16c (12.52)

Q6B —	Light ultramarine	20	
b. Watermark inverted .. 2·00			

D. Type Ib. From pane nos. QB18/QB20a (3.52)

Q6C —	Light ultramarine	20	
a. Partial *tête-bêche* pane (QB18) £1750			
b. Watermark inverted .. .. 2·00 ✓			

E. Type Ic. From pane nos. QB15 or QB15a (1.53)

Q6D —	Light ultramarine	20	
b. Watermark inverted .. 2·00			

For cylinder varieties on booklet panes, see Nos. QB19*b* and QB20*b/c*.

Q6*d*   Q6A*b*

Cylinder Numbers (Blocks of Six)
Type II. Perforation Type 5

Perforation Type 6 (no dot) and
6B (dot)

Cyl. No.					No dot	Dot
190	..	..	..	..	70	70
191	..	..	..	..	70	70
192	..	..	..	..	1·50	70

Cyl. No.					No dot	Dot
191	..	..	..	..	70	70
192	..	..	..	∴	70	70

Top and bottom rows exist with the arrows omitted from cylinder 192 dot.

Booklet Panes of Six
Type Ic
From Booklets BD32 and H1/6
QB15 Watermark upright 3·00

QB15a Watermark inverted 15·00

Booklet Panes of Four
Type II
From Booklet BD7/a made up from sheets
Selvedge at top
QB16 Watermark upright 3·00

From Booklet BD7
Selvedge at bottom
QB16a Watermark upright 3·00

Type Ia
From Booklets BD8/10
QB16b Watermark upright 4·00

QB16c Watermark inverted 12·00

Booklet Panes of Two
Type II
From Booklet BD5 made up from sheets
QB17 Watermark upright 2·00

Booklet Panes with Printed Labels
Type Ib
Panes of six comprising three stamps and three labels

QB18/a

From Booklets BD20, BD31, F1/5, F7, F9, F11 and F14
" MINIMUM INLAND PRINTED PAPER RATE 1½d." 17 mm. high
QB18 Watermark upright 14·00   QB18a Watermark inverted 14·00

QB19/a

From Booklets F6, F8 and F10
" MINIMUM INLAND PRINTED PAPER RATE 1½d."   15 mm. high
QB19 Watermark upright   20·00   QB19a Watermark inverted 20·00
                                            b. Spur on R (No. 2) ..   .. 45·00

QB20/a

From Booklets F12/13
" SHORTHAND IN ONE WEEK "
QB20 Watermark upright   22·00   QB20a Watermark inverted 22·00
  b. Major retouch (Nos. 1 and 2) 40·00   *c.* Spur on R (No. 2) ..   .. 50·00

316

Listed Varieties

QB19*b*, 20*c*   QB20*b*

Major retouch extends from back of head in No. 1 to front
of face in No. 2 giving a mottled effect to the background.
The main differences are found in the thickening of the
letters " REVEN " in No. 1 and " STAGE " in No.2

Booklet Cylinder Numbers

Panes of six

					Perf. Type	
					B3(I)	B6(Ie)
Cyl. No.					No dot	Dot
F 8 ..	..	..	..	..	7·00	7·00

Panes of two

						Perf. Type	
					E	I	E
Cyl. No.					No dot	No dot	Dot
191 ..	..	..	..	..	†	†	5·00
192 ..	..	..	..	..	5·00	—	5·00

Panes of six including three labels

			Perf. Type	
			B3(I)	B6(Ie)*
Advert.		Cyl. No.	No dot	Dot
" MINIMUM INLAND RATE 1½d." (17 mm.)	..	F 5	28·00	28·00
Ditto (15 mm). Spacing error** ..	..	F 7	40·00	40·00
Ditto (15 mm.) Spacing corrected† ..	..	F 7	—	—
" SHORTHAND IN ONE WEEK "	..	F 7	35·00	35·00

* This is as Type B5 but imperf. margins and with one extension hole at top instead of bottom.
    The extension hole is at the top of the pane instead of at the bottom because the panes containing three
stamps had the cylinder number etched one row lower than the panes of six on the cylinder (row 18 for panes of
six and row 19 others).

**Unlike cylinder F 5, where the labels were included on the cylinder, cylinder F 7 contained impressions
of the stamps only, the labels being printed typographically in a separate operation.   There was an error
of spacing on the third label where the vertical distance between " RATE " and " 1½d." was 2 mm. instead
of 1 mm.

†In a later printing this was corrected.

Coils

Type II
Vertical delivery printed in continuous reels

Code No.	Issued	Number in roll	Face value	
B	May 1951	960	£4.0.0	Bottom delivery
E	May 1951	480	£2.0.0	Bottom delivery
X	May 1951	960	£4.0.0	Bottom delivery
Z	May 1951	1920	£8.0.0	Bottom delivery
EXP*	Feb. 1952	240	£1.0.0	Bottom delivery
AB*	May 1954	240	£1.0.0	Bottom delivery

Type I
Sideways delivery printed in continuous reels with watermark sideways

O	May 1951	480	£2.0.0	Left side delivery

*The EXP (exposed) and AB coils were used in vending machines in exposed positions

Imprimaturs from the National Postal Museum Archives

Imperforate, watermark Type W20

Watermark upright
Watermark inverted
Watermark sideways
Tête-bêche pair
Tête-bêche pair with vertical gutter margin

Booklet pane of four. Imperforate, watermark Type W20

Two panes as No. QB16b arranged vertically *tête-bêche* with horizontal gutter margin

Booklet pane with printed labels. Imperforate, watermark Type W20

Two panes as No. QB18 arranged *tête-bêche*

1½d. Type Q1

1937 (JULY 30). RED-BROWN

Cat. No.	S.G. No.		Shades		Mint	Used
Q7	464		Red-Brown		20 ✓	12 ✓

a. Watermark inverted (8.37)   7·00   50 ✓
b. Watermark sideways (2.38)   90 ✓   70 ✓
c. Imperf. three sides (pair) . .
d. Crown flaw (Cyl. 145 Dot,
　　150 Dot, R.19/7)   . .   . .   18·00   e. "Cancelled", Type 33P   . .   9·00

Q7d

Controls and Cylinder Numbers (Blocks of Six)

Perforation Type 5.   Without pick up bar

Cyl. No.	Control	No dot	Dot	Cyl. No.	Control	No dot	Dot	Cyl. No.	Control	No dot	Dot
1	A 37	1·10	1·10	18	B 37	1·00	1·00	33	B 37	10·00	—
12	A 37	1·10	1·10	22	B 37	1·00	1·00	35	B 37	†	40·00
14	A 37	1·10	1·10	30	B 37	1·00	1·00				
17	B 37	1·00	1·00	32	B 37	1·00	1·00				

With pick up bar

Cyl. No.	Control	No dot	Dot	Cyl. No.	Control	No dot	Dot	Cyl. No.	Control	No dot	Dot
38	B 37	1·00	1·00	84	C 38	1·10	1·10	123	E 39	1·00	1·00
42	B 37	1·00	1·00	85	C 38	1·10	1·10	124	E 39	1·00	1·00
45	B 37	1·00	1·00	86	C 38	1·00	1·00	125	E 39	1·00	1·00
46	B 37	1·00	1·00	88	C 38	1·10	1·10	126	E 39	1·00	1·00
48	B 37	1·00	1·00	89	C 38	4·50	40·00	128	E 39	1·00	1·00
49	B 37	1·00	1·00	90	C 38	1·10	1·10	135	E 39	1·00	1·00
50	B 37	1·00	1·00	91	C 38	1·20	1·20	136	E 39	2·00	2·00
51	B 37	1·00	1·00	92	C 38	1·00	1·00	138	E 39	2·50	†
52	B 37	2·00	2·00	93	C 38	1·10	1·10	139	E 39	2·00	2·00
54	B 37	1·00	1·00	93	D 38	1·10	1·10	141	F 39	1·10	1·10
55	B 37	1·00	1·00	95	C 38	1·10	1·10	144	E 39	1·10	1·10
56	B 37	1·10	1·10	96	C 38	1·10	2·00	145	E 39	1·10	1·10
59	B 37	1·00	1·00	98	C 38	1·00	1·00	148	E 39	1·10	1·10
60 (i)	B 37	1·10	1·10	102	D 38	1·00	1·00	148	F 39	2·00	2·00
60 (ii)	B 37	1·10	1·10	104	C 38	2·00	2·00	149	F 39	2·00	2·00
61	B 37	1·20	1·20	104	D 38	2·00	1·00	150	E 39	2·00	2·00
64	B 37	1·00	1·00	106	D 38	7·00	7·00	150	F 39	2·00	2·00
65	B 37	1·00	1·00	107	D 38	1·00	1·00	151	E 39	1·10	1·10
68	B 37	1·10	1·10	108	D 38	1·00	1·00	152	E 39	1·10	1·10
68	C 38	1·10	1·10	109	D 38	1·00	1·00	153	F 39	1·00	1·00
69	C 38	1·10	1·10	110	D 38	1·00	1·00	154	E 39	1·10	1·10
70	C 38	1·00	1·00	112	D 38	1·00	1·00	156	E 39	1·10	1·10
71	B 37	1·00	1·00	113	D 38	1·00	1·00	159	F 39	1·00	1·00
71	C 38	1·10	1·10	116	D 38	1·00	1·00	161	F 39	1·10	1·10
74	C 38	1·00	1·00	120	D 38	2·00	2·00	164	F 39	2·50	2·50
76	C 38	1·00	1·00	120	E 38	1·00	1·00	165	G 40	2·50	2·50
77	C 38	1·00	1·00	121	D 38	2·00	2·00	167	F 39	1·10	1·10
81	C 38	1·00	1·00	122	D 38	1·10	1·10	173	G 40	1·00	1·00
83	C 38	1·10	1·10	122	E 39	1·00	1·00				

In cylinder 98 the figure " 9 " is retouched.

Perforation Type 6 (no dot) and 6B (dot)

83	C 38	2·00	2·00	145	E 39	4·50	4·50	161	F 39	4·00	4·00

Perforation Type 2A

106	D 38	†	14·00	135		39	†	30·00

Varieties:
The left pane of cylinder 12 has a tiny dot after the " 12.", later erased.
Cylinder 60 exists in two states. In state (ii) the cylinder has been rechromed, and the control on both panes is weak and irregular in depth.
Control C 38 with cylinder 96. exist normal, both much weaker and lightly retouched and practically invisible with no trace of dot.
Control D 38 with cylinder 107 exists normal and in various weaker states to being practically invisible.
The right pane of cylinder 110 was without dot. It may be distinguished by the pick up bar under the first stamp, which has a nick in base at left.
In the right pane of cylinder 112 the cylinder number is engraved very close to the stamp, causing the stop sometimes to be perforated out. Can be identified if the cutting line is present.

Retouched controls

The following controls were retouched before the cylinders were put to press:

E 39 Cyl. 120.
F 39 Cyl. 141, 141. and 149

" Shadow " controls

Distinct traces of previous control are seen on the following:

C 38 Cyl. 71. (B 37)
D 38 Cyl. 106 (fraction bar of C 38) later removed
E 39 Cyl. 120, 122, 122., 124, 124., 125, 125. (D 38)
F 39 Cyl. 141, 141., 149 (E 39)
G 40 Cyl. 165, 165., 173. (F 39)

Booklet Panes of Six

From Booklets BD11/12 and BD21/24

QB21 Watermark upright   8·00
  s. "Cancelled", Type 33P .. 60·00
  sa. "Cancelled", Type 33 ..

QB21a Watermark inverted 60·00
  as. "Cancelled", Type 33P .. 60·00

Booklet Panes of Two

From Booklets BD1/a and BD2/a

QB22 Watermark upright   5·00

QB22a Watermark inverted 18·00

QB23/a (various advertisements, type (8) (shown))

Booklet Panes with Advertising Labels

Panes of six, comprising two labels printed in *black* and two stamps
From Booklets BD11/12 and BD23/24

QB23 Watermark upright   35·00
  s. "Cancelled", Type 33P .. 50·00

QB23a Watermark inverted 50·00
  as. "Cancelled", Type 33P .. 70·00
  at. "Cancelled", Type 33 ..

		Wmk Upright	Wmk Inverted
(1)	"Cash's name tapes / J. & J. Cash Ltd." (*numbered* 405)	60·00	70·00
(2)	"Cash's satin lingerie ribbons / Booklet containing samples" (*numbered* 453)	60·00	70·00
(3)	"Cash's satin lingerie ribbons / Booklet containing patterns" (*numbered* 459, 467, 473, 482, 492 *or* 498) ..	35·00 ✓	50·00
(4)	"Cash's satin lingerie ribbons / Samples of Cash's ribbons" (*numbered* 21, 389, 395, 410, 416, 424, 430, 441, 448 *or* 460) ..	35·00	50·00
(5)	"Fontana Note / Wm. Collins, Sons & Co. Ltd." ..	60·00	70·00
(6)	"Drages. 50 Pay-Way / Drages Ltd." ..	50·00	60·00
(7)	"Drages. Terms to suit YOU / Drages Ltd." ..	35·00	50·00
(8)	"Saving is Simple ["is" 3·5 mm. high]/Home Safe" ..	35·00	50·00
(9)	"Saving is Simple ["is" 4·5 mm. high]/Home Safe" ..	35·00	50·00
(10)	"Send your good wishes/by Greetings Telegram" ..	35·00	50·00
(11)	"You can reach your / friends at sea by Radio Telegram"	35·00	50·00
(12)	"Atlantic Holidays / Cunard White Star"	60·00	70·00
(13)	"Post Early / In The Day"	35·00	50·00
(14)	"Commander Stephen / King-Hall" (text on both labels sideways)	60·00	70·00
(15)	"Times Furnishing Company / London, W.C.1" ..	60·00	70·00

The numbers on panes QB23(1) (4) correspond to the numbers of the booklets in which they were issued
See Appendix 2.

Booklet Cylinder Numbers
Panes of six

Cyl. No.	B3(I) No dot	B3A(P) Dot		Cyl. No.	B4(E) No dot	B4A(I) Dot	B4B(E) Dot
G 8	20·00	20·00		G 8	15·00	15·00	15·00
G 29	15·00	†		G 19	15·00	15·00	15·00
G 30	15·00	†		G 20	15·00	15·00	15·00
G 34	15·00	†		G 28	15·00	15·00	15·00
G 36	15·00	†		G 49	15·00	15·00	†
G 40	15·00	†		G 50	15·00	15·00	20·00
G 44	25·00	†					
G 45	15·00	†					
G 48	20·00	†					
G 57	15·00	†					
G 58	15·00	†					
G 61	25·00	†					
G 69	15·00	†					
G 71	18·00	†					

Panes of two

Cyl. No.	B3(I) No dot		Cyl. No.	B4(E) No dot	B4A(I) Dot	B4B(E) Dot
G 19	15·00		G 19	†	15·00	20·00
G 20	15·00		G 20	†	15·00	†
G 28	15·00		G 28	20·00	†	†
G 50	20·00		G 50	20·00	†	†

Panes of six including two labels

Cyl. No.	Advert. No.	B3(I) No dot	B3A(P) Dot	B4(E) No dot	B4A(I) Dot	B4B(E) Dot
G 10	QB23(4) No. 389	†	†	70·00	70·00	70·00
	QB23(5)	†	†	£110	95·00	†
	Wmk inverted	†	†	£120	£100	†
	QB23(6)	†	†	95·00	†	95·00
	Wmk inverted	†	†	95·00	†	95·00
	QB23(7)	†	†	65·00	†	65·00
	QB23(8)	†	—	£110	£110	£110
	Wmk inverted	†	—	£110	†	£110
	QB23(9)	†	—	†	†	†
	Wmk inverted	†	—	†	†	†
G 18	QB23(1) No. 405	†	†	†	95·00	†
	QB23(4) No. 21	†	†	65·00	65·00	†
	No. 395	†	†	†	65·00	†
	No. 410	†	†	65·00	65·00	†
	No. 416	†	†	65·00	65·00	†
	No. 424	†	†	65·00	65·00	†
	No. 430	†	†	65·00	65·00	†
	No. 448	†	†	70·00	70·00	†
	QB23(7)	70·00	†	65·00	65·00	70·00
	QB23(8)	†	†	65·00	70·00	†
	QB23(9)	†	—	65·00	65·00	65·00
	QB23(10)	†	†	65·00	65·00	65·00
	QB23(11)	†	†	65·00	65·00	65·00
	QB23(12)	†	†	95·00	†	95·00

Single Pane cylinders (no dot)

Cyl. No.	Advert. No.			Perf. Type B3(I)	B3A(P)	Cyl. No.	Advert. No.			Perf. Type B3(I)	B3A(P)
G 29	QB23(8)‡	..	..	80·00	†	G 46	QB23(9)	..	..	—	†
	QB23(8) Re-engraved			90·00	†		QB23(10)	..	..	65·00	†
	QB23(10)	..	..	65·00	†		QB23(11)	..	..	65·00	†
	QB23(11)‡	..	..	80·00	†		QB23(13)	..	..	65·00	†
	QB23(11) Re-engraved			80·00	†		QB23(14)	..	..	95·00	†
							QB23(15)	..	..	95·00	†
G 37	QB23(4) No. 441	..		65·00	65·00						
	No. 448	..		65·00	65·00	G 59	QB23(3) No. 482	..		70·00	†
	QB23(8)	..	..	65·00	65·00		No. 492	..		70·00	†
	QB23(9)	..	..	65·00	65·00		QB23(9)	..	..	70·00	†
	QB23(10)	..	..	65·00	65·00		QB23(10)	..	..	65·00	†
	QB23(11)	..	..	65·00	65·00		QB23(13)	..	..	65·00	†
G 41	QB23(2) No. 453	..		80·00	†	G 67	QB23(10)	..	..	80·00	†
	QB23(3) No. 459	..		65·00	†						
	QB23(10)	..	..	65·00	†	G 70	QB23(3) No. 498	..		65·00	†
	QB23(11)	..	..	65·00	†		QB23(9)	..	..	65·00	†
	QB23(13)	..	..	80·00	†		QB23(10)	..	..	65·00	†
G 46	QB23(3) No. 467	..		65·00	†		QB23(13)	..	..	65·00	†
	No. 473	..		70·00	†						

‡The cylinder number was originally engraved incorrectly on the advertisement pane. This was later erased and re-engraved in its correct position in the margin.

Coils

Vertical delivery printed in continuous reels

Code No.	Issued	Number in roll	Face value	
K	1937	960	£6.0.0	Top delivery
K	1937	960	£6.0.0	Bottom delivery
L	1937	480	£3.0.0	Top delivery

Sideways delivery printed in continuous reels with watermark sideways

N	Feb. 1938	480	£3.0.0	Left side delivery

Imprimatur from the National Postal Museum Archives

Imperforate, watermark Type W20
Watermark upright

Specimen overprint from the National Postal Museum Archives

Booklet pane of six. Perf. 15 × 14, watermark Type W20
"Specimen", Type 32 and upper left stamp with punch hole

1942 (SEPTEMBER 28). PALE RED-BROWN

Cat. No.	S.G. No.		Shades	Mint	Used
Q8	487		Pale red-brown	65 ✓	35 ✓

a. Coil join (horiz. pair) (6.50)
c. Retouched forehead (Cyl. 192 No dot, R.19/1) .. 20·00
d. Spot in daffodil leaf (Cyl. 192 Dot, R.10/10) .. .. 20·00
e. Extended serif to 1 of ½ (Cyl. 192 Dot , R.7/11) .. .. 20·00

s. "Specimen", Type 9 ..
t. "Cancelled", Type 28 ..
u. "Cancelled", Type 33 ..

Q8/9e

Controls and Cylinder Numbers (Blocks of Six)

Perforation Type 5

Cyl. No.	Control	No dot	Dot	Cyl. No.	Control	No dot	Dot	Cyl. No.	Control	No dot	Dot
174	N 43	5·00	5·00	183	O 44	5·00	5·00	186	S 46	5·00	5·00
175	L 42	5·00	5·00	184	S 46	5·00	5·00	187	U 47	5·00	5·00
175	N 43	5·00	5·00	185	S 46	5·00	5·00	187	None	5·00	5·00
176	L 42	5·00	5·00	185	U 47	5·00	5·00	191	None	5·00	5·00
179	Q 45	5·00	5·00	185	None	7·50	7·50	192	None	5·00	5·00
183	N 43	5·00	5·00	186	R 45	5·00	5·00				

Perforation Type 6

Cyl. No.	Control	No dot 6	6B	Dot 6	Cyl. No.	Control	No dot 6	6B	Dot 6	Cyl. No.	Control	No dot 6	6B	Dot 6
178	O 44	5·00	5·00	5·00	178	P 44	5·00	5·00	†	183	O 44	5·00	7·00	5·00

Perforation Type 5AE, no dot cylinder only

179   Q 45   9·00

On cylinder 183 the control O 44 has been retouched on both panes
On cylinder 187 dot the arrow is missing in the bottom margin

Booklet Panes of Four

From Booklet BD6/a made up from sheets

Selvedge at top	Selvedge at bottom
QB24 Watermark upright —	QB24a Watermark upright —

Booklet Panes of Two

From Booklet BD4 made up from sheets
QB25 Watermark upright   2·00

Booklet Cylinder Numbers

Panes of two

Cyl. No.					Perf. Type E No dot	Dot
185 ..	..	..	..	..	6·00	6·00
187 ..	..	..	..	..	6·00	6·00

Coils

Sideways delivery made up from sheets with joins every 12th stamp

Code No.	Issued	Number in roll	Face value	
N	June 1950	480	£3.0.0	**Left side delivery**

Imprimatur from the National Postal Museum Archives

Imperforate, watermark Type W20
Watermark upright

1951 (MAY 3). PALE GREEN

Cat. No. S.G. No.		Shades	Mint	Used
Q9 505		Pale green	25 ✓	30 ✓

a. Watermark inverted .. 2·00 60 ✓
b. Watermark sideways (14.9.51) .. .. 2·00 ✓ 2·50 ✓
c. Retouched forehead (Cyl. 192 No dot, R.19/1) .. 20·00
d. Spot in daffodil leaf (Cyls. 192 Dot, 195 Dot, 196 Dot, R.10/10) .. .. 15·00
e. Extended serif to 1 of ½ (Cyls. 192 Dot, 195 Dot, R.7/11) .. .. 15·00
f. Coil join (vert. pair) ..
g. Coil join (horiz. pair) ..
h. Malformed fleur-de-lis at right (Cyl. 194 Dot, R.19/8)

$Q9h$

Cylinder Numbers (Blocks of Six)
Perforation Type 5

Cyl. No.				No dot	Dot		Cyl. No.				No dot	Dot
190	..	..	..	2·00	2·00		195	..	..	..	2·00	2·00
192	..	..	..	15·00*	2·00		196	..	..	..	2·00	2·00
193	..	..	..	2·00	2·00		197	..	..	..	2·00	2·00
194	..	..	..	2·00	2·00		199	..	..	..	3·00	3·00

Perforation Type 6 (no dot) and 6B (dot)

				No dot	Dot						No dot	Dot
195	..	..	..	2·00	2·00		**197**	..	..	..	2·00	2·00

Booklet Panes of Six
From Booklets BD20 and BD31/32

QB26 Watermark upright   4·00   QB26a Watermark inverted   14·00

Booklet Panes of Four
From Booklets BD7/10   From Booklet BD7
Selvedge at top   Selvedge at bottom
QB27 Watermark upright   3·00   QB27a Watermark upright   3·00

From Booklets BD8/10
Selvedge at top
QB27b Watermark inverted   10·00

Booklet Panes of Two
From Booklet BD5 made up from sheets
QB28 Watermark upright   3·00

Booklet Cylinder Numbers
Panes of six

	Perf. Type	
	B3(I)	B6(Ie)
Cyl. No.	No dot	Dot
G 4	9·00	9·00

Panes of two

Cyl. No.				Perf. Type	E		Cyl. No.				Perf. Type	E
				No dot	Dot						No dot	Dot
192	..	..	..	†	9·00		196	..	..	..	†	10·00
194	..	..	..	9·00	†		199	..	..	..	†	9·00
	..	..	..	†	15·00							

Coils

Vertical delivery made up from sheets with joins every 20th stamp

Code No.	Issued	Number in roll	Face value	
K	May 1951	960	£6.0.0	Bottom delivery
L	May 1951	480	£3.0.0	Top delivery

Sideways delivery made up from sheets with joins every 12th stamp

N	May 1951	480	£3.0.0	Left side delivery

Vertical delivery printed in continuous reels

K	Sept. 1951	960	£6.0.0	Bottom delivery
L	Sept. 1951	480	£3.0.0	Top delivery

Sideways delivery printed in continuous reels with watermark sideways

N	14.9.51	480	£3.0.0	Left side delivery

Imprimatur from the National Postal Museum Archives

Imperforate, watermark Type W20

Watermark upright

2d. Type Q1

1938 (JANUARY 31). ORANGE

Cat. No.	S.G. No.			Shades		Mint	Used

Qro   465   Orange   1·25 ✓   35 ✓

a.	Bisected (1d.) *Used on cover*	†	20·00 ✓			
b.	Watermark inverted (6.40)	38·00	3·00 ✓	d.	Coil join (vert. pair)	..
c.	Watermark sideways (2.38)	60·00 ✓	25·00 ✓	t.	" Cancelled ", Type 33P .. 13·00	

Bisects: In Guernsey on 27 December 1940, authority was given by Post Office notice, that prepayment of penny postage could be effected by using half a British 2d. stamp, diagonally bisected. Such stamps were used in Guernsey during the German occupation. Earliest known date 27 December 1940. The 2d. stamps available were the 1937 definitive and the 1940 Stamp Centenery commemorative. Examples of George V 2d. stamps bisected were also accepted by the Post Office, as were, in most instances, bisects of other values which had not been authorised. Bisects remained valid for postage in Guernsey until 22 February 1941, although examples are recorded two days later. The 24 February was a Monday and letters prepaid with a bisected stamp, which missed the final Saturday collection, were accepted and postmarked 24 February.

Controls and Cylinder Numbers (Blocks of Six)

Perforation Type 5

Cyl. No.	Control	No dot	Dot	Cyl. No.	Control	No dot	Dot	Cyl. No.	Control	No dot	Dot
1	B 37	9·00	9·00	11	F 39	10·00	10·00	15	G 40	9·00	9·00
1	C 38	16·00	16·00	11	G 40	10·00	10·00	15	H 40	14·00	14·00
7	D 38	9·00	9·00	12	E 39	9·00	9·00	17	H 40	9·00	9·00
8	D 38	9·00	9·00	12	G 40	9·00	9·00	17	I 41	9·00	9·00
10	E 39	9·00	9·00	14	G 40	9·00	9·00	20	I 41	12·00	12·00
11	E 39	9·00	9·00	14	H 40	10·00	10·00				

Perforation Type 6 (no dot) and 6B (dot)

10	E 39	10·00	10·00	11	F 39	10·00	10·00	12	F 39	9·00	9·00
11	E 39	10·00	10·00	12	E 39	10·00	10·00				

Retouched Controls

The following Controls were retouched before the cylinders were put to press:
F39   Cyl. 11, 12, 12.

" Shadow " Controls

Distinct traces of the previous Control are seen on the following:
G 40   Cyl. 12. (traces of F 39)

Booklet Panes of Six

From Booklets BD13/15 and BD25

QB29 Watermark upright   25·00
  s. " Cancelled ", Type 33P .. 85·00

QB29a Watermark inverted £300
  as. " Cancelled ", Type 33P .. 85·00

Booklet Cylinder Numbers

Panes of six from single pane cylinders (no dot)

Cyl. No.				Perf. Type B3(I)	Cyl. No.				Perf. Type B3(I)
H 1	..	..	..	.. 40·00	H 5	..	..	..	.. 45·00
H 2	..	..	..	.. 40·00	H 6	..	..	..	.. 45·00
H 4	..	..	..	.. 45·00	H 7	..	..	..	.. 45·00

Coils

Vertical delivery made up from sheets with joins every 20th stamp

Code No.	Issued	Number in roll	Face value	
Q	1937	960	£8.0.0	Bottom delivery
R	1937	480	£4.0.0	Top delivery

Sideways delivery printed in continuous reels with watermark sideways

T	Feb. 1938	480	£4.0.0	Left side delivery

Imprimaturs from the National Postal Museum Archives

Imperforate, watermark Type W20

Watermark upright
Watermark inverted
Watermark sideways
Tête-bêche pair
Tête-bêche pair with vertical gutter margin

1941 (OCTOBER 6). PALE ORANGE

Cat. No.	S.G. No.			Shades	Mint	Used
Q11	488			Pale orange	50	25 ✓

a.	Watermark inverted	..	2·75	20 ✓		
b.	Watermark sideways (6.42)	11·00 ✓	12·00 ✓			
c.	Tête-bêche (horizontal pair)			*f.*	Coil join (vert. pair)	..
d.	Imperf. (pair)	..	.. £1500†	*s.*	"Specimen ", Type 9	..
e.	Imperf. pane of 6*	..		*t.*	" Cancelled ", Type 33	..

*Booklet error. See General Notes.
†No. Q11*d* exists from NPM archive sales.

Controls and Cylinder Numbers (Blocks of Six)

Perforation Type 5

Cyl. No.	Control	No dot	Dot	Cyl. No.	Control	No dot	Dot	Cyl. No.	Control	No dot	Dot
23	M 43	5·00	5·00	34	P 44	3·00	3·00	47	U 47	3·00	3·00
24	J 41	3·00	3·00	36	Q 45	3·00	3·00	49	U 47	3·00	3·00
24	K 42	3·00	3·00	38	P 44	3·00	3·00	50	U 47	3·00	3·00
25	J 41	3·00	3·00	39	P 44	3·00	3·00	52	None	3·00	3·00
25	K 42	3·00	3·00	39	Q 45	3·00	3·00	54	None	3·00	3·00
25	L 42	3·00	3·00	40	Q 45	3·00	3·00	55	None	5·00	5·00
25	M 43	3·00	3·00	40	R 45	5·00	5·00	58	None	3·00	3·00
26	L 42	5·00	5·00	41	R 45	3·00	3·00	59	None	3·00	3·00
30	M 43	3·00	3·00	42	S 46	3·00	3·00	60	None	3·00	3·00
30	N 43	3·00	3·00	42	U 47	3·00	3·00	61	None	3·00	3·00
32	N 43	3·00	3·00	45	R 45	3·00	3·00	62	None	3·00	3·00
32	O 44	5·00	5·00	45	T 46	3·00	3·00	67	None	5·00	5·00
33	O 44	3·00	3·00	47	T 46	3·00	3·00	68	None	8·00	8·00

Perforation Type 6 (no dot) and 6B (dot)

Cyl. No.	Control	No dot	Dot	Cyl. No.	Control	No dot	Dot	Cyl. No.	Control	No dot	Dot
25	J 41	5·00	†	47	T 46	3·00	3·00	61	None	3·00	3·00
25	L 42	3·00	5·00	52	None	3·00	3·00	62	None	5·00	5·00
34	P 44	3·00	†	53	None	5·00	5·00	64	None	3·00	3·00
38	P 44	3·00	3·00	55	None	3·00	3·00	67	None	5·00	5·00
45	S 46	3·00	3·00	58	None	5·00	5·00	68	None	12·00	12·00
45	T 46	3·00	3·00	59	None	5·00	5·00				

Perforation Type 6 (dot)

25	J 41		5·00	34	P 44		3·00	38	P 44		3·00
25	L 42		3·00								

Perforation Type 5AE, no dot cylinder only

39	P 44	—
40	Q 45	—

Retouched controls

The following controls were retouched before the cylinders were put to press:
U 47   Cyl. 47, 47.

Booklet Panes of Six

From Booklets BD16/18 and BD26/29
QB30 Watermark upright   6·00   QB30a Watermark inverted 20·00

Booklet Cylinder Numbers

Panes of six
Single Pane cylinders (no dot)

Cyl. No.					Perf. Type B3(I)	Cyl. No.					Perf. Type B3(I)
H 10	..	..	..	..	15·00	H 16	..	..	..	..	15·00
H 11	..	..	..	..	15·00	H 17	..	..	..	..	60·00
H 14	..	..	..	..	15·00	H 18	..	..	..	..	15·00
H 15	..	..	..	..	15·00						

Double Pane cylinders

Cyl. No.					B4(E) No dot	B4A(I) Dot	Cyl. No.				B3(I) No dot	B5(BP) Dot	B6(Ie) Dot
H 20	..	..	..	..	22·00	22·00	H 20	..	..		15·00	15·00	22·00
							H 22	..	..		22·00	22·00	22·00

Cyl. No.					B3(I) No dot	B6(Ie) Dot	Cyl. No.					B3(I) No dot	B6(Ie) Dot
H 23	..	..	..	..	15·00	15·00	H 32	..	..	..	..	14·00	14·00
H 24	..	..	..	..	15·00	15·00	H 34	..	..	..	..	15·00	15·00
H 25	..	..	..	..	28·00	28·00	H 41	..	..	..	..	15·00	15·00
H 26	..	..	..	..	28·00	28·00	H 45	..	..	..	..	14·00	14·00
H 28	..	..	..	..	14·00	14·00	H 46	..	..	..	..	15·00	15·00
H 29	..	..	..	..	14·00	14·00	H 47	..	..	..	..	28·00	28·00
H 31	..	..	..	..	14·00	14·00							

Coils

Vertical delivery printed from sheets with joins every 20th stamp

Code No.	Issued	Number in roll	Face value	
Q	1942	960	£8.0.0	Bottom delivery
R	1942	480	£4.0.0	Top delivery
V	Mar. 1949	960	£8.0.0	Bottom delivery

Sideways delivery printed in continuous reels with watermark sideways

T	June 1942	480	£4.0.0	Left side delivery

Imprimaturs from the National Postal Museum Archives

Imperforate, watermark Type W20

Watermark upright
Watermark inverted
Watermark sideways
Tête-bêche pair
Tête-bêche pair with vertical gutter margin

1951 (MAY 3). PALE RED-BROWN

Cat. No.	S.G. No.						Shades	Mint	Used
Q12	506						(1) Pale red-brown	25 ✓	20 ✓
a.	Watermark inverted	..	2·75	3·50			(2) Bright red-brown	1·50	45
b.	Watermark sideways								
	Shade (1)	..	..	80	1·10 ✓				
	Shade (2)	..	..	1·80 ✓	1·10				
c.	Tête-bêche (horiz. pair)	..	£2000						
d.	Imperf. three sides (pair)	..	£800						
e.	"Swan head" to 2 (wmk.								
	sideways)	..	..	15·00					
f.	Ditto retouched								
	Shade (1)	..	..	6·00					
	Shade (2)	..	..	10·00					

g. Retouches to Rose, Thistle and Cross on Crown (Cyl. 75 No dot, R.1/3 & 4) .. .. 25·00
h. Missing jewel in Crown (Cyl. 75 No dot, R.19/1) .. 15·00
i. Coil join (vert. pair) ..

Q12*e*

Q12*f*
Tip of 2 less rounded than normal and slightly shorter

Q12*g* (R.1/3)

Q12*h*

Cylinder Numbers (Blocks of Six)
Perforation Type 5

Cyl. No.					No dot	Dot	Cyl. No.					No dot	Dot
67	..	..	..	..	5·00	5·00	72	..	..	..	..	3·00	3·00
68	..	..	..	..	3·00	3·00	73	..	..	..	..	3·00	3·00
69	..	..	..	..	3·00	3·00	75	..	..	..	..	12·00*	3·00
71	..	..	..	..	3·00	3·00							

Perforation Type 6 (no dot) and 6B (dot)

69	..	..	..	..	3·00	3·00	71	..	..	..	..	3·00	3·00
70	..	..	..	..	8·00	8·00							

Booklet Panes of Six
From Booklets BD19, BD30, BD32 and H1/7

QB31 Watermark upright   5·00   QB31a Watermark inverted   25·00

Booklet Cylinder Numbers
Panes of six

Cyl. No.					Perf. Type B3(I) No dot	B6(Ie) Dot	Cyl. No.					Perf. Type B3(I) No dot	B6(Ie) Dot
H 41	..	..	..	..	12·00	12·00	H 48	..	..	..	..	30·00	30·00
H 47	..	..	..	..	12·00	12·00							

Coils
Vertical delivery made up from sheets with joins every 20th stamp

Code No.	Issued	Number in roll	Face value	
Q	May 1951	960	£8.0.0	Bottom delivery
R	May 1951	480	£4.0.0	Top delivery
V	May 1951	960	£8.0.0	Bottom delivery

Sideways delivery printed in continuous reels with watermark sideways

T	May 1951	480	£4.0.0	Left side delivery

Vertical delivery printed in continuous reels

Q	Dec. 1951	960	£8.0.0	Bottom delivery
R	Jan. 1952	480	£4.0.0	Top delivery
V	Dec. 1951	960	£8.0.0	Bottom delivery

Imprimaturs from the National Postal Museum Archives
Imperforate, watermark Type W20

Watermark upright
Watermark inverted
Watermark sideways
Tête-bêche pair
Tête-bêche pair with vertical gutter margin

2½d. Type Q1

1937 (MAY 10). ULTRAMARINE

Cat. No.	S.G. No.						Shades		Mint	Used
Q13	466						Ultramarine		25 ✓	5 ✓

a.	Watermark inverted (6.40)	25·00	2·00 ✓
b.	Watermark sideways (6.40)	75·00 ✓	12·00 ✓
c.	Tête-bêche (horizontal pair)		
d.	Coil join (vert. pair)	..	
e.	Coil join (horiz. pair)	..	
s.	"Cancelled", Type 33	..	
t.	"Cancelled", Type 33P	..	12·00

Controls and Cylinder Numbers (Blocks of Six)

Perforation Type 5.   Without pick up bar

Cyl. No.	Control	No dot	Dot	Cyl. No.	Control	No dot	Dot	Cyl. No.	Control	No dot	Dot
1	A 37	25·00	25·00	2	B 37	1·40	1·40	2	D 38	4·00	4·00
2	A 37	1·40	1·40								

Perforation Type 6 (no dot) and 6B (dot)

2	A 37	1·40	1·40	2	D 38	1·40	1·40

With pick up bar.   Perforation Type 5

Cyl. No.	Control	No dot	Dot	Cyl. No.	Control	No dot	Dot	Cyl. No.	Control	No dot	Dot
3	E 39	1·40	1·40	22	H 40	1·40	1·40	44	I 41	2·00	2·00
3	G 40	2·00	2·00	23	H 40	2·50	2·50	45	I 41	1·40	1·40
6 (i)	G 40	2·00	2·00	25	H 40	1·40	1·40	48	I 41	1·40	1·40
6 (ii)	G 40	3·50	3·50	28	H 40	1·40	1·40	53	I 41	1·40	1·40
6	H 40	1·40	1·40	30	H 40	2·50	2·50	56	I 41	1·40	1·40
7	G 40	1·75	1·75	34	H 40	1·75	1·40	57	I 41	1·40	1·40
10	G 40	1·75	1·75	36	H 40	1·75	1·40	58	I 41	1·40	1·40
10	H 40	9·00	9·00	40	H 40	2·00	2·00	59	I 41	1·75	1·75
13 (i)	G 40	1·75	—	41	H 40	1·75	1·75	61	I 41	1·40	1·40
13 (ii)	G 40	2·50	2·50	41	I 41	1·40	1·40	62	I 41	2·00	2·00
15	G 40	2·50	2·50	43	H 40	2·50	2·50	63	I 41	1·75	1·75
15	H 40	2·50	2·50	43	I 41	2·00	2·00	64	I 41	2·00	2·00
20	H 40	2·00	2·00	44	H 40	1·40	1·40	65	I 41	2·00	75·00

Perforation Type 6 (no dot) and 6B (dot)

Cyl. No.	Control	No dot	Dot	Cyl. No.	Control	No dot	Dot	Cyl. No.	Control	No dot	Dot
6 (i)	G 40	1·75	2·75	20	H 40	2·00	2·00	30	H 40	1·40	1·40
6 (ii)	G 40	2·00	2·00	22	H 40	7·00	7·00	41	H 40	8·00	8·00
8	G 40	2·25	2·25	23	H 40	2·00	2·00				
10	H 40	2·00	2·00	25	H 40	2·50	2·50				

Varieties:

Cylinder 6 Control G 40 exists in two states:
> (i) Control faint
> (ii) Control heavily retouched

Cylinder 13 exists in two states:
> (i) Control faint
> (ii) Control heavily retouched

Retouched controls

> The following controls were retouched before the cylinders were put to press:
> > G 40 Cyl. 7, 7.
> > I 41 Cyl. 41, 41., 43, 43.

"Shadow" controls

> Distinct traces of the previous control are seen on the following:
> > D 38 Cyl. 2 (C 38)
> > H 40 Cyl. 6 (G 40)
> > I 41 Cyl. 44 (H 40)

Booklet Panes of Six

From Booklets BD13/15 and BD25

QB32 Watermark upright	30·00		QB32a Watermark inverted	£200		
s. "Cancelled", Type 33P ..	80·00		as. "Cancelled", Type 33P ..	80·00		

Booklet Cylinder Numbers

Panes of six from single pane cylinders (no dot)

Cyl. No			Perf. Type B3(I)	Cyl. No.			Perf. Type B3(I)
J 3	..	.. ..	45·00	J 7	..	.. ..	45·00
J 5	..	.. ..	45·00	J 10	..	.. ..	45·00

Coils

Vertical delivery made up from sheets with joins every 20th stamp

Code No.	Issued	Number in roll	Face value	
F	1937	960	£10.0.0	Bottom delivery

Sideways delivery made up from sheets with joins every 12th stamp

M	1937	480	£5.0.0	Left side delivery

Vertical delivery printed from continuous reels

F	1940	960	£10.0.0	Bottom delivery

Sideways delivery printed from continuous reels with watermark sideways

M	June 1940	480	£5.0.0	Left side delivery

Imprimatur from the National Postal Museum Archives

Imperforate, watermark Type W20

Watermark upright

Specimen overprint from the National Postal Museum Archives

Booklet pane of six. Perf. 15 × 14, watermark Type W20

"Speçimen", Type 23 and upper left stamp with punch hole

1941 (JULY 21).   LIGHT ULTRAMARINE

Cat. No.	S.G. No.			Shades	Mint	Used
Q14	489			Light ultramarine	12	10

a.	Watermark inverted (3.42)	1·00	40
b.	Watermark sideways (1942)	16·00	10·00
c.	Tête-bêche (horizontal pair)	£1300	
d.	Imperf. (pair)	£2000†	
e.	Imperf. pane of 6*	£2500	

f. b for d in value (Cyl. 239 Dot, R.18/3) .. .. .. 17·00
s. "Specimen", Type 9 ..
t. "Cancelled", Type 28 ..
u. "Cancelled", Type 33 ..

*Booklet error. See General Notes.
†No. Q14d exists from NPM archive sales.

Q14f

Controls and Cylinder Numbers (Blocks of Six)

Perforation Type 5

Cyl. No.	Control	No. dot	Dot	Cyl. No.	Control	No dot	Dot	Cyl. No.	Control	No dot	Dot
69	J 41	60	60	135	M 43	60	60	203	S 46	60	60
70	J 41	60	60	135	N 43	60	60	203	T 46	60	60
72	J 41	60	60	136	N 43	60	60	204	T 46	60	60
73	J 41	16·00		138	N 43	60	60	204	U 47	60	60
75	J 41	3·00	3·00	142	N 43	60	60	205	S 46	60	60
77	J 41	60		142	O 44	60	60	205	T 46	60	60
80	J 41	60	60	143	N 43	2·00	2·00	206	S 46	60	60
80	K 42	60	60	144	N 43	60	60	209	U 47	60	60
81	J 41	60	60	145	N 43	60	60	210	T 46	60	60
81	K 42	60	60	145	O 44	60	60	211	U 47	60	60
82	J 81	†	16·00	146	N 43	2·00	2·00	212	U 47	60	60
83	J 41	60	60	146	O 44	60	60	213	U 47	60	60
83	K 42	60	60	147	O 44	60	60	216	U 47	60	60
84	J 41	60	60	148	O 44	60	60	217	U 47	60	60
84	K 42	60	60	149	O 44	60	60	219	None	3·00	3·00
84	L 42	60	60	150	O 44	60	60	220	U 47	60	60
86	K 42	60	60	151	P 44	60	60	222	None	60	60
87	K 42	60	60	152	O 44	60	60	223	None	60	60
90	K 42	60	60	152	P 44	60	60	224	None	60	60
92	K 42	60	60	153	O 44	60	60	225	U 47	60	60
95	K 42	60	60	154	O 44	60	60	225	None	2·50	2·50
95	L 42	60	60	155	O 44	60	60	226	None	2·50	2·50
96	K 42	60	60	155	P 44	60	60	227	U 47	60	60
96	L 42	2·50	2·50	156	P 44	60	60	228	None	60	60
97	L 42	60	60	157	P 44	60	60	229	None	60	60
99	L 42	60	60	159	P 44	60	60	230	None	60	60
100	L 42	2·00	2·00	162	P 44	60	60	231	None	60	60
101	L 42	60	60	164	P 44	60	60	234	None	60	60
104	L 42	60	60	165	P 44	60	60	235	None	60	60
110	L 42	—	†	166	P 44	2·50	2·50	236	None	60	60
110	M 43	60	60	168	P 44	60	60	238	None	60	60
111	L 42	60	60	172	P 44	60	60	239	None	60	60
111	M 43	60	60	172	Q 45	60	60	240	None	60	60
113	L 42	60	60	173	Q 45	60	60	241	None	60	60
113	M 43	60	60	174	P 44	60	60	244	None	2·00	2·00
114	L 42	60	60	174	Q 45	60	60	245	None	60	60
117	L 42	60	60	177	Q 45	60	60	246	None	60	60
117	M 43	60	60	178	Q 45	60	60	247	None	60	60
118	M 43	60	60	184	Q 45	—	—	248	None	60	60
119	M 43	60	60	186	Q 45	60	60	249	None	60	60
120	M 43	60	60	186	R 45	60	60	250	None	60	60
121	M 43	60	60	187	R 45	60	60	252	None	60	60
121	N 43	60	60	187	Q 45	60	60	253	None	60	60
124	M 43	60	60	190	Q 45	60	60	254	None	60	60
127	M 43	60	60	190	R 45	60	60	255	None	60	60
130	M 43	60	60	194	R 45	60	60	256	None	60	60
131	M 43	60	60	195	S 46	60	60	260	None	60	60
131	N 43	60	60	197	S 46	60	60	261	None	60	60
132	M 43	60	60	201	S 46	60	60	263	None	60	60
132	N 43	60	60	201	T 46	60	60	266	None	2·00	2·00
133	M 43	60	60	202	S 46	60	60				
133	N 43	60	60	202	T 46						

Perforation Type 6 (no dot) and 6B (dot)

Cyl. No.	Control	No dot	Dot	Cyl. No.	Control	No dot	Dot	Cyl. No.	Control	No dot	Dot
111	L 42	2·50	2·50	164	P 44	60	60	195 (i)	R 45	60	60
135	M 43	60	†	165	P 44	60	60	195 (ii)	R 45	7·50	7·50
138	N 43	60	2·00	167	P 44	60	60	196	R 45	60	60
144	N 43	60	60	172	P 44	60	60	236	None	60	60
146	N 43	60	†	173	Q 45	60	60	238	None	60	60
148	O 44	†	2·00	179	Q 45	2·00	2·00	239	None	60	60
151	N 43	60	†	184	Q 45	60	60	240	None	60	60
151	O 44	60	60	187	Q 45	60	60	246	None	2·50	2·50
152	O 44	60	60	187	R 45	60	60	260	None	60	60
156	P 44	60	†	190	Q 45	60	60	261	None	2·00	2·00
161	P 44	60	60	194	R 45	60	60	263	None	60	60

Perforation Type 6 (dot)

Cyl.	Control	Dot	Cyl.	Control	Dot	Cyl.	Control	Dot
135	M 43	60	151	O 44	60	165	P 44	60
138	N 43	60	152	O 44	60	167	P 44	60
144	N 43	60	156	P 44	60	173	Q 45	60
146	N 43	60	161	P 44	60	184	Q 45	60
151	N 43	60	164	P 44	60			

Perforation Type 5AE, no dot cylinder only

Cyl.	Control	No dot	Cyl.	Control	No dot	Cyl.	Control	No dot
142	O 44	2·00	156	P 44	7·50	184	Q 45	60
145	O 44	60	162	P 44	60	186	Q 45	60
146	N 43	2·00	164	P 44	60	219	None	5·00
148	O 44	2·00	165	P 44	60	223	None	60
149	O 44	60	172	P 44	60	248	None	60
150	O 44	60	172	Q 45	60	249	None	5·00
152	O 44	60	174	Q 45	60			
154	O 44	60	177	Q 45	60			

Varieties:

Cylinder 100 had the L and fraction bar engraved by hand.
On cylinder 146 the control N 43 has been heavily retouched on both panes. The retouches show as an outline of heavy dots.
Cylinder 195 exists in two states. In state (ii) the control has been heavily retouched.
The U 47 controls have been retouched on cylinder 212 (dot pane) and cylinder 217 (no dot pane).

Errors of engraving

Cylinder 144 (both panes) were originally engraved " 141 ". Cylinder 166 dot pane was originally engraved " 116.", and cylinder 204 (no dot pane) was originally engraved " 104 ".

" Shadow " controls

Distinct traces of the previous control are seen on L 42 cylinder 96 dot (K 42) and on O 44 cylinder 146 (both panes N 43).

Booklet Panes of Six

From Booklets BD16/18 and BD26/29

QB33 Watermark upright   5·00   QB33a Watermark inverted   8·00

Booklet Cylinder Numbers

Panes of six

Single Pane cylinders (no dot)

Cyl. No				Perf. Type B3(I)	Cyl. No.				Perf. Type B3(I)
J 15	..	..	..	12·00	J 18	..	..	..	12·00
J 16	..	..	..	12·00	J 20	..	..	..	12·00
J 17	..	..	..	12·00	J 21	..	..	..	12·00

Double Pane cylinders

Cyl. No.				B3(I) No dot	B5(BP) Dot	Cyl. No.				B4(E) No dot	B4A(I) Dot
J 23	..	..	..	10·00	10·00	J 23	..	..	..	10·00	10·00
J 25	..	..	..	10·00	10·00	J 25	..	..	..	20·00	20·00
J 28	..	..	..	12·00	12·00	J 28	..	..	..	10·00	10·00
J 29	..	..	..	10·00							
J 30	..	..	..	10·00	10·00						

Cyl. No.				B3(I) No dot	B6(Ie) Dot	Cyl. No.				B3(I) No dot	B6(Ie) Dot
J 29	..	..	..	10·00	10·00	J 50	..	..	..	10·00	10·00
J 30	..	..	..	10·00	12·00	J 51	..	..	..	12·00	12·00
J 31	..	..	..	10·00	10·00	J 52	..	..	..	10·00	10·00
J 32	..	..	..	10·00	10·00	J 53	..	..	..	10·00	10·00
J 34	..	..	..	10·00	10·00	J 54	..	..	..	10·00	10·00
J 35	..	..	..	10·00	10·00	J 58	..	..	..	10·00	10·00
J 39	..	..	..	10·00	10·00	J 59	..	..	..	10·00	10·00
J 43	..	..	..	20·00	20·00	J 60	..	..	..	10·00	10·00
J 45	..	..	..	10·00	10·00	J 61	..	..	..	10·00	10·00
J 48	..	..	..	10·00	10·00	J 62	..	..	..	12·00	12·00
J 49	..	..	..	10·00	10·00	J 65	..	..	..	15·00	15·00

Coils

Vertical delivery printed in continuous reels

Code No.	Issued	Number in roll	Face value	
F	1942	960	£10.0.0	Bottom delivery
U	Nov. 1949	1920	£20.0.0	Bottom delivery

Sideways delivery printed from continuous reels with watermark sideways

M	1942	480	£5.0.0	Left side delivery

Imprimatur from the National Postal Museum Archives

Imperforate, watermark Type W20

Watermark upright

Specimen overprints from the National Postal Museum Archives

Booklet pane of six. Perf. 15 × 14, watermark Type W20

"Specimen", Type 30

1951 (MAY 3) PALE SCARLET

Cat. No.	S.G. No.			Shades	Mint	Used
Q15	507			Pale scarlet	20✓	12✓
a.	Watermark inverted	..	60✓	35✓	*cb.* Damaged S in POSTAGE .. 10·00	
b.	Watermark sideways	..	80✓	90✓	*d.* Tête-bêche (horizontal pair)	

Q15*cb*

Cylinder Numbers (Blocks of Six)
Perforation Type 5

Cyl. No.				No dot	Dot	Cyl. No.				No dot	Dot
259	..	..	..	1·50	1·50	270	..	..	..	1·00	1·00
261	..	..	..	1·00	1·00	273	..	..	..	1·00	1·00
264	..	..	..	6·00	6·00	274	..	..	..	1·00	1·00
266	..	..	..	1·00	1·00	275	..	..	..	1·00	1·00
267	..	..	..	1·00	1·00	276	..	..	..	1·00	1·00
268	..	..	..	1·00	1·00	277	..	..	..	1·00	1·00
269	..	..	..	1·00	1·00	279	..	..	..	1·00	1·00

Booklet Panes of Six
From Booklets BD19/20 and BD30/32

QB34 Watermark upright   3·00   QB34a Watermark inverted   4·00

Booklet Cylinder Numbers
Panes of six

Cyl. No.				Perf. Type B3(I) No dot	B6(Ie) Dot	Cyl. No.				Perf. Type B3(I) No dot	B6(Ie) Dot
J 62	..	..	..	7·00	7·00	J 68	..	..	..	11·00	11·00
J 66	..	..	..	7·00	7·00	J 69	..	..	..	8·00	8·00
J 67	..	..	..	7·00	7·00	J 70	..	..	..	7·00	7·00

Coils
Vertical delivery printed from continuous reels

Code No.	Issued	Number in roll	Face value	
F	May 1951	960	£10.0.0	Bottom delivery
U	May 1951	1920	£20.0.0	Bottom delivery

Sideways delivery printed from continuous reels with watermark sideways

| M | 3.5.51 | 480 | £5.0.0 | Left side delivery |

Imprimatur from the National Postal Museum Archives
Imperforate, watermark Type W20

Watermark upright

3d. Type Q1

1938 (JANUARY 31). VIOLET

Cat. No.	S.G. No.		Shades	Mint	Used
Q16	467		Violet	5·00 ✓	60 ✓

a. Top margin imperf. ..
b. Dark spot below eye (Cyl. 11
   No dot, R. 19/1) .. ..   12·00
c. Dotted line into margin (Cyl.
   14 No dot, R. 20/1) .. ..   10·00

Broken number in value ✓

f. Coil join (vert. pair).. ..
g. Coil join (horiz. pr.) (6.38) ..

Q16b

Q16c

Controls and Cylinder Numbers (Blocks of Six)

Perforation Type 5

Cyl. No.	Control	No dot	Dot	Cyl. No.	Control	No dot	Dot	Cyl. No.	Control	No dot	Dot
3	C 38	32·00	32·00	9	D 38	32·00	32·00	17	G 40	45·00	45·00
5 (i)	C 38	32·00	32·00	11	E 39	32·00*	32·00	18	G 40	32·00	32·00
5 (ii)	C 38	†	45·00	12	E 39	32·00	32·00	18	H 40	32·00	32·00
9	C 38	35·00	35·00	14	G 40	32·00*	32·00				

Perforation Type 6 (no dot) and 6B (dot)

11	E 39	32·00	32·00	12	E 39	32·00	32·00

Varieties:

Cylinder 5 dot exists in two states:
      (i) No dot after " 5 "
      (ii) added dot after " 5 ".
Cylinders 3, 5 and 9 dot have a white dot in the " 3 " of the control with damage in the shape of two additional white dots on cylinder 9 dot.

' Shadow " controls

Distinct traces of the previous control are seen on the following:
      E 39   Cyl. 11. (D 38)
      H 40   Cyl. 18 (G 40)

Coils

Vertical delivery made up from sheets with joins every 20th stamp

Code No.	Issued	Number in roll	Face value	
C	1938	960	£12.0.0	Bottom delivery

Sideways delivery made up from sheets with joins every 12th stamp

S	June 1938	480	£6.0.0	Left side delivery

Imprimatur from the National Postal Museum Archives

Imperforate, watermark Type W20

Watermark upright

1941 (NOVEMBER 3). PALE VIOLET

Cat. No.	S.G. No.		Shades	Mint	Used
Q17	490		Pale violet	1·60 ✓	30 ✓

a. White patch in hair and
   blemish in background (Cyl.
   34 Dot, R. 9/10) .. ..   25·00
b. Ditto, retouched .. ..   22·00
c. Broken circle to value (Cyl.
   27 No dot, R. 18/2) .. ..   12·00
d. Ditto, retouched .. ..   10·00

e. Top margin imperf. ..
f. Coil join (vert. pair) (1942)..
g. Coil join (horiz. pr.) (6.43) ..
s. " Specimen ", Type 9 ..
t. " Cancelled ", Type 33 ..

Q17a   Q17b

Q17c   Q17d

Controls and Cylinder Numbers (Blocks of Six)

Perforation Type 5

Cyl. No.	Control	No dot	Dot	Cyl. No.	Control	No dot	Dot	Cyl. No.	Control	No. dot	Dot
21	J 41	10·00	10·00	25	N 43	10·00	10·00	28	Q 45	10·00	10·00
21	K 42	10·00	10·00	25	O 44	10·00	10·00	30	None	15·00	15·00
21	L 42	10·00	10·00	26	N 43	10·00	10·00	32	None	20·00	20·00
22	L 42	15·00	15·00	26	O 44	10·00	10·00	34	None	10·00	10·00
22	M 43	10·00	10·00	27	R 45	20·00*	10·00				
22	N 13	15·00	15·00	27	None	20·00*	10·00				

Perforation Type 6

Cyl. No.	Control	No dot 6	6B	Dot 6	Cyl. No.	Control	No dot 6	6B	Dot 6	Cyl. No.	Control	No dot 6	6B	Dot 6
21	J 41	10·00	10·00	15·00	22	L 42	27·00	27·00	†	29	O 44	10·00	10·00	†
21	L 42	27·00	27·00	†	28	P 44	10·00	10·00	†	29	P 44	15·00	15·00	†

Perforation Type 2A

Cyl. No.	Control	Dot
30	None	†	—

Perforation Type 5AE, no dot cylinder only

Cyl. No.	Control	No dot
25	O 44	10·00
28	Q 45	15·00

"Shadow" control

Distinct traces of the previous control are seen on K 42 cylinder 21 dot (J 41).

Error of engraving

On cylinder 27 the dividing arrow was incorrectly engraved between stamps 7 and 8 in the upper and lower margins. This was erased by lines and re-engraved in the correct position between stamps 6 and 7.

Coils

Vertical delivery made up from sheets with joins every 20th stamp

Code No.	Issued	Number in roll	Face value	
C	1942	960	£12.0.0	Bottom delivery

Sideways delivery made up from sheets with joins every 12th stamp

S	June 1943	480	£6.0.0	Left side delivery

Imprimatur from the National Postal Museum Archives

Imperforate, watermark Type W20

Watermark upright

4d. Type Q2

1938 (NOVEMBER 21). GREY-GREEN

Cat. No.	S.G. No.		Shades	Mint	Used
Q19	468		Grey-green	35 ✓	30 ✓

   a. Imperf. (pair) .. .. .. £1200†
   b. Imperf. three sides (pair) .. £1500
   s. "Specimen", Type 9 ..
   t. "Cancelled", Type 33 ..

†No. Q19*a* exists from NPM archive sales.

Controls and Cylinder Numbers (Blocks of Six)

Single Pane cylinder. Perforation Type 6B (no dot)

Cyl. No.	Control	No dot	Dot	Cyl. No.	Control	No dot	Dot	Cyl. No.	Control	No dot	Dot
1	D 38	2·75		1	I 41	2·75		1	K 42 bars ⌐	2·75	
1	E 39	2·75		1	K 42	5·00					
1	G 40	2·75		1	K 42 bar —	2·75					

Perforation Type 6 (no dot)
   1 I 41   4·25

Double Pane cylinder. Perforation Type 6 (no dot) and 6B (dot)

6	None	2·75	2·75	9	O 44 bar —	2·75	2·75	9	O 44 bars ⌐	2·75	2·75
9	O 44	2·75	2·75	9	O 44 bars ⌐	2·75	2·75				

"Shadow" controls

  Distinct traces of the previous control are seen on the following:
    I 41 Cyl. 1 (G 40)
    K 42 (incl. 1 and 2 bars)   Cyl. 1 (I 41)

Imprimatur from the National Postal Museum Archives

Imperforate, watermark Type W20

Watermark upright

1950 (OCTOBER 2). LIGHT ULTRAMARINE

Cat. No.	S.G. No.		Shades	Mint	Used
Q20	508		Light ultramarine	1·40 ✓	1·10 ✓

   a. Retouched background to POS (Cyl. 13 No dot, R.9/2)   12·00
   b. Double impression .. .. †   —
   c. Coil join (vert. pair) ..
   d. Coil join (horiz. pair) ..

A single used example is known of No. Q20*b*. This is not as clear as the King George V varieties since it is a pale stamp, but inscription and frame are doubled nevertheless. It was probably due to paper movement in the press.

Q20*a*

Cylinder Numbers (Blocks of Six)

Perforation Types

Cyl. No.				2 No dot	3 Dot	5 No dot	5 Dot	6 No dot	6B Dot
13	..	..	..	17·00	17·00	9·00	9·00	9·00	9·00

Coils

Vertical delivery made up from sheets with joins every 20th stamp

Code No.	Issued	Number in roll	Face value	
A	2.10.50	960	£16.0.0	Bottom delivery

Sideways delivery made up from sheets with joins every 12th stamp

H	2.10.50	480	£8.0.0	Left side delivery

Imprimatur from the National Postal Museum Archives

Imperforate, watermark Type W20

Watermark upright

5d. Type Q2

1938 (NOVEMBER 21). BROWN

Cat. No.	S.G. No.				Shades		Mint	Used
Q21	469				Brown		2·50 ✓	35 ✓
a.	Imperf. (pair)	..	..	..	£1250†	s. "Specimen", Type 9	..	
b.	Imperf. three sides (pair)	..	£1000					

†No. Q21a exists from NPM archive sales.

Controls and Cylinder Numbers (Blocks of Six)

Single Pane cylinder.   Perforation Type 6B (no dot)

Cyl. No.	Control	No dot	Dot	Cyl. No.	Control	No dot	Dot	Cyl. No.	Control	No dot	Dot
1	D 38	18·00		1	G 40	18·00		1	K 42	18·00	
1	E 39	18·00		1	I 41	18·00					

Perforation Type 6 (no dot)

1	I 41	35·00

Double Pane cylinder.   Perforation Type 5

3	L 42	50·00	50·00	3	L 42 bars ∟	18·00	18·00	3	L 42 bars ☐	18·00	18·00
3	L 42 bar —	18·00	18·00	3	L 42 bars ☐	18·00	18·00				

Perforation Type 6 (no dot) and 6B (dot)

3	L 42 bars ☐	18·00	18·00
4	K 42	†	25·00

Perforation Type 5AE (no dot)

3	L 42 bars ∟	25·00

" Shadow " control

Distinct traces of the previous control are seen on E 39 cylinder 1 no dot (D 38)

Variety:

Cylinder 1 no dot with control I 41 has a large smudge between the cylinder number and the stamp

Imprimatur from the National Postal Museum Archives

Imperforate, watermark Type W20

Watermark upright

6d. Type Q2

1939 (JANUARY 30). PURPLE

Cat. No.	S.G. No.		Shades	Mint	Used
Q22	470		Purple	1·25 ✓	25 ✓
a.	Coil join (vert. pair)	..			
s.	" Specimen ", Type 9	..			
t.	" Cancelled ", Type 33	..			
	Extra there in use	✓			

Controls and Cylinder Numbers (Blocks of Six)

Typographed control in black.   Single Pane cylinders.   Perforation Type 2 (no dot).

Cyl. No.	Control	No dot	Dot	Cyl. No.	Control	No dot	Dot	Cyl. No.	Control	No dot	Dot
1	D 38	7·00		25	L 42	7·00		36	T 46	7·00	
1	E 39	7·00		30	M 43	7·00		36	U 47	7·00	
10	F 39	7·00		32	L 42	7·00		36	None	7·00	
10	G 40	7·00		32	M 43	7·00		37	T 46	7·00	
10	H 40	7·00		32	N 43	7·00		37	None	7·00	
21	H 40	7·00		33	O 44	7·00		39	None	7·00	
25	J 41	7·00		33	Q 45	7·00		41	None	7·00	
25	K 42	7·00		33	T 46	22·00					

Perforation Type 3 (no dot)			Perforation Type 6B (no dot)			Perforation Type 6 (no dot)		
25	K 42	14·00	1	D 38	7·00	1	D 38	12·00
32	N 43	7·00	25	L 42	14·00	37	None	11·00

Varieties:

Cylinder 25.   With control J 41 in state 1 there is a coloured slightly diagonal line running through P of POSTAGE and extending through " 25 " which has been partly erased in state 2.   This remains faint with control K 42 and is completely removed with control L 42.

Cylinder 37.   The pick-up bar under R. 20/1 is badly damaged and under R. 20/10 it is completely omitted.

Coil

Vertical delivery made up from sheets with joins every 20th stamp

Code No.	Issued	Number in roll	Face value	
J	30.1.39	480	£12.0.0	Bottom delivery

Imprimatur from the National Postal Museum Archives

Imperforate, watermark Type W20

Watermark upright

7d. Type Q3

1939 (FEBRUARY 27). EMERALD-GREEN

Cat. No.	S.G. No.		Shades	Mint	Used
Q23	471		Emerald-green	4·50 ✓	35 ✓

  a. Imperf. three sides (pair) . . £1000
  b. Cracked cylinder (Cyl. 10 Dot, R.1–20/12) . . . .
  c. Damaged N in REVENUE (Cyls. 9 and 10 No dot, R. 20/2) . . . . . . 30·00
  t. "Cancelled", Type 33 . .

Q23*b*   Q23*c*

The illustration of No. Q23*b* is typical of a plate crack which occurred in all stamps in the 12th vertical row of cylinder 10 dot. This cylinder was withdrawn and replaced by cylinder 9.

No. Q23*c* occurred in more than one state. In its second state with control S 46 the coloured line is thinner as if an attempt had been made to remove it. Without control it is as in the second state but in addition there is damage to the V of REVENUE.

Controls and Cylinder Numbers (Blocks of Six)

Single Pane cylinders. Perforation Type 6B (no dot)

Cyl. No.	Control	No dot	Dot	Cyl No.	Control	No dot	Dot	Cyl. No.	Control	No dot	Dot
1	E 39 bar —	28·00		2	E 39 bars ☐	28·00		3	E 39 bars ☐	28·00	
1	E 39 bars ☐	28·00		2	E 39 bars ☐	28·00		3	E 39 bars ☐	28·00	
2	E 39	28·00		2	E 39 bars ☐	28·00		3	E 39 bars ☐	28·00	
2	E 39 bar —	28·00		3	E 39 bars ☐	28·00		3	E 39 bars ☐	28·00	

Perforation Type 6 (no dot)

1	E 39 bar —	28·00
2	E 39 bars ☐	28·00
3	E 39 bars ☐	28·00

Double Pane cylinders

Perforation Type 5				Perforation Type 6 (no dot) and 6B (dot)		
9	None	28·00	28·00	9	None	65·00	65·00
10	S 46	45·00*	28·00	10	S 46	45·00*	28·00
10	None	45·00*	28·00	10	None	45·00*	28·00
12	None	28·00	28·00	12	None	28·00	28·00

Imprimatur from the National Postal Museum Archives

Imperforate, watermark Type W20

Watermark upright

8d. Type Q3

1939 (FEBRUARY 27).   CARMINE

Cat. No. S.G. No.	Shades	Mint	Used
Q24 472	Bright carmine	5·00 ✓	40 ✓
s. " Specimen ", Type 9 ..	t. " Cancelled ", Type 33 ..		

Controls and Cylinder Numbers (Blocks of Six)

Single Pane cylinders.   Perforation Type 6B (no dot)

Cyl. No.	Control	No dot	Dot	Cyl. No.	Control	No dot	Dot	Cyl. No.	Control	No dot	Dot
1	E 39	55·00		1	E 39 bars ⌴	42·00		3(i)	O 44	42·00	
1	E 39 bar —	55·00		1	E 39 bars ☐	42·00		3(ii)	O 44	42·00	
1	E 39 bars ⌞	42·00		1	E 39 bars ☐	42·00		3	O 44 bar —	55·00	

Double Pane cylinders

Perforation Type 5   Perforation Type 6 (no dot) and 6B (dot)

6	S 46	42·00	42·00	6	S 46 bar —	42·00	42·00
9	None	42·00	42·00	9	None	55·00	55·00

Varieties:

The control O 44 exists in two states:
            (i) Control very faint and (ii) Control retouched with heavy outline

Imprimatur from the National Postal Museum Archives

Imperforate, watermark Type W20

Watermark upright

9d. Type Q3

1939 (MAY 1).   OLIVE-GREEN

Cat. No. S.G. No.		Shades	Mint	Used
Q25 473		Deep olive-green	5·00 ✓	40 ✓
a.	Sloping serif to top stroke of last E of PENCE and dot to right of central cross in Crown (Cyl. 3 No dot, R.18/1) .. .. 25·00			
b.	Serif touched out but dot remains (Cyl. 2 No dot, R.18/1) .. .. 25·00	s. " Specimen ", Type 9 ..		
		t. " Cancelled ", Type 33 ..		

No. Q25a is a multipositive variety occurring on cylinder 3 which was replaced by cylinder 2 where it was partially corrected. A different multipositive was used for cylinder 5.

Controls and Cylinder Numbers (Blocks of Six)

Typographed control, in black   Single Pane cylinders.   Perforation Type 2 (no dot).

Cyl. No.	Control	No dot	Dot	Cyl. No.	Control	No dot	Dot	Cyl. No.	Control	No dot	Dot
2	I 41	45·00*		2	O 44	45·00*		3	G 40	45·00*	
2	K 42	45·00*		2	P 44	45·00*		3	H 40	45·00*	
2	L 42	45·00*		2	R 45	45·00*		3	N 43	45·00*	
2	N 43	45·00*		3	E 39	45·00*					

Perforation Type 3 (no dot)

2	R 45	—

Double Pane cylinders.

Perforation Type 5 | Perforation 5AE (no dot cylinder only)

5	None	35·00	35·00		5	None	45·00

Perforation Type 6 (no dot) and 6B (dot) | Perforation Type 2 (no dot) and 2A dot

5	None	35·00	35·00		5	None	40·00	40·00

Imprimatur from the National Postal Museum Archives

Imperforate, watermark Type W20

Watermark upright

10d. Type Q3

1939 (MAY 1). TURQUOISE-BLUE

Cat. No.	S.G. No.			Shades	Mint	Used
Q26	474			Turquoise-blue	4·50 ✓	45 ✓

a. Imperf. (pair) £2000
b. Broken fleur-de-lis (Cyl. 7 No dot, R.20/7) .. .. 35·00

s. " Specimen ", Type 9 ..
t. " Cancelled " Type 33 ..

No. Q26*a* exists from NPM archive sales.

Q26*b*

Controls and Cylinder Numbers (Blocks of Six)

Typographed control, in black. Single Pane cylinder. Perforation 2 (no dot).

Cyl. No.	Control	No dot	Dot	Cyl. No.	Control	No dot	Dot	Cyl. No.	Control	No dot	Dot
ɪ	E 39	30·00		ɪ	J 41	30·00		ɪ	N 43	30·00	
ɪ	F 39	30·00		ɪ	K 42	30·00		ɪ	O 44	30·00	
ɪ	H 40	30·00		ɪ	L 42	30·00					
ɪ	I 41	30·00		ɪ	M 43	30·00					

Double Pane cylinders. Perforation Type 6 (no dot) and 6B (dot)

5	Q 45	30·00	30·00	5	U 47	30·00	30·00	6	Q 45	†	45·00
5	T 46	30·00	30·00	5	None	30·00	30·00	7	None	—	£125

Perforation Type 5

7	None	30·00	30·00

Imprimatur from the National Postal Museum Archives

Imperforate, watermark Type W20
Watermark upright

11d. Type Q3

1947 (DECEMBER 29). PLUM

Cat. No.	S.G. No.		Shades	Mint	Used
Q27	474*a*		Plum	3·00 ✓	1·25 ✓

Cylinder Number (Blocks of Six)

Double Pane Cylinder

Perforation Type 5				Perforation Type 6 (no dot) and 6B (dot)			
Cyl. No.		No dot	Dot	Cyl. No.		No dot	Dot
ɪ	.. ..	24·00	24·00	ɪ	.. ..	24·00	24·00

Imprimatur from the National Postal Museum Archives

Imperforate, watermark Type W20
Watermark upright

1s. Type Q3

1939 (MAY 1). BISTRE-BROWN

Cat. No.	S.G. No.			Shades	Mint	Used
Q28	475			Bistre-brown	5·00 ✓	25 ✓

a. Broken Crown (Cyl. 16 Dot, S 46, R.18/2) .. .. .. 40·00

s. "Specimen", Type 9 ..

t. "Specimen", Type 23 .. 28·00

u. "Cancelled", Type 33 ..

Q28a

Variety No. Q28a was corrected by retouching before control U 47 was employed with cylinder 16. It was a multipositive flaw as it first occurred on cylinder 13 but was retouched before being put to press and later retouched again by two vertical lines. It was also retouched before being put to press on cylinders 17 and 19 and on the latter there are two dots close together to the left of the central cross in the Crown.

Controls and Cylinder Numbers (Blocks of Six)

Photogravure control, in bistre-brown. Single Pane cylinder. Perforation Type 6B (no dot)

Cyl. No.	Control	No dot	Dot	Cyl. No.	Control	No dot	Dot	Cyl. No.	Control	No dot	Dot
7	E 39	32·00									
7	G 40	32·00									

Typographed control, in black. Single Pane cylinders. Perforation Type 6B (no dot)

| 6 | H 40 | 32·00 | | 6 | K 42 | 32·00 | | 6 | O 44 | 32·00 |
| 6 | J 41 | 32·00 | | 6 | M 43 | 32·00 | | 7 | H 40 | 32·00 |

Perforation Type 6 (no dot)

| 6 | J 41 | 32·00 |
| 6 | M 43 | 32·00 |

On cylinder 6 the number was originally engraved in reverse. This was corrected before the cylinder was put to press.

Double Pane cylinders. Perforation Type 6 (no dot) and 6B (dot)

13	Q 45	32·00	32·00	16	U 47	32·00	32·00	19	None	40·00	40·00
14	None	—	†	16	None	32·00	32·00				
16	S 46	32·00	65·00*	17	None	32·00	32·00				

Perforation Type 5

16	None	55·00*	32·00
17	None	32·00	32·00
19	None	32·00	32·00

"Shadow" controls

Trace of O of unissued O 44 control is seen on U 47 cylinder 16 no dot. Shadow of complete O 44 control is clearly seen on this cylinder without control.

Imprimatur from the National Postal Museum Archives

Imperforate, watermark Type W20

Watermark upright

Recess-Printed "Arms" High Values (1939-48)

PRINTER AND WATERMARK. All stamps in Sections QB and QC are watermarked "GviR" (Type **W21**) and were recess-printed by Waterlow & Sons.

SHEET LAYOUT. These stamps were issued in sheets of 40 (5 rows of 8) but the 2s. 6d., 5s. and £1 values were printed in two panes of 40 and then guillotined. Only the 10s. value was printed in sheets of 40. There were no plate numbers and the plates can only be distinguished by marginal markings. A detailed study of these by Major-General Sir Leonard Atkinson, K.B.E. appears in *The GB Journal* for July, September and November 1968.

UNUSED PRICE QUOTATIONS. Unused prices quoted in Sections QB and QC are for mint unmounted examples.

W21

Q4

(Des. E. Dulac)
(Eng. J. A. C. Harrison)

Q5

(Des. Hon. George R. Bellew, M.V.O.)

Cat. No.	S.G. No.	Perf.			Shades	Mint	Used
1939 (SEPTEMBER 4).		**2s. 6d. BROWN, TYPE Q4**					
Q29	476	14		Brown		45·00	9·00 ✓
a. Mark in Shield (R. 1/7)		..	80·00	25·00			
b. Gashed Crown (R. 2/7)		..	80·00	25·00			
c. Gashed Crown (R. 5/5)		..	80·00	20·00			
s. "Specimen", Type 23		..	£200				

Q29*a*

Q29*b*

Q29*c*

Plates. Four double plates were used.

Imprimatur from the National Postal Museum Archives

Imperforate, watermark Type W21

Watermark upright

QB   "Arms" 2s. 6d. (Q30)

Cat. No.	S.G. No.	Perf.	Shades	Mint	Used

1942 (MARCH 9).   2s. 6d. YELLOW-GREEN, TYPE Q4

Q30   476a   14   Yellow-green   10·00   90 ✓

- a. Major re-entry (R. 5/2) .. 75·00 25·00
- b. Re-entry in shield and left frame (R. 1/7) .. .. 50·00 15·00
- c. Minor re-entries .. *From* 20·00 5·00
- s. " Specimen ", Type 9 ..
- t. " Specimen ", Type 23 .. £200
- u. " Cancelled ", Type 34 ..
- v. "Specimen", Type 30 ..

Q30a

Q30b

Plates.   Ten double plates were used.

Imprimatur from the National Postal Museum Archives
Imperforate, watermark Type W21
Watermark upright

348

1939 (AUGUST 21). 5s. RED, TYPE Q4

Q31   477   14   Red   20·00   1·25 ✓
  a.   Major re-entry (R. 4/2) .. 85·00   30·00
  b.   Re-entry in harp, etc. (R. 2/1) 55·00   18·00
  c.   Minor re-entries .. *From* 35·00   5·00
  d.   Guide mark in hair (T or ⊥)
      R.2/7, 5/7 etc.)   ..   .. 35·00   6·00
  s.   " Specimen ", Type 9   ..
  t.   " Specimen ", Type 23   ..   £200
  u.   " Cancelled " Type 34   ..

Q31*a*

Plates.   Seven double plates were used.

Imprimatur from the National Postal Museum Archives

Imperforate, watermark Type W21

Watermark upright

Cat. No.	S.G. No.	Perf.			Shades	Mint	Used

1939 (OCTOBER 30). 10s. DARK BLUE, TYPE Q5

Q32 478 14 (1) Dark blue £175 18·00 ✓
a. Major re-entry (R. 3/7) .. £225 48·00   (2) Steel blue-black £200 18·00 ✓
b. Minor re-entries .. *From* £190 32·00
c. Retouched medallion (R. 4/1) £200 35·00
d. Dot on scroll (R. 2/5) .. £200 35·00
e. Retouch to lower lip (R. 2/7) £190 35·00
f. Flaws on both sides of scroll   h. Dark line across bottom
   (R.3/6) .. .. .. £190 32·00   right stem (R.1/4) .. .. £190 32·00
g. Flaw on left side of scroll   i. Gash on chin (R.4/8) .. £200 35·00
   (R.4/6) .. .. .. £190 32·00   s. "Specimen", Type 23 .. £350

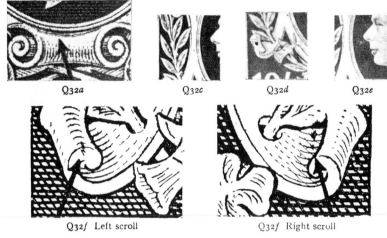

Q32*a*   Q32*c*   Q32*d*   Q32*e*

Q32*f* Left scroll   Q32*f* Right scroll

Q32*g* Left scroll   Q32*h*   Q32*i*

Plates. One single plate was used

Although only one plate was used it exists in three different states and in the third state every stamp was re-entered. We have therefore restricted our listing of re-entries and varieties to what we consider to be the more important ones.

Of these var. *d* exists in all three states; var. *c* in state 2 but with the lines of shading only doubled in state 3; vars. *e* and *h* exist in states 2 and 3; vars. *a*, *f*, *g* and *i* exist only in state 3.

States 2 and 3 have an oblique line in the margin opposite row 5.

All stamps in the eighth vertical row of state 3 have, amongst other things, the left frame retouched.

Imprimatur from the National Postal Museum Archives

Imperforate, watermark Type W21

Watermark upright

Cat. No.	S.G. No.	Perf.	Shades	Mint	Used

1942 (NOVEMBER 30). 10s. ULTRAMARINE, TYPE Q5

Q33	478*a*	14	Ultramarine	38·00	4·00 ✓
s.	" Specimen ", Type 9	..			
t.	" Specimen ", Type 23	..	£300		
u.	" Cancelled ", Type 34	..			

Plates. Official sources record three plates, but it is likely that a fourth was used according to a recent study of this value. The plates were all single pane.

Imprimatur from the National Postal Museum Archives

Imperforate, watermark Type W21

Watermark upright

Cat. No.	S.G. No.	Perf.	Shades	Mint	Used

1948 (OCTOBER 1). £1, BROWN, TYPE Q5

Q34	478*b*	14	Brown	10·00	22·00 ✓
s.	" Specimen ", Type 30	..			

Plates. One double plate was used.

Imprimatur from the National Postal Museum Archives

Perf. 14, watermark Type W21

Watermark upright

Recess-Printed "Festival" High Values (1951)

SHEET LAYOUT. All values were issued in sheets of 40 (10 horizontal rows of 4) but they were printed in two panes of 40 which were then guillotined.

Q6. H.M.S. *Victory*

Q7. White Cliffs of Dover

(Des. Mary Adshead)

Q8. St. George and the Dragon

Q9. Royal Coat-of-Arms

(Des. Percy Metcalfe, **c.v.o.**)

Cat. No.	S.G. No.	Perf.	Shades	Mint	Used
1951 (MAY 3).	**2s. 6d. YELLOW-GREEN, TYPE Q6**				
Q35	509	11 × 12	Yellow-green	8·00 ✓	75 ✓

Imprimatur from the National Postal Museum Archives
Imperforate, watermark Type W21
Watermark upright

1951 (MAY 3).	**5s. RED, TYPE Q7**				
Q36	510	11 × 12	Red	22·00 ✓	1·50 ✓

Imprimatur from the National Postal Museum Archives
Imperforate, watermark Type W21
Watermark upright

1951 (MAY 3).	**10s. ULTRAMARINE, TYPE Q8**				
Q37	511	11 × 12	Ultramarine	12·00 ✓	6·00 ✓

Imprimatur from the National Postal Museum Archives
Imperforate, watermark Type W21
Watermark upright

1951 (MAY 3). £1, BROWN, TYPE Q9

Q38	512	11 × 12	Brown	25·00 ✓ 16·00 ✓

a. Re-entry in DIEU (R. 5/1
and R. 5/4) ..   ..   .. 75·00   30·00

Imprimatur from the National Postal Museum Archives

Imperforate, watermark Type W21

Watermark upright

Q38a

Die Proofs

In black on thin card. No watermark

Head and crown for 2s. 6d. and 5s.	£850
St. George and dragon for 10s.	£750
Head only for 10s. and £1	£850

Quantitites Sold 2s. 6d. 40,723,192; 5s. 22,141,445; 10s. 10,122,720; £1 2,383,720

Commemorative Issues (1937-51)

All stamps in this Section are watermarked "GviR" (Type **W20**) and were photogravure printed by Harrison & Sons.

Except for the Stamp Centenary issue and the Silver Wedding £1 they were in sheets of 120 (20 horizontal rows of 6).

> **UNUSED PRICE QUOTATIONS.** Unused prices quoted in this Section are for mint unmounted examples.

Q10. King George VI and Queen Elizabeth
(Des. E. Dulac)

1937 (MAY 13). CORONATION OF KING GEORGE VI

Cat. No.	S.G. No.	Type No.	Perf.	Description	Mint	Used
QCom1	461	**Q10**	15×14	1½d. Maroon	40 ✓	25 ✓

a.	Ray flaw	..	1·00 ✓			
b.	Ray flaw corrected	..	1·50	*j.*	Crack in Orb	3·50
c.	Colon flaw	..	1·75 ✓	*k.*	Short foot to 2	7·00
d.	"Comet" flaw ..	..	25·00	*l.*	Patch in oval	3·50
e.	Spur to A in MAY ..	..	1·50	*m.*	Long tail to S	3·50
f.	Extra decoration ..	..	12·00	*n.*	Extended bar to E ..	3·50
g.	Pearl behind tiara ..	..	10·00	*p.*	"Beetle" on monogram ..	25·00
h.	Spot in lacing by Orb	..	4·00	*q.*	Double fraction bar.. ..	16·00
ha.	White dot above Y (with			*r.*	White spot on E	
	var. *h*)	..		*s.*	"Cancelled"; Type 33	
i.	Pearl in Orb.. ..	..	1·00 ✓		(twice)	£200

> First Day Cover (QCom1) .. 28·00 ✓✓

Despite strict instructions not to issue this stamp before 13 May it is known prereleased on mail from Cheadle Hulme, Cheshire on 10 May, on 11 May (High Wycombe, Bucks) and from a number of sub-offices on 12 May, which was a Bank Holiday.

Varieties

a. Ray flaw. This was a multipositive flaw (R. 19/1) in which the right arm of the ornament in upper left corner is almost solid. It was issued on cylinders 4, 6, 7, 8, 10, 12, 16, 17, 19 and 24, all no dot.

b. Ray flaw corrected. This was corrected before issue on cylinders 2, 3, 18, 20, 23, 27 and 30 and cylinders 4, 7, 10, 16 and 19 were also reissued with the correction. Naturally there is some variation in the skill of the correction from cylinder to cylinder so it is not practical to give an illustration of this. Every stamp in position R. 19/1 no dot either has the flaw or it has been corrected.

c. Colon flaw. Two white dots between 12 and May (Cyl. 7 no dot, R. 10/1). Later corrected in the fourth printing of Cyl. 7 no dot.

d. "Comet" flaw between May and 1937 (Cyl. 6 dot, R. 10/1).

e. Spur to A in MAY (R. 18/4 on Cyls. 2, 4, 6, 7 all no dot). Later corrected.

f. Extra decoration on King's uniform in the shape of a white cross (Cyl. 7 no dot, R. 1/5).

g. Pearl behind Queen's tiara (Cyl. 7 no dot, R. 6/6). Later corrected. Also short line over G which was not corrected.

h. Spot in lacing to right of Cross of Orb (R. 7/6). This is a multipositive variety which is found on cylinders 3, 4, 6 and 7 dot but was later retouched although traces of the flaw can be found on the later cylinders. This stamp also contains another variety, a small white dot above left arm of Y in MAY but it only occurs on cylinder 6 dot.

i. Pearl in Orb. A faint white spot on lower part of Orb which is visible on all dot cylinders in position R. 18/1.

j. Crack in Orb. Very marked variety (Cyl. 20 no dot, R. 4/1).

k. Short foot in 2 of date (Cyl. 2 no dot, R. 15/5).

l. Large patch in oval at bottom right (Cyl. 19 dot, R. 13/1).

m. Long tail to bottom of S of POSTAGE (Cyl. 3 dot, R. 11/1).

n. Extended middle bar to first E of REVENUE (Cyl. 23 dot, R. 10/2).

Varieties (contd.)

p.   "Beetle" on "E" of monogram (Cyl. 19 no dot, R. 12/3).
q.   Extra fraction bar in left value (Cyl. 10 no dot, R. 4/2).
r.   White spot on E of monogram (Cyl. 12 no dot, R. 15/2).
    The variety previously listed as "inner line in 1" came from cylinder 23 no dot R. 7/2 but was not fully constant.
    There are many other flaws on this stamp which are fully described in *Great Britain. The Coronation Stamp, 1937* by L. Birch and the article by Major F. R. B. Whitehouse in *The GB Journal* for March 1971.

Controls and Cylinder Numbers (Blocks of Six)

All the following are found with control A 37.
An R shows the existence of the Ray flaw, and RC denotes Ray flaw corrected.
Perforation Type 5

Cyl. No. No dot		Cyl. No. Dot		Cyl. No. No dot		Cyl. No. Dot		Cyl. No. No dot		Cyl. No. Dot	
2	1·75	2.	2·00	10R	2·00	10.	2·00	19R	2·00	19.	2·00
3	1·75	3.	2·00	10RC	30·00			19RC	3·50		
4R	2·00	4.	2·00	12R	2·00	12.	2·00	20	1·75	20.	2·00
6R	2·00	6.	2·00	16R	1·50	16.	2·00	23	1·75 ✓	23.	2·00 ✓
7R	3·25	7.	2·00 ✓	16RC	3·50			24R	4·00	24.	4·00
7RC	2·50 ✓			17R	2·00	17.	2·00	27	2·50	27.	2·50
8R	2·00 ✗	8.	2·50 ✓	18	1·75	18.	2·00	30	1·75 ✗	30.	2·00 ✓

    It is believed that only 3 sheets were printed from cylinder 4 no dot with the ray flaw corrected. A vertical corner position strip of 3 showing the cylinder number and ray flaw corrected is known.

Imprimatur from the National Postal Museum Archives

Imperforate, watermark Type W20

Watermark upright

Quantity Sold   388,731,000

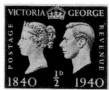

Q11.   Queen Victoria and King George VI
(Des. H. L. Palmer)

1940 (MAY 6).   CENTENARY OF FIRST ADHESIVE POSTAGE STAMPS
Printed in sheets of 160 arranged in 20 horizontal rows of 8.

Cat. No.	S.G. No.	Type No.	Perf.	Description	Mint	Used
QCom2	479	**Q11**	14½ × 14	½d. Green	30 ✓	20 ✓
a.	Hole in central cross of Crown (Cyl. 1 Dot, R. 17/3)		30·00	s. " Specimen ", Type 9 ..		
QCom3	480	**Q11**	14½ × 14	1d. Scarlet	40 ✓	40 ✓
				s. " Specimen ", Type 9 ..		
QCom4	481	**Q11**	14½ × 14	1½d. Red-brown	30 ✓	30 ✓
				s. " Specimen ", Type 9 ..		
QCom5	482	**Q11**	14½ × 14	2d. Orange	50 ✓	40 ✓
a.	Bisected (1d.) *used on cover**		†	16·00	s. " Specimen ", Type 9 ..	
QCom6	483	**Q11**	14½ × 14	2½d. Ultramarine	1·90 ✓	80 ✓
a.	Retouched neck (Cyl. 2 Dot, R. 20/2)..		15·00			
b.	Retouch to King's face and hair (Cyl. 5 No dot, R. 20/1)		12·00	c. Loop to Crown (position?)	25·00	
				s. " Specimen ", Type 9		
QCom7	484	**Q11**	14½ × 14	3d. Violet	4·50 ✓	4·00 ✓
				s. " Specimen ", Type 9 ..		

> First Day Cover (QCom2/7)..   .. 28·00

*See note after No. Q10 regarding use in the Channel Islands.

QCom2a (½d.)

QCom6a (2½d.)

QCom6b (2½d.)

QCom6c (2½d.)

Controls and Cylinder Numbers (Blocks of Six)

All the following are found with control G 40.

Type of Perforation: Bottom margin imperf., top margin perforated through and a single extension hole at each side.

Value	Cyl. No.	No dot	Dot	Value	Cyl. No.	No dot	Dot	Value	Cyl. No.	No dot	Dot
½d.	1	1·75	1·75	1½d.	2	5·00	5·00	2½d.	2	7·00	38·00*
	3	1·10	1·10		3	3·50	3·50		3	7·00	7·00
	6	1·10	1·10						4	16·00	18·00
1d.	1	2·00	2·00	2d.	1	3·50	3·50		5	28·00*	7·00 ✔
	2	7·50	7·50		2	3·50	3·50		7	9·00	9·00
	3	2·00	2·00		3	5·00	5·00				
	5	2·00	2·00					3d.	5	20·00	20·00

Imprimaturs from the National Postal Museum Archives

Nos. QCom2/7 imperforate, watermark Type W20

Watermark upright (*set of* 6)

Quantities Sold

½d. 82,896,960; 1d. 232,903,680; 1½d. 40,412,800; 2d. 121,065,120; 2½d. 312,957,440; 3d. 22,128,000

Q12

Q13

Symbols of Peace and Reconstruction

(Des. H. L. Palmer)   (Des. Reynolds Stone)

1946 (JUNE 11). VICTORY ISSUE

Cat. No.	S.G. No.	Type No.	Perf.	Description	Mint	Used
QCom8	491	**Q12**	15 × 14	2½d. Ultramarine	12 ✔	12 ✔

a. Extra port-hole aft (Cyl. 11 No dot, R. 16/1) .. .. — 10·00 ✔

b. Extra port-hole at fore (Cyl. 8 Dot, R. 5/6) .. .. .. — 15·00

s. " Specimen ", Type 9 ..
t. " Cancelled ", Type 28 ..

| QCom9 | 492 | **Q13** | 15 × 14 | 3d. Violet | 10 ✔ | 10 ✔ |

a. Shiny ink .. .. — 60   35

b. Seven berries (Cyl. 4 No dot, R. 12/5) .. .. .. — 5·00 ✔   ✔

c. Gash on temple (Cyls. 2 Dot, 4 Dot, 5 Dot, R. 9/6) .. — 7·50

s. " Specimen ", Type 9 ..
t. " Cancelled ", Type 28 ..

| First Day Cover (QCom8/9) | .. 38·00 |

QCom8*a*

QCom8*b*

QCom9*b*

Controls and Cylinder Numbers (Blocks of Six)

All the following are found with control S 46.

Perforation Type 5

Value	Cyl. No.	No dot	Dot	Value	Cyl. No.	No dot	Dot	Value	Cyl. No.	No dot	Dot
2½d.	3	80	80	2½d.	10	80	80	3d.	2	14·00	—
	4	80	80		11	80	80		4	14·00	£150
	6	†	—		12	80	80		5	5·00	5·00
	7	80	80		13	1·10	1·10				
	8	80	80		15	80	80	Cylinder 5 was printed in shiny
	9	1·25	1·25		17	80	80	ink.

Perforation Type 6 (no dot) and 6B (dot)

2½d.	9	1·10	1·10
3d.	2	80	80
	4	80	80

Cylinder 4 has a vertical line in the margin under the first stamp in the bottom row. Early printings without this line. *Price £1 each.*

Imprimaturs from the National Postal Museum Archives

Nos. QCom8/9 imperforate, watermark Type W20

Watermark upright (*set of* 2)

Quantities Sold   2½d. 307,832,500; 3d. 43,085,700

Stamps of this issue were overprinted for use in Tangier.   In the case of the 3d. value the overprint was applied to the stop panes of Cyls. 2. and 4., Perforation Type 5.

Q14

Q15

King George VI and Queen Elizabeth
(Des. G. T. Knipe and Joan Hassall from
photographs by Dorothy Wilding)

1948 (APRIL 26). ROYAL SILVER WEDDING

£1 printed in sheets of 20, arranged in 4 horizontal rows of 5.

Cat. No.	S.G. No.	Type No.	Perf.	Description	Mint	Used
QCom10	493	**Q14**	15 × 14	2½d. Ultramarine	20 ✓	20 ✓
a.	Spot on shoulder (Cyl. 5 No dot, R. 15/1)	..	.. ..	7·50 ✓		
s.	"Specimen", Type 30 ..	..				
QCom11	494	**Q15**	14 × 15	£1 Blue	38·00 ✓	35·00 ✓
s.	"Specimen", Type 30 ..	..				
t.	"Cancelled", Type 34P	..				

First Day Cover (QCom10/11)   ..   £325

QCom10a

Cylinder Numbers

2½d. Perforation Type 5. Blocks of six   £1 Blocks of four

Cyl. No					No dot	Dot
1	..	..	..	..	70	70
4	..	..	..	..	70	70
5	..	..	..	..	70	70
6	..	..	..	..	3·50	3·50

Cyl. No.					No dot	Dot
1	..	..	..	..	£150	£150

Imprimaturs from the National Postal Museum Archives

Imperforate, watermark Type W20

Watermark upright (2½d.)
Watermark upright (£1)

Quantities Sold   2½d. 147,500,000; £1 419,628.

Q16. Gathering Vraic
(Des. J. R. R. Stobie)

Q17. Islanders gathering Vraic
(From drawing by E. Blampied)

Cat. No.	S.G. No.	Type No.	Perf.	Description	Mint	Used

1948 (MAY 10).   CHANNEL ISLANDS LIBERATION

Issued to commemorate the third anniversary of the liberation, these stamps were intended primarily for use in the Channel Islands. They were also available at eight Head Post Offices in Great Britain.

For stamps issued in the Channel Islands during the German Occupation 1940–45 see APPENDIX 7.

Cat. No.	S.G. No.	Type No.	Perf.	Description		Mint	Used
QCom12	C 1	**Q16**	15 × 14	1d.	(1) Scarlet	10 ✓	10 ✓
					(2) Rose-red	2·00	50
QCom13	C 2	**Q17**	15 × 14	2½d.	Ultramarine	15 ✓	15 ✓
	a. Crown flaw (R.1/1)	..	6·00 ✓				
	b. Line across wheel (R.6/1) ..		6·00	*c.*	" Broken " wheel (R.20/5)	5·00 ✓	

First Day Cover (QCom12/13)   ..   15·00

QCom13*a*   QCom13*b*   QCom13*c*

Cylinder Numbers (Blocks of Six)
Perforation Type 6 or 6B (both no dot)

Value	Cyl. No.			Perf. 6	Type 6B	Value	Cyl. No.				Perf. 6	Type 6B
1d.	2	..	..	75	1·00	2½d.	4	..	..	..	1·10	1·25

Imprimaturs from the National Postal Museum Archives

Nos. QCom12/13 imperforate, watermark Type W20
Watermark upright (*set of 2*)

Quantities Sold   1d. 5,934,000; 2½d. 5,398,000

Essays
Photographic essays exist in an unaccepted design and in the above designs with a different crown. (*Price from* £25 *each*).

Specimens
Both values exist in Post Office archives overprinted " SPECIMEN " by a handstamp measuring 13 × 1·75 mm.

Q18. Globe and Laurel Wreath

(Des. Percy Metcalfe, c.v.o.)

Q19. " Speed "

(Des. Abram Games)

Q20. Olympic Symbol

(Des. Stanley D. Scott)

Q21. Winged Victory

(Des. Edmund Dulac)

Cat. No.	S.G. No.	Type No.	Perf.	Description	Mint	Used
1948 (JULY 29).		**OLYMPIC**	**GAMES**			
QCom14	495	**Q18**	15 × 14	2½d. Ultramarine	10 ✔	10 ✔
QCom15	496	**Q19**	15 × 14	3d. Violet	20 ✔	20 ✔
a. Crown flaw (Cyl. 1 No dot, R. 20/2)			5·00 ✔	✔		
b. Crown flaw retouch (Cyl. 1 No dot, R. 20/2)			9·00			
c. Hooked 3 (Cyl. 1 No dot, R. 19/2)			5·00 ✔			
QCom16	497	**Q20**	15 × 14	6d. Bright purple	25 ✔	20 ✔
a. Initials H.L.P. *(Strip of 3)*			£150			
b. Ditto, retouched *(Strip of 3)* *From*			85·00			
QCom17	498	**Q21**	15 × 14	1s. Brown	1·25 ✔	1·00 ✔

First Day Cover (QCom14/17) .. 30·00

In the 6d. value the initials H, L and P (H. L. Palmer) were engraved on the 4th, 5th and 6th marginal rules respectively, on the bottom row of Cylinder 9. Three attempts were made to remove these initials by retouching. In the first only the P was almost obliterated, in the second the H was removed as well and finally all three letters were touched out.

QCom15a

QCom15b

QCom15c   Part of QCom16a

Cylinder Numbers (Blocks of Six)

Perforation Type 5

Value	Cyl. No.				No dot	Dot		Value	Cyl. No.				No dot	Dot
2½d.	2	..	..	..	50	50		6d.	9	..	..	..	2·00	2·00
	3	..	..	..	50	50		1s.	3	..	..	..	6·00	6·00
3d.	1 (inc. QCom15a and													
	c) ..	..	..	..	8·00*	2·00								
	1 (inc. QCom15b/c)		..		20·00*	2·00								

Imprimaturs from the National Postal Museum Archives

Nos. QCom14/17 imperforate, watermark Type W20

Watermark upright (*set of* 4)

Quantities Sold

2½d. 155,350,980; 3d. 32,554,642; 6d. 24,397,370; 1s. 32,187,465

Q22. Two Hemispheres
(Des. Mary Adshead)

Q23. U.P.U. Monument, Berne
(Des. Percy Metcalfe, c.v.o.)

Q24. Goddess Concordia, Globe and
Points of Compass
(Des. H. Fleury)

Q25. Posthorn and Globe

(Des. George R. Bellew, m.v.o.)

1949 (OCTOBER 10). UNIVERSAL POSTAL UNION

Commemorating the 75th Anniversary

Cat. No.	S.G. No.	Type No.	Perf.	Description	Mint	Used
QCom18	499	**Q22**	15 × 14	2½d. Ultramarine	10 ✓	8 ✓
a.	Major retouch (Cyl. 5 No dot, R. 18/2)		20·00			
b.	Lake in Asia (Cyl. 3 Dot, R. 14/1)		12·00			
c.	Lake in India (Cyl. 2 No dot, R. 8/2)		10·00			
QCom19	500	**Q23**	15 × 14	3d. Violet	30 ✓	30 ✓
QCom20	501	**Q24**	15 × 14	6d. Bright purple	45 ✓	45 ✓
QCom21	502	**Q25**	15 × 14	1s. Brown	1·25 ✓	1·25 ✓
a.	Retouched background to 1/- (R.8/5)		12·00			

> First Day Cover (QCom18/21)   ..   55·00

Many retouches are known on the 2½d. value. See article by Niall Fair in March 1983 issue of Gibbons *Stamp Monthly*.

QCom18a

QCom18b

Cylinder Numbers (Blocks of Six)

Perforation Type 5

Value	Cyl. No.			No dot	Dot	Value	Cyl. No.			No dot	Dot
2½d.	2	..	..	50	50	2½d.	5	..	..	28·00*	50
	3	..	..	50	50						

Perforation Type 6 or 6B (both no dot)

				Perf. Type 6	6B					Perf. Type 6	6B
3d.	2	..	..	2·00	12·00	1s.	2	..	..	6·50	6·50
6d.	2	..	..	2·40	4·00						

Imprimaturs from the National Postal Museum Archives

Nos. QCom18/21 imperforate, watermark Type W20

Watermark upright (*set of* 4)

Quantities Sold   2½d. 135,150,000; 3d. 16,450,000; 6d. 11,450,000; 1s. 11,400,000

Q26. " Commerce and Prosperity "
(Des. Edmund Dulac)

Q27.   Festival Symbol
(Des. Abram Games)

Cat. No.	S.G. No.	Type No.	Perf.	Description	Mint	Used
1951 (MAY 3).		**FESTIVAL OF BRITAIN**				
QCom22	513	**Q26**	15 × 14	2½d. Scarlet	10	8
QCom23	514	**Q27**	15 × 14	4d. Ultramarine	35	35

First Day Cover (QCom22/3)	..	16·00

Cylinder Numbers (Blocks of Six)
Perforation Type 5

Value	Cyl. No.			No dot	Dot	Value	Cyl. No.			No dot	Dot
2½d.	3	..	..	..	2·00	†	4d.	1	..	..	..	2·50	†
	5	..	..	..	1·50	1·50						

Imprimaturs from the National Postal Museum Archives
Nos. QCom22/23 imperforate, watermark Type W20

Watermark upright (*set of* 2)

Quantities Sold   2½d. 260,142,000 ; 4d. 22,197,000

The Postage Due Stamps

General Notes

INTRODUCTION. In the Post Office circular No. 5 (April 14 1914) the announcement was made of the introduction on 20 April of Postage Due Labels of the values ½d., 1d., 2d., and 5d.

PRINTERS. Preliminary printings of the ½d., 1d., 2d. and 5d. were made at Somerset House and then by Harrison and Sons. The 1s. in the Simple Cypher watermark was printed exclusively at Somerset House, and the remaining values, which were introduced later, were printed by Harrison. The Somerset House and Harrison printings of the ½d., 1d., 2d. and 5d. can only be distinguished with certainty when they have control attached; the Somerset House controls always having a stop after the letter.

From 1924 to 1934 the contract was held by Waterlow and Sons who first printed the 1d. on thick chalk-surfaced paper with the Simple Cypher watermark and thereafter all values, with the addition of the 2s. 6d., on the Block Cypher watermarked paper.

In 1934 the contract reverted to Harrison but again these printings can only be distinguished from the Waterlow issues when they have control attached. Harrison continued to print all the Postage Due issues during the reigns of King Edward VIII and King George VI.

The stamps were typographed in sheets of 240, arranged in 12 horizontal rows of 20, and perforated 14 × 15.

WATERMARKS. Except for R3, R6 and R8, normal stamps have the watermark *sideways*. Varieties exist with sideways-inverted, sideways and reversed, and sideways-inverted and reversed watermarks, and the following four illustrations show these watermark positions *as seen from the back of the stamp:*

Sideways

Sideways-inverted

Sideways and
Reversed

Sideways-inverted
and Reversed

The preliminary Somerset House printings almost always have the watermark sideways-inverted.

King George V Postage Dues (1914-31)

R1 " POSTAGE DUE "

R2 "TO PAY "

Cat. No.	S.G. No.	Date	Description	Unused	Used

1914 (20 APRIL)–23. TYPE R1. WMK. SIMPLE CYPHER, TYPE W14, SIDEWAYS -INVERTED ON 1½d., 4d. AND 1s. AND SIDEWAYS ON OTHERS

Printed at Somerset House and by Harrison & Sons

R1 D1 20.4.14
a. Wmk. sideways-inverted .. 80 60
b. Wmk. sideways and reversed 12·00
c. Wmk. sideways-inverted and reversed .. .. ..
d. Varnish ink .. .. ..

½d. Emerald 40 40 ✓
s. " Specimen ", Type 23 .. 10·00

R2 D2/2a 20.4.14
a. Wmk. sideways-inverted .. 80 40
b. Wmk. sideways-inverted and reversed .. .. .. 10·00
c. No watermark .. .. ..
d. Varnish ink. Shade (1) .. £1500

1d. (1) Carmine 50 40 ✓
1d. (2) Pale carmine 75 40 ✓

s. " Specimen ", Type 23 .. 10·00

R3 D3 1923
a. Wmk. sideways .. .. 30·00 15·00

1½d. Chestnut 32·00 15·00
s. " Specimen ", Type 23 .. 30·00

R4 D4 20.4.14
a. Wmk. sideways-inverted .. 1·75 85
b. Wmk. sideways-inverted and reversed .. .. .. 5·00
c. No watermark.. .. ..

2d. Agate 50 40 ✓

s. " Specimen ", Type 23 .. 15·00
t. " Specimen ", Type 26 .. 9·00
(wmk. sideways, invtd.)

R5 D5/5a 1918
a. Wmk. sideways-inverted .. 11·00 1·75

3d. (1) Violet 2·00 1·00 ✓
3d. (2) Bluish violet 2·50 3·00
s. " Specimen ", Type 23 .. 15·00
t. " Specimen ", Type 26 .. 30·00

R6 D6 1921
a. Wmk. sideways .. ..

4d. Dull grey-green 18·00 1·75 ✓
s. " Specimen ", Type 23 .. 15·00

R7 D7 20.4.14
a. Wmk. sideways-inverted .. 25·00 10·00

5d. Brownish cinnamon 2·50 1·50 ✓
s. " Specimen ", Type 23 .. 10·00

R8 D8/8a 1915
a. Wmk. sideways .. .. 55·00 20·00

1s. (1) Bright blue 20·00 2·00 ✓
1s. (2) Deep bright blue 20·00 2·00
s. " Specimen ", Type 23 .. 15·00
t. " Specimen ", Type 26 ..

The 1d. is known bisected and used to make up a 1½d. rate on understamped letters from Ceylon (1921) and to pay ½d. on a returned printed paper matter envelope at Kilburn, London (1923). The 2d. was bisected and used as a 1d. at West Kensington, Streatham and at Malvern, Worcestershire in the same year.

Watermark Varieties. The following have been recorded:

½d.
Wmk sideways: Types II, III
Wmk sideways-inverted: Types I, II, III

3d.
Wmk sideways: Types II, III
Wmk sideways-inverted: Types II, III

1d.
Wmk sideways: Types II, III
Wmk sideways-inverted: Types I, II, III

4d.
Wmk sideways: Type III
Wmk sideways-inverted: Type III

1½d.
Wmk sideways: Type III
Wmk sideways-inverted: Types II, III

5d.
Wmk sideways: Type II
Wmk sideways-inverted: Type I

2d.
Wmk sideways: Types II, III
Wmk sideways-inverted: Types I, III

1s.
Wmk sideways: Type III
Wmk sideways-inverted: Types II, III

Controls. Prices are for unused singles.

Somerset House Printings:

½d.	I.	P.		2d.	I.	P.		1s.	I.	P.
D. 14	†	3·50	D. 14		†	5·00	F. 15		†	25·00
							O. 19		†	32·00
1d.			**5d.**				S. 21		†	32·00
D. 14	†	3·50	D. 14		†	20·00	V. 23		40·00	†

Watermark varieties known:
Wmk sideways-inverted, Type I: ½d. D. 14; 1d. D. 14; 2d. D. 14; 5d. D. 14.
Wmk sideways-inverted, Type II: 1s. F. 15.
Wmk sideways, Type III: 1s. V. 23.
Wmk sideways-inverted, Type III: 1s. O. 19, S. 21.

Harrison Printings:

½d.		I.	P.	1d.		I.	P.	2d.		I.	P.
D 14		70	70	Q 21		3·50	6·00	O 19		1·60	1·60
I 16		85	85	R 21		70	1·00	P 20		1·25	1·85
N 19		70	85	S 21		70	70	R 21		1·25	2·50
R 21		70	2·25	S 22		70	70	U 23		6·00	3·75
S 22		†	70	T 22		85	85	**3d.**			
U 22		70	4·50	U 23		70	70	L 18		3·00	5·00
W 23		3·00	3·00					O 20		3·00	3·00
1d.				**1½d.**				T 22		3·00	3·00
D 14		85	85	U 22		45·00	†	V 23		3·00	3·00
E 14		80	70	U 23		45·00	†	W 23		3·00	6·00
G 15		70	6·00	V 23		45·00	35·00	**4d.**			
I 16		70	85	**2d.**				Q 20		15·00	12·00
K 17		70	70	D 14		1·50	1·50	**5d.**			
N 19		85	70	H 16		1·25	1·25	D 14		15·00	60·00
P 20		70	†	I 16		1·50	2·00				
Q 20		3·00	†	K 17		3·00	1·25				

Watermark varieties known:
Wmk sideways, Type II: ½d. D 14, I 16, W 23; 1d. D 14, E 14, G 15, I 16, T 22, U 23; 2d. D 14, H 16, I 16, P 20; 3d. T 22, V 23, W 23; 5d. D 14.
Wmk sideways-inverted, Type II: ½d. W 23; 1d. U 23; 1½d. V 23; 3d. V 23, W 23.
Wmk sideways, Type III: ½d. N 19, R 21, S 22, U 22; 1d. K 17, N 19, P 20, Q 20, Q 21, R 21, S 21, S 22, T 22, U 23; 1½d. U 22, U 23; 2d. K 17, O 19, P 20, R 21, U 23; 3d. L 18, O 20, T 22, V 23; 4d. Q 20.
Wmk sideways-inverted, Type III: ½d. N 19, U 22; 1d. Q 21, R 21, S 21, S 22, T 22; 1½d. U 22 U 23; 2d. R 21, U 23; 3d. T 22; 4d. Q 20.

Die Proofs

In black on white glazed card ½d., 1d., 2d., 5d., 1s. ... ... *From* £1500

Colour Trials.

No watermark. Imperf. ..

½d. orange £750

Wmk. Simple Cypher (sideways-inverted). Imperf.

1s. value in 14 different colours and ovptd. "CANCELLED", Type 28 .. *Each* £250

Wmk Simple Cypher (sideways-inverted). Perf 14 × 15:

2d. value in 18 different colours .. .. *Each* 30·00
As above, but ovptd "SPECIMEN", Type 23: Colours Nos. 1, 6, 10.. .. *Each* 35·00
The 2d. in the trial colours were described as No. 1 Carmine, No. 2 Claret, No. 3 Magenta, No. 4 Scarlet, No. 5 Red-brown, No. 6 Bartolozzi brown, No. 7 Fawn, No. 8 Umber, No. 9 Bronze green, No. 10 Green, No. 11 Faenza green, No. 12 Agate (as issued), No. 13 Mauve, No. 14 Violet, No. 15 Azure blue, No. 16 Royal blue, No. 17 Orange, No. 18 Blue, No. 19 Green.

Imprimaturs from the National Postal Museum Archives

Imperforate, watermark Type W14

1½d. value, watermark sideways-inverted
3d. value, watermark sideways
4d. value, watermark sideways-inverted
1s. value, watermark sideways-inverted

1924. TYPE R1. THICK CHALK-SURFACED PAPER. WMK. SIMPLE CYPHER, TYPE W14, SIDEWAYS

Printed by Waterlow & Sons

Cat. No.	S.G. No.		Description	Unused	Used
R9	D9		1d. Carmine	2·25	3·00

Controls.   Prices are for unused singles.

		I.	*P.*
B 24	..	6·50	†
C 25	..	6·50	†

1924-31. TYPES R1 AND R2 (2s. 6d.). WMK. BLOCK CYPHER, TYPE W15, SIDEWAYS

Cat. No.	S.G. No.	Date			Description	Unused	Used

Printed by Waterlow & Sons, and later (from 1934) by Harrison & Sons

Cat. No.	S.G. No.	Date			Description	Unused	Used
R10	D10	6.25			½d. Emerald	30	30✓
a.	Wmk. sideways-inverted ..	4·00	70				
				s.	"Specimen", Type 23	..	
				t.	"Specimen", Type 26	..	
				u.	"Specimen", Type 30	..	
R11	D11	4.25			1d. Carmine	50	30✓
a.	Wmk. sideways-inverted ..						
				s.	"Specimen", Type 23	..	
				t.	"Specimen", Type 26	..	
				u.	"Specimen", Type 30	..	
R12	D12	10.24			1½d. Chestnut	26·00	15·00✓✓
a.	Wmk. sideways-inverted ..			s.	"Specimen", Type 23	..	
R13	D13	7.24			2d. Agate	1·60	40✓
a.	Wmk. sideways-inverted ..			s.	"Specimen", Type 23	..	
				t.	"Specimen", Type 30	..	
				u.	"Cancelled", Type 33	..	
R14	D14	10.24			3d. Dull violet	2·00	40✓
a.	Wmk. sideways-inverted ..	7·50					
b.	Experimental paper, Wmk. W.16	35·00	25·00				
c.	Printed on the gummed side (Control L 29)	£100	†	s.	"Specimen", Type 23	..	
R15	D15	10.24			4d. Dull grey-green	12·00	2·00✓
a.	Wmk. sideways-inverted ..	25·00		s.	"Specimen", Type 23	..	
				t.	"Specimen", Type 26	..	
R16	D16	1.31			5d. Brownish cinnamon	21·00	25·00✓✓
R17	D17	9.24			1s. Deep blue	6·00	75✓
a.	Wmk. sideways-inverted ..			s.	"Specimen", Type 23	..	
				t.	"Cancelled", Type 33	..	
R18	D18	10.24			2s. 6d. Purple/*yellow*	40·00	1·75✓✓
a.	Wmk. sideways-inverted ..			s.	"Specimen", Type 23	..	
				t.	"Specimen", Type 30	..	
				u.	"Cancelled", Type 28	..	

The 2d. is known bisected and used to make up a 2½d. rate on an understamped letter from Malta at Perranwell Station, Cornwall (1932).

Controls. Prices are for unused singles.
Waterlow Printings:

		I.	*P.*				*I.*	*P.*				*I.*	*P.*
		½d.					**2d.**					**4d.**	
B	24 ..	†	70	M	30 ..		2·00	†	T	33 ..		45·00	†
F	26 ..	70	†	O	31 ..		2·25	†				**5d.**	
I	28 ..	70	†	P	31 ..		2·00	†	N	30 ..		22·00	†
K	29 ..	†	70	Q	32 ..		2·25	†	O	31 ..		20·00	†
L	29 ..	70	†	R	32 ..		2·50	†	Q	32 ..		22·00	†
M	30 ..	70	†	T	33 ..		15·00	†	S	33 ..		25·00	†
O	31 ..	90	†				**3d.**					**1s.**	
P	31 ..	70	†	B	24 ..		3·75	†	A	24 ..		£160	†
Q	32 ..	70	†	D	25 ..		4·00	†	B	24 ..		14·00	†
S	33 ..	70	†	E	26 ..		3·50	†	C	25 ..		14·00	†
		1d.		F	26 ..		3·50	†	E	26 ..		—	14·00
B	24 ..	4·00	†	G	27 ..		3·50	†	F	26 ..		7·00	†
F	26 ..	85	2·25	H	27 ..		†	8·00	G	27 ..		7·00	†
I	28 ..	85	†	I	28 ..		3·75	†	I	28 ..		7·00	†
K	29 ..	85	9·00	K	29 ..		3·50	†	K	29 ..		7·00	†
L	29 ..	85	†	L	29 ..		3·75	†	M	30 ..		14·00	†
N	30 ..	1·10	†	N	30 ..		3·75	†	O	31 ..		10·00	†
O	31 ..	85	†	O	31 ..		3·75	†	Q	32 ..		7·00	†
Q	32 ..	85	†	Q	32 ..		3·75	†	R	32 ..		7·00	†
S	33 ..	85	9·00	R	32 ..		3·75	†	S	33 ..		8·00	†
		1½d.		T	33 ..		3·75	†					
B	24 ..	35·00	†				**4d.**					**2s. 6d.**	
		2d.		A	24 ..		18·00	†	B	24 ..		30·00	†
A	24 ..	2·25	†	B	26 ..		10·00	†	H	27 ..		32·00	†
C	25 ..	2·10	†	E	26 ..		12·00	†	I	28 ..		30·00	†
E	26 ..	2·25	†	F	26 ..		10·00	†	K	29 ..		32·00	—
F	26 ..	2·10	†	I	28 ..		†	14·00	L	29 ..		32·00	†
H	27 ..	15·00	†	K	29 ..		10·00	†	N	30 ..		38·00	†
I	28 ..	2·00	†	L	29 ..		10·00	†	O	31 ..		32·00	†
K	29 ..	2·00	†	N	30 ..		10·00	†	Q	32 ..		30·00	†
L	29 ..	2·00	†	Q	32 ..		10·00	†	R	32 ..		30·00	†
				R	32 ..		10·00	†	S	33 ..		35·00	†

The sole 1½d. control must have existed with the watermark sideways-inverted.

Waterlow Printing. Experimental wmk **W16:**

		I.	*P.*
		3d.	
D 25	..	60·00	†

Harrison Printings:

		I.	*P.*				*I.*	*P.*				*I.*	*P.*
		½d.					**2d.**					**5d.**	
U	34 ..	5·00	†	V	34 ..		12·00	†	U	34 ..		24·00	†
U	34 [streaky gum]	1·00	†	X	35 ..		2·25	†	W	35 ..		24·00	†
W	35 ..	1·00	†	Y	36 ..		2·25	†				**1s.**	
Y	36 ..	70	†						U	34 ..		15·00	†
							3d.		W	35 ..		17·00	†
		1d.		W	35 ..		8·00	†	X	35 ..		20·00	†
U	34 ..	11·00	11·00	Y	36 ..		4·00	5·50				**2s. 6d.**	
W	35 ..	5·50	†						U	34 ..		45·00	†
Y	36 ..	1·50	—				**4d.**		V	34 ..		45·00	†
				V	34 ..		17·00	†	X	35 ..		45·00	†
				X	35 ..		15·00	†	Z	36 ..		32·00	†

The U 34 controls are generally on smooth-gummed paper but all the later controls are on paper with streaky gum.

Colour Trial

½d. purple on yellow £450

Imprimaturs from the National Postal Museum Archives

Imperforate, watermark Type W15 (sideways)
½d., 1d., 1½d., 2d., 3d., 4d., 5d., 1s., 2s. 6d.

King Edward VIII Postage Dues (1936-37)

> UNUSED PRICE QUOTATIONS. Unused prices quoted for R19–26 are for mint unmounted examples.

Cat. No.	S.G. No.	Date	Description	Mint	Used
1936-37. TYPES R1 AND R2 (2s. 6d.). WMK. " E 8 R ", TYPE W19, SIDEWAYS					
Printed by Harrison & Sons					
R19	D19	June 1937	½d. Emerald	5·50	5·00
R20	D20	May 1937	1d. Carmine	1·00	1·60 ✔
R21	D21	May 1937	2d. Agate	7·50	5·00 ✔
R22	D22	Mar. 1937	3d. Dull violet	1·60	1·60 ✔
			s. " Specimen ", Type 30 ..		
R23	D23	Dec. 1936	4d. Dull grey-green	12·00	15·00
			s. " Specimen ", Type 30 ..		
R24	D24/a	Nov. 1936	5d. (1) Brownish cinnamon	38·00	20·00
			(2) Yellow-brown ('37)	12·00	15·00
			s. " Specimen ", Type 30 ..		
R25	D25	Dec. 1936	1s. Deep blue	7·50	4·50
			s. " Specimen ", Type 30 ..		
R26	D26	May 1937	2s. 6d. Purple/*yellow*	£160	8·00

The 1d. is known bisected (Solihull, 3 July 1937).

Controls. Prices are for mint singles.

	I.	*P.*		*I.*	*P.*		*I.*	*P.*
½d.			**3d.**			**1s.**		
A 37 ..	.. 12·00	†	A 37 ..	.. 3·25	†	A 36 ..	.. 12·00	†
1d.			**4d.**					
A 37 ..	.. 2·50	†	A 36 ..	.. 20·00	†	**2s. 6d.**		
			5d.			A 37 ..	.. £175	†
2d.			A 36 ..	.. 50·00	†	C 38 ..	.. £300	†
A 37 ..	.. 7·50	†	A 37 ..	.. 30·00	†			

Imprimaturs from the National Postal Museum Archives

Imperforate, watermark Type W19 (sideways)

½d., 1d., 2d., 3d., 4d., 5d., 1s., 2s. 6d.

King George VI Postage Dues (1937-52)

UNUSED PRICE QUOTATIONS. Unused prices quoted for R27–39 are for mint unmounted examples.

Cat. No. S.G. No.	Date	Description	Mint	Used

1937-38. TYPES R1 AND R2 (2s. 6d.). WMK. " GviR ", TYPE W20, SIDEWAYS

Printed by Harrison & Sons

R27	D27	1938	½d. Emerald	7·00	3·25 ✓
a. Broken " 2 " in " ½ " (R. 3/14)		20·00	s. " Specimen ", Type 9	..	
R28	D28	1938	1d. Carmine	1·75	40 ✓
a. Wmk. sideways-inverted ..			s. " Specimen ", Type 9	..	
			t. " Cancelled ", Type 33	..	
R29	D29	1938	2d. Agate	1·75	40 ✓
a. Wmk. sideways-inverted ..		9·00	s. " Specimen ", Type 9	..	
			t. " Cancelled ", Type 33	..	
R30	D30	1938	3d. Violet	8·00	40 ✓
a. Wmk. sideways-inverted ..		20·00	s. " Specimen ", Type 9	..	
			t. " Cancelled ", Type 33	..	
R31	D31	1937	4d. Dull grey-green	45·00	7·50 ✓
a. Wmk. sideways-inverted ..			s. " Specimen ", Type 9	..	
			t. " Cancelled ", Type 33	..	
R32	D32	1938	5d. Yellow-brown	7·00	1·00 ✓
a. Wmk. sideways-inverted ..		30·00	s. " Specimen ", Type 9	..	
			t. " Cancelled ", Type 33	..	
R33	D33	1937	1s. Deep blue	48·00	75 ✓
a. Wmk. sideways-inverted ..		24·00	s. " Specimen ", Type 9	..	
			t. " Cancelled ", Type 33	..	
R34	D34	1938	2s. 6d. Purple/*yellow*	55·00	1·50 ✓
			s. " Specimen ", Type 9	..	
			t. " Cancelled ", Type 33	..	

The 2d. is known bisected (St. Albans, 5 June 1951; Harpenden, 4 June 1951 and 30 October 1954).

Controls. Prices are for mint singles.

	I.	P.			I.	P.			I.	P.
	½d.			**3d.**				**5d.**		
C 38 ..	.. 8·00	†	B 37 ..	.. 9·00	†	O 44 ..	.. 18·00	†
E 39 ..	.. 8·00	—	C 38 ..	.. 9·00	†	P 44 ..	.. 12·00	†
G 40 ..	.. 20·00	35·00	D 38 ..	.. 10·00	†	T 46 ..	.. 12·00	—
			F 39 ..	.. †	30·00			
	1d.		I 41 ..	.. †	9·50		**1s.**	
C 38 ..	.. 2·50	†	K 42 ..	.. 30·00	†	B 37 ..	.. 50·00	†
E 39 ..	.. 2·25	†	M 43 ..	.. 9·00	†	C 38 ..	.. 50·00	†
G 40 ..	.. 2·50		O 44 ..	.. 12·00	†	E 39 ..	.. 55·00	†
I 41 ..	.. 2·25	2·25	R 45 ..	.. 12·00	†	G 40 ..	.. 50·00	†
K 42 ..	.. †	2·25	U 47 ..	.. 9·00	—	J 41 ..	.. 50·00	†
M 43 ..	.. 2·25	†				K 42 ..	.. 50·00	†
O 44 ..	.. 3·00	†		**4d.**		M 43 ..	.. 50·00	†
P 44 ..	.. —	†	B 37 ..	.. 60·00	†	O 44 ..	.. 50·00	†
Q 45 ..	.. 30·00	†	C 38 ..	.. 60·00	†	P 44 ..	.. 50·00	—
U 47 ..	.. 2·50	†	E 39 ..	.. 60·00	†	R 45 ..	.. 50·00	†
			G 40 ..	.. †	80·00	S 46 ..	.. 60·00	†
	2d.		H 40 ..	.. 80·00	†			
C 38 ..	.. 2·50	†	I 41 ..	.. †	60·00		**2s. 6d.**	
E 39 ..	.. 3·00	†	K 42 ..	.. †	60·00	C 38 ..	.. 65·00	†
G 40 ..	.. —	3·00	M 43 ..	.. 60·00	†	D 38 ..	.. 65·00	85·00
I 41 ..	.. —	18·00	O 44 ..	.. 90·00	†	E 39 ..	.. 75·00	†
K 42 ..	.. —	2·25	P 44 ..	.. 60·00	†	I 41 ..	.. £110	
M 43 ..	.. 2·25	†	T 46 ..	.. 60·00	†	K 42 ..	.. £150	£130
O 44 ..	.. 20·00	†				L 42 ..	.. £110	
Q 44 ..	.. †	—		**5d.**		O 44 ..	.. 75·00	†
Q 45 ..	.. 2·25	†	C 38 ..	.. 12·00	†	P 44 ..	.. 75·00	†
U 47 ..	.. 2·25	†	E 39 ..	.. 10·00	†	Q 45 ..	.. £150	†
			G 40 ..	.. 12·00	†	S 46 ..	.. £150	†
			I 41 ..	.. †	7·00	U 47 ..	.. —	†
			M 43 ..	.. 18·00	†			

Imprimaturs from the National Postal Museum Archives

Imperforate, watermark Type W20 (sideways)

½d., 1d., 2d., 3d., 4d., 5d., 1s.

Perf. 14 × 15, watermark Type W20 (sideways)

2s. 6d.

Cat. No.	S.G. No.	Date	Description	Mint	Used

1951–55?. COLOURS CHANGED AND NEW VALUE. TYPE R1. WMK. "GviR", TYPE W20, SIDEWAYS

Printed by Harrison & Sons

R35	D35	18.9.51	½d. (1) Yellow-orange	1·75	2·00 ✓
a. Broken " 2 " in " ½ " (R.3/14) .. .. .. 30·00			(2) Bright-orange (1955?)		
R36	D36	6.6.51	1d. Violet-blue	1·10	75 ✓
a. Wmk. sideways-inverted ..					
R37	D37	11.2.52	1½d. Green	1·75	1·75
a. Wmk. sideways-inverted .. 6·00					
b. Stop after THREE.. .. 30·00					
R38	D38	14.8.51	4d. Blue	22·00	9·00 ✓
R39	D39	6.12.51	1s. Ochre	26·00	4·00 ✓

The dates of issue given above are those on which the stamps were first issued by the Supplies Department to postmasters.

R35(2) comes from two sheets on the George VI watermarked paper which were found amongst a supply of stamps in the distinct bright orange shade with Tudor Crown watermark (Z1).

The 1d. is known bisected (Dorking, 14 April and 23 June, 1952 and Camberley, 6 April, 1954).

On 7 June 1951, the post office at Bury St. Edmunds ran out of 1d. Postage Due stamps. Two unofficial handstamps were made on the instructions of the postmaster, and the overprint " POSTAGE DUE " applied to the current 1d. postage stamp (No. Q6). About a hundred were said to have been used on that day. In addition 20 unused examples were sold over the post office counter to an individual who then sold them to dealers. *Price £150 used on piece.*

Imprimaturs from the National Postal Museum Archives

Imperforate, watermark Type W20 (sideways)

½d., 1d., 1½d., 4d., 1s.

Appendixes

APPENDIX 1

Perforators

King Edward VII

The gauge of the perforators continued to be 14×14, until September 1911 when it was altered to 15×14 for some of the later printings made by Harrison & Sons. This was done to facilitate easier and equal separation.

Horizontal Comb Machines

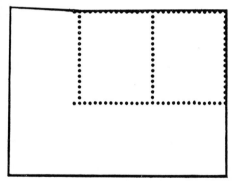

Type H1

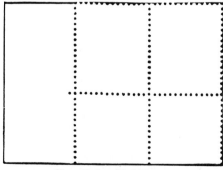

Type H1A or H2A Types

Type H1   With a single extension pin at each end.   Bottom feed.

Type H1A   As above, but top feed.

Set to perforate the sheet either from bottom to top or from top to bottom giving sheet margins as follows:

Bottom feed—
Bottom margin — Imperforate.
Top margins — Perforated through.
Side margins — A single extension hole at each side.

Top feed—
Bottom margin — Perforated through.
Top margin — Imperforate.
Side margins — A single extension hole.

This machine was used solely by De la Rue and perforated all values with bottom feed. The ½d., 1d., 2½d., 5d. and 6d. are also known with top feed.

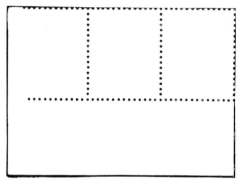

Type H2(c)

Type H2(a)   With a nine pin extension spur at the left and a single extension pin at the right.   Bottom feed.

Type H2A(b)   As (a) but with ten pin extension spur.   Top feed.

Type H2(c)   As (a) but with eleven pin extension spur.   Bottom feed.

Type H2A(c)   As above but top feed.

Type H2(d)   As (a) but with twelve pin extension spur.   Bottom feed.

Type H2A(d)   As above but top feed.

Type H2(e)   As (a) but with fourteen pin extension spur.   Bottom feed.

Type H2A(e)   As above but top feed.

Type H2(f)   As (a) but extension spur of seventeen pins at left.

Type H2(g)   As above but extension spur of thirteen pins at right.

Set to perforate the sheet either from bottom to top or from top to bottom giving sheet margins as follows:

Bottom feed—
Bottom margin — Imperforate.
Top margin — Perforated through.
Left margin — Perforated through with eleven pins.
Right margin — A single extension hole.
This is as Type I for King George V typographed issues.

Top feed—
Bottom margin — Perforated through.
Top margin — Imperforate.
Left margin — A single extension hole.
Right margin — Perforated through with eleven pins.
This is as Type IA for King George V typographed issues.

This machine was used by Harrison and Sons for the perf. 14 printings of the ½d., 1d. 3d. and 4d. values, and also by Somerset House for the £1 value only.

Vertical Comb Machines

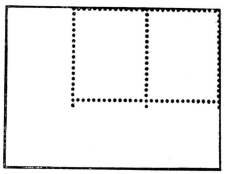

Type V1 or Type V4

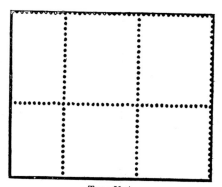

Type V1A
(This illustration is perf. 15 × 14 (Type V3A))

Type V1   With seventeen pin extension spur in top margin. Bottom margin one extension hole. Left feed.

Type V1A   As above but right feed.

Set to perforate the sheet from side to side and gave sheet margins as follows:

Left feed—   Bottom margin   A single extension hole.
              Top margin   Perforated through with seventeen pins.
              Left margin   Imperforate.
              Right margin   Perforated through

Right feed—   Bottom margin   Perforated through with seventeen pins.
              Top margin   A single extension hole.
              Left margin   Perforated through.
              Right margin   Imperforate.

This machine was used by all three contractors.

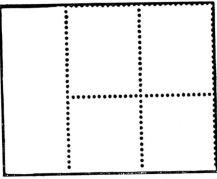

Type V2

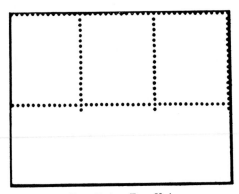

Type V2A or Type V4A

Type V2   With thirteen pin extension spur in bottom margin.   Top margins one
extension hole.   Left feed.

Type V2A   As above but right feed.

Set to perforate the sheet from side to side and gave sheet margins as follows:

Left feed—	Bottom margin	Perforated through with thirteen pins.
	Top margin	A single extension hole.
	Left margin	Imperforate.
	Right margin	Perforated through.
Right feed—	Bottom margin	A single extension hole.
	Top margin	Perforated through with thirteen pins.
	Left margin	Perforated through.
	Right margin	Imperforate.

This machine was only used by De la Rue for ½d. and 1d. values (both feeds) on Controls
A to J 10.   The 4d. value, green and brown on coated paper is also recorded.

Type V2(a).   As Type V2 but the bottom margin is perforated through with only twelve
pins. It exists only in the ½d. and 1d. with Controls E 5 and F 6.

Types V3 and V3A.   These produce the same perforation patterns as Types V1 and V1A
above, except that the perforation is 15 × 14 and not 14.

Types V4 and V4A.   This is a recently found type of vertical perforator yielding a single extension hole in both *top* and bottom margins.   So far it is only known to exist for the ½d. and 1d. values perforated 14.   As a control piece would be as Type V1 with left feed and V2A with right feed, the three vertical types can only be distinguished by at least a complete vertical strip of twenty.

There is evidence to believe that Types V4 and V4A were employed quite extensively but were not recognised at the time.   Information is needed from those who have complete vertical control strips from any of the three vertical perforators.

Typographed Booklet Panes

The letter in brackets below the following three diagrams refers to the booklet selvedge at left.
(E)   Extension hole in the margin in each row
(P)   Perforated margin
(I)   Imperforate margin

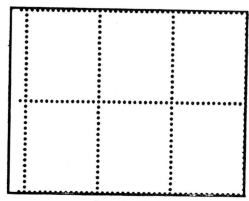

Type B1 (E)

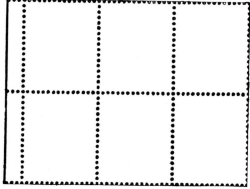

Type B1A (P)

Types B1   A horizontal comb perforator with a single extension pin at each end of the
and B1A   comb head (Type B1(E)) but which also perforated through the central gutter
so that panes from gutter margins were Type B1A(P).   Employed by De La
Rue for Booklets (1) to (6).

For Booklet (7) Harrison used a different horizontal comb which also had a single pin on each side of the central gutter, hence this only occurs as Type B1(E). This continued in use for the King George V booklets until about 1918.

Type B2   The above machine, as adapted for the Silver Jubilee issue.

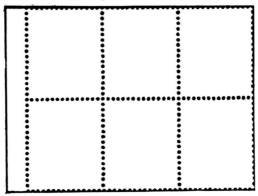

Type B3 (I)

Types B3   A vertical comb perforator. With left feed the left-hand pane (without
and B3A   horizontal bars and watermark upright) was imperforate as shown above and all other panes were perforated through (as Type B1A(P)). With right feed the right-hand pane (without horizontal bars and watermark inverted) was imperforate and all other panes perforated through. All Georgian panes have vertical marginal rules at the side and the centre panes have horizontal rules as well.

This was employed regularly by Harrison from 1918 and also for the provisional printings by Waterlow and Harrison. The use of right feed by Waterlow is rare and is not known in the Harrison provisional printing.

Type B3 was also used for the ½d. and 1d. Downey Head Die 1B watermark Crown booklet panes and the 2d. Die 1 Profile Head watermark Royal Cypher booklets. In the Downey Head booklets, panes from the centre of the sheet (with horizontal bars in the margin) have imperforate margin (Type B3(I)) and the outer panes (without horizontal bars) are perforated through (Type B3A(P)).

King George V
1911-24. Typographed. ½d. to 1s.

The gauge of perforation was 14½ or 15 horizontally by 14 vertically, the exception being the Die 1A ½d. and 1d. which have been found perf. 14, and the 6d. perf. 14 issued in 1920–21 when the 15 × 14 machine was out of action.

Type 1   As for Types H2(a), H2(d) and H2(e) of King Edward VII.   Also two new machines with extension spurs of fifteen and sixteen pins respectively.

Type 1A   As above, but top feed.

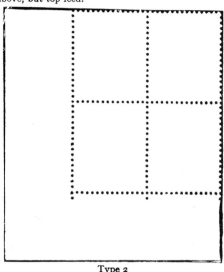

Type 2

Type 2A

Type 2   In general use throughout the period. Extension spur of fourteen pins at left.

Left feed—		
	Bottom margin	A single extension hole.
	Top margin	Perforated through.
	Left margin	Imperforate.
	Right margin	Perforated through.

Type 2A

Right feed—		
	Bottom margin	Perforated through.
	Top margin	A single extension hole.
	Left margin	Perforated through.
	Right margin	Imperforate.

Type 2(c) (left feed). Variety with single extension hole missing in the bottom margin.

Type 2 was a vertical comb perforator perforating a sheet from left to right or right to left as the case may be.   The comb spurs each contain 14 pins and therefore give the perforation 15 × 14. At least two comb-

heads are known. In one of them, the pins are set so that the 14 pins perforate a distance one-half milli-
meter in excess of the other comb-head. Stamps from this comb-head can be recognized by the fact that
the outer top corner perforation is thinner than normal and the gauge is something like 14¾.

Type 3

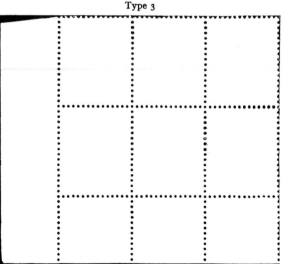

Type 3A

Type 3   Extension spur at right.
    Right feed—   Bottom margin   A single extension hole.
                   Top margin   Perforated through.
                   Left margin   Perforated through.
                   Right margin   Imperforate.
Type 3A
    Left feed—   Bottom margin   Perforated through.
                   Top margin   A single extension hole.
                   Left margin   Imperforate.
                   Right margin   Perforated through.

Type 3A is believed not to exist for 1d. Downey Head issues and those that have been so
described have been found to be Type 1A, the bottom corners being similar.

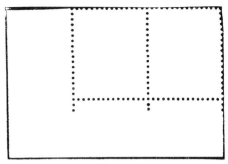

Type 4

Type 4   As for Type 2, but the bottom margin shows two extension holes with left feed.

1913-30.   Engraved.   2s. 6d. to £1

The gauge was 11 horizontally by 12 vertically and two machines were in operation:—

- (a) Used exclusively by Waterlow and Layton, gave the marginal perforation similar to Type 1 (top feed).
- (b) Used by the other two contractors, gave marginal perforations similar to Type 5 (bottom feed).   Bradbury, Wilkinson also used the top feed which gave marginal perforations similar to Type 6B.

Photogravure

The perforating was done on a separate machine.   The photogravure stamps issued prior to the Silver Jubilee issue were generally perforated on the machines in use at the end of the typographed period—Type 2.   Occasionally Type 4 and rarely Type 3 were also used.

Later, the general perforator in use was a new type of single comb head set to perforate the undivided web from bottom to top.   At each end of the comb head on both dot and no dot panes was a single extension pin (Type 5).

Type 5 perforator was adapted for the Silver Jubilee issued by the removal of alternate sets of vertical pins.

Later still a supplementary perforator in use was as Type 6.   This is a continuous web perforator with a triple comb head enabling three rows of stamps to be perforated at a time. The outer ends of the comb heads were without extension pins, and the pins crossed the interpane margins.

The machine was soon modified by the removal of the pins in the interpane margin, leaving only single extension pins.   Cylinder blocks from the no dot pane show no alteration.

Type 5.   Cylinder blocks from dot and no dot panes.

Left margin	A single extension hole.
Bottom margin	Imperforate.

Type 6.   Cylinder blocks from the no dot pane.

Left margin	Imperforate.
Bottom margin	Perforated through.

Type 6A.   Cylinder blocks from the dot pane.

Left margin	Perforated through.
Bottom margin	Perforated through.

Type 6B.   Cylinder blocks from the dot pane.

Left margin	A single extension hole.
Bottom margin	Perforated through.

The ½d., 1½d., 2d., 2½d. and 3d. King George VI pale colours of 1941–42 were at first printed from single pane cylinders with dot but were perforated with the left-pane perforator, Type 6.

Similarly, early printings of the 4d., 5d., 6d., 7d., 8d. and 1s. King George VI were from single pane cylinders without dot but were perforated with the right-pane perforator, Type 6B.

Type 6 (no dot) and Type 6B (dot) are the same as Types B and C as described under " Perforators " in Vol. 3 of this work.

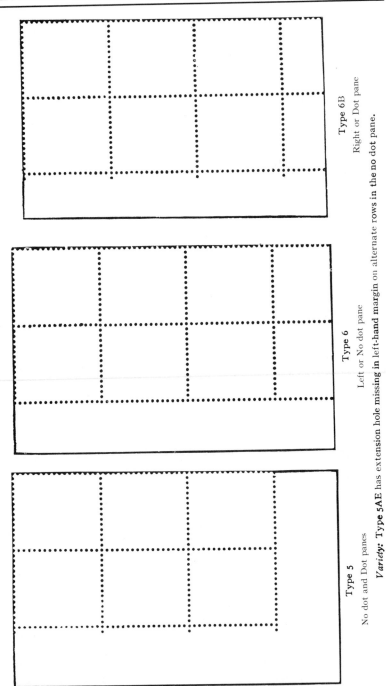

Type 6B
Right or Dot pane

Type 6
Left or No dot pane

Type 5
No dot and Dot panes

Variety: **Type 5AE** has extension hole missing **in left-hand margin** on alternate rows in the no dot pane.

Booklet Panes

A new machine (B4) was introduced for the booklets containing the stamps printed in photogravure, although occasional use was made of the original B3 perforator of the typographed issue.   Booklet panes with cylinder numbers may be found with the following perforations:

Type	Cyl. No. Pane	Perforation
B3	No dot	Imperf. margin. (Known as I.)
B3A	Dot	Perf. margin. (Known as P.)
B4	No dot	Extension hole in the margin in each row. (Known as E.)
B4A	Dot	Imperf. margin. (Known as I.)
B4B	Dot	Extension hole in the margin in each row. (Known as E.)
B5	Dot	Perforations at bottom only extend across margin. (Known as BP.)
B6	Dot	As for B5 except that the two perforation pins next to the stamp margin have been removed (leaving a single $\frac{1}{2}$ hole in the margin). (Known as Ie.)

For illustrations of **E, P** and **I** see B1, B1A and B3 respectively under **King Edward VII.**

The descriptions for Types B5 and B6 apply only to the cylinder panes.   On non cylinder panes the three perforation holes (or one hole in the case of B6) can be either in the top, middle or bottom row.   In both cases the watermark is either upright (panes from dot cylinder adjoining the central gutter) or inverted (panes from no dot cylinder adjoining the central gutter).

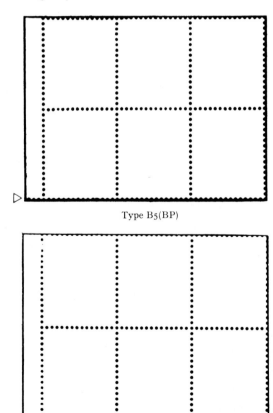

Type B5(BP)

Type B6(Ie)

APPENDIX 2

Post Office Booklets of Stamps

> **BOOKLET PRICES.** Prices in this Appendix are for booklets containing panes with "average" perforations (i.e. full perforations on two edges of the pane only). Booklets containing panes with complete perforations are worth more.

KING EDWARD VII

2s. BOOKLETS

Series 1

The first fourteen editions were without a number on the cover, each edition being identifiable by some feature peculiar to itself and, for the sake of convenience, these early editions are referred to by numbers in brackets, viz., No. (1) to No. (14). After this the printing contract was awarded to Harrison & Sons who instituted the numbering of the booklets on the cover, starting with No. 8.

For all the King Edward VII editions, i.e., Nos. (1) to (7) an additional ½d. was charged for the booklet itself in addition to the price of the stamps. No. (1) was sold over the counter for 2s. 0½d.; Nos. (2) to (7) contained only 1s. 11½d. worth of stamps, one of the stamps on one of the ½d. panes being printed with a green cross. Since that time no charge has ever been made for any British Post Office booklet of stamps other than the price of the stamps it contained. Originally there were two basic requirements for booklets which were:—

(a) The stamps should always be upright when the booklet was opened, (b) There should always be a binding margin on the left of each pane.

Type **1**

Type **2**

1904 (March 16). The first booklet issued contained four panes of six, i.e., 24 × 1d. K.E. VII stamps, printed by De La Rue, with watermark Crown, normal or inverted. It was bound with staples in a red cover bearing the Edwardian P.O. cypher and interleaved with plain grease proof paper.

Cat. No.

BA1 Edition No. (1) (sold for 2s. 0½d.). Red cover as T **1** £130
Edition BA1 is known without interleaves.

1906 (June). As before, but make-up changed to include 12 × 1d. and 23 × ½d. stamps and one green cross.

BA2 Edition No. (2) (contents 1s. 11½d.). Red cover as T **2** £400

1907 (August). As before, but make-up changed to include 18 × 1d. and 11 × ½d. and one green cross.

BA3 Edition No. (3) (contents 1s. 11½d.). Red cover as T **2** £400

1908 (August). As before, but interleaves used for Post Office notices printed in red.

BA4 Edition No. (4) (contents 1s. 11½d.). Red cover as T **2** £400

1909 (August). As before, but interleaves of plain white paper printed on one side with trade advertisements in green. Edition: No. (5)—third advertisement Chas. Baker & Co.; No. (6)—third advertisement Brimsdown lamps.

Cat. No.

BA5   Edition Nos. (5) & (6) (contents 1s. 11½d.). Red cover as T **2** £400

1911 (June). As before, but containing stamps printed by Harrison & Sons and showing a larger Post Office cypher on cover. Interleaves printed on one side with Post Office notices in green.

BA6   Edition No. (7) (contents 1s. 11½d.). Red cover as T **2** £450

KING GEORGE V
2s. BOOKLETS
Series 1

1911 (August). As King Edward VII issue, but make-up changed to include 18 × 1d. and 12 × ½d. stamps of the new reign (Die 1B) with watermark Crown, normal or inverted. Interleaves printed on both sides with trade advertisements in green: No. (8)—first advertisement Aitchison & Co.; No. (9)—first advertisement Gresham Fire and Accident Insurance Society; No. (10)—first advertisement Empire Hotels. Georgian Post Office cypher on cover.

BB1   Edition Nos. (8), (9) & (10). Red cover as T **2** £200

Edition No. 8 exists without the 5th interleaf.

Type **3**   Type **4**

1912 (April). Cover redrawn to allow space for inland postage rates, otherwise as before. No. (11)—first advertisement Marsuma Cigarettes; No. (12)—first advertisement Palethorpes Sausages.

BB2   Edition Nos. (11) & (12). Red cover as T **3** £300

1912 (September). As before, but stamps (Die 1b) with watermark Simple Cypher.

BB3   Edition No. (13). Red cover as T **3** £375

1912 (November). As before, but with redesigned cover showing foreign and colonial as well as inland rates of postage.

BB4   Edition No. (14). Red cover as T **4** £375

1913 (January). As before, but bearing booklet number on the cover.

BB5   Edition Nos. 8 & 9. Red cover as T **4** £375

Edition No. 9 exists without interleaves.

1913 (April). As before, but containing stamps of the 1912–22 issue with watermark Simple Cypher, normal or inverted.

BB6   Edition Nos. 10 to 35. Red cover as T **4** £100

Edition No. 13 is found containing advertisements of edition No. 12. It is also known without interleaves. Edition No. 15 is also known containing interleaves of Edition No. 16.

1915 (November). As before, except lower panel of front cover, which was changed to show " NEW RATES OF POSTAGE ".

BB7   Edition Nos. 36 to 42. Red cover as T 4   .. .. £110

1916 (May). As before, but advertisements on interleaves printed in black instead of green.

Cat. No.

BB8   Edition Nos. 43 to 45. Red cover as T 4   .. .. £150

Edition No. 45 exists containing the ½d. pane of 6 in which the last stamp (R. 2/3) is overprinted with a red cross and surcharged ½d. This was a suggestion for a Red Cross surcharge, but the plan was never adopted.

1916 (July). As before, but colour of cover changed from red to orange.

BB9   Edition Nos. 46 to 64. Orange cover as T 4   .. .. £125

Edition No. 48 (without stamps) has been seen with covers printed on red card. Two examples of Edition No. 56 are known with the interleaves duplicated.

Edition Nos. 63/4 exist with covers stapled or stitched.

Series 1 booklets Nos. 62 to 64 exist stitched as well as stapled.   From No. 65 onwards booklets were normally stitched, but stapling was sometimes resorted to when booklets had to be re-assembled because of mis-stitching (mainly during the King Edward VIII and early King George VI periods).   Black thread was the rule but other colours were occasionally used.

Type 5

1917 (September). As before, but rates of postage transferred to an interleaf and the lower panel of the front cover used for a trade advertisement.

BB10   Edition Nos. 65 to 81. Orange covers as T 5   .. .. £150

    These booklets were replaced by the 3s. booklets (Series 2) in October 1918, following the increase of the inland letter rate from 1d. to 1½d.

Series 4

A new series was introduced, bound in blue covers, selling at 2s., concurrently with Series 3. A feature of this series (except the Special Jubilee booklets) and of Series 5, is the first pane of 1½d. stamps, which contained only four postage stamps. The remaining two spaces, i.e., those on the left next to the margin, being printed with trade advertisements or postal notices.

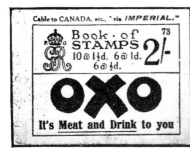

Type **6**   Type **7**

1924 (February). Containing 10 × 1½d., 6 × 1d. and 6 × ½d. stamps of the 1912–1922 issue with Simple Cypher watermark, normal or inverted.
Cat. No.
BB11   Edition Nos. 1 & 2. Blue cover as T **6** £400

1924 (March). As before, but containing stamps with the Block Cypher watermark printed by Waterlow & Sons.

Varieties
   1924 (June). The *se-tenant* advertisements were accidentally inverted. Booklet No. 8.
   1924 (September). The upper *se-tenant* advertisement was deliberately inverted. Edition No. 12.
   1924 (November). Some of the advertisement panes were printed on paper with watermark sideways. Edition No. 15. (Booklets containing these are very rare.)
   1927 (November). The upper *se-tenant* advertisement was deliberately inverted. Edition No. 67.
   1931 (September). The *se-tenant* advertisements were printed in green. Edition No. 171.
   1933 (October). As a trial, 478,000 covers were printed on unglazed paper of a deeper blue. The remaining production of 38,500 had normal covers. Edition No. 242.

BB12   Edition Nos. 3 to 102 and 108 to 254. Blue covers at T **6** £100

   Edition Nos. 27, 29, 31 and 100 exist with stapled covers. There were two types of Edition Nos. 37 and 38, the advertisement panes in each being different. Some advertisement panes in Edition No. 37 were omitted or misplaced and advertisers were given advertisement panes in Edition No. 38 to compensate.

1929 (May). As before, but cover of special design printed in blue on buff and containing stamps of the P.U.C. issue.
BB13   Edition Nos. 103 to 107. Blue on buff cover as T **7** £250

1934 (February). As before, but containing stamps with the Block Cypher watermark printed by Harrison & Sons.
BB14   Edition Nos. 255 to 287. Blue cover as T **6** £125

1935 (January). As before, but containing stamps of the photogravure issue intermediate format with the *se-tenant* advertisements etched on the cylinder and were printed in red-brown. From Booklet No. 289 an interleaf Air Mail label was included.

BB15   Edition Nos. 288 to 297. Blue cover as T **6** £250

Type **8**

1935 (May).   Silver Jubilee issue of booklets larger in size than the normal with cover of special design printed in blue on buff, containing 12 × 1½d., 4 × 1d. and 4 × ½d. and no *se-tenant* advertisements.

BB16   Edition Nos. 298 to 304. Blue on buff cover as T **8** . .   . .   35·00

Edition No. 298 exists with stapled covers or Air Mail label omitted.

1935 (July).   As Edition No. 297, but containing stamps of the photogravure issue small format with *se-tenant* advertisements printed in black.

BB17   Edition Nos. 305 to 353. Blue cover as T **6**   . .   . .   55·00

Edition No. 305. Early printings of this edition contained *se-tenant* advertising labels for Telephone Service and Air Mails. The former included the words "Installed free", which for sometime had been incorrect. These words were deleted by hand on later printings.
Edition Nos. 309–14 were bound using purple thread.
Edition No. 350. The *se-tenant* advertising labels exist transposed vertically with Safety of Capital (top) and Universal Fixed Trust (bottom). This was caused by a horizontal row of stamps being folded over during stacking. Four examples have been found of this variety.

3s. BOOKLETS
Series 2

Type **9**   Type **10**

1918 (October).   The minimum inland postage rate having been increased from 1d. to 1½d., a new series was introduced to replace Series 1, containing 12 × 1½d.; 12 × 1d. and 12 × ½d. stamps of the 1912–22 issue with watermark Simple Cypher, normal or inverted. Bound in orange covers and fully interleaved.

Cat. No.

BB18   Edition Nos. 1 to 11. Orange cover as T **9** £150

1919 (July).   Make-up altered to contain 18 × 1½d., 6 × 1d. and 6 × ½d.   Otherwise as before.

BB19   Edition Nos. 12 to 26. Orange cover as T **9** £150
With the increase in the inland postage rate to 2d. in July 1920 Series 2 continued as 3s. 6d. booklets.

1921 (April). An experimental booklet bound in blue covers was issued containing 18 × 2d. stamps (Die I or II), which sold at 3s. concurrently with the 3s. 6d. booklets.

BB20   Edition Nos. 35 and majority of 37. Blue cover as T **10** £200
Series 2 booklets were replaced by Series 3, also containing 3s. and 3s. 6d. booklets, in August 1921.

Series 3

1921 (December).   An experimental booklet bound in blue covers, similar to Edition Nos. 35 and 37 of Series 2, was issued containing 18 × 2d. stamps (Die II), costing 3s. and sold concurrently with the 3s. 6d. books.

BB21   Edition Nos. 12, 13 and part of 37. Blue cover as T **10** £200

Type **11**

1922 (May).   With the reduction of the minimum inland postage rate from 2d. to 1½d., the make-up was changed to include 18 × 1½d.; 6 × 1d. and 6 × ½d.   Bound in scarlet covers and fully interleaved.

BB22   Edition Nos. 19, 20, 22, 23 and 25 to 54. Scarlet cover as T **11** £175
Edition No. 22 exists bound with staples.

1922 (June).   An experimental booklet was issued bound in blue covers, similar to Edition Nos. 12 and 13, but containing 24 × 1½d. stamps.   Sold concurrently with Edition Nos. 20, 22, 23 and 25.

Cat. No.

BB23   Edition Nos. 21 and 24. Blue cover as T **11** £225

1924 (February).   As Edition No. 54, but containing stamps with the Block Cypher watermark printed by Waterlow & Sons.   Airmail label included from Edition No. 191.

BB24   Edition Nos. 55 to 167 and 173 to 273. Scarlet cover as T **11** .. .. ..   55·00

1929 (May).   As before, but cover of special design printed in red on buff and containing stamps of the P.U.C. issue.

BB25   Edition Nos. 168 to 172. Red on buff cover as T **7** £200

1934 (March).   As Edition No. 273, but containing stamps with the Block Cypher watermark printed by Harrison & Sons.

BB26   Edition Nos. 274 to 288. Scarlet cover as T **11** .. ..   95·00

1935 (January).   As before, but containing stamps of the photogravure issue intermediate format.

BB27   Edition Nos. 289 to 293. Scarlet cover as T **11** £200

1935 (May). Silver Jubilee issue of booklets larger in size than the normal with cover of special design printed in red on buff, containing 20 × 1½d.; 4 × 1d. and 4 × ½d. Silver Jubilee stamps, watermark Block Cypher, normal or inverted.

BB28   Edition Nos. 294 to 297. Red on buff cover as T 8 .. ..   35·00

1935 (July).   As Edition No. 293, but containing stamps of the photogravure issue small format.

BB29   Edition Nos. 298 to 319. Scarlet cover as T 11 .. ..   75·00

A special cover card was used to produce 4,000 of edition No. 312 prior to the introduction of new cover material for edition No. 314.

Edition No. 313 was issued in June 1936 with an error on the air mail interleaf. The words "AIR MAIL" in the third line of the last paragraph read "AIR MAII". The labels remained in use until July 1937 but the misprint was never corrected.

Edition No. 318 exists with a stapled cover.

3s. 6d. BOOKLETS
Series 2

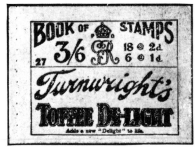

Type **12**   Type **13**

1920 (July).   With the increase of the minimum inland postage rate from 1½d. to 2d., the make-up was changed to 18 × 2d. and 6 × 1d., and the price was increased from 3s. to 3s. 6d.   Otherwise as Cat. No. BB19.

BB30   Edition Nos. 27 to 32. Orange cover as T 12 .. ..   £200

1921 (January). Make-up changed to 12 × 2d.; 6 × 1½d.; 6 × 1d. and 6 × ½d.

BB31   Edition Nos. 33, 34, 36 and 38. Orange-red cover as T 13 .. ..   £175

Series 2 booklets were replaced by Series 3, also containing 3s. and 3s. 6d. booklets, in August 1921.

Series 3

1921 (August).   A new series was introduced to replace Series 2, containing 12 × 2d. (Die I Edition Nos. 1, 2, 4 or Die II others); 6 × 1½d., 6 × 1d. and 6 × ½d. stamps of the 1912-22 issue with watermark Simple Cypher, normal or inverted. Bound in orange-red covers, fully interleaved.

Cat. No.

BB32   Edition Nos. 1 to 11 and 14 to 18. Orange-red cover as T 13 .. ..   £200

The inland postage rate was reduced from 2d. to 1½d. in May 1922 and from that date Series 3 was issued as 3s. booklets.

5s. BOOKLETS
Series 5

Type **14**
The letters " P " and " O " are on either side of crown
on the King George V booklets, as shown in Type **11**

1931 (August).   A new series was introduced, bound in green covers, selling at 5s.
concurrently with Series 3 and 4, and containing 34 × 1½d.; 6 × 1d. and 6 × ½d. stamps with
Block Cypher watermark printed by Waterlow & Son, the first 1½d. pane being similar
to that in Series 4 and having four postage stamps and two *se-tenant* advertisements.
BB33   Edition No. 1. Green cover as T **14** £500

1932 (June).   As before, but with buff covers.   From Booklet No. 4 an interleaf Air
Mail label was included.
BB34   Edition Nos. 2 to 6. Buff cover as T **14** £150

1934 (July).   As before, but containing stamps with the Block Cypher watermark printed
by Harrison & Sons.
BB35   Edition Nos. 7 and 8. Buff cover as T **14** £150

1935 (February).   As before, but with stamps of the photogravure issue intermediate
format and with *se-tenant* advertisements etched on the cylinder and were printed in red-brown.
BB36   Edition No. 9. Buff cover as T **14** £350

1935 (July).   As before, but with stamps of the photogravure issue small format and
with the *se-tenant* advertisements printed in black.
BB37   Edition Nos. 10 to 15. Buff cover as T **14** ..   ..   85·00

KING EDWARD VIII
6d. BOOKLETS SOLD FROM SLOT-MACHINES
Series 6. Sub-series A

1936.   Booklets containing 4 × 1½d. stamps, in small panes of two, were obtainable
from slot-machines placed outside 40 of the larger London Post Offices.   No interleaves
and stamps either watermark normal or inverted.   Bound in buff unglazed covers without
inscription.
BC1   No edition number. Unprinted buff cover   ..   ..   25·00

2s. BOOKLETS
Series 4

1936 (October).   As Cat. No. BB17, except for the K.E.VIII cypher on the cover and
containing stamps of the new reign.
Cat. No.
BC2   Edition Nos. 354 to 385. Blue cover as T **6** ..   ..   40·00
Edition Nos. 357, 362, 370, 372, 375, 378, 381 and 385 are known with a stapled cover (without
stitching holes).

3s. BOOKLETS
Series 3

1936 (November). As Cat. No. BB29, except for the K.E.VIII cypher on the cover and without " P " and " O " on either side of crown, and containing stamps of the new reign.

BC3   Edition Nos. 320 to 332. Scarlet cover as T **11** .. ..   35·00

5s. BOOKLETS
Series 5

1937 (March). As Cat. No. BB37, but with the K.E.VIII cypher on the cover and containing stamps of the new reign.

BC4   Edition Nos. 16 and 17. Buff cover as T **14** .. ..   90·00
Edition Nos. 16 and 17 are known with a stapled cover (without stitching holes).

KING GEORGE VI
6d. BOOKLETS SOLD FROM SLOT-MACHINES
Series 6. Sub-series A

1938 (January). As Cat. No. BC1, but containing stamps of the new reign in the original dark colours, with watermark normal or inverted. With or without interleaf.

BD1   No edition number. Unprinted buff cover .. ..   18·00
      a. With interleaf .. ..   18·00

Series 6. Sub-series B

1938 (February). Make-up changed to contain 2 × 1½d.; 2 × 1d. and 2 × ½d. stamps in the original dark colours, with watermark normal or inverted. Bound in plain pink unglazed covers, with or without interleaves.

BD2   No edition number. Unprinted pink cover .. ..   55·00
      a. With interleaves .. ..   55·00

Series 6. Sub-series C

1940 (June). Make-up changed to contain 4 × 1d. and 4 × ½d. stamps in the original dark colours in panes of four with watermark sideways, either with margin at top of stamps or at bottom; bound in pale green plain covers with interleaves. Booklets obtainable only from a slot-machine placed inside the G.P.O., King Edward Building, E.C.1.

BD3   No edition number. Unprinted green cover. Margin at top .. ..   55·00
      a. Margin at bottom .. ..   55·00
      b. One pane with margin at top, other inverted with margin at bottom £125

1s. BOOKLETS SOLD FROM SLOT-MACHINES
Series 6. Sub-series D

1947 (December). Make-up changed to contain 4 × ½d.; 4 × 1d. and 4 × 1½d. stamps in the pale shades in panes of two, all with watermark normal. Bound in plain unglazed cream covers without interleaves.

BD4   No edition number. Unprinted cream cover .. ..   12·00

1951 (May). As before, but containing stamps in the changed colours.

BD5   No edition number. Unprinted cream cover .. ..   12·00

Series 6. Sub-series E

1948. Make-up changed to contain 4 × ½d.; 4 × 1d. and 4 × 1½d. stamps of the pale shades in panes of four with watermark normal. Cover cream. A very rare booklet.

Cat. No.
BD6   No edition number. Unprinted cream cover. Margin at top .. ..
      a. Margin at bottom .. ..

1951 (May).   As before, but stamps in the new colours all watermark normal, margin either at the top or at the bottom.   These booklets were on sale outside the Festival of Britain Post Office on the South Bank.

BD7   No edition number. Unprinted cream cover. Margin at top   .. .. 14·00
    a.   Margin at bottom .. .. 14·00
    ab. Panes in wrong order, 1d., 1½d., ½d. .. .. 30·00

Type 15

Type 16

1952 (December).   As before, but with printed covers with stamps either watermark normal or inverted and with margins only at the top.   At first available at Paignton head office, but later at other places.   Back cover printed: " 1½d. Minimum Postage Rate for Inland Printed Papers 1½d. ".

BD8   No edition number. Cream cover as T 15   .. .. 14·00
    a.   1½d. pane reversed and stitched through stamps   .. ..

1953 (September).   As before with Inland Letter rate on inside cover corrected in ink.

BD9   No edition number. Cream cover as T 15   .. .. 12·00

1954.   As before, with Inland Postage rates correctly printed.   GPO emblem with St. Edward's crown and oval frame on the front cover and new notice on the back cover: " Minimum Foreign Letter Rate FOUR PENCE ".

BD10 No edition number. Cream cover as T 16   .. .. 14·00

2s. BOOKLETS
Series 4

1937 (August).   As Cat. No. BC2, except for the K.G.VI cypher on the cover and containing stamps of the new reign in the original dark colours.

BD11   Edition Nos. 386 to 412. Blue cover as T 6   .. .. £120
    Edition No. 405 exists which had been both stitched and stapled.

Type 17

1938 (April).   As before, but with redesigned front cover showing GPO emblem instead of royal cypher.

Cat. No.

BD12   Edition Nos. 413 to 508. Blue cover as T **17** £120

Examples of Edition No. 454 were bound in error with two front covers.

Series 2 booklets were replaced by the 2s. 6d. booklets of Series 7 when the inland postage rate was increased from 1½d. to 2½d. in June 1940.

2s. 6d. BOOKLETS
Series 7

Type **18**   Type **19**

1940 (June).   The minimum inland postage rate having been increased from 1½d. to 2½d., a new series of booklets was introduced to replace Series 3 and 4, containing 6 × 2½d.; 6 × 2d. and 6 × ½d. stamps in the dark colours. Fully interleaved and bound in red covers to use up surplus card left over from Series 3.

BD13   Edition Nos. 1 to 7. Scarlet cover as T **18** £250

1940 (September).   As before, but covers changed to blue to use up surplus card left over from Series 4.

BD14   Edition Nos. 8 to 13. Blue cover as T **18** £250

1940 (October).   As before, but with glazed green covers of changed design.

BD15   Edition Nos. 14 to 94. Green cover as T **19** £150

1942 (March).   As before, but containing stamps in the pale shades.

BD16   Edition Nos. 95 to 146 (part). Green cover as T **19** . . . .' £150

1942 (October).   As before, but with unglazed green covers.

BD17   Edition Nos. 146 (part) to 214. Green cover as T **19** £125

Type **20**

1943 (August).   After Edition No. 214, the booklets were no longer numbered, but were dated with the month of issue.   At the same time commercial advertising ceased, covers and interleaves being used for Post Office slogans.   Changed cover design, with GPO emblem in centre.

Varieties: In the first printing the Forces parcel rate for 3 lb. was wrongly given as 6d.; October 1943, corrected to 9d. by means of a handstamp, with or without interleaving; November 1943 to August 1944, with thinner or rougher interleaving or not interleaved; September 1944 onwards, no interleaving.

Cat. No.

BD18   Edition dates as below. Green cover as T **20**   ..   ..   15·00

Booklet No. BD18

(1) AUG 1943	22·00	(46) MAY 1947		15·00
(2) SEPT 1943	22·00	(47) JUNE 1947		15·00
(3) OCT 1943	22·00	(48) JULY 1947		15·00
(4) NOV 1943	22·00	(49) AUG 1947		15·00
(5) DEC 1943	22·00	(50) SEPT 1947		15·00
(6) JAN 1944	22·00	(51) OCT 1947		15·00
(7) FEB 1944	22·00	(52) NOV 1947		15·00
(8) MAR 1944	22·00	(53) DEC 1947		15·00
(9) APR 1944	22·00	(54) JAN 1948		15·00
(10) MAY 1944	22·00	(55) FEB 1948		15·00
(11) JUNE 1944	22·00	(56) MAR 1948		15·00
(12) JULY 1944	22·00	(57) APR 1948		15·00
(13) AUG 1944	22·00	(58) MAY 1948		15·00
(14) SEPT 1944	22·00	(59) JUNE 1948		15·00
(15) OCT 1944	22·00	(60) JULY 1948		15·00
(16) NOV 1944	22·00	(61) AUG 1948		15·00
(17) DEC 1944	22·00	(62) SEPT 1948		15·00
(18) JAN 1945	22·00	(63) OCT 1948		15·00
(19) FEB 1945	22·00	(64) NOV 1948		15·00
(20) MAR 1945	22·00	(65) DEC 1948		15·00
(21) APR 1945	22·00	(66) JAN 1949		15·00
(22) MAY 1945	22·00	(67) FEB 1949		15·00
(23) JUNE 1945	22·00	(68) MAR 1949		15·00
(24) JULY 1945	22·00	(69) APR 1949		15·00
(25) AUG 1945	22·00	(70) MAY 1949		15·00
(26) SEPT 1945	22·00	(71) JUNE 1949		15·00
(27) OCT 1945	22·00	(72) JULY 1949		15·00
(28) NOV 1945	22·00	(73) AUG 1949		15·00
(29) DEC 1945	22·00	(74) OCT 1949		15·00
(30) JAN 1946	15·00	(75) NOV 1949		15·00
(31) FEB 1946	15·00	(76) DEC 1949		15·00
(32) MAR 1946	15·00	(77) JAN 1950		15·00
(33) APR 1946	15·00	(78) FEB 1950		15·00
(34) MAY 1946	15·00	(79) MAR 1950		15·00
(35) JUNE 1946	15·00	(80) APR 1950		15·00
(36) JULY 1946	15·00	(81) MAY 1950		15·00
(37) AUG 1946	15·00	(82) JUNE 1950		15·00
(38) SEPT 1946	15·00	(83) JULY 1950		15·00
(39) OCT 1946	15·00	(84) AUG 1950		15·00
(40) NOV 1946	15·00	(85) SEPT 1950		15·00
(41) DEC 1946	15·00	(86) OCT 1950		15·00
(42) JAN 1947	15·00	(87) NOV 1950		15·00
(43) FEB 1947	15·00	(88) DEC 1950		15·00
(44) MAR 1947	15·00	(89) JAN 1951		15·00
(45) APR 1947	15·00	(90) FEB 1951		15·00

1951 (May). As before, but containing stamps in the new colours. The June and some July 1951 editions exist with a correction in red to the printed paper rate on the cover. From July 1951 the printed paper rate reference was corrected to read " 1½d. " in black.

Cat. No.

BD19   Edition dates as below. Green cover as T **20**   ..   ..   16·00

Booklet No. BD19

(1) MAY 1951	16·00	(6) OCT 1951		16·00
(2) JUNE 1951	16·00	(7) NOV 1951		16·00
(3) JULY 1951	16·00	(8) DEC 1951		16·00
a. Rate corrected in		(9) JAN 1952		16·00
red		(10) FEB 1952		16·00
(4) AUG 1951	16·00			
(5) SEPT 1951	16·00			

1952 (March).   Make-up changed to contain 6 × 2½d.; 6 × 1½d.; 3 × 1d. and 6 × ½d.   The 1d. pane comprised three stamps in the top row and a Post Office notice in the lower row reading " MINIMUM INLAND PRINTED PAPER RATE 1½d." and measuring 17 mm. high.   Otherwise as before.

BD20   Edition dates as below. Green cover as T **20**   .. ..   16·00

Booklet No. BD20

(1) MAR 1952 .. .. 16·00	(9) NOV 1952 .. .. 16·00
(2) APR 1952 .. .. 16·00	(10) DEC 1952 .. .. 16·00
(3) MAY 1952 .. .. 16·00	(11) JAN 1953 .. .. 16·00
(4) JUNE 1952 .. .. 16·00	(12) FEB 1953 .. .. 16·00
(5) JULY 1952 .. .. 16·00	(13) MAR 1953 .. .. 16·00
(6) AUG 1952 .. .. 16·00	(14) APR 1953 .. .. 16·00
(7) SEPT 1952 .. .. 16·00	(15) MAY 1953 .. .. 16·00
(8) OCT 1952 .. .. 16·00	

Type **21**   Type **22**

1953 (May).   Composite booklets introduced, containing stamps of King George VI *and* Queen Elizabeth II.   Make-up: 6 × 2½d.   Q.E. II (S51), 6 × 1½d.   Q.E. II (S25), 3 × 1d. K.G. VI and three labels (QB18/a), 6 × ½d.   K.G. VI (Q3) in panes of six.   Green cover as T **21** not interleaved.

F1   Edition date MAY 1953   .. ..   14·00
F2   Edition date JUNE 1953   .. ..   15·00
F3   Edition date JULY 1953   .. ..   15·00
F4   Edition date AUG 1953   .. ..   15·00

> In Booklets F5–14 below, Panes QB18/a read " MINIMUM INLAND PRINTED PAPER RATE 1½d.", 17 mm. high.   Panes QB19/a read the same, but 15 mm. high.   Panes QB20/a read "SHORTHAND IN ONE WEEK ".

1953 (September).   As before, but with the addition of two interleaving pages, one at each end. Green cover as T **21**.

F5   Edition date SEPT 1953 (contains panes QB18/a) .. ..   55·00
F6   Edition date SEPT 1953 (contains panes QB19/a) .. ..   20·00

1953 (October).   As before, but new style green cover as T **22**.

Cat. No.

F7   Edition date OCT 1953 (contains panes QB18/a) .. ..   15·00
F8   Edition date OCT 1953 (contains panes QB19/a) .. ..   15·00
F9   Edition date NOV 1953 (contains panes QB18/a) .. ..   15·00
F10   Edition date NOV 1953 (contains panes QB19/a) .. ..   40·00
F11   Edition date DEC 1953 (contains panes QB18/a) .. ..   15·00
F12   Edition date JAN 1954 (contains panes QB19/a) .. ..   15·00
F13   Edition date FEB 1954 (contains panes QB20/a) .. ..   15·00

1954 (March).   As before, but pane of 6 × ½d.   Q.E. II (S1) in place of 6 × ½d.   K.G. VI.

F14   Edition date MAR 1954. Green cover as T **22** (contains panes QB18/a)   ..   £250

3s. BOOKLETS
Series 3

1937 (August).   As Cat. No. BC3, except for K.G.VI cypher on the cover and containing stamps of the new reign in the original dark colours.

BD21   Edition Nos. 333 to 343. Scarlet cover as T **11** £180

1938 (April).   As before, but with redesigned front cover showing GPO emblem instead of royal cypher.

BD22   Edition Nos. 344 to 377. Scarlet cover as T **17** £180

Series 3 booklets were replaced by the 2s. 6d. booklets of Series 7 in June 1940.

5s. BOOKLETS :
Series 5

1937 (August).   As Cat. No. BC4, but with K.G.VI cypher on the cover and containing stamps of the new reign in the original dark colours.

BD23   Edition Nos. 18 to 20. Buff cover as T **14** £180

Type **23**

1938 (May).   As before, but with redesigned front cover showing GPO emblem instead of royal cypher.

BD24   Edition Nos. 21 to 29. Buff cover as T **23** £180

Edition No. 29 initially had glazed covers, but in the later part of the printing unglazed card was introduced.

Series 5 was replaced by Series 8, also of 5s. booklets, in July 1940.

Series 8

1940 (July).   The minimum inland postage rate having been raised from 1½d. to 2½d. a new series of 5s. booklets was introduced to replace Series 5, containing 18 × 2½d.; 6 × 2d. and 6 × ½d. stamps in the original dark colours.   Bound in glazed buff covers and fully interleaved.

BD25   Edition Nos. 1 to 16 (part). Buff cover as T **23** £180

1942 (March).   During the life of Edition No. 16 stamps in the pale shades were brought into use.   Otherwise as before.

Cat. No.

BD26   Edition Nos. 16 (part) to 29 (part). Buff cover as T **23** £150

1943 (February).   As before, but cover changed to rough unglazed buff.

BD27   Edition Nos. 29 (part) to 36. Buff cover as T **23** £125

Type **24**

Type **25**

1943 (September). As before, but with changed cover design with GPO emblem in centre. Booklets dated and no longer numbered. Commercial advertising ceased and interleaves were used for war slogans. With or without interleaving (August 1944), later without interleaving (October 1944 onwards).

In the earlier printing an error in the Forces parcel rate—the 3 lb. rate being shown as 6d. instead of 9d.—was corrected with a hand stamp, but this was later correctly printed.

BD28   Edition dates as below. Buff cover as T 24   . .   . .   35·00

Booklet No. BD28

(1) SEPT 1943	40·00	(26) JUNE 1947	35·00
(2) OCT 1943	40·00	(27) AUG 1947	35·00
(3) NOV 1943	40·00	(28) OCT 1947	35·00
(4) DEC 1943	40·00	(29) DEC 1947	35·00
(5) FEB 1944	40·00	(30) FEB 1948	35·00
(6) MAR 1944	40·00	(31) APR 1948	35·00
(7) AUG 1944	40·00	(32) JUNE 1948	35·00
(8) OCT 1944	40·00	(33) JULY 1948	35·00
(9) NOV 1944	40·00	(34) AUG 1948	35·00
(10) JAN 1945	35·00	(35) OCT 1948	35·00
(11) FEB 1945	35·00	(36) DEC 1948	35·00
(12) APR 1945	35·00	(37) FEB 1949	35·00
(13) JUNE 1945	35·00	(38) APR 1949	35·00
(14) AUG 1945	35·00	(39) JUNE 1949	35·00
(15) OCT 1945	35·00	(40) AUG 1949	35·00
(16) DEC 1945	35·00	(41) SEPT 1949	35·00
(17) JAN 1946	35·00	(42) OCT 1949	35·00
(18) MAR 1946	35·00	(43) DEC 1949	35·00
(19) MAY 1946	35·00	(44) FEB 1950	35·00
(20) JUNE 1946	35·00	(45) APR 1950	35·00
(21) AUG 1946	35·00	(46) JUNE 1950	35·00
(22) OCT 1946	35·00	(47) AUG 1950	35·00
(23) DEC 1946	35·00	(48) OCT 1950	35·00
(24) FEB 1947	35·00	(49) DEC 1950	35·00
(25) APR 1947	35·00		

1944 (April). As before, but with changed cover design. With or without interleaving.

BD29   Edition dates as below. Buff cover as T 25   . .   . .   30·00

Booklet No. BD29

(1) APR 1944	30·00	(2) JUNE 1944	30·00

1951 (May). As Cat. No. BD28, but containing stamps in the new colours.

Cat. No.
BD30   Edition dates as below. Buff cover as T 24   . .   . .   15·00

Booklet No. BD30

(1) MAY 1951	15·00	(4) NOV 1951	17·00
(2) JULY 1951	15·00	(5) JAN 1952	17·00
(3) SEPT 1951	17·00		

1952 (March). Make-up changed to contain 18 × 2½d.; 6 × 1½d.; 3 × 1d. and 6 × ½d., the 1d. pane having three stamps in the top row and Post Office notice in the lower row reading " MINIMUM INLAND PRINTED PAPER RATE 1½d." and measuring 17 mm. high. Otherwise as before.

BD31   Edition dates as below. Buff cover as T **24**   .. .. 15·00

Booklet No. BD31

(1) MAR 1952	..	..	15·00	(4) SEPT 1952	..	..	16·00
(2) MAY 1952	..	..	16·00	(5) NOV 1952	..	..	16·00
(3) JULY 1952	..	..	15·00				

1953 (January). Make-up again altered to include the 2d. value and containing 12 × 2½d.; 6 × 2d.; 6 × 1½d.; 6 × 1d. and 6 × ½d. Otherwise as before.

BD32   Edition dates as below. Buff cover as T **24**   .. .. 24·00

Booklet No. BD32

(1) JAN 1953	..	..	24·00	(2) MAR 1953	.. ..	24·00

1953 (May). Composite booklets introduced, containing stamps of King George VI *and* Queen Elizabeth II. Make-up: 12 × 2½d. Q.E. II (S51), 6 × 2d. K.G. VI (Q12), 6 × 1½d. Q.E. II (S25), 6 × 1d. K.G. VI (Q6), 6 × ½d. K.G. VI (Q3) in panes of six. Not interleaved. Buff cover as T **21**.

H1   Edition date MAY 1953   .. .. 20·00
H2   Edition date JULY 1953   .. .. 20·00

1953 (September). As before, but with the addition of two interleaving pages, one at each end.

H3   Edition date SEPT 1953. Buff cover as T **21**   .. .. 20·00

1953 (November). As before but buff cover in new style as T **22**.

H4   Edition date NOV 1953   .. .. 20·00
H5   Edition date JAN 1954   .. .. 20·00

1954 (March). As before but pane of 6 × ½d. Q.E. II (S1) in place of 6 × ½d. K.G. VI.
H6   Edition date MAR 1954. Buff cover as T **22**   .. .. 60·00

1954 (March). As before but pane of 6 × ½d. Q.E. II (S1) in place of 6 × ½d. K.G. VI *and* 6 × 1d. Q.E. II (S13) in place of 6 × 1d. K. G. VI.
H7   Edition date MAR 1954. Buff cover as T **22**   .. .. 60·00

Booklet Pane Pre-Cancellations

Pre-cancellations were applied to booklet panes to prevent their being used for postal purposes. The types of pre-cancellation are illustrated and described below; pre-cancelled booklet panes are listed and priced in the main catalogue.

On Booklets (1) to (4) of Series 1, pre-cancellation Type A was applied by hand on make-up trials and on sample booklets distributed to sub-offices. From Booklet (5), when advertisement pages were introduced, the primary purpose of the pre-cancellations was for use on advertisers' voucher copies. However, some booklets continued to be overprinted with " Specimen " or " Cancelled " for official reference purposes or for use as colour standards, up to the issue of King Edward VIII.

Usually, two or more strikes were applied to each pane, but later on it became customary to prepare a handstamp containing the number of impressions required to cancel each pane with a single strike.

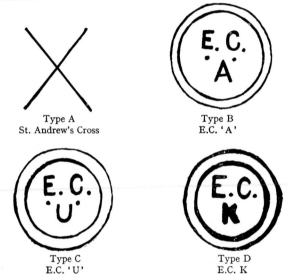

Type A
St. Andrew's Cross

Type B
E.C. 'A'

Type C
E.C. 'U'

Type D
E.C. K

Type A was handwritten in pen and ink across each stamp in the pane and was employed in booklets (1) to (6) (Nos. BA1/5).

Types B, C and D were used only on booklet (6) (No. BA5).

Type E
London Chief Office, E.C.
(Double Circle)

Type F
London (Chief Office) E.C.
(Single Circle)

Type E was employed on the K.E. VII Harrison booklet (7) (No. BA6) and later on the K.G. V Downey Head issue with Crown watermark (Nos. BB1/2). However it has also been discovered on panes from the K.E. VII De La Rue booklet (6) (No. BA5) and these are very rare.

Type F was used only on the Downey Head stamps with Crown watermark (Nos. BB1/2).

Type G	Type H	Type I
	" London, E.C. " Types	
(Double Circle)	(Single Circle)	(Double Circle
Code No. varies	Also exists with 25 mm.	with Curved Bars)
	diameter	

Type G was used only on the Downey Head stamps with Crown watermark (Nos. BB1/2).

Type H was used on the Downey Head stamps with Crown watermark (Booklets BB1/2) and with Simple Cypher watermark (Booklets BB3/5) and on Profile Head stamps (Booklets BB6, etc.).

Type I was used on the Profile Head stamps (Booklets BB6/11, BB18/23, BB30/32) and for a short time in 1924 with Block watermark stamps (Booklets BB12 and BB24).

Type J	Type K
(Curved Line)	(Curved and Straight Lines)

" London Chief Office " Types

Types J and K were made with rubber stamps and were applied (in violet) on Block watermark stamps (Booklets BB12 and BB24).

From about 1926 the stamps were overprinted " Specimen " or " Cancelled " and from 1928 they were additionally punched (Type P) for further security. After 1940, voucher copies of booklets were either made up with unprinted paper or dummy stamps, or simply had the stamps removed.

APPENDIX 4

"Specimen" and "Cancelled" Overprints

General Notes

INTRODUCTION. Between 1847 and 1873 it was the custom for examples of major changes in design or colour and new values to be distributed with circulars to Postmasters and to be overprinted "SPECIMEN". From 1879 this was also done on stamps sent to the Universal Postal Union for distribution to member nations. However from 1892 it was decided to overprint only the values from 2s. 6d. upwards, the lower values being sent without overprint, but from 1913 onwards the 1s. values were also overprinted. The use of "SPECIMEN" overprints on stamps sent to the U.P.U. ceased completely in March 1948.

Stamps overprinted "SPECIMEN" or "CANCELLED" were made for many purposes, such as for official record copies, trial printings and on coil stamps and booklet panes. It was also the practice to preserve sheets or blocks of six of printings which varied in shade from their predecessors to serve as colour standards for matching future printings.

All the "SPECIMEN" and "CANCELLED" stamps listed are known to exist in private hands, some being very rare. Others are known to exist only in official records and are not listed.

THE OVERPRINTS. Information on "Specimen" stamps from official sources has always been very difficult to obtain. The overprints were applied by or on behalf of the authorities controlling the production of the stamps (the Postage Stamp Department of the Inland Revenue until 1915 and the Post Office Stores Department thereafter), or by the printers. There was a tendency for the overprints to remain in use in their original form, or slightly modified, for long periods, even after a change in controller or printer.

The overprints were either handstamped or printed from type settings, some by both means. Some of the type settings were of such poor quality that they cannot be distinguished from handstamps unless the stamps are in multiples. Overprints composed from the same type to fit stamps or sheets of various shapes or sizes may differ slightly in dimensions. In the interests of simplification some of the types we illustrate comprise groups of overprints of similar character but differing slightly from one another, these bearing an asterisk after the Type number.

The uses to which the various types were put at various times are indicated below:—

KING EDWARD VII. Type 16 on the De La Rue 2s. 6d., 5s., 10s. and £1 were supplied to the U.P.U.; Types 15 (16 on the lower values) and 17 were used on reference copies; Types 18 to 20 were used for colour standards and Type 22 was probably used for the same purpose on the 1911–12 issues; Type 21 was used on Harrison coil trials.

When the De La Rue printing contract ended in 1910 the Inland Revenue instructed them to return all the British stamps in their possession, but they were allowed to retain items mounted in their correspondence books on condition that they were cancelled. Issued stamps were defaced by having the word "Cancelled" written across them in manuscript, while items of proof status were cancelled with pen strokes.

KING GEORGE V. The only "Specimen" overprints sent to the U.P.U. were of Type 26 on the 1s. Royal Cypher watermark and the Waterlow 2s. 6d., 5s., 10s. and £1 and of Type 32 in black on the photogravure 1s. and in red on the £1 Postal Union Congress. Otherwise Types 23, 25, 26, 28, 30, 32 and 33 were generally used for colour standards. Types 23 and 28 were also used for trial printings, while Type 24 was almost exclusively used for this purpose. Type 27 is seen on Waterlow high values which were used for forensic tests. The purpose for which Type 29 was used is unknown. Type 31 (a handstamp) was used on the 1s. Royal Cypher watermark and the Bradbury, Wilkinson 2s. 6d., 5s. and 10s. and it is believed that they were supplied in response to a request from a foreign administration.

APPENDIX 4 "Specimen" and "Cancelled" Overprints

Types of Overprints

SPECIMEN	SPECIMEN	SPECIMEN	(SPECIMEN curved)	CANCELLED
9*	15*	16	17	18
14¾×1¾–2	14½×2–2¼	15½×2½	16×2¾	14¼×1½
(1871–1900)	(1891–1911)	(1891–1909)	(1904–07)	(1900–07)

CANCELLED	CANCELLED	CANCELLED.	SPECIMEN	SPECIMEN
19	20	21	22	23*
14×1½	12¼×1½	24×2½	14¾×2	9¾–10×1¾
(1906–09)	(1910)	(1911)	(1911–12)	(1912–42)

CANCELLED	CANCELLED	SPECIMEN	CANCELLED	CANCELLED
24*	25	26*	27	28*
15×2	12¾×1¼	12½×2	27×2¾	11¾×1½
(1911–20)	(1912)	(1911–24)	(1913)	(1912–46)

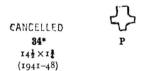

SPECIMEN	SPECIMEN	SPECIMEN	SPECIMEN	CANCELLED
29	30*	31	32	33*
11¼×1¼	13×1¼	12¼×1¾	10½×2	11–12×1¾–2
(1913)	(1924–51)	(1918)	(1924–37)	(1924–46)

CANCELLED
34*
14½×1¾
(1941–48)

P

Types of Overprints referred to in the Lists
Sizes given in millimetres

*These Types represent groups comprising several similar types differing slightly from one another within the measurements given.

Type **P** was a handpunch used on booklet panes already overprinted " CANCELLED ". They come from voucher booklets sent to the advertisers.

The dates quoted represent the main periods of usage of the overprints or groups of overprints. They do not necessarily encompass the dates of issue of all the stamps on which they are found—they may have been used on pre-issue proofs or on stamps long after their dates of issue, after new overprint types had come into use.

Types 22, 23, 24, 28, 30 and 33 were also used on booklet panes.   Stamps from sheets with the same overprints are considerably scarcer and some can be identified only if they are marginal copies or in multiples greater than blocks of six (3 × 2).

Types 23, 24 and 28 have been used to cancel specimen sheets of unprinted watermarked paper but such items are not listed.

In 1924 folders containing sets of the contemporary definitive stamps to 10s. and the British Empire Exhibition Commemorative stamps were prepared for presentation to delegates at the Stockholm U.P.U. Congress.   One of these folders exists with each stamp overprinted with Type 15.

A set comprising the low values in the Block Cypher watermark overprinted with Type 32 (the 6d. with Type 26) and the Bradbury, Wilkinson high values overprinted with Type 23, all additionally overprinted with Type 34 at a much later date, is of unknown status.

KING EDWARD VIII.   Types 30 and 32 have been recorded on a very small number of stamps in private hands.   Type 33 was used on booklet panes.

KING GEORGE VI.   The first issue: 1s., 2s. 6d. (both colours), 5s. and 10s. (both colours) overprinted with Type 23 were for supplies sent to the U.P.U.   Type 34 was used for colour standards and other overprints were used for the same purposes as during the previous reigns.   Apart from those sent to the U.P.U. and booklet stamps overprinted with Type 33, very few are in private hands.

In 1947 folders containing sets of the contemporary definitive stamps to 10s., the 1940 Stamp Centenary and 1946 Peace Commemorative issues, Postage Due stamps to 2s. 6d. and items of postal stationery, as well as stamps overprinted for use in the Morocco Agencies and Tangier, were prepared for presentation to delegates at the Paris U.P.U. Congress. One of these folders exists with each stamp overprinted with Type 9, which had not been used since Victorian times.   Its purpose is unknown.

Although too late for U.P.U. distribution with "Specimen" overprint, an example of the 1948 Silver Jubilee £1 is known with "CANCELLED" Type 34 and large punch holes in three corners.   Its purpose is not known.

POSTAGE DUE STAMPS.   Type 23 on the 1s. Royal Cypher watermark and the 2s. 6d. Block Cypher watermark were used for supplies sent to the U.P.U.   Otherwise the purposes of the types used on the Postage Due stamps were similar to those of the contemporary Postage stamps.

Protective Underprints

In general the practice of firms underprinting their stamps to prevent theft ceased about 1881. Sloper's perforation of stamps with initials or monogram of the firm was better and more secure, being visible from the front. These are known to philatelists as "perfins" and are outside the scope of this Catalogue. From about 1904 to 1915 two firms are known to have returned to underprinting on top of the gum and used examples exist.

Messrs. W. H. Everett & Sons Limited of London invented a hand-held roller with inking pad, six impressions of the initials being in a horizontal row, which they advertised as being with permission of the Post-master General. Although advertised at only £1 the invention does not appear to have sold as no other firms are known using one. The other firm was Messrs. S. & J. Watts of Manchester who used "Wattses", evidently printed from a metal plate.

The Post Office would not repurchase stamps underprinted or perforated, so there was little point in office boys stealing them.

KING EDWARD VII

Wattses

1   2

1903. W. H. Everett & Son Limited, Bell's Buildings, Salisbury Square, London, E.C. Underprint Type 1 in purple or red

PP230 ½d. blue-green (M1)   ..   ..
PP231 1d. red (M5)   ..   ..
PP232 1½d. purple and green (M8)   ..   ..
PP233 2d. green and red (M11)   ..   ..
PP234 2½d. blue (M16) ..   ..
PP235 6d. purple (M32)   ..   ..

We do not distinguish between inverted or sideways varieties due to the random method of application.

1904. S. & J. Watts, Manchester. Underprint Type 2 in black (18 mm. wide). (a) Vertical underprint, reading upwards

PP236 ½d. blue-green (M1)   ..   ..
PP237 ½d. yellow-green (M2) ..   ..
PP238 1d. red (M5)   ..   ..
PP239 3d. purple on yellow (M19)   ..   ..
PP240 3d. purple on yellow (M20)   ..   ..

(b) Vertical underprint, reading downwards

PP241 1d. red (M5)   ..   ..
PP242 3d. purple on yellow (M19)   ..   ..
PP243 3d. purple on yellow (M20)   ..   ..
PP244 5d. purple and blue (M28)   ..   ..

(c) As last but underprint (14 mm. wide) in black

PP245 1d. red (M5)   ..   ..
PP246 1d. red (M6)   ..   ..
PP247 1d. red (M7)   ..   ..
PP248 3d. purple on yellow (M22)   ..   ..

KING GEORGE V

1912. W. H. Everett & Son Ltd., Bell's Buildings, Salisbury Square, London, E.C. Underprint Type 1 in purple.

PP249   1d. red (N16)   ..   ..

1912. S. & J. Watts, Manchester. Underprint Type 2 (14 mm. wide). (a) Vertical underprint, reading upwards

PP250   1½d. red-brown (N18)   ..   ..

(b) Vertical underprint, reading downwards

PP251   1d. red (N16)   ..   ..

PP252   3d. violet (N22) ..   ..

APPENDIX 6

Postage Rates

Postage rates from 1635 have been researched from official records and the following extract is reproduced with kind permission of the Post Office. The rates given apply only to the period covered by this Catalogue.

Letter Post

The Treasury was empowered to regulate rates of postage, and subsequent changes were made by Treasury Warrant.

Date	*Rates of Charge*	
22 June 1897	4oz.	1d.
Then ½d. for each additional 2oz.		
1 November 1915	1oz.	1d.
	2oz.	2d.
	4oz.	2½d.
Then ½d. for each additional 2oz.		
3 June 1918	4oz.	1½d.
	6oz.	2d.
Then ½d. for each additional 2oz.		
1 June 1920	3oz.	2d.
Then ½d. for each additional 1oz.		
29 May 1922	1oz.	1½d.
	3oz.	2d.
Then ½d. for each additional oz.		
14 May 1923	2oz.	1½d.
The ½d. for each additional 2oz.		
1 May 1940	2oz.	2½d.
Then ½d. for each additional 2oz.		
1 May 1952	2oz.	2½d.
	4oz.	3d.
Then 1d. for each additional 2oz.		

Postcards

The first postcards issued by the Post Office appeared in 1870. These bore an embossed ½d. stamp and were followed in 1882 by the reply Postcard. Private postcards were permitted from 1894 and the maximum size allowed was 5½″ × 3½″, increased in 1925 to 5⅞″ × 4⅛″. The minimum size limit was 4″ × 2¾″.

Date	*Charge*
1 January 1901 ..	½d.
3 June 1918	1d.
3 June 1921	1½d.
29 May 1922 ..	1d.
1 May 1940	2d.

Printed Papers

This service was introduced as "Book Post" and had been used extensively by the subscribing Lending Libraries. On 1 January 1904 the Service was renamed the Halfpenny Packet Post with revised regulations to include all types of documents.

Date	*Rates of Charge*	
22 June 1897	2oz. only ..	½d.
Because the Letter Rate was 1d. for 4oz. and ½d. for each additional 2oz. the Book Post applied only to packets up to 2oz. in weight.		
1 November 1915	2oz.	½d.
Then ½d. for each additional 2oz. up to 5lb. Book Post.		
3 June 1918	1oz.	½d.
	2oz.	1d.
After 2oz. the letter rate applied.		
1 June 1920	1oz.	½d.
	2oz.	1d.
Then ½d. for each additional 2oz. up to 2lb. Now called Printed Paper Post.		
13 June 1921	2oz.	1d.
Then ½d. for each additional 2oz. up to 2lb.		
29 May 1922	1oz.	½d.
	2oz.	1d.
Then ½d. for each additional 2oz. up to 2lb.		
14 May 1923	2oz.	½d.
Then ½d. for each additional 2oz. up to 2lb.		
1 May 1940	2oz.	1d.
Then ½d. for each additional 2oz. up to 2lb.		
1 June 1951	4oz.	1½d.
Then ½d. for each additional 2oz. up to 2lb.		

Deferment of late posted Printed Paper Matter

When minimum rate was reduced to ½d. on 29 May 1922, the 1d. rate which had previously existed was maintained for such items as Stock Exchange quotations, etc., which could not be posted before the agreed "cut-off" time. This "cut-off" time was introduced to encourage early posting and to even out peaks of work. The ½d. differential continued by custom until 1965.

APPENDIX 6   Postage Rates

Newspaper Post

From 1870 the charge had been ½d. per copy irrespective of weight, but from 1 November 1915 the maximum weight permitted was 2lb.

Date	Charge Per Copy			
1 November 1915	Not exceeding 6oz.	..	..	½d.
	Each additional 6oz.	..	..	½d.
1 September 1920	Not exceeding 6oz.	..	..	1d.
	Each additional 6oz.	..	..	½d.
1 July 1940	Not exceeding 4oz.	..	..	1½d.
	Each additional 4oz.	..	..	½d.

Articles for the Blind

Originally introduced as Blind Literature this service was made free of charge from 17 May 1965.

Date	Rates of Charge			Date	Rates of Charge		
1 September 1906	2oz.	..	½d.	**17 February 1926**	2lb.	..	½d.
	2lb.	..	1d.		5lb.	..	1d.
	5lb.	..	1½d.		6½lb.	..	1½d.
1 February 1907	2oz.	..	½d.	**3 July 1936**	2lb.	..	½d.
	2lb.	..	1d.		5lb.	..	1d.
	5lb.	..	1½d.		8lb.	..	1½d.
	6lb.	..	2½d.		11lb.	..	2d.
				Service renamed Articles for the Blind.			
1 January 1915	2oz.	..	½d.	**1 July 1940**	2lb.	..	½d.
	5lb.	..	1d.		5lb.	..	1d.
	6lb.	..	2d.		8lb.	..	1½d.
13 June 1921	1lb.	..	½d.		11lb.	..	2d.
	5lb.	..	1d.		15lb.	..	2½d.
	6½lb.	..	2d.				

Express Services

Service 1. Express by Post Office messenger or, from 1934, special messenger all the way.

Date	Charges	Notes
1900	3d. per mile	Weight charge abolished
1906	3d. per mile	Weight charge of 3d. on packets exceeding 1lb. in weight imposed.
1 June 1906	6d. per mile plus cost of special conveyance if used. Weight fee (for packets over 1lb.) 3d.	Charge for additional articles 1d. per article after the first. Waiting fee (after 10 mins.) 2d. for each 15 mins.
1934	As above	As above but waiting fee 2d. for each 10 mins. after the first 10 mins.

Service 2. Special Delivery at the request of the sender. Charges were the same as for Service 1. From 1934 the service was by the sender's request, but by Post Office messenger from the delivery office after transmission by post, see also Service 4.

Date	Charges	Notes
1934	Full postage plus special delivery fee of 6d.	If a special conveyance was used the advised cost was charged to the sender or if unknown at 1 shilling per mile.

Service 3. Express delivery all the way at the request of the addressee. Charges were the same as for Service 1. Additional articles were charged at 1d. for every ten beyond the first. From 1934 the service changed to express from the office of delivery at the request of the addressee when the charge was the same as Service 1 including charge for additional articles.

Service 4. There was a Limited Sunday Special Delivery Service, introduced in 1921, because of the withdrawal of Sunday deliveries. Charges were as for Service 2 except the special fee was 1s. 6d. per mile in 1921. From 1934 the cost was full postage plus special fee of 1s. 6d.

Service 5. Express delivery of message received by telephone. Usual charge per telephone call and writing down fee (minimum charge 3d. for 30 words, 1d. for every additional 10 words). Express charges as for Service 1.

Official Parcel Post
This service had been first introduced on 1 August 1883.

Date	Rates of Postage			Date	Rates of Postage		
1 June 1897	1lb.	. .	3d.	**1 July 1940**	3lb.	. .	7d.
	2lb.	. .	4d.		4lb.	. .	8d.
	3lb.	. .	5d.		5lb.	. .	9d.
	4lb.	. .	6d.		6lb.	. .	10d.
	5lb.	. .	7d.		7lb.	. .	11d.
	6lb.	. .	8d.		8lb.	. .	1s. 0d.
	7lb.	. .	9d.		15lb.	. .	1s. 1d.
	8lb.	. .	10d.				
	9lb.	. .	11d.	**6 January 1947**	3lb.	. .	8d.
	11lb.	. .	1s. 0d.		4lb.	. .	9d.
					5lb.	. .	10d.
2 July 1906	1lb.	. .	3d.		6lb.	. .	11d.
	2lb.	. .	4d.		7lb.	. .	1s. 0d.
	3lb.	. .	5d.		8lb.	. .	1s. 1d.
	5lb.	. .	6d.		15lb.	. .	1s. 2d.
	7lb.	. .	7d.				
	8lb.	. .	8d.	**29 December 1947**	3lb.	. .	9d.
	9lb.	. .	9d.		4lb.	. .	11d.
	10lb.	. .	10d.		5lb.	. .	1s. 0d.
	11lb.	. .	11d.		6lb.	. .	1s. 1d.
					7lb.	. .	1s. 2d.
1 November 1915	1lb.	. .	4d.		8lb.	. .	1s. 3d.
	2lb.	. .	5d.		15lb.	. .	1s. 4d.
	3lb.	. .	6d.				
	5lb.	. .	7d.	**31 July 1950**	3lb.	. .	10d.
	7lb.	. .	8d.		4lb.	. .	1s. 0d.
	8lb.	. .	9d.		5lb.	. .	1s. 2d.
	9lb.	. .	10d.		6lb.	. .	1s. 3d.
	10lb.	. .	11d.		7lb.	. .	1s. 4d.
	11lb.	. .	1s. 0d.		8lb.	. .	1s. 5d.
					15lb.	. .	1s. 6d.
3 June 1918	3lb.	. .	6d.				
	7lb.	. .	9d.	**1 July 1951**	3lb.	. .	11d.
	11lb.	. .	1s. 0d.		4lb.	. .	1s. 1d.
					5lb.	. .	1s. 3d.
1 June 1920	2lb.	. .	9d.		6lb.	. .	1s. 5d.
	5lb.	. .	1s. 0d.		7lb.	. .	1s. 6d.
	8lb.	. .	1s. 3d.		8lb.	. .	1s. 7d.
	11lb.	. .	1s. 6d.		15lb.	. .	1s. 8d.
14 May 1923	2lb.	. .	6d.	**31 March 1952**	2lb.	. .	11d.
	5lb.	. .	9d.		3lb.	. .	1s. 1d.
	8lb.	. .	1s. 0d.		4lb.	. .	1s. 3d.
	11lb.	. .	1s. 3d.		5lb.	. .	1s. 5d.
					6lb.	. .	1s. 7d.
					7lb.	. .	1s. 9d.
1 July 1935	3lb.	. .	6d.		8lb.	. .	1s. 10d.
	4lb.	. .	7d.		11lb.	. .	1s. 11d.
	5lb.	. .	8d.		15lb.	. .	2s. 0d.
	6lb.	. .	9d.				
	7lb.	. .	10d.				
	8lb.	. .	11d.				
	15lb.	. .	1s. 0d.				

Railex

This was a new service, introduced on 1 January 1934. It provided for the conveyance of a postal packet to a railway station by Post Office messenger for despatch on the first available train, and for its immediate delivery by Post Office messenger from the station of destination.

Date	Charge		
1 January 1934	Not exceeding 2oz.	..	2s. 6d.
	Over 2oz. and up to 1lb. ..	..	3s. 0d.
1 July 1940	Not exceeding 2oz.	..	3s. 0d.
	Over 2oz. and up to 1lb. ..	..	3s. 6d.

Channel Islands. The German Occupation 1940–1945

A. GUERNSEY

Following the German Occupation the existing supplies of current British stamps continued in use until stocks became exhausted. It had earlier been decided that locally printed stamps should be supplied, but in the event these were not ready for issue until 18 February 1941. Faced with a dearth of 1d. stamps the authorities announced, on 27 December 1940, that bisected 2d. values would be allowed to do duty for 1d. stamps. The 2d. stamps available were the 1937 definitive and the 1940 Stamp Centenary commemorative. Examples of George V 2d. stamps bisected were also accepted by the Post Office, as were, in most instances, bisects of other values which had not been authorised. Bisects remained valid for postage in Guernsey until 24 February 1941, although examples are recorded two days later. On Sark their use continued until 31 May 1941.

The German Commandant had a swastika overprint applied to a number of the bisected 1940 Stamp Centenary 2d. stamps and submitted these to Berlin for approval, but this scheme was turned down, as was another which involved a similar overprint on the 1937 1d. value. Examples of both exist, but are very rare.

As previously mentioned, the locally printed 1d. stamps were issued on 18 February 1941. The ½d. stamp was released on 7 April 1941 and the 2½d. on 12 April 1944. This last stamp was issued in an effort to economise on the use of paper as it was found that sealed letters were franked with two 1d. stamps and one ½d. or a larger number of ½d's, a gross waste in times of shortage. Many printings of these stamps were made, the most notable being on the French bank-note paper in 1942.

Shades of these issues abound, the more outstanding ones being the bluish green (4th) and olive-green (8th) printings of the ½d, and the vermilion (11th) printing of the 1d. These stamps continued to be used after the liberation in 1945 until 13 April 1946.

1940. Swastika overprints. *Stamps of Great Britain optd.*
>   (*a*) 1937 *Geo. VI definitive optd. with a number of small swastikas*
>   GW1 1d. scarlet (Q4) £800

(*b*) 1940 *Stamp Centenary commemorative, intended for bisection, optd. with a swastika on each half of the stamp*
>   GW2 2d. orange (QCom5).. .. .. .. £800

Nos. GW1/2 were prepared for use, but not issued. They are, therefore, only known unused.

Example of bisected 1940 Stamp Centenary 2d. stamp

1940 (27 Dec). *Stamps of Great Britain bisected.*

(*a*) *George V definitives*

					Price on cover
GW3	2d. orange (N20) (1912–22 issue)	..	..	..	£175
GW4	2d. orange (N36) (1924–26 issue)	..	..	..	£175
GW5	2d. orange (N55) (1934 issue)	..	..	..	£200

(*b*) *George VI 1937–39 definitives*

GW6	1d. scarlet (Q4)	..	..	..	..	..	£450
GW7	2d. orange (Q10) (Head Office c.d.s)		..	..	18·00
GW7a		(Machine cancel) ..		..	..	20·00
GW7b		(Sub-office cancel)		..	*from*	20·00

(c) 1940 *Stamp Centenary commemoratives*

GW8	1d. scarlet (QCom3) ..	..	..	£450
GW9	2d. orange (QCom5) (Head Office c.d.s)	..	..	16·00 ✓
GW9a	(Machine cancel)	..	..	18·00
GW9b	(Sub-office cancel)	..	*from*	10·00
GW10	2½d. ultramarine (QCom6) ..	..	..	£600
GW11	3d. violet (QCom7) ..	..	..	—

GW1 Arms of Guernsey

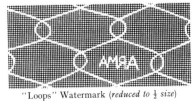

"Loops" Watermark *(reduced to ½ size)*

(Designed by E. W. Vaudin)
(Printed in typography by Guernsey Press Co. Ltd.)

1941–44. *Rouletted. (a) White paper. No wmk*

			Printing		
GW12 (= S.G.1) **GW1**	½d.	light green (7.4.41)	(1 (*part*))	3·00	2·50
	a.	*Emerald-green* (7.4. & 6.4.41) ..	(1 (*part*) 2, 3)	2·50	2·50
	b.	*Bluish green* (11.41)	(4)	42·00	28·00
	c.	*Bright green* (2.42)	(6)	24·00	12·00
	d.	*Dull green* (9.42)	(7)	4·50	3·50
	e.	*Olive-green* (2.43)	(8)	20·00	22·00
	f.	*Deep yellow-green* (7.43 & 10.43)	(9, 10)	2·50	2·50
	g.	*Pale yellow-green* (1.44 and later)	(11, 12, 13)	2·50	2·50
	h.	Imperf. (pair)		£150	
	i.	Imperf. between (horiz. pair) ..		£600	
	j.	Imperf. between (vert. pair) ..		£700	
	k.	Imperf. between stamp and margin		£100	
	l.	Printed on the gummed side ..		80·00	
GW13 (= S.G.2)	1d.	scarlet (18.2.41)	(1–10)	2·25	1·25
	a.	*Pale vermilion (shades)* (7.43) ..	(11)	4·00	2·50
	b.	*Carmine* (12.43 and later) ..	(12–16)	4·00	3·50
	c.	Imperf. (pair)		£150	75·00
	d.	Imperf. between (horiz. pair) ..		£600	
	e.	Imperf. between (vert. pair) ..		£700	
	ea.	Imperf. vert. (centre stamp of horiz. strip of 3)			
	f.	Imperf. between stamp and margin		£100	
	g.	Printed double (scarlet shade) ..		75·00	
GW14 (= S.G.3)	2½d.	ultramarine (shades) (12.4.44) ..	(1)	6·00	6·00
	a.	*Deep ultramarine* (4.44–11.44) ..	(2, 3 (*part*) & 4)	6·00	4·50
	b.	*Pale ultramarine* (7.44)	(3 (*part*))	4·50	3·50
	c.	Imperf. (pair)		£350	
	d.	Imperf. between (horiz. pair) ..		£800	
		(b) Bluish French bank-note paper. Wmk. loops			
GW15 (= S.G.4) **GW1**	½d.	bright green (11.3.42)	(5)	14·00 ✓	22·00 ✓
	a.	Watermark inverted		16·00	22·00
	b.	Watermark reversed		16·00	22·00
	c.	Watermark inverted and reversed		16·00	22·00
GW16 (= S.G.5)	1d.	scarlet (9.4.42)	(7)	8·00 ✓	22·00 ✓
	a.	Watermark inverted		15·00	22·00
	b.	Watermark reversed		15·00	22·00
	c.	Watermark inverted and reversed		15·00	22·00

The dates given for the shades of Nos. 1–3 are the months in which they were printed as indicated on the printer's imprints. Others are issue dates.

Nos. GW15/6 with a watermark variety can only be identified when the word "ARMA" forms part of the watermark. The reversed watermark appears to be the normal when viewed through the *front* of the stamp.

First Day Cover (No. GW12)	..	..	..	..	.. 6·00
First Day Cover (No. GW13)	..	..	..	..	.. 6·00
First Day Cover (No. GW14)	..	..	..	..	.. 7·50
First Day Cover (No. GW15)	..	..	..	..	.. 75·00
First Day Cover (No. GW16)	..	..	..	..	.. 40·00

Commercial Covers. Covers from personal or commercial correspondence franked with Nos. GW12, GW13 or GW14 are worth from twice the value quoted for used stamps. Similar covers franked with No. GW15 or No. GW16 are valued at three times the price quoted for used stamps.

Forgeries

All three values have been forged since 1945, the colours being almost identical with one or other of the shades of the actual stamps. They were printed in sheets of 25 instead of 60, have no imprint and do not contain the varieties, neither are the "Vs" in the corners at all clear. Even so, single copies are difficult to detect and care should be exercised in buying these stamps.

Imprints and Printings (Blocks of Four)

Imprint block of ½d. 4th printing

The various printings can be identified from the sheet imprints as follows:

½d.	1st Printing 240M/3/41	18·00
	2nd Printing 2 × 120M/6/41	20·00
	(a) Large white flaw above "G" of "GUERNSEY" on bottom right stamp	24·00
	3rd Printing C × 120M/6/41	20·00
	4th Printing 4 × 120M/11/41	£150
	5th Printing 5 × 120M/2/42	60·00
	6th Printing 6 × 240M/2/42	70·00
	7th Printing 7 × 120M/9/42	30·00
	8th Printing 8 × 120M/2/43	£130
	9th Printing 9 × 120M/7/43	14·00
	10th Printing 10 × 120M/10/43	14·00
	11th Printing Guernsey Press Co. (*stop and comma*) ..	14·00
	12th Printing Guernsey Press Co. (*stop only, margin at bottom 23 to 27 mm*)	14·00
	13th Printing Guernsey Press Co. (*stop only, margin at bottom 15 mm*)	14·00
1d.	1st Printing 120M/2/41	18·00
	2nd Printing 2 × 120M/2/41	15·00
	3rd Printing 3 × 120M/6/41	10·00
	4th Printing 4 × 120M/6/41	15·00
	5th Printing 5 × 120M/9/41	16·00
	6th Printing 6 × 240M/11/41	12·00
	7th Printing 7 × 120M/2/42	60·00
	8th Printing 8 × 240M/4/42	14·00
	9th Printing 9 × 240M/9/42	10·00
	10th Printing 10 × 240M/1/43	10·00
	11th Printing 11 × 240M/7/43	20·00
	12th Printing Guernsey Press Co.	30·00
	13th Printing PRESS TYP.	18·00
	14th Printing "PRESS" (*inverted commas unlevel*)	18·00
	15th Printing "PRESS" (*inverted commas level, margin at bottom 28 mm*)	20·00
	16th Printing "PRESS" (*inverted commas level, margin at bottom 12 mm*)	15·00
2½d.	1st Printing Guernsey Press Co.	22·00
	2nd Printing "PRESS" (*inverted commas unlevel*)	20·00
	3rd Printing "PRESS" (*inverted commas level, margin at bottom 22 mm*)	25·00
	4th Printing "PRESS" (*inverted commas level, margin at bottom 15 mm*)	20·00

The numbered imprints occur in the left-hand corner, bottom margin on the 1st printing of the 1d., and central, bottom margin on all other printings of all three values.

In the numbered imprints, for example, 2 × 120M/6/41, the "2" indicates the number of the printing; "120M" denotes the number of stamps printed in thousands, in this case 120,000; and "6/41" denotes the date of the printing, June 1941.

In the first ten printings of the ½d. and the first eleven printings of the 1d. the printing details are prefixed by the name of the printer, "Guernsey Press Co.".

Varieties

½d. All printings show a break in the left outer frame line on R. 7/1 and another in the right outer frame line on R. 8/6 (*Price twice normal*)

1d. All printings from the eighth onwards show a break near the bottom of the right outer frame line which extends into the adjacent pearl on R. 4/3 and R. 9/3 (*Price twice normal*)

Sheets: 60 (6 × 10).

Quantities Printed: ½d. 1,772,160; 1d. 2,478,000; 2½d. 416,640.

Withdrawn and Invalidated: 13.4.46, but last day postmark 14.4.46. The stamps could be used in Great Britain for a short time after liberation, but were soon declared to be invalid there.

B. JERSEY

Soon after Jersey was occupied by German troops the Commandant ordered the Postmaster to forward stocks of the currently available (British) stamps to Bigwoods, the Jersey printers, to be overprinted with a swastika and "JERSEY 1940". The Bailiff of Jersey protested at this action and, after reference to Berlin, the Commandant ordered the stocks of overprinted stamps to be destroyed. Only four complete sets and a few singles are known to have survived. One of the complete sets is in the Jersey Postal Headquarters archives.

Bigwoods also prepared a local 1d. stamp depicting the Arms of Jersey and inscribed "ETATS DE JERSEY", with and without an overprint of a swastika and "1940". These also were destroyed, except for two sheets now in museums, two further sheets which were cut up for collectors and a complete (but damaged) sheet with the overprint.

(JW1)
(Overprinted by Bigwoods, States of Jersey Printers)

Two locally printed stamps followed during 1941–42 the designer, Major N. V. L. Rybot, incorporating an "A" in each corner of the 1d. design to stand for *Ad Avernum Adolf Atrox* (to hell with you atrocious Adolf). On the subsequent ½d. value an "A" appeared in each of the upper corners and a "B" in the lower. These stood for "Atrocious Adolf, Bloody Benito".

This tradition of "hidden" inscriptions was continued by E. Blampied who incorporated the Royal Cypher into the design of the 3d. view.

1940. Swastika overprints. *Stamps of Great Britain optd. with Type* **JW1.**

(a) On 1937–39 George VI definitives

JW1	½d. green ..	£500
JW2	1½d. red-brown	£500
JW3	2d. orange..	£525
JW4	2½d. ultramarine ..	£525
JW5	3d. violet ..	£525
JW6	4d. grey-green	£525
JW7	5d. brown ..	£525
JW8	6d. purple ..	£525
JW9	7d. emerald-green	£525
JW10	8d. bright carmine	£525
JW11	9d. deep olive-green	£525
JW12	10d. turquoise-blue	£525
JW13	1s. bistre-brown ..	£525

(b) On 1940 Stamp Centenary issue

JW14	½d. green ..	£600
JW15	1½d. red-brown	£600
JW16	2d. orange..	£600
JW17	2½d.ultramarine ..	£600
JW18	3d. violet ..	£600

As Nos. JW1/18 were prepared but not issued, they are only known unused.

Proofs: Proof overprints made from a single block exist on the Edward VIII 1½d. and on the Stamp Centenary set (except the 1d.).

Forgeries

Forgeries of the swastika overprints were reported in circulation in 1974. They are cruder in appearance and differ from the genuine examples as follows: (1) the swastika is much thinner on the forgeries and can be at the wrong angle; (2) the ink is much thinner, many forged overprints revealing large white patches under the glass; (3) the swastika and "JERSEY 1940" have been applied separately.

JW2

(Designed by R. W. Cutland)

. (Printed in typography by Bigwoods)

1940. *No wmk. Imperf.* (*a*) *Type* **JW2**

JW19	1d. scarlet	..	..	..	..	..	£800

(*b*) *Type* **JW2** *overprinted as Type* **JW1** *but without* "JERSEY"

JW20	1d. scarlet	..	..	..	..	..	£800

Nos. JW19/20 were prepared but not issued. They do not exist in used condition.

Sheets: 30 (10 × 3).
A proof sheet of 6 (2 × 3) of No. JW20 exists on laid paper, ungummed and rouletted.

JW3 Arms of Jersey

(Designed by Major N. V. L. Rybot)
(Printed in typography by *Evening Post*, Jersey)

1941–43. *White paper* (*thin to thick*). *No wmk. P11*

JW21 (= S.G.1)	**JW3**	½d. bright green (29.1.42)	..	..	..	..	3·75	2·50
		a. Imperf. between (vert. pair)		..	..	..	£650
		b. Imperf. between (horiz. pair)		..	..	..	£550
		c. Imperf. (pair) ..	..	..	..	..	£175
		d. Imperf. between stamp and margin		..	..	50·00
		e. On greyish paper	..	..	..	..	5·50	6·50
		f. Stop before 2 (R.1/6)	..	..	..	7·00
		g. Line from lion's claw (R. 6/6)	..	..	..	7·00
		h. Break above T (R. 8/1)	..	..	..	6·00
		i. Three breaks in P (R. 8/3) ..	..	..	..	6·00
		j. White circle flaw (R. 8/6)	..	..	..	7·00
JW22 (= S.G.2)		1d. scarlet (1.4.41)	..	..	..	..	4·00	3·50
		a. Imperf. between (vert. pair)		..	..	..	£650
		b. Imperf. between (horiz. pair)		..	..	..	£550
		c. Imperf. (pair) ..	..	..	..	..	£200
		d. On chalk-surfaced paper (10.41)		..	..	38·00	40·00
		e. On greyish paper (1.43)	..	..	..	4·25	6·50

First Day Cover (No. JW21)	..	..	..	..	..	4·50
First Day Cover (No. JW22)	..	..	..	..	..	4·50

PLATE VARIETIES
Listed Flaws

JW21*f*
Dark spot before 2 in tablet
at right
(R. 1/6)

JW21*g*
Heavy line from lion's claw
to S in POSTAGE
(R. 6/6)

JW21*h*
Small white break joins
T to shield
(R. 8/1)

JW21*i*
Three breaks in P
(R. 8/3)

JW21*j*
Large white circle after
Y of JERSEY
(R. 8/6)

Imprints (Blocks of Six)

½d. "EVENING POST", JERSEY, JANUARY 1942	..	..	18·00
On greyish paper	..	..	..	..	..	28·00
1d. "EVENING POST", JERSEY, 17/3/41	..	..	18·00
On chalk-surfaced paper	..	..	..	..	£250
On greyish paper	..	..	..	..	..	28·00

Plate Flaws: Distinctive and positioned flaws are listed but many plate flaws exist on these stamps and most are worth twice normal.

Sheets: 60 (6 × 10).

Numbers Printed: ½d., 750,000; 1d., 1,000,000.

Withdrawn and Invalidated: 13.4.46, but last day postmark 14.4.46. The stamps could be used in Great Britain for a short time after liberation, but were soon declared to be invalid there.

Forgeries
Both values exist in different colours from the originals as imperforate forgeries.

Plate Proofs (Pairs)

½d. on thin paper in black	..	..	..	..	£125
1d. on thick card in black	..	..	..	..	60·00

JW4 Old Jersey Farm   **JW5** Portelet Bay   **JW6** Corbière Light-
house

JW7 Elizabeth Castle   **JW8** Mont Orgueil   **JW9** Gathering Vraic
Castle   (seaweed)

(Designed by E. Blampied. Engraved by H. Cortot)
(Printed in typography by French Govt. Ptg. Works, Paris)

1943–44. *No wmk. P13½.*

JW23 (= S.G.3) **JW4**	½d. green (1.6.43)		7·00	3·75
	a. Rough grey paper (6.10.43)		8·50	11·00
JW24 (= S.G.4) **JW5**	1d. scarlet (1.6.43)		1·00	50
	a. On newsprint (28.2.44)		2·00	2·75
JW25 (= S.G.5) **JW6**	1½d. brown (8.6.43)		3·00	3·00
JW26 (= S.G.6) **JW7**	2d. orange-yellow (8.6.43)		3·00	2·25
JW27 (= S.G.7) **JW8**	2½d. blue (29.6.43)		1·50	2·25
	a. Thin paper with design showing through back (25.2.44)		£175	
	b. On newsprint (25.2.44)		1·00	2·00
JW28 (= S.G.8) **JW9**	3d. violet (29.6.43)		1·00	4·00

First Day Covers (3) .. .. 16·00

The dates quoted for the paper varieties are those on which they were printed.
The 3d. value is known bisected from Rouge-Bouillon.

Forgeries
All values exist as imperforate forgeries in different shades.

Imprints and Printings. (Blocks of Four)

½d.	1st printing 1/5/43	..	..	..	..	..	16·00
	2nd printing 3/5/43	..	..	..	..	..	16·00
	3rd printing 6/10/43	..	..	..	..	..	40·00
1d.	1st printing 7/5/43	..	..	..	..	..	6·00
	2nd printing 8/5/43	..	..	..	..	..	6·00
	3rd printing 7/10/43	..	..	..	..	..	8·00
	4th printing 28/2/44	..	..	..	..	..	8·00
1½d.	1st printing 17/5/43	..	..	..	..	..	9·00
	2nd printing 18/5/43	..	..	..	..	..	9·00
2d.	1st printing 20/5/43	..	..	..	..	..	10·00
	2nd printing 21/5/43	..	..	..	..	..	10·00
2½d.	1st printing 31/5/43	..	..	..	..	..	12·00
	2nd printing 25/2/44	..	..	..	..	..	10·00
3d.	1st printing 4/6/43	..	..	..	..	..	7·00
	2nd printing 5/6/43	..	..	..	..	..	7·00

Sheets: 120 (four panes 3 × 10), separated by interpanneau margins.

Imprint: None.

Numbers Printed: ½d., 360,000, grey paper, 120,000; 1d., 960,000, newsprint, 240,000; 1½d., 360,000; 2d., 360,000; 2½d., 360,000, newsprint, 360,000; 3d., 360,000.

Withdrawn and Invalidated: 13.4.46, but last day postmark 14.4.46. The stamps could be used in Great Britain for a short time after liberation, but were soon declared to be invalid there.

Proofs and Essays

Die proofs in black on rough paper, signed Cortot	..	£100
Colour proofs, signed Cortot	*from*	£120
Colour proofs, unsigned	*from*	£100
Black presentation proofs on good quality wove paper ..		£200
Epreuves-de-luxe in issued colours, with imprint "Atelier de Fabrication des Timbres-Poste, PARIS" and covered with tissue paper	*each*	30·00
Mise en train proofs in black on pink paper, ½d., 1d., 1½d. and 2d. only..	*each*	50·00
Half-size essays of ½d. and 1d. in single or two colours on wove or India paper	*from (each)*	£125

OFFICIAL STAMPS

JW10

JW11

1940 (July). *Typo. Imperf.*
JWO1 **JW10** (−) black £250   £350
No. JWO1 was used by Capt. Gussek, the first Jersey Commandant, on his official mail and occasionally on documents.

1940. *Inscr. "HAFEN/KOMMANDANT/JERSEY" with anchor in centre. Imperf.*
JWO2 **JW11** (−) black £250   £400

1940. *As No. JWO2, but inscr. "HAFEN/KAPITAN/etc."*
JWO3 (−) black £250   £400

Nos. JWO2/3 were used by the Harbour Master and appear more frequently on permits or documents than on letters.

Further Reading

The list below is representative of major works relating to British postal history, stamps and postmarks of the reigns of King Edward VII to King George VI. It is culled from *A List of Books on the Postal History, and Adhesive Postage and Revenue Stamps of Great Britain,* compiled by Arnold M. Strange (2nd edition, 1971, Great Britain Philatelic Society, London), to which reference should be made for additional works. Later publications to date and appropriate titles on the Channel Islands are also included.

POSTAL HISTORY

Dagnall, Harry. *The Mechanised Sorting of Mail.* (1976. The Author, Leicester.)

Daunton, M. J. *Royal Mail: The Post Office since 1840.* (1985. The Athlone Press, London.)

Farrugia, Jean and Gammons, Tony. *Carrying British Mails.* (1980. The National Postal Museum, London.)

Hay, Ian. *The Post Office Went to War.* (1946. H.M. Stationery Office, London.)

Jackson, G. Gibbard. *From Post Boy to Air Mail. The Story of the British Post Office.* (Sampson Low, Marston & Co., London.)

Kay, George F. *Royal Mail. The Story of the Posts in England from the Time of Edward IV to the Present Day.* (1951. Rockliffe Publishing Corporation Ltd.)

Marshall, C. F. Dendy. *The British Post Office from its Beginnings to the End of 1925.* (1926. Oxford University Press.)

Murray, Sir Evelyn, K.C.B., Secretary to the Post Office. *The Post Office.* (1927. Putnam & Co., Ltd., London.)

Robinson, Howard. *The British Post Office. A History.* (1948. Princeton University Press.)

Robinson, Howard. *Carrying British Mails Overseas.* (1964. George Allen & Unwin Ltd., London.)

Staff, Frank. *The Penny Post 1680–1918.* (1964. Lutterworth Press, London.)

GENERAL

Alcock, R. C. and Meredith, C. W. *British Postage Stamp Varieties Illustrated. Queen Victoria Surface-Printed Issues to King George VI.* (1949. R. C. Alcock, Cheltenham.)

Hamilton, Patrick. *British Stamps. A Description of the Postage Stamps of the United Kingdom.* (1948. Peter Davies, London.)

Hamilton, Patrick. Supplement to the above. (1954. Harris Publications Ltd., London.)

Lowe, Robson. *The Encyclopaedia of British Empire Postage Stamps, 1661–1951.* (1952. 2nd Edn. Robson Lowe Ltd., London.) Reprinted in Billig's Philatelic Handbook series (2 Vols.). (HJMR Co., North Miami, Florida.)

Mackay, James A. *Great Britain. The Story of Great Britain and her Stamps.* (1967. Philatelic Publishers, London.)

Mackay, James A. *British Stamps.* (1985. Longman Group Ltd., London.)

Oliver, Sidney A. R. and Vallancey, F. Hugh. *The Postage Stamps of Great Britain, 1840–1922.* (1923. *Stamp Collecting,* London.)

Rigo de Righi, A. G. *The Stamp of Royalty; British Commemorative Issues for Royal Occasions 1935–1972.* (1973. The National Postal Museum, London.)

Rose, Stuart. *Royal Mail Stamps—A Survey of British Stamp Design.* (1980. Phaidon Press, Oxford.)

Rowell, Reginald B. *Notes on Controls. Part II. Edwardian and Georgian Periods.* (1916. Stamp Collecting Handbook, London.)

Todd, T. *A History of British Postage Stamps.* (1949. Duckworth, London.)

Ward, W. *A Book about British Books of Stamps and Rolls.* (1925. Lytham.)

Williams, L. N. and M. *Commemorative Postage Stamps of Great Britain.* (1967. Arco Publications, London.)

Wilson, Sir John, Bart. *The Royal Philatelic Collection.* (1952. The Dropmore Press, London.)

PHILATELIC PERIODICALS DEVOTED TO GREAT BRITAIN

The British Philatelist (1908–54) (Chas. Nissen & Co., Ltd., London.)

The GB Journal (From 1956) (The Great Britain Philatelic Society, London.)

The G.B. Philatelist (1961–65) (The Regent Stamp Co., Ltd., London.)

Gibbons Stamp Monthly (*British Stamps* supplement from October 1981, January, April and July 1982, monthly since October 1982.)

British Philatelic Bulletin (From 1963) (title was *Philatelic Bulletin*, 1963–83). (The Post Office, London.)

The Philatelist/Philatelic Journal of Great Britain (1981–83) (The P.J.G.B., 1891–1980, is now merged with *The Philatelist*, after March 1966 the former was wholly devoted to Great Britain (Robson Lowe Ltd., London.)

The Philatelic Review (From 1977) (Candlish, McCleery Ltd., Melton Mowbray.)

"SPECIMEN" STAMPS

Samuel, Marcus and Huggins, Alan. *Specimen Stamps and Stationery of Great Britain.* (1980. The Great Britain Philatelic Society, London.)

KING EDWARD VII

Beaumont, K. M. and Adams, H. C. V. *The Postage Stamps of Great Britain. The Embossed Issues. The Surface-Printed Issues of Queen Victoria and King Edward VII.* (1954. The Royal Philatelic Society, London. Revised 1964 by K. M. Beaumont and John Easton.)

Bernstein, I. J. *The Official Stamps of Great Britain.* (1906. Philatelic Record Handbook.)

Buckley, Sam C. *The Marginal Varieties of the Edwardian Stamps of Great Britain, 1902–1912.* (1912. Oswald Marsh, London.)

Doupé, H. S. *A Study of the Cracked Units of the K. E. VII De La Rue One Penny Stamp, 1902–10.* (1962. The Great Britain Philatelic Society, London.)

Melville, Fred J. *Great Britain. King Edward VII Stamps.* (1911. Melville Stamp Books, London.)

Phillips, Stanley. *Great Britain. The Harrison and Somerset House Printings (1911–1912) and How to Distinguish Them.* (1913. Stanley Gibbons Ltd., London.)

Wiseman, W. A. *Great Britain: The De La Rue-Years 1878–1910 Vol. 1.* (1984. Bridger & Kay Ltd., London.)

KING GEORGE V

Beaumont, K. M. and Stanton, J. B. M. *The Postage Stamps of Great Britain, Part IV. The Issues of King George V.* (1957. The Royal Philatelic Society, London.)

Hacket, Alastair. *The 1935 Silver Jubilee Issue of Great Britain.* (1982. Edinburgh Stamp Shop.)

Knight, Donald R. and Sabey, Alan D. *The Lion Roars at Wembley: British Empire Exhibition 60th Anniversary 1924–1925.* (1984. Donald R. Knight, New Barnet, Herts.)

Phillips, Stanley. *The Stamps of Great Britain (1911–1921).* (1921. Stanley Gibbons Ltd.)

Stanton, J. B. M. and Rushworth, K. G. *King George V. A Study of the Provisional Issues of 1934 and 1935.* (1960. Stanley Gibbons Ltd., London on behalf of the Great Britain Philatelic Society.)

Stitt-Dibden, W. G. *Selected Works. Vol. 1. Wembley & Olympic Issues.* (No date. The Postal History Society and the G.B. Philatelic Society, London.)

Vallancey, Hugh. *Check List of British Photogravure and Jubilee Stamps, 1934–36.* (1936. The Vallancey Press, London.)

Vallancey, Hugh. *Check List of British Photogravure Stamps of King George V including Stamps overprinted for Morocco.* (1939. The Vallancey Press, London.)

KING EDWARD VIII

Kirk, A. J. *King Edward VIII. A Study of the Stamps of the Reign of King Edward VIII.* A revised edition of J. B. M. Stanton's book. (1974. 2nd Edn. The Great Britain Philatelic Society, London.)

Stanton, J. B. M. *King Edward VIII. A Study of the Stamps of the Reign of King Edward VIII.* (1958. The Great Britain Philatelic Society, London.)

KING GEORGE VI

Anon. *A Catalogue of Cylinder Flaws on King George VI Great Britain Commemoratives.* (1954. Crabtree Press, Brighton.)

Bert, A. L. *Great Britain. Check List of King George VI Controls and Cylinder Numbers, 1937–1954.* (1954. West Croydon.)

Birch, L. *Great Britain. The Coronation Stamp, 1937. Its Aberrations, Flaws and Abnormalities.* (No date. Midland Stamp Co., Birmingham.)

Langston, Colin W. and Corless, H. C. *Stamps of Great Britain issued in Rolls and the Machines which Use Them. An Historical Survey including a Check List of the Rolls issued since 1938.* (1961. The Authors, London.)

Stitt-Dibden, W. G. *Selected Works. Vol. 1. Wembley & Olympic Issues.* (No date. The Postal History Society and the G.B. Philatelic Society, London.)

POSTMARKS

Alcock, R. C. and Holland, F. C. *The Postmarks of Great Britain and Ireland, being a Survey of the British Postmarks from 1660 to 1940.* (1940. R. C. Alcock Ltd., Cheltenham.) Part II issued later.

Bennett, J. Bruce, Parsons, Cyril, R. H., and Pearson, G. R. *Current Machine Postmarks of the United Kingdom.* (1963. British Postmark Society, London.)

Brummell, G. *British Post Office Numbers, 1884–1906.* (1946. R. C. Alcock Ltd., Cheltenham.)

Brummell, G. *Postmarks of the British Isles. A Short History with Notes on Collecting.* (1930. Bournemouth Guardian Ltd., Bournemouth.)

Brummell, G. *The Postmark Slogans of Great Britain.* (1938. R. C. Alcock, Cheltenham.)

Cohen, Stanley, F. and Rosenblat, Daniel G. *Squared Circle Postmarks of the London Suburban District Offices.* (1983. Harry Hayes, Batley, West Yorkshire.)

Holland, F. C. *Introduction to British Postmark Collecting.* (1971.)

Langston, Colin M. *Surcharged and Explanatory Dies of Great Britain.* (1964. The Author.)

Mackay, James A. *Scottish Postmarks 1693–1978.* (1978. The Author, Dumfries.)

Mackay, James A. *English and Welsh Postmarks since 1840.* (1980. The Author, Dumfries.)

Mackay, James A. *British Post Office Numbers 1924–1969.* (1981. The Author, Dumfries.)

Mackay, James A. *Irish Postmarks since 1840.* (1982. The Author, Dumfries.)

Mackay, James A. *The Parcel Post of the British Isles.* (1982. The Author, Dumfries.)

Mackay, James A. *Registered Mail of the British Isles.* (1983. The Author, Dumfries.)

Mackay, James A. *Official Mail of the British Isles.* (1983. The Author, Dumfries.)

Mackay, James A. *Surcharged Mail of the British Isles.* (1984. The Author, Dumfries.)

Parsons, Cyril R. H., Peachey, Colin G. and Pearson, George R. *Collecting Slogan Postmarks.* (1986. The Authors, Aylesbury.) (Includes listings of slogan postmarks, 1917–69.)

Reynolds, Paul. *The Machine Cancellations of Wales 1905–1985.* (1985. Welsh Philatelic Society, Swansea.)

Peach, Jack. *U.K. Machine Marks.* (1982. 2nd. Edn. Vera Trinder Ltd., London.)

Pearson, George. *Special Event Postmarks of the United Kingdom.* (1984. 3rd. Edn. British Postmark Society, London.)

Swan, V. *British Slogan Cancellations, 1917–1960.* (1960. The Author, Alton.)

Whitney, Dr. J. T. *Collect British Postmarks.* (1983. 3rd. Edn. The Author, Benfleet, Essex.)

CHANNEL ISLANDS

Backman, A. and Forrester, R. *The Postage Stamps of the Smaller Channel Islands.* (1989. Ilford.)

Further Reading

Cruickshank, Charles. *The German Occupation of The Channel Islands.* (1975. London.) Official history, non-philatelic.

Danan, Yves Maxime. *Emissions Locales et Affranchissements de Guerre des Iles da la Manche.* (1969. Paris.)

Danan, Yves Maxime. *Histoire Postale des Isles de la Manche,* Tome 1 and Tome 2. (1976 and 1978. Paris.)

Griggs, Ian. *The 1942 Jersey ½d. Arms; a Plating Study.* (1982. Ilford.)

Harris, R. E. *Islanders Deported Parts 1 and 2.* (1980. Chippenham.)

Mayne, Richard. *Mailships of the Channel Islands 1771–1971.* (1971. Chippenham.)

McKenzie, Donald. *The Red Cross Mail Service for Channel Island Civilians 1940–1945.* (1975. Chippenham.)

Möhle, Heinz. *Die Briefmarken von den Kanel-Inseln; Guernsey und Jersey, Deutsche Besetzung 1940–45.* (1970. Frankfurt.)

Newport, William. *Stamps and Postal History of the Channel Islands.* (1972. London.)

Trotter, J. M. Y. "Early Guernsey Postal History and Private Agents for Guernsey Letters." *Transactions of the Société Guernesaise,* 1950. *Postal History Society Bulletin,* 1950.

Wieneke, M. *The German Field Post Office in the Channel Islands.* (1981. Jersey.)

Notes

1661-1937

WHATEVER YOU COLLECT IN GREAT BRITAIN YOU SHOULD CONTACT ME.

I GIVE A SPECIALISED APPROVAL SERVICE TO THE BASIC COLLECTOR THE SPECIALIST OR EXHIBITOR

- ★ **ISSUED STAMPS**
- ★ **POSTAL HISTORY**
- ★ **TELEGRAPHS**
- ★ **FISCALS**
- ★ **SHADES**
- ★ **CINDERELLAS**
- ★ **S.P. ABNORMALS**

- ★ **SPECIMENS**
- ★ **PROOFS**
- ★ **IMPRIMATURS**
- ★ **OFFICIALS**
- ★ **POSTAGE DUES**
- ★ **USED ABROAD**
- ★ **COLLEGE STAMPS**

YOU NAME IT AND I CAN USUALLY FIND SOMETHING USEFUL IN STOCK.

YOUR WANTS LIST OR SPECIALITIES WELCOMED

 W. P. BIRD

FLAT 4, THE FRIARY, OLD WINDSOR, BERKS SL4 2NS

Tel. Windsor (0753) 840164   Callers by Appointment Please

GREAT BRITAIN 1840-1950

For the connoisseur and specialist. . .

. . . we provide an ever-changing range of items to which the description "quality" and "rarity" may aptly be applied.

THE SELECTED ITEMS SECTION of our regular stock-list contains items for the G.B. Specialist of most reigns, but in particular those of Queen Victoria. . .

. . . KING EDWARD VII, KING GEORGE V and KING GEORGE VI

Line engraved with scarcer Plates and MX's, Surface Printed cds used, Certified shades of both KEVII and GV, varieties, rare multiples, etc., etc.

The 'Bargains Section' will also interest the Specialist with its hundreds of less expensive items from fillers at only 2% of Cat. to fine mint & VFU singles. Lots of unusual postmarks, Used Abroad, shades, flaws, etc, from QV to QEII make this a most fascinating source of choice for the GB collector.

GB SPECIALISTS ARE INVITED TO SEND FOR THIS LIST, WHICH IS COMPLETELY FREE OF CHARGE.

GB POSTAL AUCTION

Our regular GB-only Postal Auction provides the collector with the opportunity to purchase at 'dealer prices'. From Postal History through to QEII varieties, from basic stamps through to major rarities.

A free catalogue for our next sale is always available

Items you could expect to find in our List or our Auction

KING EDWARD VII

1902 1d Rose-carmine, Spec, M5 (4) u/m £28.00
1910 7d Deep grey-black, SG249A, u/m with Cert £65.00
1902 10d Carmine-pink, Spec, M42(3) u/m with Cert £225.00
1911 3d Grey/lemon, SG285a,1/m with Cert..........................£1,950.00
1911 ½d Bright green, SG271, vfu, light cds £75.00
1911 1d intense rose-red, Spec,M6(3) u/m with Cert £250.00

KING GEORGE V

1911 ½d Bluish-green, SG323,u/m with Cert.............................£275.00
1912½d Deep cobalt green, Spec,N14(18) u/m with Cert...£150.00
1912 2½d Deep bright-blue, Spec.N21(5), vfu,cds £45.00
1915 2/6 Blackish-brown, Spec.N64(11), fine 1/m with Cert £450.00
1915 10s Bright 'Cambridge' blue, Spec.N70(5), fine 1/m with Cert......... ....£1,950.00
1918 10s Steel-blue, Spec. N71(3), fine 1/m with Cert.............£1,750.00

WANTS LISTS

We constantly supply medium to rare items to clients whose collections range from average to Gold Medal standard - so make sure we are aware of you, and of your requirements in G,B,

WE URGENTLY REQUIRE

Fine quality and rare items or collections of Great Britain.
To obtain the best price it has always paid to contact the specialists first, so contact Barry Fitzgerald at:

Embassy Philatelists

THE BRITISH PHILATELIC FEDERATION
PTS

MANFIELD HOUSE (7th Floor)
376 THE STRAND, LONDON WC2R 0LR ENGLAND
Tel: 01-240-1527 VAT-No 228 8653 31

1902 —1951
Our free, monthly
ILLUSTRATED CATALOGUES
Normally contain
some of the following

BOOKLETS & PANES

BOTTOM ROWS

CANCELLED CLICHES

COIL LEADERS & JOINS

COLOUR TRIALS

CONTROLS

COVERS

CYLINDERS

DIE PROOFS

DOUBLE PRINTS

ERRORS

ESSAYS

FLAWS

IMPERFORATES

IMPRIMATURES

INKS

OFFSETS

PERFORATION TYPES

PLATE PROOFS

PLATING PIECES

PLUG REPAIRS

RECESSION FLAWS

SHADES

SPECIMENS

VARIETIES

WATERMARKS

SHOULDN'T YOU RECEIVE THEM?

Malcolm Sprei
M & S STAMPS
77 The Strand
London WC2R 0DR
Tel: 01 240 3778

Please send me a copy of your free catalogue

Name ....

Address ....

ACCESSORIES

From Stamp Hinges to Ultra Violet Lamps; from Tweezers and Magnifiers to Colour Keys and Watermark Detectors – Stanley Gibbons accessories are the answer to every collector's requirements.

The range has been completely revised with an improved selection of tweezers and the addition of a drying book and photo mounts for cover and postcard collectors.

The magnifiers have been completely revised to allow a wider variety of choice with each item having been carefully selected for its quality and value for money.

Current details of our superb range are available direct from Stanley Gibbons or your favourite supplier.

**Stanley Gibbons Publications Ltd.,
5 Parkside, Christchurch Road,
Ringwood, Hampshire BH24 3SH**

Telephone 0425 472363

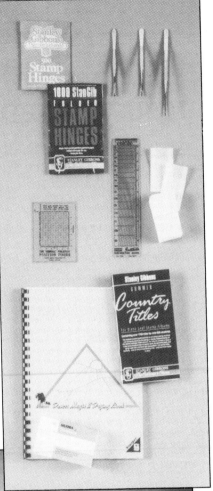

COMPLETE YOUR SET

No stamp collector likes to have incomplete sets – whether you are talking about Tudor Crowns, St Edward Crowns or the Crown of the SG Catalogue range – the **Great Britain Specialised Catalogue.**

Volume 1 (item 0285) **Queen Victoria**
Volume 2 (item 0286) **King Edward VII to King George VI**
Volume 3 (item 2810) **Queen Elizabeth II pre-decimal issues**
Volume 4 (item 2820) **Queen Elizabeth II decimal definitive issues**
Volume 5 (item 2891) **Queen Elizabeth II decimal special issues**

Volumes 1 & 2 are available either case bound or paperback.

HOW TO KEEP RIGHT UP TO DATE

A handbook-catalogue such as this volume can only be published every two or three years. For more simplified but up to date details of the current GB market it is wise to augment the information provided in the Great Britain Specialised Catalogue with

Collect British Stamps (item 0289) – published each November. The World's most successful Catalogue, published in full colour.

Great Britain CONCISE Stamp Catalogue (item 2887) – published each May. A one-volume Catalogue based on the GB listing in Part I with a host of additional information.

THE MAGAZINE FOR THE GB COLLECTOR

Each month **Gibbons Stamp Monthly** contains a 'British Stamps' section with regular coverage of new issues, Machins, varieties and books, including the supplements to the Great Britain Specialised Catalogue. Feature articles cover a variety of topics from Queen Victoria line-engraved to modern postal history and a varied selection of advertisements provide the very latest in market information.

Please send for a free specimen copy and subscription details to **Hugh Jefferies, Stanley Gibbons Magazines, Parkside, Ringwood, Hampshire BH24 3SH.**

BLANK SPRINGBACK ALBUMS

These fine albums give the more advanced collector the freedom and flexibility he needs to arrange his collection exactly as he wants it.

Leaves are finely printed with a feint quadrille and most have side and centre markings to aid arrangement.

Albums and binders are now supplied with a sheet of self-adhesive, gold-blocked title panels, a selection of country titles and a run of volume numbers; allowing them to be clearly identifiable on the shelf or left blank if you prefer.

1. Tower (Item 0331) A choice of red, green, or black binder with 100 leaves of white cartridge 11⅛″ × 9⅞″. Boxed.

2. Senator Medium (Item 0384) A very popular 'first blank leaved album for many years now. 50 leaves 10⅜″ × 8¾″, a choice of three binder colours; black, green or red.

3. Senator Standard (Item 0386) As the Senator Medium but with 100 larger sized leaves (11⅛″ × 9⅞″). One of our best selling albums!

4. Simplex Medium (Item 3810) Fifty leaves of high quality cream paper with a subtle decorative border (10⅜″ × 8¾″). Binder choice of green or red.

5. Simplex Standard (Item 3812) 100 larger sized leaves (11⅛″ × 9⅞″), otherwise the same style as the Simplex Medium. Boxed. Popular with generations of stamp collectors!

6. Utile (Item 3821) 25 white cartridge special double linen-hinged transparent faced leaves (11⅛″ × 9⅞″) designed to lie flat when album is opened. Attractive binder in choice of green or red.

Transparent Interleaving Fine quality glazed transparent paper in packs of 100 sheets for Tower, Senator, Simplex or similar types of loose-leaf springback albums.

Item 3310 Standard size 11″ × 9⅝″.

Item 3311 Medium size 10″ × 8⅛″.

For further details visit your favourite stamp shop or, in case of difficulty, write to:

**Stanley Gibbons Publications Ltd.,
5 Parkside, Christchurch Road,
Ringwood, Hampshire BH24 3SH
Telephone 0425 472363**

PEG-FITTING
BLANK LOOSE-LEAF ALBUMS

Stanley Gibbons blank albums give you the freedom and flexibility you need to arrange your collection exactly as you want it.

All those items which can add real interest to a collection: shades, inverted watermarks, gum variations, cylinder blocks, unusual cancellations, etc. can be easily accommodated and there is no need to be frustrated by empty spaces perpetually reminding you of the stamps you do not have.

Peg-fitting albums represent the very peak of Stanley Gibbons range – albums which have stood the test of time from the Devon, now in its 30th year of production to the Philatelic which has been housing the great collections of the world for over a century!

The Devon
A strong elegant, large-capacity binder containing 100 fine quality cartridge leaves (10⅜ × 9¾ in.). Choice of maroon, green, black or blue. Ideal for collections where that extra capacity is required. Transparent interleaving available, boxed.

The Exeter
A quality binder in a choice of red, blue or green containing 40 leaves (10¼ × 9¾ in.) of fine white cartridge. All leaves are double linen-hinged with transparent facing so that leaves lie flat when the album is opened and damaging friction is minimised.

An illustrated colour brochure giving prices of these and all other Stanley Gibbons Publications Products is available by post from

**Stanley Gibbons Publications Ltd.,
5 Parkside, Christchurch Road,
Ringwood, Hampshire BH24 3SH.
Telephone 0425 472363**

The Plymouth
Maroon, black, green or blue, a connoisseur's album in a strong matching slip-case. Supplied with 40 double linen-hinged leaves (10⅜ × 9¾ in.) with glassine facing for additional protection.

The Philatelic
The largest album in the Stanley Gibbons range, it not only accommodates more stamps per page than other albums but also allows sheets, blocks, etc., to be arranged and mounted on its 12⅞ × 10¾ in. leaves. Bound in handsome deep green cloth with leather corners and spine, supplied with 80 double linen-hinged, transparent faced leaves and presented in a sturdy deep green slip-case.

The Oriel
Supreme among luxury blank albums, the Oriel will enhance the very finest collection. Half bound in rich red leather with gold tooling, each album contains 50 superior gilt-edged double linen-hinged leaves (10⅜ × 9⅝ in.) with transparent facings and is supplied in a luxury matching slip-case.

The most prestigious home for your stamps.

Additional binders and leaves are available for all Stanley Gibbons peg-fitting albums.

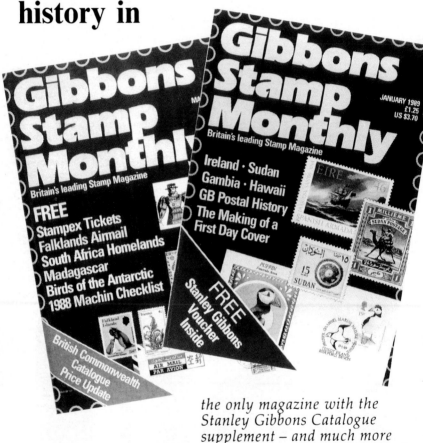